Beliefs-Preferences Gauge Symmetry Group and Replication of Contingent Claims in a General Market Environment

Beliefs-Preferences Gauge Symmetry Group and Replication of Contingent Claims in a General Market Environment

Valery A. Kholodnyi

IES Press

Beliefs-Preferences Gauge Symmetry Group and Replication of Contingent Claims in a General Market Environment

Valery A. Kholodnyi

Published by:
IES Press
104 T.W. Alexander Dr., Bldg. 3/P.O. Box 14008
Research Triangle Park, NC 27709

First Printing 1998
Printed in the United States of America

Publishers Cataloging-in-Publication
(*Provided by Quality Books, Inc.*)

Kholodnyi, Valery A., 1964-
Beliefs-preferences gauge symmetry group and replication of contingent claims in a general market environment / Valery A. Kholodnyi.
p. cm.
Includes bibliographical references and index.
Preassigned LCCN: 98-85188
ISBN 0-9663032-1-0

1. Options (Finance)–Valuation–Mathematical models.
2. Derivative securities–Valuation–Mathematical models.
3. Symmetry groups. I. Title.

HG6024.A3K3956 1998 332.63'228
QBI98-797

About the Author

Valery A. Kholodnyi received his Ph.D. in Applied Mathematics from the Moscow Institute of Electronics and Mathematics in 1990. He has held university positions in various departments, such as the Department of Microwave and Quantum Electronics, the Department of Mathematical Modeling of Physical Processes, and the Department of Physics, in both Russia and the United States. He has authored or co-authored two monographs and over 60 research papers in finance, mathematics, theoretical physics and engineering, and has published in journals, such as the *Journal of Mathematical Physics*, the *Journal of Integral Equations and Applications* and *Nonlinear Analysis, Theory, Methods and Applications.* He was an Invited Speaker at the Second World Congress of Nonlinear Analysts and at numerous international and national conferences, as well as at research seminars in university departments and industry. Currently, he is the Vice-President of Research and Development for Integrated Energy Services, L.C., an independent research institute for financial capital markets.

Statement of the Publisher

Integrated Energy Services L. C. scientists conduct leading-edge research in the field of Theoretical Finance. IES Press is dedicated to bringing into the public domain the results of their efforts.

Patrick D. Bosold
Director of Publications
IES Press

Preface

In 1900, Louis Bachelier invented the seeds of stochastic calculus. His motivation was the problem of modeling the random character of the dynamics of prices of underlying securities in financial markets, with the aim of analyzing financial derivatives.

Financial derivatives, or contingent claims, roughly speaking, are contracts whose specifications are determined by, that is, are derived from the prices of the underlying securities, such as stock or foreign currency. Although Bachelier's work lay relatively dormant for nearly half a century, his pioneering application of stochastic calculus, through the work of giants in the field of finance, culminated in the celebrated option pricing model of Fischer Black and Myron Scholes in 1973. Options are one of the most widely traded types of financial derivatives. Black and Scholes's groundbreaking work met with overwhelming success among both practitioners and academic researchers and presented a landmark understanding of this field. The Black and Scholes model was so successful, even too successful, in that its very success led the study of actual financial phenomena, which was the original goal, to be virtually identified and later even replaced by the study of mathematical aspects of stochastic calculus, which was just a tool. The means were mistaken for the ends. The subject of financial derivatives literally became a subset of stochastic calculus.

In this book, we are making an attempt to come back to the original goal, namely, to the study of actual financial phenomena. In particular, we study the financial phenomenon underlying the valuation of financial derivatives. It is our view that the study of financial phenomena is on the brink of a revolution similar to that of quantum physics in the 1920s. The revolution in quantum physics was based on the study of actual physical phenomena that led to the thorough review and renewal of the very foundations of physics. It is this return to foundations that led, in turn, to the invention and elaboration of one of the most powerful and rich areas of mathematics and mathematical physics in this century.

History shows that virtually all the major revolutions in physics, revolutions that revealed the deepest insights into Nature, were made through recognizing that a range of seemingly unrelated phenomena actually represent a common underlying phenomenon. Such a unification of seemingly unrelated phenomena indicates the presence of an inherent symmetry in the underlying phenomenon. A standard way to formalize such a symmetry mathematically is in terms of group theory.

Among these symmetries one of the major roles was played by the so-called gauge symmetries. Gauge symmetries were responsible for such major revolutions in physics as the creation of the theory of the classical electromagnetic field by Maxwell, the general theory of relativity by Einstein which provided the theory for the classical gravitational field, and all the successful modern unified quantum field theories which are responsible for the unification of all known interactions in nature, namely electromagnetic, weak, strong and gravity.

In 1996, Kholodnyi and Price authored two articles, [18] and [19], that introduced a fundamental symmetry in foreign exchange markets. These articles gave rise to further research on foreign exchange option symmetry (see articles [14], [12], [13], [17], and monographs [21], [22]). Article [18] was presented at the Session on Derivatives Pricing at the Conference on Computational Intelligence for Financial Engineering, organized by the International Association of Financial Engineers and the Institute of Electrical and Electronic Engineers held in New York, New York in March 1997. An extended summary of this article was published in the proceedings of this conference [20]. Also, articles [18] and [19] were the subject of two invited papers presented at the Session on Financial Engineering and Mathematics of the 18th International Federation for Information Processing Conference on Modeling and Optimization held in Detroit, Michigan in July 1997.

The practical significance of this research on foreign exchange option symmetry for electric power markets, as they move from a regulated environment to a deregulated environment, was recognized by *Energy Marketing* [24]. The practical impact of this research on derivatives markets in general was also acknowledged in *Derivatives Week* [23].

As was indicated in the original article [18] it was conceptually based on article [6] in 1995 by the author which, to the best of our knowledge, introduced for the first time to finance such fundamental notions from modern theoretical physics as observables, invariant or coordinate-free descriptions of a phenomenon, symmetries and related group-theoretical methods. In this regard, it was the methodology employed in article [6] that led the author to formulate the science of Theoretical Finance, which was announced by him at the Special Session on Derivatives and Financial Mathematics of the 909th Meeting of the American Mathematical Society held in Iowa City, Iowa and at the Second World Congress of Nonlinear Analysts held in Athens, Greece, both in 1996. Briefly speaking, Theoretical Finance is related to Finance in a similar manner as Theoretical Physics is related to Physics. It is the purpose of this book to publish article [6].

Article [6] introduced a fundamental symmetry, gauge symmetry between beliefs of market participants and their preferences in a general market environment for a market with exchange of an arbitrary but fixed number n of arbitrary underlying securities. The beliefs of a market participant are formalized as the family of positive evolution operators determined by the subjective transition probabilities for the prices of the underlying securities. The preferences of a market participant are formalized as the family of marginal utilities of consumption of a unit of account at a particular time and at a particular state of the market as expressed by the prices of the underlying securities. In this way a market participant is formalized as a pair of these beliefs and preferences.

We observe that the well-known equation for pricing of capital assets possesses a symmetry between the beliefs of market participants and their preferences. This equation equates the loss in utility associated with the sacrifice of a consumption good due to the purchase of one additional unit of a capital good and carrying it over a period of time with the expected gain in utility associated with the consumption of the consumption good due to selling this additional unit of the capital good at the next period of time. If market participants have agreed upon the market values of a set of European contingent claims with everywhere dense payoffs, that is, if such a set of European contingent claims is actually traded, then the beliefs of market participants can be transformed into preferences in such a way that the established market prices for these European contingent claims remain unchanged. Therefore the beliefs and preferences of these market participants, which are unobservable, are related by a symmetry. Since the operator of multiplication by a marginal utility as a function of time and the state of the market as expressed by the prices of the underlying securities is just a particular case of the operator of multiplication by a function of time and these prices, we recognize that the symmetry between the beliefs and preferences of these market participants is nothing but a gauge symmetry with the gauge group given by the set of all positive real numbers with the group operation being standard multiplication. This provides us with the complete description of the degrees of freedom that such market participants have in terms of their beliefs and preferences: market participants, or more precisely beliefs and preferences of market participants can only differ by a gauge transformation. In this regard, the set of all such market participants with all possible beliefs and preferences is nothing but the orbit of the gauge group and each representative market participant from the class of indistinguishable market participants with the same beliefs and preferences can be characterized as a point in this orbit, that is, using the terminology of modern theoretical physics, by a particular choice of gauge.

If the beliefs of market participants are Markovian and are sufficiently smooth functions of time admitting a description in terms of a, generally speaking, time-dependent infinitesimal generator, the beliefs-preferences gauge symmetry group can be restated in terms of this generator. In this case a, generally speaking, time-dependent infinitesimal generator of a market environment plays the role of a connection on the vector bundle with the fiber being the vector space of payoffs contingent on the current state of the market as expressed by the prices of the underlying securities and with the base space being the trading time set. In this regard, the evolution equation for the values of European contingent claims with this infinitesimal generator of the market environment states that the value of a European contingent claim is such a section of this vector bundle, that is, a vector field, that its covariant derivative is identically zero, that is, it is parallel to itself. Hence the Cauchy problem for this equation states that the value of a European contingent claim, as an element of the vector space of all payoffs contingent on the current state of the market, at an inception time is a result of a parallel transport, given by an evolution operator from the market environment, of its value at an expiration time, that is, its payoff. This covariant derivative enables us to rewrite the evolution equation for the values of European contingent claims in a covariant form, that is, independently of a particular choice of the beliefs-preferences gauge.

Representing the generator of the Markovian beliefs as a pseudodifferential operator, that is, roughly speaking, as a function of the operators of multiplication by the prices of the underlying securities and the operators of differentiation with respect to these prices, the gauge transformations can be represented in a standard way in terms of covariant derivatives with respect to time and the underlying security prices. In this regard, the evolution equation for the values of European contingent claims with the infinitesimal generator of a market environment can be represented in a covariant form by replacing the operators of differentiation with respect to time and the underlying security prices with the operators of covariant differentiation with respect to time and the underlying security prices. These covariant derivatives arise due to a connection on the vector bundle with the fiber being the vector space of real numbers $\mathbb{R}$ and the base space being the price-time space, that is, a subspace $\mathbb{R}^{n+1}_{++}$ of $\mathbb{R}^{n+1}$ consisting of $n+1$-tuples $(s_1, s_2, \ldots, s_n, t)$ with positive entries where s_i is the price of the i-th underlying security at time t. It is in this way that we can physically, or more precisely financially unite the set of all prices and the set of all trading times, that is, the trading time set into a set that we call *price-time*.

As an example we show that in the case of Markovian beliefs given by general multidimensional diffusion processes, gauge transformations take the form of the changes of measure due to the Girsanov theorem. In this regard we interpret the changes of measure due to gauge transformations in the case of general Markovian beliefs as a generalization of the changes of measure due to the Girsanov theorem.

Having described by the beliefs-preferences gauge symmetry the degrees of freedom that market participants have in terms of their beliefs and preferences we obtain an evolution equation that determines, in a general market environment, the values of European contingent claims independent of these beliefs and preferences. We obtain this evolution equation under the assumption that the market participants have agreed upon the market values of a certain minimal set of European contingent claims, that is, under the assumption that this set of European contingent claims is actually traded. It is this minimal set of European contingent claims that dynamically spans the market and we also obtain an equation determining the portfolio of these European contingent claims that is needed to dynamically replicate a given European contingent claim. In this regard we actually define, for a general market environment, the very concepts *to dynamically span* for a set of European contingent claims, *a dynamically complete* for a market, *to dynamically replicate* and *dynamically replicating portfolio* for a given European contingent claim.

As an illustration we show that in the case of Markovian beliefs given by general multidimensional diffusion processes, the evolution equation that determines, in a general market environment, the values of European contingent claims independent of the beliefs and preferences of market participants is nothing but the Black and Scholes equation. Moreover, the dynamically spanning set of European contingent claims can be chosen as the underlying securities themselves and a pure discount bond with the dynamically replicating portfolio chosen according to standard delta hedging.

Representing the generator of Markovian beliefs as a quasidifferential operator introduced by the author in 1987 (see [1], [2], [3], [5] and [4]), that is, as an operator which is, roughly speaking, a strong limit of linear partial differential operators as their orders tend to infinity, we explicitly obtain, with any desired level of accuracy, in the approximation of this generator by the linear partial differential operators, the dynamically spanning set of European contingent claims and the dynamically replicating portfolio for a given European contingent claim. This enables one, by reading with any desired level of accuracy from market data the generator of a market environment and hence the generator of Markovian beliefs, to obtain, with any desired level of accuracy, the actual dynamically spanning set of European contingent claims and the actual dynamically replicating portfolio for a given European contingent claim at a current time. In this regard the assumption that the beliefs are of a Markovian type is irrelevant for the dynamic replication of European contingent claims and can be omitted.

Finally we note that, being able to dynamically replicate general European contingent claims in a general market environment, we can dynamically replicate contingent claims of a general type such as universal contingent claims introduced by the author in 1995 (see [7], [9], [8], [11], [10], [15], and [16]) also in a general market environment.

The practical applications of the beliefs-preferences gauge symmetry presented in this book are significant and far-reaching. We mention a few of the main applications here:

- The beliefs-preferences gauge symmetry group allows one to screen out, directly from market data, inconsistencies in market values of European contingent claims, providing a practical means for detecting, analyzing and utilizing true arbitrage opportunities in derivative markets;

- The beliefs-preferences gauge symmetry group allows one to explicitly construct a dynamically replicating portfolio for a given European contingent claim in a general market environment directly from market data;

- The beliefs-preferences gauge symmetry group allows one to explicitly obtain a minimal set of European contingent claims that dynamically spans the market in a general market environment directly from market data;

- The beliefs-preferences gauge symmetry group is applicable to the dynamic replication of contingent claims of a general type, such as universal contingent claims, as well as European contingent claims.

Our book is written for a wide audience covering the whole spectrum of readers from financial practitioners to researchers in the areas of finance, mathematics, or physics:

- Relative value traders who would like to take advantage of a true arbitrage that is relatively easy to execute;

- Independent private traders with minimal experience and limited technical and financial resources;

- Financial advisors and practitioners who need to apply the most up-to-date methods of finance in their daily professional activities in order to maintain their competitive edge, either personally or for their institutions;

- Financial professionals with a background in quantitative finance, who seek to stay up-to-date with current progress in modern finance, or those with a background in mathematics, who do not wish to be encumbered with mathematical proofs but seek deeper understanding of current trends in mathematical finance;

- Ph.D.s and other researchers in finance and mathematical finance;

- Mathematicians and physicists with or without knowledge of finance, who are interested in entering the field of modern mathematical finance;

- Students and teachers of finance, mathematics or physics who would enjoy taking or giving a course in the field of modern finance, especially in view of the current trends towards interdisciplinary programs in quantitative finance and risk management;

- Anyone with a background in mathematics or finance or both, who is interested in recent developments in modern finance.

Finally we note that the results of this book are not limited to the analysis of financial capital markets. For example, these results can also be applied to the analysis of the dynamics of a multiple species population in ecology and to the behavioral sciences in general.

References

[1] V. A. Kholodnyi. The linear operator method for the analysis of problems in classical electrodynamics. *Reports of Moscow Institute of Electronics and Mathematics*, 1:67–88, 1987.

[2] V. A. Kholodnyi. *The Operator Method for Classical Electrodynamics.* MS thesis, Moscow Institute of Electronics and Mathematics, 1987.

[3] V. A. Kholodnyi. The analysis of a coupled meander-line slow-wave system by the method of pseudodifferential operators. In N. Kopylova, editor, *The 44th All-Union Research Conference Devoted to the Day of Radio, Volume II*, pages 123–124, Moscow, Russia, 1989. Radio and Communication.

[4] V. A. Kholodnyi. *Invention and elaboration of the method of quasidifferential operators for the analysis of slow-wave systems.* PhD thesis, Moscow Institute of Electronics and Mathematics, 1990.

[5] V. A. Kholodnyi. The method of quasidifferential operators for the analysis of slow-wave systems. In *The Workshop on Electrodynamics of Periodic and Irregular Structures*, page 10, Orjonikidze, Russia, 1990.

[6] V. A. Kholodnyi. Beliefs-preferences gauge symmetry group and replication of contingent claims in a general market environment. *Preprint, Integrated Energy Services, Inc.*, 1995.

[7] V. A. Kholodnyi. A nonlinear partial differential equation for American options. *Preprint, Integrated Energy Services, Inc.*, 1995.

[8] V. A. Kholodnyi. On the linearity of Bermudan and American options with general time-dependent payoffs in partial semimodules. *Preprint, Integrated Energy Services, Inc.*, 1995.

[9] V. A. Kholodnyi. Semilinear evolution equation for general derivative contracts. *Preprint, Integrated Energy Services, Inc.*, 1995.

[10] V. A. Kholodnyi. Semilinear evolution equation for universal contingent claims. *Preprint, Integrated Energy Services, Inc.*, 1995.

[11] V. A. Kholodnyi. Universal contingent claims. *Preprint, Integrated Energy Services, Inc.*, 1995.

[12] V. A. Kholodnyi. Approximation of foreign exchange options preserving the foreign exchange option symmetry. *Preprint, Integrated Energy Services, Inc.*, 1996.

[13] V. A. Kholodnyi. Foreign exchange option symmetry in the exchange-rate homogeneous market environment. *Preprint, Integrated Energy Services, Inc.*, 1996.

[14] V. A. Kholodnyi. Foreign exchange symmetry for universal contingent claims. *Preprint, Integrated Energy Services, Inc.*, 1996.

[15] V. A. Kholodnyi. A nonlinear partial differential equation for American options in the entire domain of the state variable. *Nonlinear Analysis, Theory, Methods and Applications*, 30(8):5059–5070, 1997. Proceedings of the Second World Congress of Nonlinear Analysts, Athens, Greece, 1996.

[16] V. A. Kholodnyi. A semilinear evolution equation for general derivative contracts. In J. F. Price, editor, *Derivatives and Financial Mathematics*, pages 119–138, Commack, New York, 1997. Nova Science Publishers, Inc.

[17] V. A. Kholodnyi and G. Paslaski. Foreign exchange symmetry for barrier options with time-dependent barriers in a market environment which admits the method of images. *Preprint, Integrated Energy Services, Inc.*, 1997.

[18] V. A. Kholodnyi and J. F. Price. Foreign exchange option symmetry in a general market environment. *Preprint, Integrated Energy Services, Inc.*, 1996.

[19] V. A. Kholodnyi and J. F. Price. Foreign exchange option symmetry in a multiple currency general market environment. *Preprint, Integrated Energy Services, Inc.*, 1996.

[20] V. A. Kholodnyi and J. F. Price. Foreign exchange option symmetry based on domestic-foreign payoff invariance. In J. F. Marshall and R. J. Marks, editors, *Conference on Computational Intelligence for Financial Engineering*, pages 164–170. IEEE, 1997.

[21] V. A. Kholodnyi and J. F. Price. *Foreign Exchange Option Symmetry.* World Scientific, River Edge, New Jersey, 1998.

[22] V. A. Kholodnyi and J. F. Price. *Foundations of Foreign Exchange Option Symmetry.* IES Press, Fairfield, Iowa, 1998.

[23] S. Rideout. The general Kelvin transform symmetry. *Derivatives Week*, 6(40):8–9, October 1997.

[24] S. Rideout. Sophisticated, unique technology revolutionizes risk management industry. *Energy Marketing*, pages 7–10, September 1997.

Acknowledgments

I would like to acknowledge the great help I received at all the stages of our work on the book.

I thank, first of all, Integrated Energy Services, L.C. for financially supporting the realization and publishing of this book, but most importantly for creating a unique environment that brought together practitioners and researchers. In my opinion, only in such a challenging and stimulating mixture of viewpoints can fresh and fruitful ideas, approaches, and solutions arise. The work that is the subject of this book represents the kernel of one of the many products for risk management offered by this company.

I thank Steven Rideout for his constant attention to this book and for his many practical insights into the nature of financial markets.

I thank Patrick Bosold and George Paslaski for their help in editing the manuscript.

I thank my parents Antonina and Alexander for sharing their fascination with the world around us, what it is made from and how it works, but more importantly for their sleepless nights, care and warmth.

I thank my newborn son Nikita for overseeing the final stages of the project from his favorite spot on my left shoulder in front of the computer screen, but more importantly for needing my sleepless nights, care and warmth.

Saving the best for last, I thank my wife Larisa Kholodnaya for her love, patience and actual help in preparing the book.

Contents

Beliefs-Preferences Gauge Symmetry Group and Replication of Contingent Claims in a General Market Environment

Valery A. Kholodnyi

Integrated Energy Services, Inc.
52 North Third Street
Fairfield, IA 52556
U.S.A.

October, 1995

Abstract

We introduce a fundamental symmetry, a gauge symmetry, between beliefs of market participants and their preferences in a general market environment for a market with exchange of an arbitrary but fixed number n of arbitrary underlying securities. The beliefs of a market participant are formalized as the family of positive evolution operators determined by the subjective transition probabilities for the prices of the underlying securities. The preferences of a market participant are formalized as the family of marginal utilities of consumption of a unit of account at a particular time and at a particular state of the market as expressed by the prices of the underlying securities. In this way a market participant is formalized as a pair of these beliefs and preferences.

We observe that the well-known equation for pricing of capital assets possesses a symmetry between the beliefs of market participants and their preferences. This equation equates the loss in utility associated with the sacrifice of a consumption good due to the purchase of one additional unit of a capital good and carrying it over a period of time with the expected gain in utility associated with the consumption of the consumption good due to selling this additional unit of the capital good at the next period of time. If market participants have agreed upon the market values of a set of European contingent claims with everywhere dense payoffs, that is, if such a set of European contingent claims is actually traded, then the beliefs of market participants can be transformed into preferences in such a way that the established market prices for these European contingent claims remain unchanged. Therefore, the beliefs and preferences of these market participants, which are unobservable, are related by a symmetry. Since the operator of multiplication by a marginal utility as a function of time and the state of the market as expressed by the prices of the underlying securities is just a particular case of the operator of multiplication by a function of time and these prices, we recognize that the symmetry between the beliefs and preferences of these market participants is nothing but a gauge symmetry with the gauge group given by the set of all positive real numbers with the group operation being standard multiplication. This provides us with the complete description of the degrees of freedom that such market participants have in terms of their beliefs and preferences: market participants, or more precisely beliefs and preferences of market participants can only differ by a gauge transformation. In this regard, the set of all such market participants with all possible beliefs and preferences is nothing but the orbit of the gauge group and each representative market participant from the class of indistinguishable market participants with the same beliefs and preferences can be characterized as a point in this orbit, that is, using the terminology of modern theoretical physics, by a particular choice of gauge.

If the beliefs of market participants are Markovian and are sufficiently smooth functions of time admitting a description in terms of a, generally speaking, time-dependent infinitesimal generator, the beliefs-preferences gauge symmetry group can be restated in terms of this generator. In this case a, generally speaking, time-dependent infinitesimal generator of a market environment plays the role of a connection on the vector bundle with the fiber being the vector space of payoffs contingent on the current state of the market as expressed by the prices of the underlying securities and with the base space being the trading time set. In this regard, the evolution equation for the values of European contingent claims with this infinitesimal generator of the market environment states that the value of a European contingent claim is such a section of this vector bundle, that is, a vector field, that its covariant derivative is identically zero, that is, it is parallel to itself. Hence the Cauchy problem for this equation states that the value of a European contingent claim, as an element of the vector space of all payoffs contingent on the current state of the market, at an inception time is a result of a parallel transport, given by an evolution operator from the market environment, of its value at an expiration time, that is, its payoff. This covariant derivative enables us to rewrite the evolution equation for the values of European contingent claims in a covariant form, that is, independently of a particular choice of the beliefs-preferences gauge.

Representing the generator of Markovian beliefs as a pseudodifferential operator, that is, roughly speaking, as a function of the operators of multiplication by the prices of the underlying securities and the operators of differentiation with respect to these prices, the gauge transformations can be represented in a standard way in terms of covariant derivatives with respect to time and the underlying security prices. In this regard, the evolution equation for the values of European contingent claims with the infinitesimal generator of a market environment can be represented in a covariant form by replacing the operators of differentiation with respect to time and the underlying security prices with the operators of covariant differentiation with respect to time and the underlying security prices. These covariant derivatives arise due to a connection on the vector bundle with the fiber being the vector space of real numbers $\mathbb{R}$ and the base space being the price-time space, that is, a subset $\mathbb{R}^{n+1}_{++}$ of $\mathbb{R}^{n+1}$ consisting of $n+1$-tuples $(s_1, s_2, \ldots, s_n, t)$ with positive entries, where s_i is the price of the i-th underlying security at time t. It is in this way that we can physically, or more precisely financially unite the set of all prices and the set of all trading times, that is, the trading time set into a set that we call *price-time.*

As an example we show that in the case of Markovian beliefs given by general multidimensional diffusion processes the gauge transformations take the form of the changes of measure due to the Girsanov theorem. In this regard we interpret the changes of measure due to the gauge transformations in the case of general Markovian beliefs as a generalization of the changes of measure due to the Girsanov theorem.

Having described by the beliefs-preferences gauge symmetry the degrees of freedom that market participants have in terms of their beliefs and preferences we obtain an evolution equation that determines, in a general market environment, the values of European contingent claims independent of these beliefs and preferences. We obtain this evolution equation under the assumption that the market participants have agreed upon the market values of a certain minimal set of European contingent claims, that is, under the assumption that this set of European contingent claims is actually traded. It is this minimal set of European contingent claims that dynamically spans the market and we also obtain the equations determining the portfolio of these European contingent claims that is needed to dynamically replicate a given European contingent claim. In this regard we actually define, for a general market environment, the very concepts *to dynamically span* for a set of European contingent claims, *a dynamically complete* for a market, *to dynamically replicate* and *dynamically replicating portfolio* for a given European contingent claim.

As an illustration we show that in the case of Markovian beliefs given by general multidimensional diffusion processes the evolution equation that determines, in a general market environment, the values of European contingent claims independent of the beliefs and preferences of market participants is nothing but the Black and Scholes equation. Moreover, the dynamically spanning set of European contingent claims can be chosen as the underlying securities themselves and a pure discount bond with a dynamically replicating portfolio chosen according to standard delta hedging.

Representing the generator of Markovian beliefs as a quasidifferential operator introduced by the author in 1987, that is, as an operator which is, roughly speaking, a strong limit of linear partial differential operators as their orders tend to infinity, we explicitly obtain, with any desired level of accuracy, in the approximation of this generator by the linear partial differential operators, the dynamically spanning set of European contingent claims and the dynamically replicating portfolio for a given European contingent claim. This enables one, by reading with any desired level of accuracy from market data the generator of a market environment and hence the generator of Markovian beliefs, to obtain, with any desired level of accuracy, the actual dynamically spanning set of European contingent claims and the dynamically replicating portfolio for a given European contingent claim at a current time. In this regard the assumption that the beliefs are of a Markovian type is irrelevant for the dynamic replication of European contingent claims and can be omitted.

Finally we note that, being able to dynamically replicate general European contingent claims in a general market environment, we can dynamically replicate contingent claims of a general type introduced by the author in 1995 also in a general market environment.

1 Introduction

History shows that virtually all major revolutions in physics that have revealed the deepest insights into nature were made through recognizing that a range of seemingly different phenomena actually represent a common underlying phenomenon. Such a unification indicates the presence of an inherent symmetry in the underlying phenomenon. A standard way to formalize such a symmetry mathematically is in terms of group theory.

Among these symmetries one of the major roles was played by the so-called gauge symmetries. Gauge symmetries were responsible for such major revolutions in physics as the creation of the theory of the classical electromagnetic field by Maxwell, the general theory of relativity by Einstein which provided the theory for the classical gravitational field, and all the successful modern unified quantum field theories which are responsible for the unification of all known interactions in nature, namely

---

Key words and phrases. Contingent claims, dynamic replication, gauge symmetry group.

I thank Integrated Energy Services, Inc. for financial support.

I thank Steve Rideout and Brad Stewart for their constant attention to this work.

I thank my parents Antonina and Alexander for their love, care and understanding.

electromagnetic, weak, strong and gravity.

We introduce a fundamental symmetry, a gauge symmetry, between beliefs of market participants and their preferences in a general market environment for a market with exchange of an arbitrary but fixed number n of arbitrary underlying securities. The beliefs of a market participant are formalized as a family of positive evolution operators determined by the subjective transition probabilities for the prices of the underlying securities. The preferences of a market participant are formalized as a family of marginal utilities of consumption of a unit of account at a particular time and at a particular state of the market as expressed by the prices of the underlying securities. In this way a market participant is formalized as a pair of these beliefs and preferences.

We observe that the well-known equation for pricing of capital assets possesses a symmetry between the beliefs of market participants and their preferences. This equation equates the loss in utility associated with the sacrifice of a consumption good due to the purchase of one additional unit of a capital good and carrying it over a period of time with the expected gain in utility associated with the consumption of the consumption good due to selling this additional unit of the capital good at the next period of time. If market participants have agreed upon the market values of a set of European contingent claims with everywhere dense payoffs, that is, if such a set of European contingent claims is actually traded, then the beliefs of market participants can be transformed into preferences in such a way that the established market prices for these European contingent claims remain unchanged. Therefore the beliefs and preferences of these market participants, which are unobservable, are related by a symmetry. Since the operator of multiplication by a marginal utility as a function of time and the state of the market as expressed by the prices of the underlying securities is just a particular case of the operator of multiplication by a function of time and these prices, we recognize that the symmetry between the beliefs and preferences of these market participants is nothing but a gauge symmetry with the gauge group given by the set of all positive real numbers with the group operation being standard multiplication. This provides us with the complete description of the degrees of freedom that such market participants have in terms of their beliefs and preferences: market participants, or more precisely beliefs and preferences of market participants can only differ by a gauge transformation. In this regard, the set of all such market participants with all possible beliefs and preferences is nothing but the orbit of the gauge group and each representative market participant from the class of indistinguishable market participants with the same beliefs and preferences can be characterized as a point in this orbit, that is, using the terminology of modern theoretical physics, by a particular choice of gauge.

If the beliefs of market participants are Markovian and are sufficiently smooth functions of time admitting a description in terms of a, generally speaking, time-dependent infinitesimal generator, the beliefs-preferences gauge symmetry group can be restated in terms of this generator. In this case a, generally speaking, time-dependent infinitesimal generator of a market environment plays the role of a connection on the vector bundle with the fiber being the vector space of payoffs contingent on the current state of the market as expressed by the prices of the underlying securities and with the base space being the trading time set. In this regard, the evolution equation for the values of European contingent claims with this infinitesimal generator of the market environment states that the value of a European contingent claim is such a section of this vector bundle, that is, a vector field, that its covariant derivative is identically zero, that is, it is parallel to itself. Hence the Cauchy problem for this equation states that the value of a European contingent claim, as an element of the vector space of all payoffs contingent on the current state of the market, at an inception time is a result of a parallel transport, given by the evolution operator from the market environment, of its value at expiration time, that is, its payoff. This covariant derivative enables us to rewrite the evolution equation for the values of European contingent claims in a covariant form, that is, independently of a particular choice of the beliefs-preferences gauge.

Representing the generator of the Markovian beliefs as a pseudodifferential operator, that is, roughly speaking, as a function of the operators of multiplication by the prices of the underlying securities and the operators of differentiation with respect to these prices, the gauge transformations can be represented in a standard way in terms of covariant derivatives with respect to time and the underlying security prices. In this regard, the evolution equation for the values of European contingent claims with the infinitesimal generator of a market environment can be represented in a covariant form by replacing the operators of differentiation with respect to time and the underlying security prices with the operators of covariant differentiation with respect to time and the underlying security prices. These covariant derivatives arise due to a connection on the vector bundle with the fiber being the vector space of real numbers $\mathbb{R}$ and the base space being the price-time space, that is, a subset $\mathbb{R}^{n+1}_{++}$ of $\mathbb{R}^{n+1}$ consisting of $n+1$-tuples $(s_1, s_2, \ldots, s_n, t)$ with positive entries, where s_i is the price of the i-th underlying security at time t. It is in this way that we can physically, or more precisely financially unite the set of all prices and the set of all trading times, that is, the trading time set into a set that we call *price-time.*

As an example we show that in the case of Markovian beliefs given by general multidimensional diffusion processes the gauge transformations take the form of the changes of measure due to the Girsanov theorem. In this regard we interpret the changes of measure due the gauge transformations in the case of general Markovian beliefs as a generalization of the changes of measure due to the Girsanov theorem.

Having described by the beliefs-preferences gauge symmetry

the degrees of freedom that market participants have in terms of their beliefs and preferences we obtain an evolution equation that determines, in a general market environment, the values of European contingent claims independent of these beliefs and preferences. We obtain this evolution equation under the assumption that the market participants have agreed upon the market values of a certain minimal set of European contingent claims, that is, if this set of European contingent claims is actually traded. It is this minimal set of European contingent claims that dynamically spans the market and we also obtain an equation determining the portfolio of these European contingent claims that is needed to dynamically replicate a given European contingent claim. In this regard we actually define, for a general market environment, the very concepts *to dynamically span* for a set of European contingent claims, *a dynamically complete* for a market, *to dynamically replicate* and *dynamically replicating portfolio* for a given European contingent claim.

As an illustration we show that in the case of Markovian beliefs given by general multidimensional diffusion processes the evolution equation that determines, in a general market environment, the values of European contingent claims independent of the beliefs and preferences of market participants is nothing but the Black and Scholes equation. Moreover, the dynamically spanning set of European contingent claims can be chosen as the underlying securities themselves and a pure discount bond with a dynamically replicating portfolio chosen according to standard delta hedging.

Representing the generator of Markovian beliefs as a quasidifferential operator introduced by the author in 1987 (see [26], [27], [29], [31] and [30]), that is, as an operator which is, roughly speaking, a strong limit of linear partial differential operators as their orders tend to infinity, we explicitly obtain, with any desired level of accuracy, in the approximation of this generator by the linear partial differential operators, the dynamically spanning set of European contingent claims and the dynamically replicating portfolio for a given European contingent claim. This enables one, by reading with any desired level of accuracy from market data the generator of a market environment and hence the generator of Markovian beliefs, to obtain with any desired level of accuracy the actual dynamically spanning set of European contingent claims and the dynamically replicating portfolio for a given European contingent claim at a current time. In this regard the assumption that the beliefs are of a Markovian type is irrelevant for the dynamic replication of European contingent claims and can be omitted.

Finally we note that being able to dynamically replicate general European contingent claims in a general market environment, we can dynamically replicate contingent claims of a general type introduced by the author in 1995 (see [32], [38] and [33] and also articles [40] and [39] in preparation) also in a general market environment.

The article is organized as follows. In Section (2) we present the prerequisite financial and mathematical concepts used throughout the article. In Section (3) we formalize the concepts of a market participant and a market populace and introduce the beliefs-preferences gauge symmetry group on a market populace. In Sections (4) and (5) we illustrate the beliefs-preferences gauge symmetry group in the particular case of a market populace that consists of market participants with beliefs determined by general multidimensional diffusion processes. In Section (6) we apply the beliefs-preferences gauge symmetry group to the dynamic replication of European contingent claims in a general market environment and establish the equation determining a portfolio of European contingent claims that dynamically replicates an arbitrary European contingent claim and the evolution equation determining the value of an arbitrary European contingent claim independent of the beliefs and preferences of the market participants. In Section (7) we illustrate the application of the beliefs-preferences gauge symmetry group to the dynamic replication of European contingent claims in the particular case of a market populace that consists of market participants with beliefs determined by general multidimensional diffusion processes. In Section (8) we introduce a method of quasidifferential operators that allows one to approximately determine with any desired level of accuracy a portfolio of European contingent claims that dynamically replicates an arbitrary European contingent claim and the value of an arbitrary European contingent claim independent of the beliefs and preferences of market participants.

2 Preliminaries

For the sake of financial clarity, and in order not to overload the article with details of a purely mathematical nature, we present our results rather formally from the rigorous mathematical standpoint, supporting them whenever possible with appropriate financial justification.

For convenience of reference, we present here the standard definitions of a vector space, a partially ordered vector space, and a vector lattice.

2.1. Definition. A set A is called a *partially ordered set* if there exists a binary relation $\preceq$ on A, called a *partial order*, with the following properties:

(i) $a \preceq a$,

(ii) if $a \preceq b$ and $b \preceq a$, then $a = b$, and

(iii) if $a \preceq b$ and $b \preceq c$, then $a \preceq c$,

for all a, b and c in A. A partially ordered set A with a binary relation $\preceq$ will be denoted by $(A, \preceq)$.

We write $a \succeq b$ to mean $b \preceq a$, $a \prec b$ to mean $a \preceq b$ and $a \neq b$, and $a \succ b$ to mean $a \succeq b$ and $a \neq b$.

2.2. Definition. Let $(A, \preceq)$ be a partially ordered set. If $a \preceq c$ and $b \preceq c$, then c is called an *upper bound* for a and b. Furthermore, if $c \preceq d$ whenever d is an upper bound for a and b, we call c the *least upper bound* or the *supremum* of a and b and denote it by $a \vee b$. Similarly, if $c \preceq a$ and $c \preceq b$, then c is called a *lower bound* for a and b. Furthermore, if $d \preceq c$ whenever d is a lower bound for a and b, we call c the *greatest lower bound* or the *infimum* of a and b and denote it by $a \wedge b$.

A partially ordered set $(A, \preceq)$ is called a *lattice* if $a \vee b$ and $a \wedge b$ exist in A for all a and b in A.

2.3. Definition. A *group* is a pair $(H, \cdot)$ where H is a nonempty set and $\cdot$ is a binary operation on H such that:

(i) the binary operation $\cdot$ is associative, that is $a \cdot (b \cdot c) = (a \cdot b) \cdot c$ for all a, b and c in H,

(ii) there exists an *identity* e in H such that $e \cdot a = a \cdot e = a$ for all a in H, and

(iii) for each a in H there exists an *inverse* a^{-1} in H such that $a \cdot a^{-1} = a^{-1} \cdot a = e$.

If the binary operation $\cdot$ is *commutative*, that is, if $a \cdot b = b \cdot a$ for all a and b in H, then the group $(H, \cdot)$ is said to be *abelian*.

2.4. Remark. Whenever ambiguity is unlikely we will denote a group $(H, \cdot)$ simply by H.

2.5. Definition. Let $(G, \circ)$ and $(H, \bullet)$ be two groups. The *direct product* $(G, \circ) \otimes (H, \bullet)$ of the groups $(G, \circ)$ and $(H, \bullet)$ is the group $(G \times H, \cdot)$ with the group operation $\cdot$ defined by

$$(g_1, h_1) \cdot (g_2, h_2) = (g_1 \circ g_2, h_1 \bullet h_2)$$

for all g_1 and g_2 in G and for all h_1 and h_2 in H.

2.6. Remark. In the light of Remark (2.4), whenever ambiguity is unlikely we will denote the direct product $(G, \circ) \otimes (H, \bullet)$ of the groups $(G, \circ)$ and $(H, \bullet)$ simply by $G \times H$.

2.7. Definition. A *real vector space* V is a set which is

- equipped with the structure of an abelian group written additively, that is:

  (i) $x + y$ is in V for every x and y in V,

  (ii) $x + (y + z) = (x + y) + z$ for every x, y and z in V,

  (iii) there exists an element $\mathbf{0}$ in V such that $x + \mathbf{0} = \mathbf{0} + x = x$ for every x in V,

  (iv) for every x in V there exists $-x$ in V such that $x + (-x) = (-x) + x = \mathbf{0}$,

(v) $x + y = y + x$ for every x and y in V,

- equipped with everywhere defined external composition law $\mathbb{R} \times V \to V$ written multiplicatively such that:

  (vi) $r\,x$ is in V for every r in $\mathbb{R}$ and x in V,

  (vii) $r\,(x + y) = r\,x + r\,y$ for every r in $\mathbb{R}$ and x and y in V,

  (viii) $(r + s)\,x = r\,x + s\,x$ for every r and s in $\mathbb{R}$ and x in V,

  (ix) $r\,(s\,x) = (r\,s)\,x$ for every r and s in $\mathbb{R}$ and x in V,

  (x) $1\,x = x$ for every x in V,

  where $\mathbb{R}$ is the set of real numbers.

2.8. Remark. Similarly to the real vector space or a vector space over the field of real numbers $\mathbb{R}$ one can define a complex vector space or a vector space over the field of complex numbers $\mathbb{C}$.

2.9. Definition. A real vector space E is called a *partially ordered vector space* if it is a partially ordered set with partial order $\preceq$ with the properties:

(i) if $x \preceq y$, then $x + z \preceq y + z$,

(ii) if $x \preceq y$, then $\lambda x \preceq \lambda y$,

for x, y and z in E and λ in $\mathbb{R}_+$, the set of nonnegative real numbers.

2.10. Definition. A partially ordered vector space $(E, \preceq)$ with the partial order generated by the nonnegative cone E_+ is called *nonnegatively generated* (see, for example, [5] page 31) if for each x in E there exist (not necessarily unique) x_1 and x_2 in E_+ such that $x = x_1 - x_2$, or equivalently:

$$E = E_+ - E_+.$$

2.11. Definition. A set K in a real vector space E is called a *cone* if the following properties hold:

(i) $K + K \subseteq K$,

(ii) $\lambda K \subseteq K$ for all λ in $\mathbb{R}_+$,

(iii) $K \cap (-K) = \{0\}$.

For a partially ordered vector space $(E, \preceq)$, the subset $E_+ = \{x \in E : 0 \preceq x\}$ is a cone called the *nonnegative cone* of E. The subset $E_{++} = \{x \in E : 0 \prec x\}$ is called the *positive cone* of E. In turn, each cone K in a real vector space E generates a partial order on E as follows:

$$x \preceq y \text{ if } y - x \in K.$$

In this case, K is a nonnegative cone in E.

2.12. Definition. Let $(E, \preceq)$ be a partially ordered vector space with a nonnegative cone E_+. A linear operator $A : E \to E$ is called *nonnegative* if it preserves the nonnegative cone E_+ of E, that is, if Ax is in E_+ whenever x is in E_+.

2.13. Definition. Let $(E, \preceq)$ be a partially ordered vector space with a positive cone E_{++}. A linear operator $A : E \to E$ is called *positive* if it preserves the positive cone E_{++} of E, that is, if Ax is in E_{++} whenever x is in E_{++}.

2.14. Remark. Let $(E, \preceq)$ be a partially ordered vector space with a nonnegative cone E_+ and a positive cone E_{++}. It is clear if $A : E \to E$ is a positive linear operator then it is also a nonnegative linear operator.

2.15. Definition. A partially ordered vector space $(E, \preceq)$ that is also a lattice is called a *vector lattice*.

Finally, we present the definition of a Lie algebra (see, for example, [45] page 1).

2.16. Definition. Let $\mathfrak{F}$ be either the field $\mathbb{R}$ of real numbers or the field $\mathbb{C}$ of complex numbers. A pair $(V, [,])$ of a vector space V over $\mathfrak{F}$ and a binary operation $[,]$ on V is called a *Lie algebra* if:

(i) the map $x \mapsto [x, y]$ is linear for all y in V,

(ii) $[x, y] = -[y, x]$ for all x and y in V,

(iii) the *Jacobi identity*

$$[x, [y, z]] + [y, [z, x]] + [z, [x, y]] = \mathbf{0}$$

holds for all x, y and z in V, where $\mathbf{0}$ is the identity element of the abelian group $(V, +)$.

The binary operation $[,]$ in a Lie algebra $(V, [,])$ is called a *Lie product.*

2.17. Definition. Let $X = (x_1, x_2, \ldots x_n)$ be a basis of an n-dimensional Lie algebra $(V, [,])$ over $\mathfrak{F}$, where the basis and the dimension of the Lie algebra $(V, [,])$ are identified with that of the vector space V. The *structure constants* c_{ij}^k in $\mathfrak{F}$ of the Lie algebra $(V, [,])$ are defined by

$$[x_i, x_j] = \sum_{k=1}^{n} c_{ij}^k \, x_k.$$

2.1 Market Environment

We assume the general setting introduced in [33] presenting whenever we need, for convenience of reference, the relevant concepts, terminology and results of that article.

Consider an economy without transaction costs in which trading is allowed at any time in a *trading time set* $\mathcal{T}$, an arbitrary closed subset of the real numbers (see [33]).

Denote by $s_\tau = (s_\tau^1, s_\tau^2, \ldots, s_\tau^n)$ the prices (in units of account) of one unit of the (only) n underlying securities at time

τ in $\mathcal{T}$, where $s_\tau^i > 0$ is the price of one unit of the i-th underlying security of time τ.

Denote by $\mathbb{R}^n_{++}$ the set of all $x = (x_1, x_2, \ldots, x_n)$ in $\mathbb{R}^n$ such that each x_i is a positive real number. It is clear that s_τ is in $\mathbb{R}^n_{++}$.

Whenever ambiguity is unlikely, we will write s in place of s_τ and s_i in place of s_τ^i. Also whenever ambiguity is unlikely, in the case of a single underlying security, that is, if $n = 1$, we will write s_τ or s in place of s_τ^1.

Denote by $\Pi = \Pi(\mathbb{R}^n_{++})$ the vector space of all real-valued functions on the set $\mathbb{R}^n_{++}$. Let Π_+ be the nonnegative cone of Π, that is the set of all nonnegative real-valued functions on $\mathbb{R}^n_{++}$.

We note that the vector space Π with the partial order generated by the nonnegative cone Π_+ is a partially ordered vector space. Moreover, equipped with the lattice operations of supremum and infimum defined as pointwise maximum and minimum, Π is a vector lattice.

2.18. Definition. A *European option* (on the underlying securities) with inception time t, expiration time T (t and T are in $\mathcal{T}$ with $t \leq T$), and with payoff g in Π_+ is a contract that gives the right, but not the obligation, to receive payoff $g(s_T)$ (in units of account) at expiration time T, where the prices of the underlying securities are s_T at this time T.

For each t and T in $\mathcal{T}$ with $t \leq T$, denote [33] by $\mathbf{V}(t,T)$ the operator that maps a payoff g of a European option with inception time t and expiration time T to the value $\mathcal{E}(t,T,g)$ of this option at inception time t as a function of the prices s_t of the underlying securities at this time t, that is:

$$\mathcal{E}(t,T,g) = \mathbf{V}(t,T)\, g. \tag{2.1}$$

Since the value of a European option at its expiration time is equal to its payoff, $\mathbf{V}(t,T)$ is the identity operator whenever the inception time t is equal to expiration time T.

By definition, the domain of the operator $\mathbf{V}(t,T)$ is in Π_+. Due to the no-free-lunch argument, the range of the operator $\mathbf{V}(t,T)$ is also in Π_+. Moreover, the operator $\mathbf{V}(t,T) : \Pi_+ \to \Pi_+$ is additive and positive homogeneous [33], that is

$$\mathbf{V}(t,T)(\lambda\, g + \mu\, f) = \lambda\, \mathbf{V}(t,T)\, g + \mu\, \mathbf{V}(t,T)\, f, \tag{2.2}$$

for all λ and μ in $\mathbb{R}_+$ and all admissible g and f in Π_+. Indeed, due to relation (2.1), equality (2.2) can be rewritten as follows

$$\mathcal{E}(t,T,\lambda\, g + \mu\, f) = \lambda\, \mathcal{E}(t,T,g) + \mu\, \mathcal{E}(t,T,f), \tag{2.3}$$

for all λ and μ in $\mathbb{R}_+$ and all admissible g and f in Π_+. Financially, the preceding equality (2.3) means that the value $\mathcal{E}(t,T,\lambda\, g + \mu\, f)$ at time t of the portfolio consisting of a single European option with inception time t, expiration time T and payoff $\lambda\, g + \mu\, f$ is equal to the value $\lambda\, \mathcal{E}(t,T,g) + \mu\, \mathcal{E}(t,T,f)$ at time t of the portfolio consisting of λ units of the European option with inception time t, expiration time T and payoff g, and μ units of the European option with inception time t, expiration time T and payoff f. The values of these two portfolios at time T are equal to $\lambda\, g + \mu\, f$ and hence are equal to each other. Therefore, to complete the proof of equality (2.3) and hence of equality (2.2), it is enough to note that, by the no-arbitrage argument, the values of these two portfolios are also equal to each other at time t.

The operator $\mathbf{V}(t,T) : \Pi_+ \to \Pi_+$ admits [33] a unique linear extension to an operator whose domain is a linear subspace of Π and whose range is in Π. Denote this new linear operator again by $\mathbf{V}(t,T)$.

Due to the previous discussion, the linear operator $\mathbf{V}(t,T)$ preserves the nonnegative cone Π_+ in Π, that is, $\mathbf{V}(t,T)$ is a nonnegative linear operator on Π. Moreover, due to the previous discussion, $\mathbf{V}(t,t)$ is the identity operator on Π for each t in $\mathcal{T}$.

Later in the article we will need further properties of the evolution operators $\mathbf{V}(t,T)$, which were introduced and established in [33].

From the financial standpoint [33] the only function contained in both the kernel subspace of the evolution operator $\mathbf{V}(t,T) : \Pi \to \Pi$ and in Π_+ must be the zero function $\mathbf{0}$ in Π. Indeed, due to the no-free-lunch argument there must not exist $g \neq \mathbf{0}$ in Π_+ such that $\mathbf{V}(t,T)\,g = \mathbf{0}$. This means that the evolution operator $\mathbf{V}(t,T) : \Pi \to \Pi$ preserves the positive cone Π_{++} in Π, that is, $\mathbf{V}(t,T)$ is a positive operator on Π.

Now we need the following definition of an absolutely positive operator introduced in [33].

2.19. Definition. We call a linear operator $A : \Pi \to \Pi$ an *absolutely positive operator* if $(A\,g)(s) > 0$ for each s in $\mathbb{R}^n_{++}$ whenever $g(s) > 0$ for each s in $\mathbb{R}^n_{++}$.

2.20. Remark. It is clear that if an operator $A : \Pi \to \Pi$ is absolutely positive then it is positive and hence nonnegative.

2.21. Remark. In the case when the domain and range of an operator $A : \Pi \to \Pi$ consist of measurable functions then the inequalities in Definition (2.19) are understood to hold for almost all s in $\mathbb{R}^n_{++}$.

2.22. Remark. We comment that the concept of an absolutely positive operator was in fact defined in [33] for an arbitrary partially ordered vector space and for a general, not necessarily linear, operator.

From the financial standpoint [33] the evolution operator $\mathbf{V}(t,T) : \Pi \to \Pi$ must be absolutely positive. Indeed, due to the no-free-lunch argument there must not exist s in $\mathbb{R}^n_{++}$ such that $\big(\mathbf{V}(t,T)\,g\big)(s) = 0$ whenever $g(s) > 0$ for each s in $\mathbb{R}^n_{++}$.

These are all the structural properties of the evolution operators $\mathbf{V}(t,T)$ that we need in order to present beliefs-preferences gauge symmetry in a general market environment. For the complete analysis of the minimal set of such properties, as dictated by financial reasons, see [33].

2.23. Remark. We comment that there are important reasons for not imposing any further technical restrictions on the operators $\mathbf{V}(t,T)$ such as their domains and ranges. First, as we indicated earlier in this Section, we do not wish to overload the article with too many fine details only of interest to pure mathematicians. Second, these details might obscure the structure of the beliefs-preferences gauge symmetry, which is essentially algebraic in nature. Third, and much more importantly, we want to be as independent as possible of assumptions on the particular nature of a stochastic process for the prices of the underlying securities. Moreover, we would like to be free of the very assumption of the existence of such a stochastic process. One way in which these stochastic issues might arise from such further technical restrictions is as follows. The kernel $\mathbf{V}(t,T)(s_t, s_T)$ of the operator $\mathbf{V}(t,T)$, as a function of s_t, is financially the value at inception time t of the European option with expiration time T and with the Dirac delta function $\delta(\cdot - s_T)$ as its payoff, that is, the value of the Arrow-Debreu security understood in the generalized sense. If a model of a marketplace is chosen that treats the dynamics of the prices of the underlying securities as a stochastic process, then this kernel can be financially interpreted as the discounted transition probability distribution of the prices of the underlying securities. Therefore, any such further restrictions on the operator $\mathbf{V}(t,T)$ are effectively assumptions on the particular nature of the stochastic process for the prices of the underlying securities.

The operators $\mathbf{V}(t,T)$, with t and T in $\mathcal{T}$ and $t \leq T$, contain all the information about the model of a market in which European options are being priced. This justifies the following definition.

2.24. Definition. We will say [33] that a *market environment* is given by, or simply is, the family of evolution operators

$$\mathbf{V} = \{\mathbf{V}(t,T) : \Pi \to \Pi \,|\, t,T \in \mathcal{T}, t \leq T\}.$$

2.25. Definition. We call [33] a market environment $\mathbf{V}$ in which the evolution operators $\mathbf{V}(t,T)$ are functions of $T-t$ a *time-homogeneous market environment.*

2.26. Remark. We comment [33] that the concept of a market environment can be defined in the generality of each $\mathbf{V}(t,T)$ being, in fact, an operator from Π_T to Π_t, where each Π_t with t in $\mathcal{T}$ is a copy of Π. Financially, Π_t with t in $\mathcal{T}$ is the space of all payoffs contingent on the state of the market as expressed by the prices of the underlying securities at time t.

Denote by g^+ and g^- the nonnegative and nonpositive parts of g in Π, that is $g^+ = g \vee 0$ and $-g^- = g \wedge 0$, where 0 is the zero function in Π. It is clear that

$$g = g^+ - g^-, \quad g \in \Pi.$$

It is also clear that g^+ and g^- are in Π_+ for each g in Π.

2.27. Definition. A *European contingent claim* (on the underlying securities) with inception time t, expiration time T (t and T are in $\mathcal{T}$ with $t \leq T$), and with payoff g in Π is a portfolio consisting of:

- a long position on the European option with inception time t, expiration time T and with the payoff g^+, and
- a short position on the European option with inception time t, expiration time T and with the payoff g^-.

2.28. Remark. It is clear that, due to the definition of the evolution operator $\mathbf{V}(t,T)$, the value in Π at the inception time t of a European contingent claim with expiration time T and with a payoff g in Π is given by $\mathbf{V}(t,T)\,g$.

2.2 Intervention Condition

Equipped with the framework of a market environment, we are now in a position to introduce a particular type of market environment crucial for the future presentation.

2.29. Definition. A market environment $\mathbf{V}$, that is, the family of evolution operators

$$\mathbf{V} = \{\mathbf{V}(t,T) : \Pi \to \Pi \,|\, t, T \in \mathcal{T},\, t \leq T\},$$

is said [33] to satisfy the *intervention condition* if for each t, τ, and T in $\mathcal{T}$ such that $t \leq \tau \leq T$ the following relation holds:

$$\mathbf{V}(t,\tau)\mathbf{V}(\tau,T) = \mathbf{V}(t,T). \tag{2.4}$$

The intervention condition financially expresses the requirement of intertemporal no-arbitrage in a derivative market and is a generalization to a general market environment of a semigroup intertemporal no-arbitrage condition introduced by Garman in [22] which, in our terminology, is applicable only to a time-homogeneous market environment. Indeed, in terms of European options the intervention condition reads:

$$\mathcal{E}(t,T,g) = \mathcal{E}(t,\tau,\mathcal{E}(\tau,T,g)), \tag{2.5}$$

for any t, τ, and T in $\mathcal{T}$ such that $t \leq \tau \leq T$. Financially the preceding relationship (2.5) states that the value $\mathcal{E}(t,T,g)$ at inception time t of the European option with expiration time T and payoff g is equal, by the no-arbitrage argument, to the value $\mathcal{E}(t,\tau,\mathcal{E}(\tau,T,g))$ at inception time t of the European option with expiration time τ with $t \leq \tau \leq T$ and payoff equal to the value $\mathcal{E}(\tau,T,g)$ at inception time τ of the European option with expiration time T and payoff g. It is relationship (2.5) that gives rise, according to the definition of the evolution operators $\mathbf{V}(t,T)$, to the intervention condition (2.4).

2.3 Generators of a Market Environment

A market environment $\mathbf{V}$ that satisfies the intervention condition and is such that its trading time set $\mathcal{T}$ is an interval, either finite or infinite, of nonnegative real numbers and its evolution operators $\mathbf{V}(t,T)$ are sufficiently smooth functions of time, admits the following simple characterization given by the author in [33], [32] and [38].

2.30. Definition. We say that the one-parameter family of linear operators

$$\boldsymbol{L} = \{\boldsymbol{L}(t) : \Pi \to \Pi \,|\, t \in \mathcal{T}\},$$

generates a market environment $\mathbf{V}$ if for each t and T in the trading time set $\mathcal{T}$ with $t \leq T$ and for each admissible payoff v_T in Π the function $\mathbf{V}(t,T)v_T$ of t is a solution, possibly generalized, of the Cauchy problem for the evolution equation

$$\begin{aligned} \frac{d}{dt}v + \boldsymbol{L}(t)v = 0, \quad t < T, \\ v(T) = v_T. \end{aligned} \tag{2.6}$$

An operator $\boldsymbol{L}(t)$ in the family $\boldsymbol{L}$ is called a *generator at time* t, or simply a *generator*.

2.31. Remark. We comment that the class of admissible payoffs can be characterized by the properties of the evolution operator $\mathbf{V}(t,T)$ as an operator-valued function of t and T and is beyond the scope of this article. The analysis of this admissibility issue is presented in [33].

2.32. Remark. We comment that, suitably interpreted, the generators $\boldsymbol{L}(t)$ of a market environment $\mathbf{V}$ are dispersive operators. (For the definition of a dispersive operator see, for example [55] and [19]).

2.33. Remark. If a market environment $\mathbf{V}$ is generated by the family of linear operators $\boldsymbol{L}$ then, according to Cauchy problem (2.6), each evolution operator $\mathbf{V}(t,T)$ from $\mathbf{V}$ is formally given by

$$\mathbf{V}(t,T) = e^{\int_t^T \boldsymbol{L}(\tau)d\tau}, \tag{2.7}$$

where each generator $\boldsymbol{L}(\tau)$ at time τ acts in the order opposite to that of τ.

2.34. Remark. We note that the Cauchy problem for the evolution equation (2.6) can be rewritten in terms of $\mathbf{V}(t,T)$ as follows

$$\begin{gathered} \frac{d}{dt}\mathbf{V}(t,T) + \boldsymbol{L}(t)\,\mathbf{V}(t,T) = 0, \quad t < T, \\ \mathbf{V}(t,T)|_{t=T} = \boldsymbol{I}, \end{gathered} \tag{2.8}$$

where $\boldsymbol{I}$ is the identity operator on Π.

We comment that because of the definition of the evolution operators $\mathbf{V}(t,T)$, for each admissible v_T in Π_+ the solution $\mathbf{V}(t,T)v_T$ in Π_+ at time t of the Cauchy problem for the evolution equation in (2.6) is the value at inception time t of the European option with expiration time T and payoff v_T in the market environment $\mathbf{V}$. Hence the evolution equation in (2.6) determines the values of European options in this market environment. Approximating the time derivative $\frac{d}{dt}v$ in this evolution equation by an appropriate finite difference $(v(t)-v(t-\Delta t))/\Delta t$, it is easy to see that the generator $\boldsymbol{L}(t)$ at time t determines an infinitesimal change in the values of such European options at this time t

$$v(t-\Delta t) = v(t) + \Delta t\,\boldsymbol{L}(t)\,v(t) + o(\Delta t)$$

where $o(\Delta t)$ stands for a function in Π of order higher than Δt with respect to an appropriate topology.

Similarly, because of the definition of the evolution operators $\mathbf{V}(t,T)$, for each admissible v_T in Π the solution $\mathbf{V}(t,T)v_T$ in Π at time t of the Cauchy problem for the evolution equation in (2.6) is the value at inception time t of the European contingent claim with expiration time T and payoff v_T in the market environment $\mathbf{V}$. Hence the evolution equation in (2.6) determines the values of European contingent claims in this market environment. Approximating the time derivative $\frac{d}{dt}v$ in this evolution equation by an appropriate finite difference $(v(t)-v(t-\Delta t))/\Delta t$, it is easy to see that the generator $\boldsymbol{L}(t)$ at time t determines an infinitesimal change in the values of such European contingent claims at this time t

$$v(t - \Delta t) = v(t) + \Delta t\, \boldsymbol{L}(t)\, v(t) + o(\Delta t)$$

where $o(\Delta t)$ stands for a function in Π of order higher than Δt with respect to an appropriate topology.

2.4 Abstract Market Environment

In order to present beliefs-preferences gauge symmetry in an invariant or coordinate-free setting we need the concepts of a generalized or abstract payoff and a generalized or abstract European contingent claim introduced by the author in [33]. Following this article, we financially define a *generalized or abstract payoff* as a measure of satisfaction or, more precisely, marginal utility and in this sense as a measure of an abstract wealth. For convenience of reference, we outline here the derivation given in [33] of the mathematical structure of a vector lattice for the *space of all generalized or abstract payoffs* denoted by $\mathbf{\Pi}$.

First we show that financially $\mathbf{\Pi}$ admits a structure of a real vector space.

We assume that financially an agent can have a privilege to solely receive a satisfaction without an obligation to deliver a satisfaction and can have an obligation to solely deliver a satisfaction without a privilege to receive a satisfaction. Denote by $\mathbf{\Pi}_+$ the set of all abstract payoffs that correspond to a privilege to solely receive a satisfaction without an obligation to deliver a satisfaction.

We interpret financially a portfolio consisting of an abstract payoff x in $\mathbf{\Pi}_+$ as a long position on x.

If an agent has a privilege to receive a portfolio consisting of two abstract payoffs x and y in $\mathbf{\Pi}_+$ then this portfolio itself financially represents an abstract payoff z which corresponds to a privilege to solely receive a satisfaction without an obligation to deliver a satisfaction, that is, represents an abstract payoff

z in $\mathbf{\Pi}_+$. Moreover, financially it is irrelevant in what order these abstract payoffs x and y enter into the portfolio, that is, whether the portfolio consists of the abstract payoffs x and y or abstract payoffs y and x it represents the same abstract payoff z. In symbols this means that for any generalized payoffs x and y in $\mathbf{\Pi}_+$ there exists a generalized payoff z in $\mathbf{\Pi}_+$ which we denote as $x + y = y + x$. We comment that the abstract payoffs x and y are received at the same time and therefore we do not interpret the order with which x and y enter into the portfolio as a chronological order in which x and y are to be received.

Furthermore, if an agent has a privilege to receive a portfolio of three generalized payoffs x, y and z in $\mathbf{\Pi}_+$, then this portfolio itself financially represents an abstract payoff w which corresponds to a privilege to solely receive a satisfaction without an obligation to deliver a satisfaction, that is, represents an abstract payoff w in $\mathbf{\Pi}_+$. Then financially the abstract payoff w can be received in two equivalent ways:

- as a portfolio of the abstract payoff x and the abstract payoff that represents the portfolio of the abstract payoffs y and z,
- as a portfolio of the abstract payoff that represents the portfolio of the abstract payoffs x and y and the abstract payoff z.

In symbols this means that for any generalized payoffs x, y and z in $\mathbf{\Pi}_+$ there exists a generalized payoff w in $\mathbf{\Pi}_+$ that we denote as $x + (y + z) = (x + y) + z$ and hence simply as $x + y + z$.

It is clear that financially there exists an abstract payoff in $\mathbf{\Pi}_+$ that corresponds to a privilege to receive no satisfaction without an obligation to deliver a satisfaction. Denote this abstract payoff by $\mathbf{0}$. It is also clear that this abstract payoff $\mathbf{0}$ is neutral in the sense that an agent would be indifferent to having the privilege to receive either:

- a portfolio of an abstract payoff x in $\mathbf{\Pi}_+$ and the abstract payoff $\mathbf{0}$, or

- the arbitrary abstract payoff x in $\mathbf{\Pi}_+$ itself.

In symbols this means that there exists an abstract payoff $\mathbf{0}$ in $\mathbf{\Pi}_+$ such that for each abstract payoff x in $\mathbf{\Pi}_+$ we have that $x + \mathbf{0} = \mathbf{0} + x = x$.

Now for each abstract payoff x in $\mathbf{\Pi}_+$ that, by definition, corresponds to a privilege to solely receive a satisfaction without an obligation to deliver a satisfaction there exists financially an abstract payoff in $\mathbf{\Pi}$ that corresponds to the obligation to solely deliver a satisfaction without a privilege to receive a satisfaction such that their portfolio corresponds to the neutral abstract payoff $\mathbf{0}$ in $\mathbf{\Pi}$. Denote this abstract payoff in $\mathbf{\Pi}$ that corresponds to the obligation to solely deliver a satisfaction without a privilege to receive a satisfaction by $-x$. We interpret financially this abstract payoff $-x$ as a short position on the abstract payoff x. In symbols we have that for each abstract payoff x in $\mathbf{\Pi}_+$ there exists an abstract payoff $-x$ in $\mathbf{\Pi}$ such that $x + (-x) = (-x) + x = \mathbf{0}$. Equivalently, the set of all abstract payoffs in $\mathbf{\Pi}$ that corresponds to the obligation to solely deliver a satisfaction without a privilege to receive a satisfaction is $-\mathbf{\Pi}_+$.

We note that the neutral abstract payoff $\mathbf{0}$ in $\mathbf{\Pi}$ is the only abstract payoff that simultaneously corresponds to a privilege to solely receive a satisfaction without an obligation to deliver a satisfaction and to the obligation to solely deliver a satisfaction without a privilege to receive a satisfaction. In symbols this means that $\mathbf{\Pi}_+ \cap (-\mathbf{\Pi}_+) = \{\mathbf{0}\}$.

If an agent has a portfolio of a long position on an abstract payoff x_1 in $\mathbf{\Pi}_+$ and a short position on an abstract payoff x_2 in $\mathbf{\Pi}_+$, that is, if an agent has a privilege to solely receive a satisfaction without an obligation to deliver a satisfaction that corresponds to x_1 in $\mathbf{\Pi}_+$ and the obligation to solely deliver a satisfaction without a privilege to receive a satisfaction that corresponds to $-x_2$ in $-\mathbf{\Pi}_+$, we will say that an agent is to receive the abstract payoff $x = x_1 - x_2$ in $\mathbf{\Pi}$.

Now each abstract payoff x in $\mathbf{\Pi}$ can be financially identified with a portfolio of an abstract payoff x_1 in $\mathbf{\Pi}_+$ and an abstract payoff $-x_2$ in $-\mathbf{\Pi}_+$, or equivalently with a portfolio of a long position on the abstract payoff x_1 in $\mathbf{\Pi}_+$ and a short position on the abstract payoff x_2 in $\mathbf{\Pi}_+$. In symbols this means that for each abstract payoff x in $\mathbf{\Pi}$ there exist abstract payoffs x_1 and x_2 in $\mathbf{\Pi}_+$ such that $x = x_1 - x_2$. Equivalently, the space of all abstract payoffs $\mathbf{\Pi}$ admits the decomposition $\mathbf{\Pi} = \mathbf{\Pi}_+ - \mathbf{\Pi}_+$.

With this decomposition $\mathbf{\Pi} = \mathbf{\Pi}_+ - \mathbf{\Pi}_+$ in mind, we financially interpret a portfolio of two abstract payoffs $x = x_1 - x_2$ and $y = y_1 - y_2$ in $\mathbf{\Pi}$ as a portfolio of a long position on the abstract payoff $x_1 + y_1$ in $\mathbf{\Pi}_+$ and a short position on the abstract payoff $x_2 + y_2$ in $\mathbf{\Pi}_+$. Then this portfolio of the abstract payoffs $x = x_1 - x_2$ and $y = y_1 - y_2$ in $\mathbf{\Pi}$ itself financially represents an abstract payoff $z = z_1 - z_2$ in $\mathbf{\Pi}$ with $z_1 = x_1 + y_1$ and $z_2 = x_2 + y_2$ in $\mathbf{\Pi}_+$. In symbols this means that for each abstract payoff $x = x_1 - x_2$ and $y = y_1 - y_2$ in $\mathbf{\Pi} = \mathbf{\Pi}_+ - \mathbf{\Pi}_+$ there exists an abstract payoff $z = z_1 - z_2$ in $\mathbf{\Pi} = \mathbf{\Pi}_+ - \mathbf{\Pi}_+$ with $z_1 = x_1 + y_1$ and $z_2 = x_2 + y_2$ in $\mathbf{\Pi}_+$ which we denote by $x + y$. In this way $+$ defines a binary operation on $\mathbf{\Pi}$ which we call a *summation.*

It is clear that, equipped with the binary operation of summation, the space of all abstract payoffs $\mathbf{\Pi}$ is an abelian group, that is, the properties (i)-(v) in Definition (2.7) hold for $\mathbf{\Pi}$ and $+$.

If an agent has a privilege to receive an abstract payoff x in $\mathbf{\Pi}_+$ then the agent has the privilege to receive a portfolio of any amount r in $\mathbb{R}_+$ of units of this abstract payoff x. This portfolio itself financially represents an abstract payoff y which corresponds to a privilege to solely receive a satisfaction without an obligation to deliver a satisfaction, that is, represents an abstract payoff y in $\mathbf{\Pi}_+$. In symbols this means that for any abstract payoff x in $\mathbf{\Pi}_+$ and any r in $\mathbb{R}_+$ there exists a generalized payoff y in $\mathbf{\Pi}_+$ that we denote as $r\,x$.

Moreover, a portfolio of r in $\mathbb{R}_+$ units of the portfolio of abstract payoffs x and y in $\mathbf{\Pi}_+$ is financially equivalent to a portfolio of r units of the abstract payoff x and r units of the abstract payoff y. In symbols this means that for each abstract payoff x and y in $\mathbf{\Pi}_+$ and each r in $\mathbb{R}_+$ we have $r\,(x+y) = r\,x + r\,y$.

Furthermore, a portfolio of $r+s$, with r and s in $\mathbb{R}_+$, units of an abstract payoff x in $\mathbf{\Pi}_+$ financially is equivalent to a portfolio of r units of the abstract payoff x and s units of the abstract payoff x. In symbols this means that for each r and s in $\mathbb{R}_+$ and each x in $\mathbf{\Pi}_+$ we have $(r+s)\,x = r\,x + s\,x$.

Also a portfolio of $r\,s$, with r and s in $\mathbb{R}_+$, units of an abstract payoff x in $\mathbf{\Pi}_+$ financially is equivalent to a portfolio of r units of the portfolio of s units of the abstract payoff x. In symbols this means that for each r and s in $\mathbb{R}_+$ and each x in $\mathbf{\Pi}_+$ we have $(r\,s)\,x = r\,(s\,x)$.

Finally a portfolio of 1 unit of an abstract payoff x in $\mathbf{\Pi}_+$ financially is equivalent to the abstract payoff x itself. In symbols this means that for each x in $\mathbf{\Pi}_+$ we have $1\,x = x$.

With this structure on $\mathbf{\Pi}_+$ we financially interpret a portfolio of r in $\mathbb{R}$ units of an abstract payoff $x = x_1 - x_2$ in $\mathbf{\Pi} = \mathbf{\Pi}_+ - \mathbf{\Pi}_+$ as a portfolio of:

- a long position on a portfolio of r^+ in $\mathbb{R}_+$ units of the abstract payoff x_1 in $\mathbf{\Pi}_+$ and a portfolio of r^- in $\mathbb{R}_+$ units of the abstract payoff x_2 in $\mathbf{\Pi}_+$, and

- a short position on a portfolio of r^+ in $\mathbb{R}_+$ units of the abstract payoff x_2 in $\mathbf{\Pi}_+$ and a portfolio of r^- in $\mathbb{R}_+$ units of the abstract payoff x_1 in $\mathbf{\Pi}_+$,

where $r = r^+ - r^-$ with nonnegative part $r^+ = \max\{r, 0\}$ and nonpositive part $r^- = -\min\{r, 0\}$. In symbols, this means that for each $r = r^+ - r^-$ in $\mathbb{R}$ and each $x = x_1 - x_2$ in $\mathbf{\Pi} = \mathbf{\Pi}_+ - \mathbf{\Pi}_+$ we have $r\,x = r^+x_1 + r^-x_2 - (r^+x_2 + r^-x_1)$. Defined in this way, we call the external composition law $\mathbb{R} \times \mathbf{\Pi} \to \mathbf{\Pi}$ a *multiplication by real numbers*.

It is clear that the space of all abstract payoffs $\mathbf{\Pi}$ with the binary operation of summation and the external composition law of multiplication by real numbers satisfy the properties (vi)-(x) in Definition (2.7).

Therefore the space of all abstract payoffs $\mathbf{\Pi}$ equipped with the binary operation of summation and the external composition law of multiplication by real numbers admits a structure of a real vector space. Moreover, it is clear from the preceding discussion that the set $\mathbf{\Pi}_+$ of all abstract payoffs that correspond to a privilege to solely receive a satisfaction without an obligation to deliver a satisfaction is a cone of $\mathbf{\Pi}$. Therefore $\mathbf{\Pi}$ is a partially ordered vector space with the partial order generated by the cone $\mathbf{\Pi}_+$. In this way $\mathbf{\Pi}_+$ is in fact a nonnegative cone of $\mathbf{\Pi}$. Moreover, by construction, partial ordered vector space $\mathbf{\Pi} = \mathbf{\Pi}_+ - \mathbf{\Pi}_+$ is nonnegatively generated.

We comment that the partial order in $\mathbf{\Pi}$ generated by the nonnegative cone $\mathbf{\Pi}_+$ has the following financial interpretation. An abstract payoff x in $\mathbf{\Pi}$ is preferred or equivalent to an abstract payoff y in $\mathbf{\Pi}$, that is, $x - y$ is in $\mathbf{\Pi}_+$ if an abstract payoff $x - y$ that represents the portfolio of a long position on x and a short position on y corresponds to a privilege to solely receive a satisfaction without an obligation to deliver a satisfaction.

Now we are ready to show that $\mathbf{\Pi}$ admits in fact a structure of a vector lattice.

Assume that an agent is to receive an abstract payoff $x = x_1 - x_2$ in $\mathbf{\Pi} = \mathbf{\Pi}_+ - \mathbf{\Pi}_+$. The decomposition $x = x_1 - x_2$, as we have mentioned above, is clearly not unique. For example, for any $y = y_1 - y_2$ in $\mathbf{\Pi}$ such that $x_1 \preceq y_1$ and $x_2 \preceq y_2$ and $y_1 - x_1 = y_2 - x_2$, or equivalently for any $y = y_1 - y_2$ in $\mathbf{\Pi}$ such that $y_1 = x_1 + z$ and $y_2 = x_2 + z$ for some z in $\mathbf{\Pi}_+$, we have $x = y_1 - y_2$. In this regard it is financially reasonable to require that for each abstract payoff $x = x_1 - x_2$ in $\mathbf{\Pi}$ an agent is capable of selecting an abstract payoff among all possible abstract payoffs x_1 in $\mathbf{\Pi}_+$ such that it corresponds to a minimal satisfaction that is guaranteed to be solely received without an obligation for a satisfaction to be delivered. Similarly, it is financially reasonable to require that for each abstract payoff $x = x_1 - x_2$ in $\mathbf{\Pi}$ an agent is capable of selecting an abstract payoff among all possible abstract payoffs $-x_2$ in $-\mathbf{\Pi}_+$ such that it corresponds to the maximum satisfaction, that is, of selecting an abstract payoff among all possible abstract payoffs x_2 in $\mathbf{\Pi}_+$ such that it corresponds to a minimal satisfaction that is obligated to be solely delivered without a privilege for a satisfaction to be received.

More precisely, it is financially reasonable to require that for each abstract payoff $x = x_1 - x_2$ in $\mathbf{\Pi}$ an agent is capable of selecting an abstract payoff x^+ in $\mathbf{\Pi}$, in fact in $\mathbf{\Pi}_+$ such that it is minimal among all abstract payoffs that are simultaneously preferred or equal to the neutral abstract payoff $\mathbf{0}$ and to the abstract payoff x:

(i) $\mathbf{0} \preceq x^+$ and $x \preceq x^+$,

(ii) for any y in $\mathbf{\Pi}$ such that $\mathbf{0} \preceq y$ and $x \preceq y$ we have that $x^+ \preceq y$.

In symbols, for each x in $\mathbf{\Pi}$ there exists x^+ in $\mathbf{\Pi}$, in fact in $\mathbf{\Pi}_+$, such that it is the least upper bound or supremum for x and $\mathbf{0}$.

Similarly, it is financially reasonable to require that for each abstract payoff $x = x_1 - x_2$ in $\mathbf{\Pi}$ an agent is capable of selecting an abstract payoff $-x^-$ in $\mathbf{\Pi}$, in fact in $-\mathbf{\Pi}_+$ such that it is maximal among all abstract payoffs that the neutral abstract payoff $\mathbf{0}$ and the abstract payoff x are simultaneously preferred or equal to:

(i) $-x^- \preceq \mathbf{0}$ and $-x^- \preceq x$,

(ii) for any y in $\mathbf{\Pi}$ such that $y \preceq \mathbf{0}$ and $y \preceq x$ we have that $y \preceq -x^-$.

In symbols, for each x in $\mathbf{\Pi}$ there exists $-x^-$ in $\mathbf{\Pi}$, in fact in $-\mathbf{\Pi}_+$, such that it is the greatest lower bound or infimum for x and $\mathbf{0}$.

Equivalently, it is financially reasonable to require that for each abstract payoff $x = x_1 - x_2$ in $\mathbf{\Pi}$ an agent is capable of selecting an abstract payoff x^- in $\mathbf{\Pi}$, in fact in $\mathbf{\Pi}_+$ such that it is minimal among all abstract payoffs that are simultaneously preferred or equal to the neutral abstract payoff $\mathbf{0}$ and to the abstract payoff $-x$:

(i) $\mathbf{0} \preceq x^-$ and $-x \preceq x^-$,

(ii) for any y in $\mathbf{\Pi}$ such that $\mathbf{0} \preceq y$ and $-x \preceq y$ we have that $x^- \preceq y$.

In symbols, for each x in $\mathbf{\Pi}$ there exists x^- in $\mathbf{\Pi}$, in fact in $\mathbf{\Pi}_+$, such that it is the least upper bound or supremum for $-x$ and $\mathbf{0}$.

Having defined x^+ and x^- for each abstract payoff x in $\mathbf{\Pi}$ we can, for any abstract payoffs x and y in $\mathbf{\Pi}$, define the abstract payoff $x \vee y = x + (y - x)^+$ and $x \wedge y = x - (y - x)^-$ (Compare with [50] page 51).

It is clear by the definition of x^+ for an abstract payoff x in $\mathbf{\Pi}$ that $x \vee y$ is the least upper bound or supremum of the abstract payoffs x and y in $\mathbf{\Pi}$. It is also clear by the definition of x^- for an abstract payoff x in $\mathbf{\Pi}$ that $x \wedge y$ is the greatest lower bound or infimum of the abstract payoffs x and y in $\mathbf{\Pi}$.

Therefore, equipped with the binary operations of supremum $\vee$ and infimum $\wedge$, the partially ordered vector space $\mathbf{\Pi}$ admits a structure of a vector lattice.

It is clear that any vector lattice $(E, \preceq)$ is nonnegatively generated (see [50] page 58) since for each x in E we have

$$x = x^+ - x^- \tag{2.9}$$

where x^+ with x^- are in E_+. In fact, it is well known (see [5] page 49) that in any vector lattice $(E, \preceq)$ the decomposition $x = x_1 - x_2$ with x_1 and x_2 in E_+ implies that $x^+ \preceq x_1$ and $x^- \preceq x_2$, which is the essence of our line of financial justification of the vector lattice structure of the space of all abstract payoffs $\mathbf{\Pi}$.

2.35. Remark. As an example of the vector lattice of all abstract payoffs $\mathbf{\Pi}$ we consider the vector lattice of all payoffs Π

contingent on the state of the market as expressed by the prices of the underlying securities. We recall that Π is a vector lattice with the partial order generated by the nonnegative cone Π_+ and with the lattice operations of supremum and infimum defined as pointwise maximum and minimum.

2.36. Remark. Another example of the vector lattice of all abstract payoffs $\mathbf{\Pi}$ is as follows. Assume that there exist two countries with completely separate economies so that, in particular, their currencies are not traded. Let there exist an investor who has a portfolio x of a payoff x_1 in $\Pi^{(1)}$ contingent on the prices of the underlying securities of the first country and a payoff x_2 in $\Pi^{(2)}$ contingent on the prices of the underlying securities of the second country, where $\Pi^{(1)}$ and $\Pi^{(2)}$ are copies of Π, and where for the sake of simplicity we have assumed that the number of the underlying securities is the same in both countries. We interpret such a portfolio x as an abstract payoff $x = (x_1, x_2)$ in the space of all abstract payoffs $\mathbf{\Pi} = \Pi \bigoplus \Pi$. We comment that the vector lattice structure on $\mathbf{\Pi}$ is induced by those in Π. More precisely, the nonnegative cone $\mathbf{\Pi}_+$ of $\mathbf{\Pi}$ is defined as the set of all $x = (x_1, x_2)$ in $\mathbf{\Pi}$ such that x_1 is in $\Pi_+^{(1)}$ and x_2 is in $\Pi_+^{(2)}$ and the lattice operations of supremum $\vee_{\mathbf{\Pi}}$ and infimum $\wedge_{\mathbf{\Pi}}$ in $\mathbf{\Pi}$ are defined by

$$x \vee_{\mathbf{\Pi}} y = (x_1 \vee_{\Pi^{(1)}} y_1, x_2 \vee_{\Pi^{(2)}} y_2),$$

and

$$x \wedge_{\mathbf{\Pi}} y = (x_1 \wedge_{\Pi^{(1)}} y_1, x_2 \wedge_{\Pi^{(2)}} y_2)$$

for each $x = (x_1, x_2)$ and $y = (y_1, y_2)$ in $\mathbf{\Pi}$. We comment that here $\vee_{\Pi^{(1)}}$ and $\wedge_{\Pi^{(1)}}$ stand for the lattice operations of supremum and infimum on $\Pi^{(1)}$ and that $\vee_{\Pi^{(2)}}$ and $\wedge_{\Pi^{(2)}}$ stand for the lattice operations of supremum and infimum on $\Pi^{(2)}$.

2.37. Remark. In contrast to numerical utility which assumes the total or linear ordering on the set of all "satisfactions" (see, for example, [47] page 26) we have only partial ordering on the space of all abstract payoffs $\mathbf{\Pi}$.

2.38. Remark. The natural counterpart of the requirement that the mixture operation $p\,v + q\,u$ with p and q in $[0,1]$ such that $p+q=1$ must be defined for numerical utility (see, for example, [47] page 24) is the convexity of the nonnegative cone $\mathbf{\Pi}_+$ of the space of all abstract payoffs $\mathbf{\Pi}$.

Having defined the vector lattice structure on the space of all abstract payoffs $\mathbf{\Pi}$ we are in a position, following [33], to define options with abstract payoffs that we will call generalized or abstract options. In particular, the relevant type of generalized or abstract options that we need for the presentation of the beliefs-preferences gauge symmetry group are European generalized or abstract options.

2.39. Definition. A *generalized or abstract European option* with inception time t, expiration time T (t and T are in $\mathcal{T}$, and $t \le T$), and with abstract payoff g in $\mathbf{\Pi}_+$ is a contract that gives the right, but not the obligation, to receive abstract payoff g at expiration time T.

For each t and T in $\mathcal{T}$ with $t \le T$, denote by $\mathcal{V}(t,T)$ the operator that maps an abstract payoff g of an abstract European option with inception time t and expiration time T to the abstract value of the option denoted by $\mathcal{E}(t,T,g)$ at inception time t, that is

$$\mathcal{E}(t,T,g) = \mathcal{V}(t,T)g, \tag{2.10}$$

where g is in $\mathbf{\Pi}_+$. Since, by the no-arbitrage argument, the value of an abstract European option at its expiration time is equal to its abstract payoff, $\mathcal{V}(t,T)$ is the identity operator whenever inception time t is equal to expiration time T.

By definition, the domain of the operator $\mathcal{V}(t,T)$ is in $\mathbf{\Pi}_+$. Due to the no-free-lunch argument, the range of the operator $\mathcal{V}(t,T)$ is also in $\mathbf{\Pi}_+$. Moreover, the operator $\mathcal{V}(t,T) : \mathbf{\Pi}_+ \to \mathbf{\Pi}_+$ is additive and positive homogeneous [33], that is:

$$\mathcal{V}(t,T)(\lambda\, g + \mu\, f) = \lambda\, \mathcal{V}(t,T)\, g + \mu\, \mathcal{V}(t,T)\, f, \tag{2.11}$$

for all λ and μ in $\mathbb{R}_+$ and all admissible g and f in $\mathbf{\Pi}_+$. Indeed, due to the relation (2.10) the equality (2.11) can be rewritten as follows

$$\boldsymbol{\mathcal{E}}(t,T,\lambda\, g+\mu\, f)=\lambda\,\boldsymbol{\mathcal{E}}(t,T,g)+\mu\,\boldsymbol{\mathcal{E}}(t,T,f), \tag{2.12}$$

for all λ and μ in $\mathbb{R}_+$ and all admissible g and f in $\mathbf{\Pi}_+$. Financially the preceding equality (2.12) means that the value $\boldsymbol{\mathcal{E}}(t,T,\lambda\, g+\mu\, f)$ at time t of the portfolio consisting of a single abstract European option with inception time t, expiration time T and abstract payoff $\lambda\, g+\mu\, f$ is equal to the value $\lambda\,\boldsymbol{\mathcal{E}}(t,T,g)+\mu\,\boldsymbol{\mathcal{E}}(t,T,f)$ at time t of the portfolio consisting of λ units of the abstract European option with inception time t, expiration time T and abstract payoff g and μ units of the abstract European option with inception time t, expiration time T and abstract payoff f. The values of these two portfolios at the time T are equal to $\lambda\, g+\mu\, f$ and hence are equal to each other. Therefore, to complete the proof of equality (2.12) and hence of equality (2.11) it is enough to note that, by the no-arbitrage argument, the values of these two portfolios are also equal to each other at time t.

The operator $\boldsymbol{\mathcal{V}}(t,T):\mathbf{\Pi}_+\rightarrow\mathbf{\Pi}_+$ admits [33] a unique linear extension to an operator whose domain is a linear subspace of $\mathbf{\Pi}$ and whose range is in $\mathbf{\Pi}$. Denote this new linear operator again by $\boldsymbol{\mathcal{V}}(t,T)$. We call $\boldsymbol{\mathcal{V}}(t,T)$ a *generalized or abstract evolution operator.*

Due to the previous discussion, the linear operator $\boldsymbol{\mathcal{V}}(t,T)$ preserves the nonnegative cone $\mathbf{\Pi}_+$ in $\mathbf{\Pi}$, that is, $\boldsymbol{\mathcal{V}}(t,T)$ is a nonnegative linear operator on $\mathbf{\Pi}$. Moreover, due to the previous discussion, $\boldsymbol{\mathcal{V}}(t,t)$ is the identity operator on $\mathbf{\Pi}$ for each t in $\mathcal{T}$.

These are all the structural properties of the abstract evolution operators $\boldsymbol{\mathcal{V}}(t,T)$ that we need in order to present the beliefs-preferences gauge symmetry. For the complete analysis of the minimal set of such properties, as dictated by financial reasons, see [33].

The operators $\mathcal{V}(t,T)$, with t and T in $\mathcal{T}$ and $t \leq T$, contain all the information about the model of a market in which abstract European options are being priced. This justifies the following definition.

2.40. Definition. We will say [33] that a *generalized or abstract market environment* is given by, or simply is, the family of abstract evolution operators

$$\mathcal{V} = \{\mathcal{V}(t,T) : \mathbf{\Pi} \to \mathbf{\Pi} \,|\, t, T \in \mathcal{T}, t \leq T\}.$$

2.41. Remark. We comment that the concept of an abstract market environment can be defined in the generality of each $\mathcal{V}(t,T)$ being, in fact, an operator from $\mathbf{\Pi}_T$ to $\mathbf{\Pi}_t$, where each $\mathbf{\Pi}_t$ with t in $\mathcal{T}$ is a copy of $\mathbf{\Pi}$. Financially, $\mathbf{\Pi}_t$ is the space of all abstract payoffs at time t.

Denote by g^+ and g^- the nonnegative and nonpositive parts of g in $\mathbf{\Pi}$, that is, $g^+ = g \vee 0$ and $-g^- = g \wedge 0$, where $\mathbf{0}$ is the neutral abstract payoff in $\mathbf{\Pi}$ and where $\vee$ and $\wedge$ are the lattice operations of supremum and infimum in $\mathbf{\Pi}$. It is clear that

$$g = g^+ - g^-, \quad g \in \mathbf{\Pi}.$$

It is also clear that g^+ and g^- are in $\mathbf{\Pi}_+$ for each g in $\mathbf{\Pi}$.

2.42. Definition. A *generalized or abstract European contingent claim* with inception time t, expiration time T (t and T are in $\mathcal{T}$ with $t \leq T$), and with abstract payoff g in Π is a portfolio consisting of:

- a long position on the abstract European option with inception time t, expiration time T and with an abstract payoff g^+, and
- a short position on the abstract European option with inception time t, expiration time T and with an abstract payoff g^-.

2.43. Remark. It is clear that due to the definition of the evolution operator $\mathcal{V}(t,T)$, the value in $\mathbf{\Pi}$ at inception time t of an abstract European contingent claim with expiration time T and abstract payoff g in $\mathbf{\Pi}$ is given by $\mathcal{V}(t,T)\,g$.

2.5 Intervention Condition for an Abstract Market Environment

Equipped with the framework of a generalized or abstract market environment we are now in a position to introduce a particular type of abstract market environment crucial for the future presentation.

2.44. Definition. A generalized or abstract market environment $\mathcal{V}$, that is, the family of abstract evolution operators

$$\mathcal{V} = \{\mathcal{V}(t,T) : \mathbf{\Pi} \to \mathbf{\Pi} \,|\, t, T \in \mathcal{T},\, t \le T\},$$

is said [33] to satisfy the *intervention condition* if for each t, τ, and T in $\mathcal{T}$ such that $t \le \tau \le T$ the following relation holds:

$$\mathcal{V}(t,\tau)\mathcal{V}(\tau,T) = \mathcal{V}(t,T). \tag{2.13}$$

The intervention condition financially expresses the requirement of intertemporal no-arbitrage for abstract European contingent claims. Indeed, in terms of abstract European options, the intervention condition reads:

$$\mathcal{E}(t,T,g) = \mathcal{E}(t,\tau,\mathcal{E}(\tau,T,g)), \tag{2.14}$$

for any t, τ, and T in $\mathcal{T}$ such that $t \le \tau \le T$. Financially, the preceding relationship (2.14) states that the value $\mathcal{E}(t,T,g)$ at inception time t of the abstract European option with expiration time T and abstract payoff g is equal, by the no-arbitrage argument, to the value $\mathcal{E}(t,\tau,\mathcal{E}(\tau,T,g))$ at inception time t of the abstract European option with expiration time τ, with $t \le \tau \le T$, and the abstract payoff equal to the value $\mathcal{E}(\tau,T,g)$ at inception time τ of the abstract European option with expiration time T and payoff g. It is the relationship (2.14) that gives rise, according to the definition of the generalized or abstract evolution operators $\mathcal{V}(t,T)$, to the intervention condition (2.13).

2.6 Generators of an Abstract Market Environment

An abstract market environment $\mathcal{V}$ that satisfies the intervention condition and is such that its trading time set $\mathcal{T}$ is an interval, either finite or infinite, of nonnegative real numbers and its abstract evolution operators $\mathcal{V}(t,T)$ are sufficiently smooth functions of time, admits the following simple characterization given by the author in [33].

2.45. Definition. We say that the one-parameter family of linear operators

$$\mathcal{L} = \{\mathcal{L}(t) : \mathbf{\Pi} \to \mathbf{\Pi} \,|\, t \in \mathcal{T}\},$$

generates an abstract market environment $\mathcal{V}$ if, for each t and T in the trading time set $\mathcal{T}$ with $t \leq T$ and for each admissible abstract payoff v_T in $\mathbf{\Pi}$, the function $\mathcal{V}(t,T)v_T$ of t is a solution, possibly generalized, of the Cauchy problem for the evolution equation

$$\begin{aligned} \frac{d}{dt}v + \mathcal{L}(t)v = 0, \quad t < T, \\ v(T) = v_T. \end{aligned} \tag{2.15}$$

An operator $\mathcal{L}(t)$ in the family $\mathcal{L}$ is called a *generalized or abstract generator at time t*, or simply a *generalized or abstract generator.*

2.46. Remark. We comment that the class of admissible payoffs can be characterized by the properties of the generalized or abstract evolution operator $\mathcal{V}(t,T)$ as an operator-valued function of t and T and is beyond the scope of this article. The analysis of this admissibility issue is presented in [33].

2.47. Remark. We comment that, suitably interpreted, the generators $\mathcal{L}(t)$ of a generalized or abstract market environment $\mathcal{V}$ are dispersive operators.

2.48. Remark. If a generalized or abstract market environment $\mathcal{V}$ is generated by the family of linear operators $\mathcal{L}$ then, according to Cauchy problem (2.15), each generalized or abstract evolution operator $\mathcal{V}(t,T)$ from $\mathcal{V}$ is formally given by

$$\mathcal{V}(t,T) = e^{\int_t^T \mathcal{L}(\tau)d\tau}, \tag{2.16}$$

where each generator $\mathcal{L}(\tau)$ at time τ acts in the order opposite to that of τ.

2.49. Remark. We note that the Cauchy problem for the evolution equation (2.15) can be rewritten in terms of $\mathcal{V}(t,T)$ as follows

$$\begin{aligned} \frac{d}{dt}\mathcal{V}(t,T) + \mathcal{L}(t)\mathcal{V}(t,T) = 0, \quad t < T, \\ \mathcal{V}(t,T)|_{t=T} = \mathcal{I}, \end{aligned} \tag{2.17}$$

where $\mathcal{I}$ is the identity operator on $\mathbf{\Pi}$.

We comment that because of the definition of the abstract evolution operators $\mathcal{V}(t,T)$, for each admissible abstract payoff v_T in $\mathbf{\Pi}_+$ the solution $\mathcal{V}(t,T)v_T$ in $\mathbf{\Pi}_+$ at time t of the Cauchy problem for the evolution equation in (2.15) is the value at inception time t of the abstract European option with expiration time T and abstract payoff v_T in the abstract market environment $\mathcal{V}$. Hence the evolution equation in (2.15) determines the values of abstract European options in this abstract market environment. Approximating the time derivative $\frac{d}{dt}v$ in this evolution equation by an appropriate finite difference $(v(t) - v(t-\Delta t))/\Delta t$, it is easy to see that the generalized or abstract generator $\mathcal{L}(t)$ at time t determines an infinitesimal change in the values of such abstract European options at this time t

$$v(t - \Delta t) = v(t) + \Delta t\, \mathcal{L}(t)\, v(t) + o(\Delta t)$$

where $o(\Delta t)$ stands for an element of $\mathbf{\Pi}$ of order higher than Δt with respect to an appropriate topology.

Similarly, because of the definition of the abstract evolution operators $\boldsymbol{\mathcal{V}}(t,T)$, for each admissible abstract payoff v_T in $\mathbf{\Pi}$ the solution $\boldsymbol{\mathcal{V}}(t,T)v_T$ in $\mathbf{\Pi}$ at time t of the Cauchy problem for the evolution equation in (2.15) is the value at inception time t of the abstract European contingent claim with expiration time T and abstract payoff v_T in the abstract market environment $\boldsymbol{\mathcal{V}}$. Hence the evolution equation in (2.15) determines the values of abstract European contingent claims in this abstract market environment. Approximating the time derivative $\frac{d}{dt}v$ in this evolution equation by an appropriate finite difference $(v(t) - v(t - \Delta t))/\Delta t$, it is easy to see that the generalized or abstract generator $\boldsymbol{\mathcal{L}}(t)$ at time t determines an infinitesimal change in the values of such abstract European contingent claims at this time t

$$v(t - \Delta t) = v(t) + \Delta t\, \boldsymbol{\mathcal{L}}(t)\, v(t) + o(\Delta t)$$

where $o(\Delta t)$ stands for an element of $\mathbf{\Pi}$ of order higher than Δt with respect to an appropriate topology.

2.50. Remark. In the setting of Remark (2.36), assume that times t and T are in both trading time sets of the first and second country. Consider a portfolio of two European options both with inception time t, expiration time T, and with payoffs g_1 in $\Pi_+^{(1)}$ and g_2 in $\Pi_+^{(2)}$. Denote the values of these options at inception time t by $\mathcal{E}_1(t,T,g_1)$ in $\Pi_+^{(1)}$ and $\mathcal{E}_2(t,T,g_2)$ in $\Pi_+^{(2)}$. The portfolio of these two European options can be interpreted as an abstract European option with inception time t, expiration time T and abstract payoff $g = (g_1, g_2)$ in $\mathbf{\Pi}_+$. The value $\boldsymbol{\mathcal{E}}(t,T,g)$ in $\mathbf{\Pi}_+$ of this abstract European option at inception time t is given by

$$\boldsymbol{\mathcal{E}}(t,T,g) = (\mathcal{E}_1(t,T,g_1), \mathcal{E}_2(t,T,g_2)).$$

Assume that the trading time sets of the first and second country coincide. Denote these trading time sets by $\mathcal{T}$. Let

$$\mathbf{V}_1 = \{\mathbf{V}_1(t,T) : \Pi \to \Pi \,|\, t,T \in \mathcal{T},\, t \leq T\}$$

and

$$\mathbf{V}_2 = \{\mathbf{V}_2(t,T) : \Pi \to \Pi \,|\, t,T \in \mathcal{T},\, t \leq T\}$$

stand for the market environments of the first and second countries. Then the abstract market environment

$$\boldsymbol{\mathcal{V}} = \{\boldsymbol{\mathcal{V}}(t,T) : \mathbf{\Pi} \to \mathbf{\Pi} \,|\, t,T \in \mathcal{T},\, t \leq T\}$$

is defined in such a way that each abstract evolution operator $\boldsymbol{\mathcal{V}}(t,T)$ is the following two by two diagonal matrix operator

$$\boldsymbol{\mathcal{V}}(t,T) = \begin{pmatrix} \mathbf{V}_1(t,T) & 0 \\ 0 & \mathbf{V}_2(t,T) \end{pmatrix}.$$

If the market environments $\mathbf{V}_1$ and $\mathbf{V}_2$ of the first and second countries are generated by the families

$$\boldsymbol{L}_1 = \{\boldsymbol{L}_1(t) : \Pi \to \Pi \,|\, t \in \mathcal{T}\}$$

and

$$\boldsymbol{L}_2 = \{\boldsymbol{L}_2(t) : \Pi \to \Pi \,|\, t \in \mathcal{T}\}$$

then the abstract market environment $\boldsymbol{\mathcal{V}}$ is generated by the family

$$\boldsymbol{\mathcal{L}} = \{\boldsymbol{\mathcal{L}}(t) : \mathbf{\Pi} \to \mathbf{\Pi} \,|\, t \in \mathcal{T}\},$$

where each abstract generator $\boldsymbol{\mathcal{L}}(t)$ is the following two by two diagonal matrix operator

$$\boldsymbol{\mathcal{L}}(t) = \begin{pmatrix} \boldsymbol{L}_1(t) & 0 \\ 0 & \boldsymbol{L}_2(t) \end{pmatrix}.$$

3 The Beliefs-Preferences Gauge Symmetry Group

Denote by $v(t) = v(t, s_t)$ in Π with t in $\mathcal{T}$ the value at inception time t of a European contingent claim with payoff $v(T) = v(T, s_T)$ in Π at expiration time T.

It is well known (see, for example [16], [9], [10], [8] and [14] and references therein) that at equilibrium the value $v(t) = v(t, s_t)$ is given by

$$v(t, s_t) = u'^{-1}(t, t, s_t, s_t) \times \int_{\mathbb{R}^n_{++}} u'(t, T, s_t, s_T) v(T, s_T) F(t, T, s_t, ds_T), \quad (3.1)$$

where $u'(t, T, s_t, s_T) > 0$ denotes the marginal utility of consumption of a unit of account at time T if the state of the market as expressed by the prices of the underlying securities is s_T at this time T, as viewed from time t if the state of the market as expressed by the prices of the underlying securities is s_t at this time t, and where $F(t, T, s_t, ds_T)$ stands for the transition probability of the states of the market as expressed by the prices of the underlying securities.

3.1. Remark. Relation (3.1) has the following financial interpretation. To carry one additional unit of a European contingent claim with the value $v(t, s_t)$ over the time period from t to T, $v(t, s_t)$ units of account have to be sacrificed resulting in the loss of utility $u'(t, t, s_t, s_t) v(t, s_t)$ at time t. By carrying this additional unit of the European contingent claim over the time period from t to T and selling it at time T, $v(T, s_T)$ additional units of account can be consumed resulting in the gain of utility $u'(t, T, s_t, s_T) v(T, s_T)$ at time T and, in turn, resulting in the expected gain of utility at time t

$$\int_{\mathbb{R}^n_{++}} u'(t, T, s_t, s_T) v(T, s_T) F(t, T, s_t, ds_T). \quad (3.2)$$

At equilibrium the preceding expected gain of utility at time t in (3.2) has to be equal to the loss of utility $u'(t, t, s_t, s_t)v(t, s_t)$ at time t, leading to relation (3.1).

3.2. Remark. Relation (3.1) is obtained as the standard first order condition for the optimization problem to maximize a time-additive expected or time-additive von Neumann-Morgenstern utility for each market participant. Roughly speaking, this first order condition is that the shadow prices at time t, where the state of the market as expressed by the prices of the underlying securities is s_t at this time t, for one unit of account to be received at time T, where the state of the market as expressed by the prices of the underlying securities is s_T at this time T, is equal to the marginal rate of substitution of consumption at time t and state s_t for consumption at time T and state s_T. This is another financial interpretation of relation (3.1). For the details on this optimization problem, including its formulation in terms of a Lagrangian, Bellman equation and stochastic Euler equation, see, for example, [16], [9], [14] and references therein. For the details on time-additive expected utility see, for example, [47], [20] and [16].

3.3. Remark. Relation (3.1) can be also interpreted in terms of Pareto-optimal or efficient allocation of state contingent claims or possibly generalized Arrow-Debreu securities in complete markets (see, for example, [13]).

3.4. Remark. We note that the case when the possible states of the market as expressed by the prices of the underlying securities form a discrete subset of $\mathbb{R}^n_{++}$ can be interpreted as a particular case of the possible states of the market as expressed by the prices of the underlying securities forming the set $\mathbb{R}^n_{++}$ when the probability measure $F(t, T, s_t, ds_T)$ is concentrated on this discrete subset. It is clear that in this case the integral in relation (3.1) takes the form of a sum.

3.1 Formalization of the Concept of a Market Participant

We start by formalizing the concept of the beliefs of a market participant.

3.5. Definition. We call a *belief of a market participant*, or simply a *belief* the family

$$\boldsymbol{\mathcal{B}} = \{\boldsymbol{F}(t,T) : \Pi \to \Pi \,|\, t,\, T \in \mathcal{T},\, t \le T\}$$

of linear operators $\boldsymbol{F}(t,T)$ defined by

$$(\boldsymbol{F}(t,T)\, h)(s_t) = \int_{\mathbb{R}^n_{++}} h(s_T)\, F(t,T,s_t,ds_T),$$

where h is an admissible function in Π.

By construction, each $\boldsymbol{F}(t,t)$ with t in $\mathcal{T}$ is the identity operator on Π.

3.6. Remark. Whenever ambiguity is unlikely we will also refer to an operator $\boldsymbol{F}(t,T)$ in $\boldsymbol{\mathcal{B}}$ as a belief.

3.7. Definition. We call a belief $\boldsymbol{\mathcal{B}}$ a *Markovian belief* if for each t, τ, and T in $\mathcal{T}$ such that $t \le \tau \le T$ the following relation holds

$$\boldsymbol{F}(t,\tau)\boldsymbol{F}(\tau,T) = \boldsymbol{F}(t,T).$$

Suppose that the trading time set $\mathcal{T}$ is an interval, either finite or infinite, of nonnegative real numbers. Similar to a market environment $\mathbf{V}$ that satisfies the intervention condition (2.4), a Markovian belief $\boldsymbol{\mathcal{B}}$ such that its operators $\boldsymbol{F}(t,T)$ are sufficiently smooth functions of time, admits the following simple characterization.

3.8. Definition. We say that the one-parameter family of linear operators

$$\boldsymbol{\mathfrak{L}} = \{\boldsymbol{\mathfrak{L}}(t) : \Pi \to \Pi \,|\, t \in \mathcal{T}\},$$

generates a Markovian belief $\boldsymbol{\mathcal{B}}$ if for each t and T in the trading time set $\mathcal{T}$ with $t \leq T$ and for each admissible v_T in Π the function $\boldsymbol{F}(t,T)v_T$ of t is a solution, possibly generalized, of the Cauchy problem for the evolution equation

$$\begin{gathered} \frac{d}{dt}v + \mathfrak{L}(t)v = 0, \quad t < T, \\ v(T) = v_T. \end{gathered} \tag{3.3}$$

An operator $\mathfrak{L}(t)$ in the family $\mathfrak{L}$ is called a *generator at time* t, or simply a *generator* of the Markovian belief $\boldsymbol{\mathcal{B}}$.

3.9. Remark. We comment that, suitably interpreted, the generators $\mathfrak{L}(t)$ of a Markovian belief $\boldsymbol{\mathcal{B}}$ are dispersive operators.

3.10. Remark. If a Markovian belief $\boldsymbol{\mathcal{B}}$ is generated by the family of linear operators $\mathfrak{L}$ then according to Cauchy problem (3.3) each operator $\boldsymbol{F}(t,T)$ from $\mathcal{B}$ is formally given by

$$\boldsymbol{F}(t,T) = e^{\int_t^T \mathfrak{L}(\tau)d\tau}, \tag{3.4}$$

where each generator $\mathfrak{L}(\tau)$ at time τ acts in the order opposite to that of τ.

3.11. Remark. We note that the Cauchy problem for the evolution equation (3.3) can be rewritten in terms of $\boldsymbol{F}(t,T)$ as follows

$$\begin{gathered} \frac{d}{dt}\boldsymbol{F}(t,T) + \mathfrak{L}(t)\,\boldsymbol{F}(t,T) = 0, \quad t < T, \\ \boldsymbol{F}(t,T)|_{t=T} = \boldsymbol{I}, \end{gathered} \tag{3.5}$$

where $\boldsymbol{I}$ is the identity operator on Π.

Now we introduce the concept of a generalized belief of a market participant.

Let there exist, for each t and T in $\mathcal{T}$ such that $t \leq T$ and each s_t in $\mathbb{R}^n_{++}$, a bounded measure on $\mathbb{R}^n_{++}$ with the distribution $D(t,T,s_t,ds_T)$ such that $D(t,T,s_t,ds_T)$ is the Dirac measure concentrated at s_t whenever $t = T$.

3.12. Definition. We call a *generalized belief of a market participant*, or simply a *generalized belief* the family

$$\mathfrak{B} = \{\boldsymbol{D}(t,T) : \Pi \to \Pi \,|\, t,\, T \in \mathcal{T},\, t \leq T\}$$

of linear operators $\boldsymbol{D}(t,T)$ defined by

$$\big(\boldsymbol{D}(t,T)\,h\big)(s_t) = \int_{\mathbb{R}^n_{++}} h(s_T)\, D(t,T,s_t,ds_T),$$

where h is an admissible function in Π.

By construction, each $\boldsymbol{D}(t,t)$ is the identity operator on Π.

3.13. Remark. Whenever ambiguity is unlikely we will also refer to an operator $\boldsymbol{D}(t,T)$ in $\mathfrak{B}$ as a generalized belief.

3.14. Remark. We comment that a generalized belief $\mathfrak{B}$ differs from a belief $\mathcal{B}$ in that the operators $\boldsymbol{D}(t,T)$ correspond to bounded measures on $\mathbb{R}^n_{++}$ which are not necessarily normalized to unity, while the operators $\boldsymbol{F}(t,T)$ correspond to measures on $\mathbb{R}^n_{++}$ which are normalized to unity, that is, to probability measures.

3.15. Definition. We call a generalized belief $\mathfrak{B}$ a *Markovian generalized belief* if for each t, τ, and T in $\mathcal{T}$ such that $t \leq \tau \leq T$ the following relation holds

$$\boldsymbol{D}(t,\tau)\boldsymbol{D}(\tau,T) = \boldsymbol{D}(t,T).$$

Suppose that the trading time set $\mathcal{T}$ is an interval, either finite or infinite, of nonnegative real numbers. Similar to a market environment $\mathbf{V}$ that satisfies the intervention condition (2.4) and similar to a Markovian belief $\mathcal{B}$, a generalized Markovian belief $\mathfrak{B}$ such that its operators $\boldsymbol{D}(t,T)$ are sufficiently smooth functions of time, admits the following simple characterization.

3.16. Definition. We say that the one-parameter family of linear operators

$$\mathsf{L} = \{\mathsf{L}(t) : \Pi \to \Pi \,|\, t \in \mathcal{T}\},$$

generates a Markovian generalized belief $\mathfrak{B}$ if for each t and T in the trading time set $\mathcal{T}$ with $t \leq T$ and for each admissible v_T in Π the function $\boldsymbol{D}(t,T)v_T$ of t is a solution, possibly generalized, of the Cauchy problem for the evolution equation

$$\begin{aligned} \frac{d}{dt}v + \mathbf{L}(t)v = 0, \quad t < T, \\ v(T) = v_T. \end{aligned} \tag{3.6}$$

An operator $\mathbf{L}(t)$ in the family $\mathbf{L}$ is called a *generator at time* t, or simply a *generator* of the generalized Markovian belief $\mathfrak{B}$.

3.17. Remark. We comment that, suitably interpreted, the generators $\mathbf{L}(t)$ of a Markovian generalized belief $\mathfrak{B}$ are dispersive operators.

3.18. Remark. If a generalized Markovian belief $\mathfrak{B}$ is generated by the family of linear operators $\mathbf{L}$ then, according to Cauchy problem (3.6), each operator $\boldsymbol{D}(t,T)$ from $\mathfrak{B}$ is formally given by

$$\boldsymbol{D}(t,T) = e^{\int_t^T \mathbf{L}(\tau)d\tau}, \tag{3.7}$$

where each generator $\mathbf{L}(\tau)$ at time τ acts in the order opposite to that of τ.

3.19. Remark. We note that the Cauchy problem for the evolution equation (3.6) can be rewritten in terms of $\boldsymbol{D}(t,T)$ as follows

$$\begin{aligned} \frac{d}{dt}\boldsymbol{D}(t,T) + \mathbf{L}(t)\boldsymbol{D}(t,T) = 0, \quad t < T, \\ \boldsymbol{D}(t,T)|_{t=T} = \boldsymbol{I}, \end{aligned} \tag{3.8}$$

where $\boldsymbol{I}$ is the identity operator on Π.

In order to formalize the concept of the preferences of a market participant we need the following preparation. Assume that the preferences of a market participant are given by a time-additive expected utility $u(t, T, s_t, s_T)$ of consumption of units of account at time T where the state of the market at this time T is s_T, as viewed from time t such that $t \leq T$ where the state of the market at this time t is s_t. Then the marginal utility of consumption of one unit of account at time T, where the state of the market at this time T is s_T, as viewed from time t such that $t \leq T$, where the state of the market at this time t is s_t, is given by $u'(t, T, s_t, s_T) > 0$, where the prime denotes the derivative with respect to the consumption variable.

Denote by

$$\Pi(\mathbb{R}^{2n}_{++}) = \Pi(\mathbb{R}^n_{++} \times \mathbb{R}^n_{++}) \quad \text{and}$$
$$\Pi(\mathbb{R}^{3n}_{++}) = \Pi(\mathbb{R}^n_{++} \times \mathbb{R}^n_{++} \times \mathbb{R}^n_{++})$$

the vector spaces of all real-valued functions on

$$\mathbb{R}^{2n}_{++} = \mathbb{R}^n_{++} \times \mathbb{R}^n_{++} \quad \text{and}$$
$$\mathbb{R}^{3n}_{++} = \mathbb{R}^n_{++} \times \mathbb{R}^n_{++} \times \mathbb{R}^n_{++}.$$

Let

$$\Pi_+(\mathbb{R}^{2n}_{++}) = \Pi_+(\mathbb{R}^n_{++} \times \mathbb{R}^n_{++}) \quad \text{and}$$
$$\Pi_+(\mathbb{R}^{3n}_{++}) = \Pi_+(\mathbb{R}^n_{++} \times \mathbb{R}^n_{++} \times \mathbb{R}^n_{++})$$

be the nonnegative cones of $\Pi(\mathbb{R}^n_{++} \times \mathbb{R}^n_{++})$ and $\Pi(\mathbb{R}^n_{++} \times \mathbb{R}^n_{++} \times \mathbb{R}^n_{++})$, that is, the sets of all nonnegative real-valued functions on $\mathbb{R}^n_{++} \times \mathbb{R}^n_{++}$ and $\mathbb{R}^n_{++} \times \mathbb{R}^n_{++} \times \mathbb{R}^n_{++}$.

We note that the vector spaces $\Pi(\mathbb{R}^n_{++} \times \mathbb{R}^n_{++})$ and $\Pi(\mathbb{R}^n_{++} \times \mathbb{R}^n_{++} \times \mathbb{R}^n_{++})$ with the partial order generated by the nonnegative cones $\Pi_+(\mathbb{R}^n_{++} \times \mathbb{R}^n_{++})$ and $\Pi_+(\mathbb{R}^n_{++} \times \mathbb{R}^n_{++} \times \mathbb{R}^n_{++})$ are partially ordered vector spaces. Moreover, equipped with the lattice operations of supremum and infimum defined as pointwise maximum and minimum, $\Pi(\mathbb{R}^n_{++} \times \mathbb{R}^n_{++})$ and $\Pi(\mathbb{R}^n_{++} \times \mathbb{R}^n_{++} \times \mathbb{R}^n_{++})$ are vector lattices.

We also note that Π can be viewed as a vector sublattice of $\Pi(\mathbb{R}^n_{++} \times \mathbb{R}^n_{++})$ and $\Pi(\mathbb{R}^n_{++} \times \mathbb{R}^n_{++} \times \mathbb{R}^n_{++})$. Similarly, $\Pi(\mathbb{R}^n_{++} \times$

$\mathbb{R}^n_{++})$ can be viewed as a vector sublattice of $\Pi(\mathbb{R}^n_{++} \times \mathbb{R}^n_{++} \times \mathbb{R}^n_{++})$.

It is clear that, for each t and T in $\mathcal{T}$ with $t \leq T$, the marginal utility $u'(t, T, s_t, s_T)$ is in $\Pi(\mathbb{R}^n_{++} \times \mathbb{R}^n_{++})$, in fact in $\Pi_+(\mathbb{R}^n_{++} \times \mathbb{R}^n_{++})$.

3.20. Remark. We comment that whenever t is equal to T the marginal utility $u'(t, T, s_t, s_T)$ for $s_t \neq s_T$ can be financially understood as an appropriate limit of $u'(t, T, s_t, s_T)$ with t smaller than T as t and T approach each other.

3.21. Definition. We call a *preference of a market participant*, or simply a *preference*, the family

$$\boldsymbol{\mathcal{U}} = \{\boldsymbol{u}'(t, T) : \Pi(\mathbb{R}^{2n}_{++}) \to \Pi(\mathbb{R}^{2n}_{++}) \,|\, t,\, T \in \mathcal{T}, t \leq T\}$$

of linear operators $\boldsymbol{u}'(t, T)$ defined by

$$\big(\boldsymbol{u}'(t, T)\, h\big)(s_t, s_T) = u'(t, T, s_t, s_T)\, h(s_t, s_T),$$

where h is an admissible function in $\Pi(\mathbb{R}^n_{++} \times \mathbb{R}^n_{++})$.

3.22. Remark. Whenever ambiguity is unlikely we will also refer to an operator $\boldsymbol{u}'(t, T)$ in $\boldsymbol{\mathcal{U}}$ as a preference.

3.23. Remark. We comment that an operator $\boldsymbol{u}'(t, T)$ from a preference $\boldsymbol{\mathcal{U}}$ is the operator on $\Pi(\mathbb{R}^n_{++} \times \mathbb{R}^n_{++})$ of multiplication by the function $u'(t, T, s_t, s_T) > 0$ in $\Pi(\mathbb{R}^n_{++} \times \mathbb{R}^n_{++})$, in fact in $\Pi_+(\mathbb{R}^n_{++} \times \mathbb{R}^n_{++})$ of the variables s_t and s_T and hence preserves the nonnegative cone $\Pi_+(\mathbb{R}^n_{++} \times \mathbb{R}^n_{++})$ in $\Pi(\mathbb{R}^n_{++} \times \mathbb{R}^n_{++})$.

3.24. Remark. It is clear that for each t in $\mathcal{T}$ the operator $\boldsymbol{u}'(t, t)$ on $\Pi(\mathbb{R}^n_{++} \times \mathbb{R}^n_{++})$ can be interpreted as an operator on Π viewed as a vector sublattice of $\Pi(\mathbb{R}^n_{++} \times \mathbb{R}^n_{++})$. Moreover, the operator $\boldsymbol{u}'(t, T)$ on $\Pi(\mathbb{R}^n_{++} \times \mathbb{R}^n_{++})$ can also be interpreted as an operator from Π to $\Pi(\mathbb{R}^n_{++} \times \mathbb{R}^n_{++})$, where Π is viewed as a vector sublattice of $\Pi(\mathbb{R}^n_{++} \times \mathbb{R}^n_{++})$.

Now we are ready to formalize the concept of Markovian preferences of a market participant.

It is financially reasonable to require that a market environment $\mathbf{V}$ satisfies the intervention condition (2.4), if and only if the beliefs $\boldsymbol{\mathcal{B}}$ and generalized beliefs $\mathfrak{B}$ of market participants are Markovian. This implies certain restrictions on the preferences of market participants. Indeed, for a belief $\boldsymbol{\mathcal{B}}$ due to the definitions of the evolution operator $\mathbf{V}(t,T)$ and the operators $\boldsymbol{F}(t,T)$ and $\boldsymbol{u}'(t,T)$, relation (3.1) implies that

$$\mathbf{V}(t,T) = \boldsymbol{u}'^{-1}(t,t)\boldsymbol{F}(t,T)\boldsymbol{u}'(t,T), \quad t \leq T, \tag{3.9}$$

or, more generally,

$$\mathbf{V}(\tau,T) = \boldsymbol{u}'^{-1}(t,\tau)\boldsymbol{F}(\tau,T)\boldsymbol{u}'(t,T), \quad t \leq \tau \leq T, \tag{3.10}$$

where we understand the operator

$$\boldsymbol{u}'^{-1}(t,\tau)\boldsymbol{F}(\tau,T)\boldsymbol{u}'(t,T) : \Pi \to \Pi$$

as follows.

Due to Remark (3.24) we have that $\boldsymbol{u}'(t,T) : \Pi \to \Pi(\mathbb{R}^n_{++} \times \mathbb{R}^n_{++})$ where Π is viewed as a vector sublattice of $\Pi(\mathbb{R}^n_{++} \times \mathbb{R}^n_{++})$. Then the operator $\boldsymbol{F}(\tau,T) : \Pi \to \Pi$ can be interpreted as the operator

$$\boldsymbol{F}(\tau,T) : \Pi(\mathbb{R}^n_{++} \times \mathbb{R}^n_{++}) \to \Pi(\mathbb{R}^n_{++} \times \mathbb{R}^n_{++})$$

given by

$$\big(\boldsymbol{F}(\tau,T)\,h\big)(s_t,s_\tau) = \int_{\mathbb{R}^n_{++}} h(s_t,s_T)\,F(\tau,T,s_\tau,ds_T).$$

Finally, the operator

$$\boldsymbol{u}'^{-1}(t,\tau)\boldsymbol{F}(\tau,T)\boldsymbol{u}'(t,T) : \Pi \to \Pi(\mathbb{R}^n_{++} \times \mathbb{R}^n_{++})$$

is in fact an operator with the range in Π viewed as a vector sublattice of $\Pi(\mathbb{R}^n_{++} \times \mathbb{R}^n_{++})$.

For example, in the particular case of t equal to τ the operator

$$\boldsymbol{u}'^{-1}(t,t)\boldsymbol{F}(t,T)\boldsymbol{u}'(t,T) : \Pi \to \Pi$$

is understood as follows. Due to Remark (3.24) we have that $\boldsymbol{u}'(t,T) : \Pi \to \Pi(\mathbb{R}^n_{++} \times \mathbb{R}^n_{++})$, where Π is viewed as a vector sublattice of $\Pi(\mathbb{R}^n_{++} \times \mathbb{R}^n_{++})$. In turn, the operator $\boldsymbol{F}(t,T)$: $\Pi \to \Pi$ can be interpreted as the operator

$$\boldsymbol{F}(t,T) : \Pi(\mathbb{R}^n_{++} \times \mathbb{R}^n_{++}) \to \Pi$$

given by

$$\big(\boldsymbol{F}(t,T)\,h\big)(s_t) = \int_{\mathbb{R}^n_{++}} h(s_t, s_T)\,F(t,T,s_t,ds_T).$$

Finally, due to Remark (3.24) we have that $\boldsymbol{u}'^{-1}(t,t) : \Pi \to \Pi$ where Π is viewed as a vector sublattice of $\Pi(\mathbb{R}^n_{++} \times \mathbb{R}^n_{++})$.

Now for each t, τ and T in $\mathcal{T}$ such that $t \le \tau \le T$ the relation (3.10) implies that

$$\begin{aligned} &\mathbf{V}(t,\tau)\mathbf{V}(\tau,T) = \\ &\quad \boldsymbol{u}'^{-1}(t,t)\boldsymbol{F}(t,\tau)\boldsymbol{u}'(t,\tau)\,\boldsymbol{u}'^{-1}(t,\tau)\boldsymbol{F}(\tau,T)\boldsymbol{u}'(t,T) = \\ &\quad \boldsymbol{u}'^{-1}(t,t)\boldsymbol{F}(t,T)\boldsymbol{u}'(t,T), \end{aligned} \tag{3.11}$$

where in the last equality we have made use of the assumption that the belief $\boldsymbol{\mathcal{B}}$ is Markovian.

By the assumption that the market environment $\mathbf{V}$ satisfies the intervention condition (2.4), relation (3.11) implies that

$$\mathbf{V}(t,T) = \boldsymbol{u}'^{-1}(t,t)\boldsymbol{F}(t,T)\boldsymbol{u}'(t,T)$$

which is indeed the case by relation (3.9).

At the same time, by relation (3.9) we have that

$$\mathbf{V}(t,\tau) = \boldsymbol{u}'^{-1}(t,t)\boldsymbol{F}(t,\tau)\boldsymbol{u}'(t,\tau)$$

and

$$\mathbf{V}(\tau, T) = \boldsymbol{u}'^{-1}(\tau, \tau)\boldsymbol{F}(\tau, T)\boldsymbol{u}'(\tau, T),$$

so that relation (3.11) implies that

$$\boldsymbol{u}'^{-1}(t,t)\boldsymbol{F}(t,T)\boldsymbol{u}'(t,T) = \\ \boldsymbol{u}'^{-1}(t,t)\boldsymbol{F}(t,\tau)\boldsymbol{u}'(t,\tau)\,\boldsymbol{u}'^{-1}(\tau,\tau)\boldsymbol{F}(\tau,T)\boldsymbol{u}'(\tau,T), \tag{3.12}$$

where $t \leq \tau \leq T$.

Therefore, taking into account relation (3.11) we have

$$\boldsymbol{u}'^{-1}(t,\tau)\boldsymbol{F}(\tau,T)\boldsymbol{u}'(t,T) = \\ \boldsymbol{u}'^{-1}(\tau,\tau)\boldsymbol{F}(\tau,T)\boldsymbol{u}'(\tau,T), \quad t \leq \tau \leq T. \tag{3.13}$$

The preceding identity (3.13) can be rewritten solely in terms of the preferences as follows

$$\boldsymbol{u}'^{-1}(t,\tau)\boldsymbol{u}'(t,T) = \boldsymbol{u}'^{-1}(\tau,\tau)\boldsymbol{u}'(\tau,T), \quad t \leq \tau \leq T, \tag{3.14}$$

where we interpret $\boldsymbol{u}'(t,T)$ as an operator on $\Pi(\mathbb{R}^n_{++} \times \mathbb{R}^n_{++} \times \mathbb{R}^n_{++})$ defined by

$$\big(\boldsymbol{u}'(t,T)\,h\big)(s_t, s_\tau, s_T) = u'(t,T,s_t,s_T)\,h(s_t,s_\tau,s_T).$$

In this way the preceding condition (3.14) states that the operator $\boldsymbol{u}'^{-1}(t,\tau)\boldsymbol{u}'(t,T)$ on $\Pi(\mathbb{R}^n_{++} \times \mathbb{R}^n_{++} \times \mathbb{R}^n_{++})$ restricted to $\Pi(\mathbb{R}^n_{++} \times \mathbb{R}^n_{++})$ has the range in $\Pi(\mathbb{R}^n_{++} \times \mathbb{R}^n_{++})$ viewed as the vector sublattice of $\Pi(\mathbb{R}^n_{++} \times \mathbb{R}^n_{++} \times \mathbb{R}^n_{++})$ and is equal, as an operator on $\Pi(\mathbb{R}^n_{++} \times \mathbb{R}^n_{++})$, to the operator $\boldsymbol{u}'^{-1}(\tau,\tau)\boldsymbol{u}'(\tau,T)$ on $\Pi(\mathbb{R}^n_{++} \times \mathbb{R}^n_{++})$.

3.25. Remark. In terms of the function $u'(t,T,s_t,s_T)$ the condition (3.14) can be restated as follows

$$u'^{-1}(t,\tau,s_t,s_\tau)\,u'(t,T,s_t,s_T) = \\ u'^{-1}(\tau,\tau,s_\tau,s_\tau)u'(\tau,T,s_\tau,s_T), \quad t \leq \tau \leq T, \tag{3.15}$$

where we interpret the function $u'(t,T,s_t,s_T)$ in $\Pi(\mathbb{R}^n_{++} \times \mathbb{R}^n_{++})$ as a function in $\Pi(\mathbb{R}^n_{++} \times \mathbb{R}^n_{++} \times \mathbb{R}^n_{++})$.

3.26. Definition. We call a preference of a market participant

$$\mathcal{U} = \{\boldsymbol{u}'(t,T) : \Pi(\mathbb{R}^{2n}_{++}) \to \Pi(\mathbb{R}^{2n}_{++}) \,|\, t,\, T \in \mathcal{T},\, t \le T\}$$

a *Markovian preference* if for each t, τ and T in $\mathcal{T}$ with $t \le \tau \le T$ the equality (3.14) is satisfied.

Now we present the explicit construction of a class of Markovian preferences.

Let the operator $\boldsymbol{\Lambda}(t,T) : \Pi(\mathbb{R}^n_{++} \times \mathbb{R}^n_{++}) \to \Pi(\mathbb{R}^n_{++} \times \mathbb{R}^n_{++})$ be such that

$$\boldsymbol{u}'(t,T) = e^{\boldsymbol{\Lambda}(t,T)}. \tag{3.16}$$

3.27. Remark. It is clear that $\boldsymbol{\Lambda}(t,T) : \Pi(\mathbb{R}^n_{++} \times \mathbb{R}^n_{++}) \to \Pi(\mathbb{R}^n_{++} \times \mathbb{R}^n_{++})$ is the operator of the multiplication by the function $\Lambda(t,T,s_t,s_T)$ in $\Pi(\mathbb{R}^n_{++} \times \mathbb{R}^n_{++})$ such that

$$u'(t,T,s_t,s_T) = e^{\Lambda(t,T,s_t,s_T)}. \tag{3.17}$$

In terms of the operator $\boldsymbol{\Lambda}(t,T)$ relation (3.14) can be rewritten as follows

$$\boldsymbol{\Lambda}(t,T) - \boldsymbol{\Lambda}(t,\tau) = \boldsymbol{\Lambda}(\tau,T) - \boldsymbol{\Lambda}(\tau,\tau), \tag{3.18}$$

where t, τ and T are in $\mathcal{T}$ and $t \le \tau \le T$.

Relation (3.18) states that the difference $\boldsymbol{\Lambda}(t,T) - \boldsymbol{\Lambda}(t,\tau)$ of $\boldsymbol{\Lambda}(t,T)$ and $\boldsymbol{\Lambda}(t,\tau)$ interpreted as operators on $\Pi(\mathbb{R}^n_{++} \times \mathbb{R}^n_{++} \times \mathbb{R}^n_{++})$ does not depend on t. Denote this difference by $\boldsymbol{\lambda}(\tau,T)$, that is

$$\boldsymbol{\lambda}(\tau,T) = \boldsymbol{\Lambda}(t,T) - \boldsymbol{\Lambda}(t,\tau), \tag{3.19}$$

where t, τ and T are in $\mathcal{T}$ and $t \le \tau \le T$.

It is clear that for each t, τ and T in $\mathcal{T}$ with $t \le \tau \le T$

$$\boldsymbol{\lambda}(t,T) = \boldsymbol{\lambda}(t,\tau) + \boldsymbol{\lambda}(\tau,T) \quad \text{and} \quad \boldsymbol{\lambda}(t,t) = \mathbf{0}, \tag{3.20}$$

where $\mathbf{0}$ is the zero operator on $\Pi(\mathbb{R}^n_{++} \times \mathbb{R}^n_{++})$. Indeed, the identity

$$\boldsymbol{\lambda}(t,T) = \boldsymbol{\lambda}(t,\tau) + \boldsymbol{\lambda}(\tau,T), \quad t \le \tau \le T$$

in (3.20) follows from the following chain of equalities

$$\begin{aligned} &\boldsymbol{\lambda}(t,T) = \\ &\quad \boldsymbol{\Lambda}(t,T) - \boldsymbol{\Lambda}(t,t) = \\ &\quad \boldsymbol{\Lambda}(t,\tau) - \boldsymbol{\Lambda}(t,t) + \\ &\qquad\qquad \boldsymbol{\Lambda}(t,T) - \boldsymbol{\Lambda}(t,\tau) = \\ &\quad \boldsymbol{\Lambda}(t,\tau) - \boldsymbol{\Lambda}(t,t) + \\ &\qquad\qquad \boldsymbol{\Lambda}(\tau,T) - \boldsymbol{\Lambda}(\tau,\tau) = \\ &\quad \boldsymbol{\lambda}(t,\tau) + \boldsymbol{\lambda}(\tau,T), \end{aligned}$$

where the first equality is due to the definition of $\boldsymbol{\lambda}(t,T)$ in (3.19), the second equality is due to trivial algebra, the third equality is due to relation (3.18), and the last equality is due to the definition of $\boldsymbol{\lambda}(t,\tau)$ and $\boldsymbol{\lambda}(\tau,T)$ in (3.19). Finally, the identity

$$\boldsymbol{\lambda}(t,t) = \mathbf{0}, \quad t \in \mathcal{T},$$

in (3.20) follows directly from the definition of $\boldsymbol{\lambda}(t,t)$ in (3.19).

Now according to the definition of $\boldsymbol{\lambda}(t,T)$ in (3.19) we represent $\boldsymbol{\Lambda}(t,T)$ as follows

$$\boldsymbol{\Lambda}(t,T) = \boldsymbol{\Lambda}(t,t) + \boldsymbol{\lambda}(t,T), \tag{3.21}$$

where t, τ and T in $\mathcal{T}$ with $t \le \tau \le T$.

3.28. Remark. In terms of the function $\Lambda(t,T,s_t,s_T)$ we can rewrite relation (3.18) as follows

$$\Lambda(t,T,s_t,s_T) - \Lambda(t,\tau,s_t,s_\tau) = \Lambda(\tau,T,s_\tau,s_T) - \Lambda(\tau,\tau,s_\tau,s_\tau). \tag{3.22}$$

3.29. Remark. Relation (3.22) states that the difference $\Lambda(t, T, s_t, s_T) - \Lambda(t, \tau, s_t, s_\tau)$ of $\Lambda(t, T, s_t, s_T)$ and $\Lambda(t, \tau, s_t, s_\tau)$ interpreted as functions in $\Pi(\mathbb{R}^n_{++} \times \mathbb{R}^n_{++} \times \mathbb{R}^n_{++})$ does not depend on t and s_t. Denote this difference by $\lambda(\tau, T, s_\tau, s_T)$. It is clear that

$$\begin{aligned} \lambda(t, T, s_t, s_T) = \lambda(t, \tau, s_t, s_\tau) + \lambda(\tau, T, s_\tau, s_T), \quad \text{and} \\ \lambda(t, t, s_t, s_t) = 0, \end{aligned} \tag{3.23}$$

for each t, τ and T in $\mathcal{T}$ with $t \leq \tau \leq T$. Now we can represent the function $\Lambda(t, T, s_t, s_T)$ as follows

$$\Lambda(t, T, s_t, s_T) = \Lambda(t, t, s_t, s_t) + \lambda(t, T, s_t, s_T), \tag{3.24}$$

where t, τ and T in $\mathcal{T}$ with $t \leq \tau \leq T$. Finally we comment that, as it is clear, $\boldsymbol{\lambda}(t, T)$ is the operator of multiplication by the function $\lambda(t, T, s_t, s_T)$.

The additivity of $\boldsymbol{\Lambda}(t, T)$ in (3.21) implies the following multiplicativity of $\boldsymbol{u}'(t, T)$:

$$\boldsymbol{u}'(t, T) = \boldsymbol{u}'(t, t)\, \mathbf{u}'(t, T), \quad t \leq \tau \leq T, \tag{3.25}$$

where $\mathbf{u}'(t, T) = e^{\boldsymbol{\lambda}(t, T)}$.

It is clear that, due to the relations in (3.20), we have that

$$\mathbf{u}'(t, T) = \mathbf{u}'(t, \tau)\, \mathbf{u}'(\tau, T) \quad \text{and} \quad \mathbf{u}'(t, t) = \boldsymbol{I}, \quad t \leq \tau \leq T, \tag{3.26}$$

where $\boldsymbol{I}$ stands for the identity operator on $\Pi(\mathbb{R}^n_{++} \times \mathbb{R}^n_{++})$ realized as the operator of multiplication by the function $\mathbf{1}$ in $\Pi(\mathbb{R}^n_{++} \times \mathbb{R}^n_{++})$ identically equal to unity.

3.30. Remark. The additivity of $\Lambda(t, T, s_t, s_T)$ in (3.24) implies the following multiplicativity of $u'(t, T, s_t, s_T)$:

$$u'(t, T, s_t, s_T) = u'(t, t, s_t, s_t)\, \mathrm{u}'(t, T, s_t, s_T), \quad t \leq \tau \leq T, \tag{3.27}$$

where $u'(t, T, s_t, s_T) = e^{\lambda(t,T,s_t,s_T)}$. It is clear that, due to relation (3.23), we have that

$$\begin{aligned} u'(t, T, s_t, s_T) = u'(t, \tau, s_t, s_\tau)\, u'(\tau, T, s_\tau, s_T) \quad \text{and} \\ u'(t, t, s_t, s_t) = 1, \quad t \le \tau \le T. \end{aligned} \tag{3.28}$$

3.31. Remark. The operator $\boldsymbol{\Lambda}(t, T)$ can be also represented as follows

$$\boldsymbol{\Lambda}(t, T) = \boldsymbol{\Lambda}(T, T) + \boldsymbol{\lambda}(t, T), \tag{3.29}$$

where the operator $\boldsymbol{\lambda}(t, T)$ satisfies the conditions similar to those in relation (3.20), that is:

$$\boldsymbol{\lambda}(t, T) = \boldsymbol{\lambda}(t, \tau) + \boldsymbol{\lambda}(\tau, T) \quad \text{and} \quad \boldsymbol{\lambda}(T, T) = \mathbf{0},$$

where $\mathbf{0}$ is the zero operator on $\Pi(\mathbb{R}^n_{++} \times \mathbb{R}^n_{++})$. In terms of the function $\Lambda(t, T, s_t, s_T)$ relation (3.29) states that

$$\Lambda(t, T, s_t, s_T) = \Lambda(T, T, s_T, s_T) + \lambda(t, T, s_t, s_T), \tag{3.30}$$

where the function $\lambda(t, T, s_t, s_T)$ satisfies the conditions similar to those in relation (3.23), that is:

$$\begin{aligned} \lambda(t, T, s_t, s_T) = \lambda(t, \tau, s_t, s_\tau) + \lambda(\tau, T, s_\tau, s_T), \quad \text{and} \\ \lambda(T, T, s_T, s_T) = 0 \end{aligned}$$

for each t, τ and T in $\mathcal{T}$ with $t \le \tau \le T$. We comment that, as it is clear, $\boldsymbol{\lambda}(t, T)$ is the operator of multiplication by the function $\lambda(t, T, s_t, s_T)$.

3.32. Remark. A continuous in time, in an appropriate sense, solution for $\boldsymbol{\lambda}(t, T)$ satisfying the conditions in relation (3.20) has the following form (see, for example, [6] page 93):

$$\boldsymbol{\lambda}(t, T) = \boldsymbol{\lambda}(t) - \boldsymbol{\lambda}(T), \tag{3.31}$$

where the operator $\boldsymbol{\lambda}(t)$ on Π of multiplication by the function $\lambda(t, s_t)$ in Π is interpreted as an operator on $\Pi(\mathbb{R}^n_{++} \times \mathbb{R}^n_{++})$. In this regard a continuous in time, in an appropriate sense, solution for $\lambda(t, T, s_t, s_T)$ satisfying the conditions in relation (3.23) has the following form

$$\lambda(t, T, s_t, s_T) = \lambda(t, s_t) - \lambda(T, s_T), \tag{3.32}$$

where the function $\lambda(t, s_t)$ in Π is interpreted as a function in $\Pi(\mathbb{R}^n_{++} \times \mathbb{R}^n_{++})$.

3.33. Remark. A continuous in time, in an appropriate sense, solution for $\mathbf{u}'(t, T)$ satisfying the conditions in relation (3.26) has the following form:

$$\mathbf{u}'(t, T) = \mathbf{u}'(t)\, \mathbf{u}'^{-1}(T), \tag{3.33}$$

where $\mathbf{u}(t) = e^{\boldsymbol{\lambda}(t)}$. In this regard a continuous in time, in an appropriate sense, solution for $\mathrm{u}'(t, T, s_t, s_T)$ satisfying the conditions in relation (3.28) has the following form

$$\mathrm{u}'(t, T, s_t, s_T) = \mathrm{u}'(t, s_t)\, \mathrm{u}'^{-1}(T, s_T), \tag{3.34}$$

where $\mathrm{u}'(t, s_t) = e^{\lambda(t, s_t)}$.

3.34. Remark. Due to the preceding Remark (3.33) we can rewrite relation (3.25) as follows

$$\boldsymbol{u}'(t, T) = \boldsymbol{u}'(t, t)\, \mathbf{u}'(t)\, \mathbf{u}'^{-1}(T), \quad t \le \tau \le T, \tag{3.35}$$

where $\mathbf{u}'(t) = e^{\boldsymbol{\lambda}(t)}$. In this regard, we can rewrite relation (3.27) as follows

$$u'(t, T, s_t, s_T) = u'(t, t, s_t, s_t)\, \mathrm{u}'(t, s_t)\, \mathrm{u}'^{-1}(T, s_T), \quad t \le \tau \le T, \tag{3.36}$$

where $\mathrm{u}'(t, s_t) = e^{\lambda(t, s_t)}$.

Now for a generalized belief $\mathfrak{B}$ due to the definitions of the evolution operator $\mathbf{V}(t,T)$ and the operators $\boldsymbol{D}(t,T)$ and $\boldsymbol{u}'(t,T)$ relation (3.45) presented in the next Subsection implies that

$$\mathbf{V}(t,T) = \boldsymbol{u}'^{-1}(t,t)\boldsymbol{D}(t,T)\boldsymbol{u}'(t,T), \quad t \leq T, \tag{3.37}$$

or, more generally,

$$\mathbf{V}(\tau,T) = \boldsymbol{u}'^{-1}(t,\tau)\boldsymbol{D}(\tau,T)\boldsymbol{u}'(t,T), \quad t \leq \tau \leq T, \tag{3.38}$$

where we understand the operator

$$\boldsymbol{u}'^{-1}(t,\tau)\boldsymbol{D}(\tau,T)\boldsymbol{u}'(t,T) : \Pi \to \Pi$$

as follows.

Due to Remark (3.24) we have that $\boldsymbol{u}'(t,T) : \Pi \to \Pi(\mathbb{R}^n_{++} \times \mathbb{R}^n_{++})$, where Π is viewed as a vector sublattice of $\Pi(\mathbb{R}^n_{++} \times \mathbb{R}^n_{++})$. Then the operator $\boldsymbol{D}(\tau,T) : \Pi \to \Pi$ can be interpreted as the operator

$$\boldsymbol{D}(\tau,T) : \Pi(\mathbb{R}^n_{++} \times \mathbb{R}^n_{++}) \to \Pi(\mathbb{R}^n_{++} \times \mathbb{R}^n_{++})$$

given by

$$\big(\boldsymbol{D}(\tau,T)\, h\big)(s_t, s_\tau) = \int_{\mathbb{R}^n_{++}} h(s_t, s_T)\, D(\tau, T, s_\tau, ds_T).$$

Finally, the operator

$$\boldsymbol{u}'^{-1}(t,\tau)\boldsymbol{D}(\tau,T)\boldsymbol{u}'(t,T) : \Pi \to \Pi(\mathbb{R}^n_{++} \times \mathbb{R}^n_{++})$$

is in fact an operator with the range in Π viewed as a vector sublattice of $\Pi(\mathbb{R}^n_{++} \times \mathbb{R}^n_{++})$.

For example, in the particular case of t equal to τ the operator

$$\boldsymbol{u}'^{-1}(t,t)\boldsymbol{D}(t,T)\boldsymbol{u}'(t,T) : \Pi \to \Pi$$

is understood as follows. Due to Remark (3.24) we have that $\boldsymbol{u}'(t,T) : \Pi \to \Pi(\mathbb{R}^n_{++} \times \mathbb{R}^n_{++})$, where Π is viewed as a vector sublattice of $\Pi(\mathbb{R}^n_{++} \times \mathbb{R}^n_{++})$. In turn, the operator $\boldsymbol{D}(t,T) : \Pi \to \Pi$ can be interpreted as the operator

$$\boldsymbol{D}(t,T) : \Pi(\mathbb{R}^n_{++} \times \mathbb{R}^n_{++}) \to \Pi$$

given by

$$\big(\boldsymbol{D}(t,T)\, h\big)(s_t) = \int_{\mathbb{R}^n_{++}} h(s_t, s_T)\, D(t,T,s_t,ds_T).$$

Finally, due to Remark (3.24) we have that $\boldsymbol{u}'^{-1}(t,t) : \Pi \to \Pi$, where Π is viewed as a vector sublattice of $\Pi(\mathbb{R}^n_{++} \times \mathbb{R}^n_{++})$.

Now for each t, τ and T in $\boldsymbol{T}$ such that $t \le \tau \le T$ relation (3.38) implies that

$$\begin{aligned} &\mathbf{V}(t,\tau)\mathbf{V}(\tau,T) = \\ &\quad \boldsymbol{u}'^{-1}(t,t)\boldsymbol{D}(t,\tau)\boldsymbol{u}'(t,\tau)\, \boldsymbol{u}'^{-1}(t,\tau)\boldsymbol{D}(\tau,T)\boldsymbol{u}'(t,T) = \\ &\quad \boldsymbol{u}'^{-1}(t,t)\boldsymbol{D}(t,T)\boldsymbol{u}'(t,T), \end{aligned} \tag{3.39}$$

where in the last equality we have made use of the assumption that the generalized belief $\mathfrak{B}$ is Markovian.

By the assumption that the market environment $\mathbf{V}$ satisfies the intervention condition (2.4), relation (3.39) implies that

$$\mathbf{V}(t,T) = \boldsymbol{u}'^{-1}(t,t)\boldsymbol{D}(t,T)\boldsymbol{u}'(t,T)$$

which is indeed the case by relation (3.37).

At the same time, by relation (3.37) we have that

$$\mathbf{V}(t,\tau) = \boldsymbol{u}'^{-1}(t,t)\boldsymbol{D}(t,\tau)\boldsymbol{u}'(t,\tau)$$

and

$$\mathbf{V}(\tau,T) = \boldsymbol{u}'^{-1}(\tau,\tau)\boldsymbol{D}(\tau,T)\boldsymbol{u}'(\tau,T),$$

so that relation (3.39) implies that

$$\begin{aligned} &\boldsymbol{u}'^{-1}(t,t)\boldsymbol{D}(t,T)\boldsymbol{u}'(t,T) = \\ &\quad \boldsymbol{u}'^{-1}(t,t)\boldsymbol{D}(t,\tau)\boldsymbol{u}'(t,\tau)\, \boldsymbol{u}'^{-1}(\tau,\tau)\boldsymbol{D}(\tau,T)\boldsymbol{u}'(\tau,T), \end{aligned} \tag{3.40}$$

where $t \le \tau \le T$.

Therefore, taking into account relation (3.39) we have

$$\begin{aligned} \boldsymbol{u}'^{-1}(t,\tau)\boldsymbol{D}(\tau,T)\boldsymbol{u}'(t,T) = \\ \boldsymbol{u}'^{-1}(\tau,\tau)\boldsymbol{D}(\tau,T)\boldsymbol{u}'(\tau,T), \quad t \le \tau \le T. \end{aligned} \tag{3.41}$$

Similar to the case of beliefs $\boldsymbol{\mathcal{B}}$, we can rewrite the preceding identity (3.41) solely in terms of preferences as in relation (3.14).

Now we are ready to formalize the concept of a market participant in terms of their beliefs and preferences.

3.35. Definition. We call *a market participant* a pair $\boldsymbol{\mathcal{H}} = (\boldsymbol{\mathcal{B}}, \boldsymbol{\mathcal{U}})$ where $\boldsymbol{\mathcal{B}}$ is a belief and $\boldsymbol{\mathcal{U}}$ is a preference.

3.36. Definition. We call a market participant $\boldsymbol{\mathcal{H}} = (\boldsymbol{\mathcal{B}}, \boldsymbol{\mathcal{U}})$ a *Markovian market participant* if the belief $\boldsymbol{\mathcal{B}}$ and the preference $\boldsymbol{\mathcal{U}}$ are Markovian.

3.37. Definition. We call *a market populace* $\mathbb{H}$ the set of all market participants.

3.38. Definition. We call a market populace $\mathbb{H}$ a *Markovian market populace* if it consists only of Markovian market participants.

3.39. Remark. It is clear that the market populace $\mathbb{H}$ is the Cartesian product of the set $\mathbb{B}$ of all beliefs of market participants and the set $\mathbb{U}$ of all preferences of market participants

$$\mathbb{H} = \mathbb{B} \times \mathbb{U}. \tag{3.42}$$

In other words, a market participant $\boldsymbol{\mathcal{H}} = (\boldsymbol{\mathcal{B}}, \boldsymbol{\mathcal{U}})$ in $\mathbb{H}$ can have any belief $\boldsymbol{\mathcal{B}}$ in $\mathbb{B}$ and any preference $\boldsymbol{\mathcal{U}}$ in $\mathbb{U}$.

3.40. Definition. We call the sets $\mathbb{B}$ and $\mathbb{U}$ of all beliefs and preferences of market participants $\boldsymbol{\mathcal{H}} = (\boldsymbol{\mathcal{B}}, \boldsymbol{\mathcal{U}})$ in the market populace $\mathbb{H}$ a *market populace belief* and a *market populace preference.*

Now we introduce the concept of a generalized market participant.

3.41. Definition. We call a *generalized market participant* a pair $\mathfrak{H} = (\mathfrak{B}, \mathcal{U})$, where $\mathfrak{B}$ is a generalized belief and $\mathcal{U}$ is a preference.

3.42. Remark. For a generalized market participant $\mathfrak{H} = (\mathfrak{B}, \mathcal{U})$ whenever ambiguity is likely we will call a preference $\mathcal{U}$ a *generalized preference* and denote it by $\mathfrak{U}$.

3.43. Definition. We call a generalized market participant $\mathfrak{H} = (\mathfrak{B}, \mathcal{U})$ a *Markovian generalized market participant* if the generalized belief $\mathfrak{B}$ and the preference $\mathcal{U}$ are Markovian.

3.44. Remark. For a Markovian generalized market participant $\mathfrak{H} = (\mathfrak{B}, \mathcal{U})$, whenever ambiguity is likely we will call a Markovian preference $\mathcal{U}$ a *Markovian generalized preference.*

3.45. Definition. We call *a generalized market populace* $\mathbb{H}$ the set of all generalized market participants.

3.46. Definition. We call a generalized market populace $\mathbb{H}$ a *Markovian generalized market populace* if it consists only of Markovian generalized market participants.

3.47. Remark. It is clear that the generalized market populace $\mathbb{H}$ is the Cartesian product of the set $\mathbb{B}$ of all generalized beliefs and the set $\mathbb{U}$ of all preferences

$$\mathbb{H} = \mathbb{B} \times \mathbb{U}. \tag{3.43}$$

In other words, a generalized market participant $\mathfrak{H} = (\mathfrak{B}, \mathcal{U})$ in $\mathbb{H}$ can have any generalized belief $\mathfrak{B}$ in $\mathbb{B}$ and any preference $\mathcal{U}$ in $\mathbb{U}$.

3.48. Definition. We call the set $\mathbb{B}$ of all generalized beliefs of generalized market participants $\mathfrak{H} = (\mathfrak{B}, \mathcal{U})$ in the generalized market populace $\mathbb{H}$ a *generalized market populace belief.*

3.49. Remark. For a generalized market populace $\mathbb{H} = \mathbb{B} \times \mathbb{U}$, whenever ambiguity is likely we will call the market populace preference $\mathbb{U}$ the *generalized market populace preference* and denote it by $\mathbf{U}$.

3.2 Beliefs-Preferences Gauge Symmetry Group for a Generalized Market Populace

We note first that relation (3.1) can be reformulated in the following way

$$v(t, s_t) = u'^{-1}(t, t, s_t, s_t)\,\beta(t, T, s_t) \times \int_{\mathbb{R}^n_{++}} u'(t, T, s_t, s_T)\,v(T, s_T)\,F(t, T, s_t, ds_T), \quad (3.44)$$

where $\beta(t, T, s_t) > 0$ is the state dependent discount factor for the time period from t to T (see, for example, [14]) or a "force of mortality" (see, for example [44] page 151). We comment that, generally speaking, the utilities, or more precisely the marginal utilities, in relation (3.44) differ from those in relation (3.1). In this regard, whenever ambiguity is likely, we will refer to the utilities and the marginal utilities in relation (3.44) as *generalized utilities* and *generalized marginal utilities.*

The discount factor $\beta(t, T, s_t)$ and the probability distribution $F(t, T, s_t, ds_T)$ can be absorbed into the distribution $D(t, T, s_t, ds_T)$ so that relation (3.44) can be rewritten as follows

$$v(t, s_t) = u'^{-1}(t, t, s_t, s_t) \times \int_{\mathbb{R}^n_{++}} u'(t, T, s_t, s_T) v(T, s_T) D(t, T, s_t, ds_T), \quad (3.45)$$

where

$$D(t, T, s_t, ds_T) = \beta(t, T, s_t)\,F(t, T, s_t, ds_T).$$

Therefore, relation (3.44), or equivalently (3.45), can be rewritten as follows

$$v(t) = \boldsymbol{u}'^{-1}(t,t)\boldsymbol{D}(t,T)\boldsymbol{u}'(t,T)v(T). \tag{3.46}$$

We note right away that relations (3.46) and (3.45) are invariant with respect to the following symmetry group.

3.50. Theorem. Let $\mathfrak{G}(\mathbb{R}_{++})$ be the group of positive real numbers $\mathbb{R}_{++}$ with the group operation being standard multiplication. Then for each generalized belief $\mathfrak{B}$ in $\mathbb{B}$ the operators

$$\boldsymbol{u}'^{-1}(t,t)\boldsymbol{D}(t,T)\boldsymbol{u}'(t,T) : \Pi \to \Pi$$

remain unchanged under the following group of transformations on the market populace belief $\mathbb{U}$:

$$\boldsymbol{\mathcal{U}} \to \alpha\boldsymbol{\mathcal{U}}, \quad \alpha \in \mathfrak{G}(\mathbb{R}_{++}),$$

where $\boldsymbol{D}(t,T)$ is in $\mathfrak{B}$, and where

$$\boldsymbol{\mathcal{U}} = \{\boldsymbol{u}'(t,T) : \Pi(\mathbb{R}^{2n}_{++}) \to \Pi(\mathbb{R}^{2n}_{++}) \,|\, t,\, T \in \mathcal{T}, t \leq T\}$$

and

$$\alpha\boldsymbol{\mathcal{U}} = \{\alpha\boldsymbol{u}'(t,T) : \Pi(\mathbb{R}^{2n}_{++}) \to \Pi(\mathbb{R}^{2n}_{++}) \,|\, t,\, T \in \mathcal{T}, t \leq T\}.$$

Proof. The proof immediately follows from the fact that the operator of multiplication by a constant commutes with each operator $\boldsymbol{D}(t,T)$. □

3.51. Remark. We note that the symmetry presented in the preceding Theorem (3.50) is a reflection of the fact that expected utility is unique up to an affine transformation, or marginal utility is unique up to multiplication by a positive constant (see, for example, [47] page 25 and [16] page 60).

Now we promote the symmetry from the preceding Theorem (3.50), which is global in the sense that the group elements α in $\mathfrak{G}(\mathbb{R}_{++})$ do not depend on time t and the state of the market as expressed by the prices of the underlying securities s_t in $\mathbb{R}^n_{++}$, to the local symmetry where the group elements α in $\mathfrak{G}(\mathbb{R}_{++})$ will depend on time t and the state of the market as expressed by the prices of the underlying securities s_t in $\mathbb{R}^n_{++}$, that is, to the gauge symmetry with the gauge group $\mathfrak{G}(\mathbb{R}_{++})$.

We note that the generalized belief and the preference depend on the particular market participant, or more precisely, generalized market participant although we have suppressed this dependence in relations (3.45) and (3.46). However, if all market participants, or more precisely, generalized market participants that populate a marketplace at time t have agreed upon the values at inception time t in $\mathcal{T}$ of a set of European contingent claims whose payoffs at expiration time T in $\mathcal{T}$ form a dense set then, by the no-arbitrage argument, for any pair of such market participants, or more precisely, generalized market participants $\mathfrak{H}_1 = (\mathfrak{B}_1, \mathcal{U}_1)$ and $\mathfrak{H}_2 = (\mathfrak{B}_2, \mathcal{U}_2)$ we have

$$\boldsymbol{u}_1'^{-1}(t,t)\boldsymbol{D}_1(t,T)\boldsymbol{u}_1'(t,T) = \boldsymbol{u}_2'^{-1}(t,t)\boldsymbol{D}_2(t,T)\boldsymbol{u}_2'(t,T), \tag{3.47}$$

where $\boldsymbol{D}_1(t,T)$ is in $\mathfrak{B}_1$ and $\boldsymbol{D}_2(t,T)$ is in $\mathfrak{B}_2$ and where $\boldsymbol{u}_1'(t,T)$ is in $\mathcal{U}_1$ and $\boldsymbol{u}_2'(t,T)$ is in $\mathcal{U}_2$. Therefore all such market participants, or more precisely, generalized market participants, in terms of their beliefs and generalized preferences, differ only inasmuch as allowed by equality (3.47). This provides us with a complete description of the degrees of freedom that market participants, or more precisely, generalized market participants have in terms of their generalized beliefs and preferences. Although market participants, or more precisely, generalized market participants might differ in terms of their generalized beliefs and preferences, and although their generalized beliefs and preferences are physically, or more precisely, financially unobservable, the following combination

$$\boldsymbol{u}'^{-1}(t,t)\boldsymbol{D}(t,T)\boldsymbol{u}'(t,T) \tag{3.48}$$

of their generalized beliefs and preferences is observable by relation (3.46) and is market participant, or more precisely, generalized market participant independent by equality (3.47).

Saying the same thing from another side, the degree of freedom that market participants, or more precisely, generalized market participants $\mathfrak{H} = (\mathfrak{B}, \mathcal{U})$ in $\mathbb{H} = \mathbb{B} \times \mathbb{U}$ have in terms of their generalized beliefs $\mathfrak{B}$ and preferences $\mathcal{U}$ is determined by the following abelian group of transformations $\mathfrak{G}$ of the generalized market populace $\mathbb{H} = \mathbb{B} \times \mathbb{U}$:

$$\mathfrak{H} = (\mathfrak{B}, \mathcal{U}) \to \mathfrak{g}\,\mathfrak{H} = (\mathfrak{g}_{\mathfrak{B}}\mathfrak{B}, \mathfrak{g}_{\mathcal{U}}\mathcal{U}), \quad \mathfrak{g} \in \mathfrak{G}. \tag{3.49}$$

Here each $\mathfrak{g} = (\mathfrak{g}_{\mathfrak{B}}, \mathfrak{g}_{\mathcal{U}})$ in $\mathfrak{G}$ is defined by

$$\begin{aligned} &\boldsymbol{D}(t,T) \xrightarrow{\mathfrak{g}_{\mathfrak{B}}} \mathbf{u}'^{-1}(t,t)\boldsymbol{D}(t,T)\mathbf{u}'(t,T) \quad \text{and} \\ &\boldsymbol{u}'(t,T) \xrightarrow{g_{\mathcal{U}}} \mathbf{u}'^{-1}(t,T)\boldsymbol{u}'(t,T), \end{aligned} \tag{3.50}$$

where $\boldsymbol{D}(t,T)$ is in $\mathfrak{B}$ and $\mathbf{u}'^{-1}(t,t)\boldsymbol{D}(t,T)\mathbf{u}'(t,T)$ is $\mathfrak{g}_{\mathfrak{B}}\mathfrak{B}$ and where $\boldsymbol{u}'(t,T)$ is in $\mathcal{U}$ and $\mathbf{u}'^{-1}(t,T)\boldsymbol{u}'(t,T)$ is in $\mathfrak{g}_{\mathcal{U}}\mathcal{U}$ with $\mathbf{u}'(t,T)$ being the operator of multiplication by the function $\mathrm{u}'(t,T,s_t,s_T) > 0$.

That is, the set of all generalized market participants $\mathfrak{H} = (\mathfrak{B}, \mathcal{U})$ in $\mathbb{H} = \mathbb{B} \times \mathbb{U}$ that agree at all times t in $\mathcal{T}$ upon the values of a set of European contingent claims with inception time t and expiration time T for all T in $\mathcal{T}$ such that $t \le T$ whose payoffs form a dense set is nothing but an orbit of the group $\mathfrak{G}$ in $\mathbb{H} = \mathbb{B} \times \mathbb{U}$. This financially justifies the following definition.

3.52. Definition. We call an orbit of the group $\mathfrak{G}$ in $\mathbb{H} = \mathbb{B} \times \mathbb{U}$ a *generalized market generation.*

3.53. Remark. It is clear from the preceding discussion that if there would be a market participant, or more precisely a generalized market participant $\mathfrak{H} = (\mathfrak{B}, \mathcal{U})$ that would not be from the generalized market generation that populates a marketplace, that is, if the symmetry group $\mathfrak{G}$ on the generalized market populace $\mathbb{H} = \mathbb{B} \times \mathbb{U}$ would be broken, then there would be an arbitrage opportunity in the marketplace. In this regard we conjecture that, in general, the absence of some type of arbitrage opportunity in a marketplace indicates the presence of a certain inherent symmetry, and, conversely, the presence of some type of arbitrage opportunity in a marketplace indicates the breaking of a certain inherent symmetry.

In light of relation (3.50) we will say that an element $\mathfrak{g} = (\mathfrak{g}_{\mathfrak{B}}, \mathfrak{g}_{\mathcal{U}})$ in $\mathfrak{G}$ is *generated* by $\mathfrak{u}'(t, T)$.

Now we show that the set $\mathfrak{G}$ of transformations of $\mathbb{H}$ is indeed a group, in fact an abelian group.

3.54. Theorem. The set $\mathfrak{G}$ of transformations of the generalized market populace $\mathbb{H}$ is an abelian group with the group operation of composition.

Proof. The proof directly follows from the definition of $\mathfrak{G}$ and the definition of an abelian group. □

It is clear that under the group of transformations $\mathfrak{G}$ of $\mathbb{H}$ the desired expression (3.48) remains unchanged.

3.55. Remark. It is clear that if $\mathfrak{g}_1$ and $\mathfrak{g}_2$ in $\mathfrak{G}$ are generated by $\mathfrak{u}'_1(t, T)$ and $\mathfrak{u}'_2(t, T)$ then $\mathfrak{g}_2\,\mathfrak{g}_1$ in $\mathfrak{G}$ is generated by $\mathfrak{u}'_2(t, T)\,\mathfrak{u}'_1(t, T)$.

3.56. Remark. It is clear that the sets $\mathfrak{G}_{\mathfrak{B}}$ and $\mathfrak{G}_{\mathcal{U}}$ of all transformations $\mathfrak{g}_{\mathfrak{B}}$ and $\mathfrak{g}_{\mathcal{U}}$ of the generalized market populace belief $\mathbb{B}$ and the generalized market populace preference $\mathbb{U}$ are themselves abelian groups of transformations with the group operations of composition.

3.57. Remark. It is clear that if $\mathfrak{g}_{\mathfrak{B}}^{(1)}$ and $\mathfrak{g}_{\mathfrak{B}}^{(2)}$ in $\mathfrak{G}_{\mathfrak{B}}$ are generated by $\mathbf{u'}_1(t,T)$ and $\mathbf{u'}_2(t,T)$ then $\mathfrak{g}_{\mathfrak{B}}^{(2)}\,\mathfrak{g}_{\mathfrak{B}}^{(1)}$ in $\mathfrak{G}_{\mathfrak{B}}$ is generated by $\mathbf{u'}_2(t,T)\,\mathbf{u'}_1(t,T)$.

3.58. Remark. It is clear that if $\mathfrak{g}_{\mathcal{U}}^{(1)}$ and $\mathfrak{g}_{\mathcal{U}}^{(2)}$ in $\mathfrak{G}_{\mathcal{U}}$ are generated by $\mathbf{u'}_1(t,T)$ and $\mathbf{u'}_2(t,T)$ then $\mathfrak{g}_{\mathcal{U}}^{(2)}\,\mathfrak{g}_{\mathcal{U}}^{(1)}$ in $\mathfrak{G}_{\mathcal{U}}$ is generated by $\mathbf{u'}_2(t,T)\,\mathbf{u'}_1(t,T)$.

3.59. Remark. We point out that we have used the generalized beliefs of market participants versus the beliefs of market participants, or more precisely, generalized market participants versus market participants, for the following reason. Although the transformations

$$\boldsymbol{D}(t,T) \quad \to \quad \mathbf{u}'^{-1}(t,t)\boldsymbol{D}(t,T)\mathbf{u}'(t,T)$$

preserve the property that the operators $\boldsymbol{D}(t,T)$ determine bounded measures on $\mathbb{R}^n_{++}$ (in fact, the operators

$$\mathbf{u}'^{-1}(t,t)\boldsymbol{D}(t,T)\mathbf{u}'(t,T),$$

with the appropriate domains of definition, determine bounded measures equivalent to the bounded measures determined by the operators $\boldsymbol{D}(t,T)$), the measures determined by

$$\mathbf{u}'^{-1}(t,t)\boldsymbol{D}(t,T)\mathbf{u}'(t,T)$$

might not be probability measures on $\mathbb{R}^n_{++}$, that is, they might not be normed to unity even if the original measures determined by $\boldsymbol{D}(t,T)$ are normed to unity.

The group of transformations $\mathfrak{G}$ of the generalized market populace $\mathbb{H}$ can be viewed as follows.

3.60. Definition. We call a preference

$$\boldsymbol{\mathcal{U}} = \{\boldsymbol{u}'(t,T) : \Pi(\mathbb{R}^{2n}_{++}) \to \Pi(\mathbb{R}^{2n}_{++}) \,|\, t,\, T \in \mathcal{T}, t \leq T\}$$

a *local preference* if it consists of the operators $\boldsymbol{u}'(t,T)$ of the following form:

$$\big(\boldsymbol{u}'(t,T)\,h\big)(s_t,s_T) = u'(T,s_T)\,h(s_t,s_T).$$

3.61. Remark. For a local preference $\boldsymbol{\mathcal{U}}$ each operator $\boldsymbol{u}'(t,T)$ restricted to Π viewed as a vector sublattice of $\Pi(\mathbb{R}^n_{++} \times \mathbb{R}^n_{++})$ has the range in Π also viewed as a vector sublattice of $\Pi(\mathbb{R}^n_{++} \times \mathbb{R}^n_{++})$. Therefore each operator $\boldsymbol{u}'(t,T)$ in a local preference $\boldsymbol{\mathcal{U}}$ can be interpreted as the operator $\boldsymbol{u}'(T) : \Pi \to \Pi$ defined by

$$\big(\boldsymbol{u}'(T)\, h\big)(s_T) = u'(T, s_T)\, h(s_T), \quad h \in \Pi.$$

3.62. Remark. It is clear that each local preference $\boldsymbol{\mathcal{U}}$ is a Markovian preference.

3.63. Definition. We call a market populace preference $\mathbb{U}$ a *local market populace preference* if it consists only of local preferences $\boldsymbol{\mathcal{U}}$.

3.64. Definition. We call a vector bundle $\mathfrak{A}$ with the fiber $\mathbb{R}$ and the base space $\mathbb{P} = \mathbb{R}^n_{++} \times \mathcal{T}$ an *account bundle.* We will call the base space $\mathbb{P}$ a *price-time.*

3.65. Remark. We comment that each element

$$(s,t) = (s_1, s_2, \ldots, s_n, t)$$

in the base space $\mathbb{P}$ of an account bundle $\mathfrak{A}$ financially represents the state of the market as expressed by the prices of the underlying securities

$$s = (s_1, s_2, \ldots, s_n)$$

in $\mathbb{R}^n_{++}$ at time t in $\mathcal{T}$. In this regard the base space $\mathbb{P}$ itself is, from the financial standpoint, the set of all possible states of the market as expressed by the prices of the underlying securities at all times from a trading time set. Each element from the fiber $\mathbb{R}$ over (s,t) in $\mathbb{P}$ of the account bundle $\mathfrak{A}$ financially represents the amount of units of account to be received or paid at time t in $\mathcal{T}$ if the state of the market as expressed by the prices of the underlying securities is s in $\mathbb{R}^n_{++}$ at this time t. In this regard the fiber $\mathbb{R}$ over (s,t) in $\mathbb{P}$ is, from the financial standpoint, the set of all possible amounts of units of account to be received or paid at time t in $\mathcal{T}$ if the state of the market as expressed by the prices of the underlying securities is s in $\mathbb{R}^n_{++}$ at this time t.

3.66. Remark. Later in the article we will give additional physical, or more precisely financial justifications for the terminology we have introduced for the base space $\mathbb{P}$ of an account bundle $\mathfrak{A}$ as price-time in terms of a connection on $\mathfrak{A}$.

For a Markovian generalized market populace $\mathbb{H} = \mathbb{B} \times \mathbb{U}$ with local generalized market populace preference $\mathbb{U}$, define now the gauge or local symmetry with the gauge group $\mathfrak{G}(\mathbb{R}_{++})$ as follows. Define the action of the gauge group on the fiber $\mathbb{R}$ over (s_τ, τ) in $\mathbb{P}$ of an account bundle $\mathfrak{A}$ as multiplication by $\mathrm{u}'(\tau, s_\tau) > 0$ in $\mathfrak{G}(\mathbb{R}_{++})$ so that the value $v(\tau, s_\tau)$ in the fiber $\mathbb{R}$ over (s_τ, τ) in $\mathbb{P}$ of a European contingent claim with inception time t and expiration time T with $t \leq \tau \leq T$ is transformed into $\mathrm{u}'^{-1}(\tau, s_\tau)\, v(\tau, s_\tau)$. In this regard the group of transformations $\mathfrak{G}$ in (3.50) can be represented as the following gauge group of transformations

$$\begin{aligned} \boldsymbol{D}(t,T)(t,T,s_t,ds_T) &\to \mathrm{u}'^{-1}(t,s_t)\boldsymbol{D}(t,T)(t,T,s_t,ds_T)\mathrm{u}'(T,s_T) \\ v(t,s_t) &\to \mathrm{u}'^{-1}(t,s_t)v(t,s_t). \end{aligned} \tag{3.51}$$

Therefore, in the case under consideration of the generalized market populace $\mathbb{H} = \mathbb{B} \times \mathbb{U}$ with local generalized market populace preference $\mathbb{U}$, the group of transformations (3.50) is nothing but the gauge symmetry with the gauge group $\mathfrak{G}(\mathbb{R}_{++})$. This justifies the following definition.

3.67. Definition. We call the group of transformations $\mathfrak{G}$ defined in (3.50) the *beliefs-preferences gauge symmetry group for a generalized market populace* or simply *beliefs-preferences gauge group for* $\mathbb{H}$.

For a Markovian generalized market populace $\mathbb{H} = \mathbb{B} \times \mathbb{U}$ without the assumption that the generalized market populace preference $\mathbb{U}$ is local, define now the gauge or local symmetry with the gauge group $\mathfrak{G}(\mathbb{R}_{++})$ as follows.

Fix arbitrary t_0 in $\mathcal{T}$ such that the set

$$\mathcal{T}_{t_0} = \{t \in \mathcal{T} : t > t_0\}$$

is not empty. Let the state of the market as expressed by the prices of the underlying securities at this time t_0 be s_{t_0}. Define the action of the gauge group on the fiber $\mathbb{R}$ over (s_τ, τ) in $\mathbb{P}$ of an account bundle $\mathfrak{A}$ as multiplication by

$$\mathrm{u}'_0(\tau, s_\tau) = \mathrm{u}'(t_0, \tau, s_{t_0}, s_\tau) > 0$$

in $\mathfrak{G}(\mathbb{R}_{++})$ so that the value $v(\tau, s_\tau)$ in the fiber $\mathbb{R}$ over (s_τ, τ) in $\mathbb{P}$ of a European contingent claim with inception time t and expiration time T with $t \le \tau \le T$ and t, τ and T in $\mathcal{T}_{t_0}$ is transformed into $\mathrm{u}_0'^{-1}(\tau, s_\tau)\, v(\tau, s_\tau)$. In this regard the group of transformations $\mathfrak{G}$ in (3.50) can be represented as the following gauge group of transformations

$$\begin{aligned} \boldsymbol{D}(t,T)(t,T,s_t,ds_T) &\to \mathrm{u}_0'^{-1}(t,s_t)\boldsymbol{D}(t,T)(t,T,s_t,ds_T)\mathrm{u}'_0(T,s_T) \\ v(t,s_t) &\to \mathrm{u}_0'^{-1}(t,s_t)v(t,s_t), \end{aligned} \tag{3.52}$$

where t, τ and T are in $\mathcal{T}_{t_0}$.

The group of transformations $\mathfrak{G}$ of the generalized market populace $\mathbb{H}$ can be also represented in the following equivalent way.

3.68. Definition. We call a vector bundle $\boldsymbol{\mathcal{P}}$ with the fiber Π and the base space $\mathcal{T}$ a *payoff bundle.*

3.69. Remark. We comment that each element from the fiber Π over t in $\mathcal{T}$ of a payoff bundle $\boldsymbol{\mathcal{P}}$ financially represents a payoff contingent upon the state of the market as expressed by the prices of the underlying securities at time t. In this regard the fiber Π over t in $\mathcal{T}$ is, from the financial standpoint, the set of all possible payoffs at time t contingent upon the state of the market as expressed by the prices of the underlying securities at this time t.

We need the following definition of a connection on a vector bundle (see, for example, [15]).

3.70. Definition. Let (E, M, F, π) be a vector bundle with the total space E, base space M, fiber F and projection π. Denote by $\phi = \phi(E, M, F, \pi)$ a collection $\{\phi_\gamma : \gamma \in \Omega(M)\}$ of vector space isomorphisms such that $\phi_\gamma : F_u \to F_v$ for any γ in $\Omega(u, v, M)$, where F_u is the fiber over u in M, and where $\Omega(M)$ stands for the set of all paths in M and $\Omega(u, v, M)$ stands for the set of all paths in M from u to v.

The collection $\phi = \phi(E, M, F, \pi)$ is called a *connection on the vector bundle* (E, M, F, π), or simply a *connection* if:

(i) ϕ_γ continuously depends on γ,

(ii) $\phi_{\gamma_2 \circ \gamma_1} = \phi_{\gamma_2}\phi_{\gamma_1}$ whenever the product $\gamma_2 \circ \gamma_1$ of paths γ_2 and γ_1 is defined,

(iii) $\phi_{\gamma^{-1}} = \phi_\gamma^{-1}$, and

(iv) ϕ_γ is independent of parameterization of γ.

Each element $\phi_\gamma : F_u \to F_v$ is called a *parallel transport* of fiber F_u over u to fiber F_v over v.

3.71. Remark. In the case when the base space M of a vector bundle (E, M, F, π) is discrete, the conditions (i) and (iv) in the preceding Definition of a connection $\phi = \phi(E, M, F, \pi)$ on the vector bundle (E, M, F, π) can be omitted. We comment that in this case the concept of a path in M can be defined in a similar manner to that of a path on a graph (for a discussion see, for example, [43]).

3.72. Remark. It is clear that due to the no-arbitrage argument each state of the market as expressed by the prices of the underlying securities $s = (s_1, s_2, \ldots, s_n)$ in $\mathbb{R}^n_{++}$ at time t in $\mathcal{T}$ determines a trivial connection, that is, a connection with a trivial holonomy group S on a vector lattice bundle C with the fiber $\mathbb{R}$ and the base space being the set of $n+1$ vertexes of a star graph with n edges between the vertex $n+1$ and the vertex i with $i = 1, 2, \ldots, n$. Indeed, in order to determine a trivial connection on C it is enough only to specify the parallel transports $\phi_{n+1,i}$ from the fiber $\mathbb{R}$ over the vertex $n+1$ to the fiber $\mathbb{R}$ over the vertex i with $i = 1, 2, \ldots, n$. Then each parallel transport $\phi_{i,j}$ from the fiber $\mathbb{R}$ over the vertex i to the fiber $\mathbb{R}$ over the vertex j with $i, j = 1, 2, \ldots, n$ is defined by

$$\phi_{i,j} = \phi_{n+1,j} \circ \phi^{-1}_{n+1,i}.$$

Now we define each $\phi_{n+1,i}$ in S as a multiplication by s_i^{-1}.

Financially, each vertex i with $i = 1, 2, \ldots, n$ is associated with the underlying security i and the vertex $n+1$ is associated with account so that the fiber $\mathbb{R}$ over the vertex i with $i = 1, 2, \ldots, n$ determines the possible amounts of units of the underlying security i and the fiber $\mathbb{R}$ over the vertex $n+1$ determines the possible amounts of units of account. In this regard, the edge structure of the star graph under consideration reflects the fact that account associated with the vertex $n+1$ and each underlying security associated with the vertex i with $i = 1, 2, \ldots, n$ are directly traded. In this way, each parallel transport $\phi_{i,j}$ in S from the fiber $\mathbb{R}$ over the vertex i to the fiber $\mathbb{R}$ over the vertex j with $i, j = 1, 2, \ldots, n+1$ represents the act of converting a portfolio consisting of units of the underlying security i to the portfolio consisting of units of the underlying security j where underlying security $n+1$ is identified with account. More precisely, for $i, j = 1, 2, \ldots, n+1$ a portfolio consisting of x (in the fiber $\mathbb{R}$ over the vertex i) units of the underlying security i is converted by the parallel transport $\phi_{i,j}$ to the portfolio consisting of $\phi_{i,j}(x) = s_j^{-1} s_i x$ (in the fiber $\mathbb{R}$ over the vertex j) units of the underlying security j where s_{n+1} is equal to unity. We comment that $s_i^{-1} s_j$ is nothing but the price of a unit of the underlying security j in terms of the underlying security i, or equivalently a unit-to-unit ratio of the underlying securities i and j.

Denote the set of all trivial connections S on C by $\mathbb{S}$ so that at each time t in the trading time set $\mathcal{T}$ the state of the market can be expressed by a connection $S = S_t$ in $\mathbb{S}$. In this way each (s, t) in the price-time $\mathbb{P} = \mathbb{R}^n_{++} \times \mathcal{T}$ can be identified with the pair (S, t) so that the price-time $\mathbb{P}$ itself can be identified with $\mathbb{S} \times \mathcal{T}$. The reason for representing the price-time $\mathbb{P} = \mathbb{R}^n_{++} \times \mathcal{T}$ as $\mathbb{S} \times \mathcal{T}$ is as follows. It is clear that the choice of the parallel transports $\phi_{n+1,i}$ with $i = 1, 2, \ldots, n$ that specify a trivial connection S on C among all possible $\phi_{i,j}$ with $i, j = 1, 2, \ldots, n+1$ is not unique. However the description of a state of the market at any time t in $\mathcal{T}$, by the no-arbitrage argument, must not depend on such a choice. In this way, the representation of price-time $\mathbb{P} = \mathbb{R}^n_{++} \times \mathcal{T}$ as $\mathbb{S} \times \mathcal{T}$ provides us with a description of a state of the market at any time t in $\mathcal{T}$ which is independent of this choice. We will analyze the representation of price-time $\mathbb{P} = \mathbb{R}^n_{++} \times \mathcal{T}$ as $\mathbb{S} \times \mathcal{T}$ in detail in forthcoming articles. This completes the Remark.

It is clear that a market environment $\mathbf{V}$ generated by $\boldsymbol{L}$ is a connection on the payoff bundle $\boldsymbol{\mathcal{P}}$ with the parallel transport ϕ_γ from the fiber Π over T to the fiber Π over t with $t \leq T$ defined as $\mathbf{V}(t, T)$. We comment that due to relation (2.7) the parallel transport $\phi_{\gamma^{-1}}$ from the fiber Π over t to the fiber Π over T with $t \leq T$ is formally given by

$$\mathbf{V}^{-1}(t, T) = e^{-\int_t^T \boldsymbol{L}(\tau) d\tau},$$

where each generator $\boldsymbol{L}(\tau)$ at time τ acts in the order of τ.

It is also clear that a Markovian belief $\boldsymbol{\mathcal{B}}$ generated by $\mathfrak{L}$ is a connection on the payoff bundle $\boldsymbol{\mathcal{P}}$ with the parallel transport ϕ_γ from the fiber Π over T to the fiber Π over t with $t \leq T$ defined as $\boldsymbol{F}(t, T)$. We comment that due to relation (3.4) the parallel transport $\phi_{\gamma^{-1}}$ from the fiber Π over t to the fiber Π over T with $t \leq T$ is formally given by

$$\boldsymbol{F}^{-1}(t, T) = e^{-\int_t^T \mathfrak{L}(\tau) d\tau},$$

where each generator $\mathfrak{L}(\tau)$ at time τ acts in the order of τ.

Finally, it is clear that a Markovian generalized belief $\mathfrak{B}$ generated by $\mathbf{L}$ is a connection on the payoff bundle $\boldsymbol{\mathcal{P}}$ with the parallel transport ϕ_γ from the fiber Π over T to the fiber Π over t with $t \leq T$ defined as $\boldsymbol{F}(t,T)$. We comment that due to relation (3.7) the parallel transport $\phi_{\gamma^{-1}}$ from the fiber Π over t to the fiber Π over T with $t \leq T$ is formally given by

$$\boldsymbol{D}^{-1}(t,T) = e^{-\int_t^T \mathbf{L}(\tau)d\tau},$$

where each generator $\mathbf{L}(\tau)$ at time τ acts in the order of τ.

Now our goal is to present a coordinate-free formulation for the beliefs-preferences gauge symmetry group for a Markovian generalized market populace $\mathbb{H} = \mathbb{B} \times \mathbb{U}$.

Assume that the generalized market populace preference $\mathbb{U}$ is local. Suppose that a market participant, or more precisely, a Markovian generalized market participant $\mathfrak{H}_1 = (\mathfrak{B}_1, \boldsymbol{\mathcal{U}}_1)$ is to receive at time t in $\mathcal{T}$ a payoff $h = h(s_t)$ in units of account contingent upon the state of the market at this time t as expressed by the prices of the underlying securities s_t in $\mathbb{R}^n_{++}$. Since h is a real-valued function on $\mathbb{R}^n_{++}$ it is a member of the vector lattice Π. The related marginal utility to be received by this market participant is $\boldsymbol{u'}_1(t)\, h = u'_1(t, s_t)\, h(s_t)$. Since $\boldsymbol{u'}_1(t)\, h$ is a real-valued function on $\mathbb{R}^n_{++}$ it is a member of the vector lattice Π. On the other hand, suppose that a market participant, or more precisely, a Markovian generalized market participant $\mathfrak{H}_2 = (\mathfrak{B}_2, \boldsymbol{\mathcal{U}}_2)$ is to receive at time t in $\mathcal{T}$ the payoff $h = h(s_t)$ in Π. The related marginal utility to be received by this market participant is $\boldsymbol{u'}_2(t)\, h = u'_2(t, s_t)\, h(s_t)$. Since $\boldsymbol{u'}_2(t)\, h$ is a real-valued function on $\mathbb{R}^n_{++}$ it is a member of the vector lattice Π. It is clear that the operator $\boldsymbol{u'}_2(t)\boldsymbol{u'}^{-1}_1(t)$ on Π maps the marginal utility $\boldsymbol{u'}_1(t)\, h$ to be received by the first market participant to the marginal utility $\boldsymbol{u'}_2(t)\, h$ to be received by the second market participant, both due to the payoff h in Π. Similarly, it is clear that the operator $\boldsymbol{u'}_1(t)\boldsymbol{u'}^{-1}_2(t)$ on Π maps the marginal utility $\boldsymbol{u'}_2(t)\, h$ to be received by the second market participant to the marginal utility $\boldsymbol{u'}_1(t)\, h$ to be received by the first market participant, both due to the payoff h in Π. It is clear that for two arbitrary market participants the operators $\boldsymbol{u'}_2(t)\boldsymbol{u'}_1^{-1}(t)$ and $\boldsymbol{u'}_1(t)\boldsymbol{u'}_2^{-1}(t)$ are inverse to each other and are members of the group $\mathfrak{G}_{\mathcal{U}}$. In fact, these operators are isomorphisms of Π as a vector lattice.

Define the space of all abstract payoffs $\mathbf{\Pi}$ as follows. We formalize each market participant or, more precisely, Markovian generalized market participant $\mathfrak{H} = (\mathfrak{B}, \mathcal{U})$ from a generalized market generation in a Markovian generalized market populace $\mathbb{H} = \mathbb{B} \times \mathbb{U}$ as a particular choice of basis for the space of all abstract payoffs $\mathbf{\Pi}$. For each $\mathfrak{H} = (\mathfrak{B}, \mathcal{U})$ the basis is chosen in such a way that the coordinates, indexed by s_t in $\mathbb{R}^n_{++}$, of an abstract payoff $\boldsymbol{h}$ in $\mathbf{\Pi}$ with respect to this basis are the values of the marginal utility $u'(t, s_t)\, h(s_t)$ to be received by $\mathfrak{H} = (\mathfrak{B}, \mathcal{U})$ due to the payoff $h = h(s_t)$. In this way the marginal utility $\boldsymbol{u'}(t)\, h$ in Π to be received by $\mathfrak{H} = (\mathfrak{B}, \mathcal{U})$ due to the payoff h in Π is the coordinate description of the abstract payoff $\boldsymbol{h}$ in $\mathbf{\Pi}$ in the basis associated with the Markovian generalized market participant $\mathfrak{H} = (\mathfrak{B}, \mathcal{U})$.

In this formalism, the act of changing market participants, or more precisely, Markovian generalized market participants $\mathfrak{H} = (\mathfrak{B}, \mathcal{U})$ from a generalized market generation in a Markovian generalized market populace $\mathbb{H} = \mathbb{B} \times \mathbb{U}$ is described by a linear change-of-basis operator that acts on the space Π, or more precisely, by an isomorphism of Π as a vector lattice.

In order to find the explicit form of the change-of-basis operator we note that the definition of the change-of-basis operator implies that, for any abstract payoff $\boldsymbol{h}$ in $\mathbf{\Pi}$ the operator has to map the expression $\boldsymbol{u'}_1(t)\, h$ of $\boldsymbol{h}$ in the basis associated with $\mathfrak{H}_1 = (\mathfrak{B}_1, \mathcal{U}_1)$ to the expression $\boldsymbol{u'}_2(t)\, h$ of $\boldsymbol{h}$ in the basis associated with $\mathfrak{H}_2 = (\mathfrak{B}_2, \mathcal{U}_2)$ for arbitrary $\mathfrak{H}_1 = (\mathfrak{B}_1, \mathcal{U}_1)$ and $\mathfrak{H}_2 = (\mathfrak{B}_2, \mathcal{U}_2)$ from a generalized market generation in $\mathbb{H} = \mathbb{B} \times \mathbb{U}$. Therefore it is the operator $\boldsymbol{u'}_2(t)\boldsymbol{u'}_1^{-1}(t)$ that is the change-of-basis operator from the basis associated with $\mathfrak{H}_1 = (\mathfrak{B}_1, \mathcal{U}_1)$ to the basis associated with $\mathfrak{H}_2 = (\mathfrak{B}_2, \mathcal{U}_2)$.

Therefore the set of all change-of-basis operators is in fact the group $\mathfrak{G}_{\mathcal{U}}$.

3.73. Definition. The basis associated with the market participant, or more precisely, with the Markovian generalized market participant $\mathfrak{H} = (\mathfrak{B}, \mathcal{U})$ such that $\boldsymbol{u}'(t)$ is the identity operator on Π is called a *payoff basis.*

3.74. Remark. It is clear that in the payoff basis any abstract payoff $\boldsymbol{h}$ in $\boldsymbol{\Pi}$ has as its coordinate representation the payoff h in Π.

3.75. Remark. It is easy to see that each map from $\boldsymbol{\Pi}$ to Π that associates to an abstract payoff $\boldsymbol{h}$ its coordinate representation $\boldsymbol{u}'(t)\, h$ in the basis associated with $\mathfrak{H} = (\mathfrak{B}, \mathcal{U})$ is an isomorphism of vector lattices. Therefore the vector lattices $\boldsymbol{\Pi}$ and Π are isomorphic. We comment that the structure of the vector lattice on $\boldsymbol{\Pi}$ is defined as being induced by that of Π. More precisely, the structure of a real vector space on $\boldsymbol{\Pi}$ via the operations of addition $\oplus$ and multiplication by real numbers $\odot$ is defined as follows. For any abstract payoffs $\boldsymbol{x}$ and $\boldsymbol{y}$ in $\boldsymbol{\Pi}$ the abstract payoff $\boldsymbol{z} = \boldsymbol{x} \oplus \boldsymbol{y}$ in $\boldsymbol{\Pi}$ has the coordinate representation z in the payoff basis such that $z = x + y$ where x and y are the coordinate representations of $\boldsymbol{x}$ and $\boldsymbol{y}$ in the payoff basis. For any abstract payoffs $\boldsymbol{x}$ in $\boldsymbol{\Pi}$ and r in $\mathbb{R}$ the abstract payoff $\boldsymbol{y} = r \odot \boldsymbol{x}$ in $\boldsymbol{\Pi}$ has the coordinate representation y in the payoff basis such that $y = r\, x$ where x is the coordinate representation of $\boldsymbol{x}$ in the payoff basis. Define the nonnegative cone $\boldsymbol{\Pi}_+$ of $\boldsymbol{\Pi}$ as the set of all abstract payoffs $\boldsymbol{h}$ such that their coordinate representations h in the payoff basis are in Π_+. The real vector space $\boldsymbol{\Pi}$ with the partial order generated by the nonnegative cone $\boldsymbol{\Pi}_+$ is a partially ordered vector space. Finally, define the structure of a vector lattice on $\boldsymbol{\Pi}$ via the lattice operations of supremum $\vee$ and infimum $\wedge$ defined as follows. For any abstract payoffs $\boldsymbol{x}$ and $\boldsymbol{y}$ in $\boldsymbol{\Pi}$ the abstract payoff $\boldsymbol{z} = \boldsymbol{x} \vee \boldsymbol{y}$ in $\boldsymbol{\Pi}$ has the coordinate representation z in the payoff basis such that $z = x \vee y$ where x and y are the coordinate representations of x and y in the payoff basis. Similarly, for any abstract payoffs $\boldsymbol{x}$ and $\boldsymbol{y}$ in $\mathbf{\Pi}$ the abstract payoff $\boldsymbol{z} = \boldsymbol{x} \wedge \boldsymbol{y}$ in $\mathbf{\Pi}$ has the coordinate representation z in the payoff basis such that $z = x \wedge y$ where x and y are the coordinate representations of x and y in the payoff basis. We comment that $\vee$ and $\wedge$ denote here the lattice operations of supremum and infimum for the vector lattice Π.

3.76. Remark. It is clear that each abstract payoff $\boldsymbol{h}$ in $\mathbf{\Pi}$ can be viewed as the orbit of the group $\mathfrak{G}_{\mathcal{U}}$ in Π containing h, so that the space of all abstract payoffs $\mathbf{\Pi}$ can be viewed as the set of all orbits of the group $\mathfrak{G}_{\mathcal{U}}$ in Π.

3.77. Remark. It is clear that what we have actually defined is the space of all abstract payoffs $\mathbf{\Pi}$ that explicitly depends on t in $\mathcal{T}$. To make this dependence explicit, we denote the space of all abstract payoffs $\mathbf{\Pi}$ defined for t in $\mathcal{T}$ as $\mathbf{\Pi}_t$. However, the spaces of all abstract payoffs $\mathbf{\Pi}_t$ for all t in $\mathcal{T}$ are just copies of the space of all abstract payoffs $\mathbf{\Pi}$ that can be defined independently of t as, for example, in the preceding Remark (3.76).

3.78. Definition. We call a vector bundle $\mathfrak{P}$ with the fiber $\mathbf{\Pi}$ and the base space $\mathcal{T}$ an *abstract payoff bundle.*

3.79. Remark. We comment that the fiber $\mathbf{\Pi}$ over t in $\mathcal{T}$ is $\mathbf{\Pi}_t$.

For each t and T in $\mathcal{T}$ with $t \leq T$, define an abstract evolution operator $\boldsymbol{\mathcal{V}}(t,T) : \mathbf{\Pi}_T \to \mathbf{\Pi}_t$ in such a way that in the payoff bases for $\mathbf{\Pi}_t$ and $\mathbf{\Pi}_T$ it is given by the evolution operator $\mathbf{V}(t,T)$ from a market environment

$$\mathbf{V} = \{\mathbf{V}(t,T) : \Pi \to \Pi \,|\, t,T \in \mathcal{T}, t \leq T\}.$$

If the market environment $\mathbf{V}$ is generated by

$$\boldsymbol{L} = \{\boldsymbol{L}(t) : \Pi \to \Pi \,|\, t \in \mathcal{T}\},$$

then the abstract market environment

$$\boldsymbol{\mathcal{V}} = \{\boldsymbol{\mathcal{V}}(t,T) : \mathbf{\Pi}_T \to \mathbf{\Pi}_t \,|\, t,T \in \mathcal{T}, t \leq T\}.$$

is also generated by

$$\boldsymbol{\mathcal{L}} = \{\boldsymbol{\mathcal{L}}(t) : \Pi \to \Pi \,|\, t \in \mathcal{T}\},$$

where each abstract generator $\boldsymbol{\mathcal{L}}(t)$ in the payoff basis is given by the generator $\boldsymbol{L}(t)$.

It is clear that an abstract market environment $\boldsymbol{\mathcal{V}}$ generated by $\boldsymbol{\mathcal{L}}$ is a connection on the abstract payoff bundle $\mathfrak{P}$ with the parallel transport ϕ_γ from the fiber $\boldsymbol{\Pi}_T$ over T to the fiber $\boldsymbol{\Pi}_t$ over t with $t \leq T$ defined as $\boldsymbol{\mathcal{V}}(t,T)$. We comment that, due to relation (2.16), the parallel transport $\phi_{\gamma^{-1}}$ from the fiber $\boldsymbol{\Pi}_t$ over t to the fiber $\boldsymbol{\Pi}_T$ over T with $t \leq T$ is formally given by

$$\boldsymbol{\mathcal{V}}^{-1}(t,T) = e^{-\int_t^T \boldsymbol{\mathcal{L}}(\tau)d\tau},$$

where each generator $\boldsymbol{\mathcal{L}}(\tau)$ at time τ acts in the order of τ.

3.80. Remark. We comment that the abstract generators $\boldsymbol{\mathcal{L}}(t)$ of the abstract market environment $\boldsymbol{\mathcal{V}}$ can be rigorously defined as a differential-geometric connection on the abstract payoff bundle $\mathfrak{P}$. In this way $\frac{d}{dt} + \boldsymbol{\mathcal{L}}(t)$ is nothing but a covariant derivative and Cauchy problem (2.15) states that the value $v(t)$ of an abstract European contingent claim at time t is a result of a parallel transport of the value $v(T)$ of this claim at time T given by the abstract evolution operator $\boldsymbol{\mathcal{V}}(t,T)$ from $\boldsymbol{\mathcal{V}}$ as in Remark (2.43). We will further analyze this issue later in this article.

It is clear that in the basis associated with a market participant, or more precisely, a Markovian generalized market participant $\mathfrak{H} = (\mathfrak{B}, \boldsymbol{\mathcal{U}})$ with the generalized beliefs

$$\mathfrak{B} = \{\boldsymbol{D}(t,T) : \Pi \to \Pi \,|\, t, T \in \mathcal{T}, t \leq T\}$$

and preferences

$$\boldsymbol{\mathcal{U}} = \{\boldsymbol{u}'(t) : \Pi \to \Pi \,|\, t \in \mathcal{T}\}$$

each abstract evolution operator $\boldsymbol{\mathcal{V}}(t,T)$ is given by the generalized belief $\boldsymbol{D}(t,T)$. This follows from the fact that each abstract evolution operator $\boldsymbol{\mathcal{V}}(t,T)$ in the payoff basis is given by the evolution operator $\mathbf{V}(t,T)$ which, in turn, is related to $\boldsymbol{D}(t,T)$ by the similarity transform $\boldsymbol{u}'^{-1}(t)\boldsymbol{D}(t,T)\boldsymbol{u}'(T)$, that is

$$\mathbf{V}(t,T) = \boldsymbol{u}'^{-1}(t)\boldsymbol{D}(t,T)\boldsymbol{u}'(T),$$

and from the fact that the change-of-basis for each $\mathbf{\Pi}_t$ from the payoff basis to the basis associated with $\mathfrak{H} = (\mathfrak{B}, \boldsymbol{\mathcal{U}})$ is given by the change-of-basis operator $\boldsymbol{u}'(t)$.

Now each transformation $\mathfrak{g}_{\mathfrak{B}}$ in $\mathfrak{G}_{\mathfrak{B}}$ defined in (3.50) by

$$\boldsymbol{D}(t,T) \xrightarrow{\mathfrak{g}_{\mathfrak{B}}} \mathbf{u}'^{-1}(t)\boldsymbol{D}(t,T)\mathbf{u}'(T)$$

is nothing but the similarity transform due to the change of bases for each $\mathbf{\Pi}_t$ given by the change-of-basis operator $\mathbf{u}'^{-1}(t)$.

Therefore the beliefs-preferences gauge symmetry group $\mathfrak{G}$ with transformations $\mathfrak{g} = (\mathfrak{g}_{\mathfrak{B}}, \mathfrak{g}_{\mathcal{U}})$ defined in (3.50) states nothing but that for each time t in $\mathcal{T}$ we are free to choose an arbitrary basis associated with an arbitrary $\mathfrak{H} = (\mathfrak{B}, \boldsymbol{\mathcal{U}})$ for the space of all abstract payoffs $\mathbf{\Pi}_t$. In this regard the abstract payoff bundle $\mathfrak{P}$ and the abstract market environment $\boldsymbol{\mathcal{V}}$ as a connection on $\mathfrak{P}$ provide a framework for the coordinate-free, that is, basis-independent description of the financial phenomena related to the beliefs-preferences gauge symmetry group $\mathfrak{G}$ of transformations of Markovian generalized market populace $\mathbb{H} = \mathbb{B} \times \mathbb{U}$ with local generalized market populace preference $\mathbb{U}$.

For a Markovian generalized market populace $\mathbb{H} = \mathbb{B} \times \mathbb{U}$, without the assumption that the generalized market populace preference $\mathbb{U}$ is local, define the beliefs-preferences gauge symmetry group $\mathfrak{G}$ as follows.

Fix arbitrary t_0 in $\mathcal{T}$ such that the set

$$\mathcal{T}_{t_0} = \{t \in \mathcal{T} \,:\, t > t_0\}$$

is not empty. Let the state of the market as expressed by the prices of the underlying securities at this time t_0 be s_{t_0} which we also consider to be fixed. Suppose that a market participant, or more precisely, a Markovian generalized market participant $\mathfrak{H}_1 = (\mathfrak{B}_1, \mathcal{U}_1)$ is to receive at time t in $\mathcal{T}_{t_0}$ a payoff $h = h(s_t)$ in units of account contingent upon the state of the market at this time t as expressed by the prices of the underlying securities s_t in $\mathbb{R}^n_{++}$. Since h is a real-valued function on $\mathbb{R}^n_{++}$ it is a member of the vector lattice Π. The related marginal utility to be received by this market participant is $\boldsymbol{u'}_1(t_0, t)\, h = u'_1(t_0, t, s_{t_0}, s_t)\, h(s_t)$. Since $\boldsymbol{u'}_1(t_0, t)\, h$ is a real-valued function on $\mathbb{R}^n_{++}$ it is a member of the vector lattice Π. On the other hand, suppose that a market participant, or more precisely, a Markovian generalized market participant $\mathfrak{H}_2 = (\mathfrak{B}_2, \mathcal{U}_2)$ is to receive at time t in $\mathcal{T}_{t_0}$ the payoff $h = h(s_t)$ in Π. The related marginal utility to be received by this market participant is $\boldsymbol{u'}_2(t_0, t)\, h = u'_2(t, s_t)\, h(s_t)$. Since $\boldsymbol{u'}_2(t_0, t)\, h$ is a real-valued function on $\mathbb{R}^n_{++}$ it is a member of the vector lattice Π. It is clear that the operator $\boldsymbol{u'}_2(t_0, t)\boldsymbol{u'}^{-1}_1(t_0, t)$ on Π maps the marginal utility $\boldsymbol{u'}_1(t_0, t)\, h$ to be received by the first market participant to the marginal utility $\boldsymbol{u'}_2(t_0, t)\, h$ to be received by the second market participant, both due to the payoff h in Π. Similarly, it is clear that the operator $\boldsymbol{u'}_1(t_0, t)\boldsymbol{u'}^{-1}_2(t_0, t)$ on Π maps the marginal utility $\boldsymbol{u'}_2(t_0, t)\, h$ to be received by the second market participant to the marginal utility $\boldsymbol{u'}_1(t_0, t)\, h$ to be received by the first market participant, both due to the payoff h in Π. It is clear that for two arbitrary market participants the operators $\boldsymbol{u'}_2(t_0, t)\boldsymbol{u'}^{-1}_1(t_0, t)$ and $\boldsymbol{u'}_1(t_0, t)\boldsymbol{u'}^{-1}_2(t_0, t)$ are inverse to each other and are members of the group $\mathfrak{G}_{\mathcal{U}}$. In fact, these operators are isomorphisms of Π as a vector lattice.

From this point, the presentation of beliefs-preferences gauge symmetry group $\mathfrak{G}$ for a Markovian generalized market populace $\mathbb{H} = \mathbb{B} \times \mathbb{U}$, without the assumption that the generalized market populace preference $\mathbb{U}$ is local, is completely analogous to that of a Markovian generalized market populace $\mathbb{H} = \mathbb{B} \times \mathbb{U}$ with the local generalized market populace preference $\mathbb{U}$ in which the trading time set $\mathcal{T}$ has to be replaced by $\mathcal{T}_{t_0}$.

3.3 Beliefs-Preferences Gauge Symmetry Group for a Market Populace

In order to present the beliefs-preferences gauge symmetry for a market populace and not for a generalized market populace, that is, in terms of the beliefs of market participants and not generalized beliefs of generalized market participants, we have to associate a belief of a market participant with a generalized belief of a generalized market participant. However, there is no unique way in general to accomplish this. Such uniqueness, for example, can be assured only locally in time or under the assumption that a market environment satisfies the intervention condition and that the beliefs are Markovian. These cases will be considered later in the article. However, we present now, without these previous assumptions leading to uniqueness, one obvious way to associate a belief of a market participant with a generalized belief of a generalized market participant by introducing a normalization factor for a generalized belief.

First we rewrite relation (3.1) as follows

$$v(t) = \boldsymbol{u}'^{-1}(t,t)\boldsymbol{F}(t,T)\boldsymbol{u}'(t,T)v(T). \tag{3.53}$$

We note right away that relations (3.53) and (3.1) are invariant with respect to the following symmetry group.

3.81. Theorem. Let $\mathfrak{G}(\mathbb{R}_{++})$ be the group of positive real numbers $\mathbb{R}_{++}$ with the group operation being standard multiplication. Then for each belief $\boldsymbol{\mathcal{B}}$ in $\mathbb{B}$ the operators

$$\boldsymbol{u}'^{-1}(t,t)\boldsymbol{F}(t,T)\boldsymbol{u}'(t,T) : \Pi \to \Pi$$

remains unchanged under the following group of transformations on a market populace belief $\mathbb{U}$:

$$\boldsymbol{\mathcal{U}} \to \alpha\boldsymbol{\mathcal{U}}, \quad \alpha \in \mathfrak{G}(\mathbb{R}_{++}),$$

where $\boldsymbol{F}(t,T)$ is in $\boldsymbol{\mathcal{B}}$, and where

$$\boldsymbol{\mathcal{U}} = \{\boldsymbol{u}'(t,T) : \Pi(\mathbb{R}^{2n}_{++}) \to \Pi(\mathbb{R}^{2n}_{++}) \,|\, t, T \in \mathcal{T}, t \leq T\}$$

and

$$\alpha \boldsymbol{\mathcal{U}} = \{\alpha \boldsymbol{u}'(t,T) : \Pi(\mathbb{R}^{2n}_{++}) \to \Pi(\mathbb{R}^{2n}_{++}) \,|\, t,\, T \in \mathcal{T},\, t \leq T\}.$$

Proof. The proof immediately follows from the fact that the operator of multiplication by a constant commutes with each operator $\boldsymbol{F}(t,T)$. □

3.82. Remark. We note that the symmetry presented in the preceding Theorem (3.81) is a reflection of the fact that expected utility is unique up to an affine transformation, or marginal utility is unique up to multiplication by a positive constant (see, for example, [47] page 25 and [16] page 60).

Now we promote the symmetry from preceding Theorem (3.81), which is global in the sense that the group elements α in $\mathfrak{G}(\mathbb{R}_{++})$ do not depend on time t and the state of the market as expressed by the prices of the underlying securities s_t in $\mathbb{R}^n_{++}$, to the local symmetry where the group elements α in $\mathfrak{G}(\mathbb{R}_{++})$ will depend on time t and the state of the market as expressed by the prices of the underlying securities s_t in $\mathbb{R}^n_{++}$, that is, to the gauge symmetry with the gauge group $\mathfrak{G}(\mathbb{R}_{++})$.

Let

$$\boldsymbol{D}_1(t,T) = \mathbf{u}_1'^{-1}(t,t)\boldsymbol{D}(t,T)\mathbf{u}_1'(t,T)$$

where the generalized belief $\boldsymbol{D}(t,T)$ is in fact a belief $\boldsymbol{F}(t,T)$, that is:

$$\boldsymbol{D}(t,T) = \boldsymbol{F}(t,T).$$

We construct a new belief $\boldsymbol{F}_1(t,T)$ from the generalized belief $\boldsymbol{D}_1(t,T)$ as follows

$$\boldsymbol{F}_1(t,T) = \overline{\boldsymbol{D}_1(t,T)\mathbf{1}}^{-1}\boldsymbol{D}_1(t,T)$$

where $\mathbf{1}$ is the function in Π identically equal to unity and where $\overline{\boldsymbol{D}_1(t,T)\mathbf{1}}$ is the operator on Π of multiplication by the function $\boldsymbol{D}_1(t,T)\mathbf{1}$ in Π.

3.83. Remark. Since $\mathbf{1}$ is in Π_+ it is clear that, due to the definition of a generalized belief, $\boldsymbol{D}_1(t,T)\mathbf{1}$ is in Π_+. Moreover, since the value of the function $\mathbf{1}$ at each s_T in $\mathbb{R}^n_{++}$ is positive, we have that the value of $\boldsymbol{D}_1(t,T)\mathbf{1}$ at each s_t in $\mathbb{R}^n_{++}$ is also positive, that is, $(\boldsymbol{D}_1(t,T)\mathbf{1})(s_t) > 0$ for each s_t in $\mathbb{R}^n_{++}$. Hence the operator $\overline{\boldsymbol{D}_1(t,T)\mathbf{1}}$ is invertible and the inverse operator $\overline{\boldsymbol{D}_1(t,T)\mathbf{1}}^{-1}$ preserves a nonnegative cone Π_+ in Π. Therefore, it is clear that $\boldsymbol{F}_1(t,T)$ is a belief, that is, it determines probability measures on $\mathbb{R}^n_{++}$.

3.84. Remark. The function $\boldsymbol{D}_1(t,T)\mathbf{1}$ in Π_+ can again be financially interpreted as the period discount factor (see, for example, [14]) or as a "force of mortality" (see, for example, [44] page 151).

Now we are in a position to make the following decisive step. We are going to absorb the function $\boldsymbol{D}_1(t,T)\mathbf{1}$ into the marginal utility, or more precisely we are going to absorb the operator $\overline{\boldsymbol{D}_1(t,T)\mathbf{1}}$ of the multiplication by the function $\boldsymbol{D}_1(t,T)\mathbf{1}$ into the preference by means of altering $\mathbf{u'}_1(t,T)$. That is, for a $\mathbf{u'}_1(t,T)$ define $\hat{\mathbf{u}}'_1(t,T)$ as follows

$$\hat{\mathbf{u}}'_1(t,T) = \overline{\boldsymbol{D}_1(t,T)\mathbf{1}}^{-1}\ \mathbf{u'}_1(t,T)$$

where the operator $\mathbf{u'}_1(t,T)$ acts first and the operator $\overline{\boldsymbol{D}_1(t,T)\mathbf{1}}$ acts second.

3.85. Remark. We comment that, since $\boldsymbol{F}(t,T)$ is the identity operator on Π whenever t is equal to T, we have that $\boldsymbol{D}_1(t,T)\mathbf{1}$ is equal to $\mathbf{1}$ whenever t is equal to T and hence the operator $\overline{\boldsymbol{D}_1(t,T)\mathbf{1}}$ is the identity operator on Π realized as the operator of multiplication by the function $\mathbf{1}$ whenever t is equal to T. Therefore we have

$$\hat{\mathbf{u}}'_1(t,t) = \overline{\boldsymbol{D}_1(t,t)\mathbf{1}}^{-1}\ \mathbf{u'}_1(t,t) = \mathbf{u'}_1(t,t),$$

where t is in $\mathcal{T}$.

We note that the belief and the preference depend on the particular market participant, although we have suppressed this dependence in relations (3.53) and (3.1). However, if all market participants that populate a marketplace at time t have agreed upon the values at the inception time t in $\mathcal{T}$ of a set of European contingent claims whose payoffs at the expiration time T in $\mathcal{T}$ form a dense set, then, by the no-arbitrage argument, for any pair of such market participants $\mathcal{H}_1 = (\mathcal{B}_1, \mathcal{U}_1)$ and $\mathcal{H}_2 = (\mathcal{B}_2, \mathcal{U}_2)$ we have

$$\boldsymbol{u}_1'^{-1}(t,t)\boldsymbol{F}_1(t,T)\boldsymbol{u}_1'(t,T) = \boldsymbol{u}_2'^{-1}(t,t)\boldsymbol{F}_2(t,T)\boldsymbol{u}_2'(t,T), \tag{3.54}$$

where $\boldsymbol{F}_1(t,T)$ is in $\mathcal{B}_1$ and $\boldsymbol{F}_2(t,T)$ is in $\mathcal{B}_2$, and where $\boldsymbol{u'}_1(t,T)$ is in $\mathcal{U}_1$ and $\boldsymbol{u'}_2(t,T)$ is in $\mathcal{U}_2$. Therefore all such market participants, in terms of their beliefs and preferences, differ only inasmuch as allowed by equality (3.54). This provides us with a complete description of the degrees of freedom that market participants have in terms of their beliefs and preferences. Although market participants might differ in terms of their beliefs and preferences and although their beliefs and preferences are physically, or more precisely, financially unobservable, the following combination

$$\boldsymbol{u}'^{-1}(t,t)\boldsymbol{F}(t,T)\boldsymbol{u}'(t,T) \tag{3.55}$$

of their beliefs and preferences is observable by relation (3.53) and is market participant independent by equality (3.54).

Saying the same thing from another side, the degree of freedom that market participants $\mathcal{H} = (\mathcal{B}, \mathcal{U})$ in $\mathbb{H} = \mathbb{B} \times \mathbb{U}$ have in terms of their beliefs $\mathcal{B}$ and preferences $\mathcal{U}$ is determined by the following group of transformations $\mathcal{G}$ of the market populace $\mathbb{H} = \mathbb{B} \times \mathbb{U}$:

$$\mathcal{H} = (\mathcal{B}, \mathcal{U}) \to g\mathcal{H} = (g_{\mathcal{B}}(\mathcal{B}, \mathcal{U}), g_{\mathcal{U}}(\mathcal{B}, \mathcal{U})), \quad g \in \mathcal{G}. \tag{3.56}$$

Here each $\boldsymbol{g} = (g_{\mathcal{B}}, g_{\mathcal{U}})$ in $\boldsymbol{\mathcal{G}}$ is defined by

$$\begin{aligned} (\boldsymbol{F}(t,T), \boldsymbol{u}'(t,T)) &\xrightarrow{g_{\mathcal{B}}} \hat{\mathbf{u}}'^{-1}(t,t)\boldsymbol{F}(t,T)\hat{\mathbf{u}}'(t,T) \quad \text{and} \\ (\boldsymbol{F}(t,T), \boldsymbol{u}'(t,T)) &\xrightarrow{g_{\mathcal{U}}} \hat{\mathbf{u}}'^{-1}(t,T)\boldsymbol{u}'(t,T), \end{aligned} \tag{3.57}$$

where $\boldsymbol{F}(t,T)$ is in $\boldsymbol{\mathcal{B}}$ and $\hat{\mathbf{u}}'^{-1}(t,t)\boldsymbol{F}(t,T)\hat{\mathbf{u}}'(t,T)$ is in $g_{\mathcal{B}}(\boldsymbol{\mathcal{B}},\boldsymbol{\mathcal{U}})$, and where $\boldsymbol{u}'(t,T)$ is in $\boldsymbol{\mathcal{U}}$ and $\hat{\mathbf{u}}'^{-1}(t,T)\boldsymbol{u}'(t,T)$ is in $g_{\mathcal{U}}(\boldsymbol{\mathcal{B}},\boldsymbol{\mathcal{U}})$.

That is, the set of all market participants $\boldsymbol{\mathcal{H}} = (\boldsymbol{\mathcal{B}},\boldsymbol{\mathcal{U}})$ in $\mathbb{H} = \mathbb{B} \times \mathbb{U}$ that agree at all times t in $\mathcal{T}$ upon the values of a set of European contingent claims with inception time t and expiration time T for all T in $\mathcal{T}$ such that $t \leq T$ whose payoffs form a dense set is nothing but an orbit of the group $\boldsymbol{\mathcal{G}}$ in $\mathbb{H} = \mathbb{B} \times \mathbb{U}$. This financially justifies the following definition.

3.86. Definition. We call an orbit of the group $\boldsymbol{\mathcal{G}}$ in $\mathbb{H} = \mathbb{B} \times \mathbb{U}$ a *market generation.*

3.87. Remark. We comment that the operator $\hat{\mathbf{u}}'(t,T)$ is defined by

$$\hat{\mathbf{u}}'(t,T) = \overline{\mathbf{u}'^{-1}(t,t)\boldsymbol{F}(t,T)\mathbf{u}'(t,T)\mathbf{1}}^{-1}\, \mathbf{u}'(t,T),$$

where $\overline{\mathbf{u}'^{-1}(t,t)\boldsymbol{F}(t,T)\mathbf{u}'(t,T)\mathbf{1}}$ is the operator of multiplication by the function $\mathbf{u}'^{-1}(t,t)\boldsymbol{F}(t,T)\mathbf{u}'(t,T)\mathbf{1}$ of s_t in $\mathbb{R}^n_{++}$. In this regard we will say that an element $\boldsymbol{g} = (g_{\mathcal{B}}, g_{\mathcal{U}})$ in $\boldsymbol{\mathcal{G}}$ is *generated* by $\mathbf{u}'(t,T)$.

3.88. Remark. We comment that $\hat{\mathbf{u}}'(t,T)$ is the operator of multiplication by the function

$$\begin{aligned} &\hat{\mathrm{u}}'(t,T,s_t,s_T) = \\ &\quad \Big(\big(\mathbf{u}'^{-1}(t,t)\boldsymbol{F}(t,T)\mathbf{u}'(t,T)\mathbf{1}\big)(s_t)\Big)^{-1} \mathrm{u}'(t,T,s_t,s_T). \end{aligned}$$

3.89. Remark. We comment that $g_{\mathcal{B}}$ is in fact a map from $\mathbb{B}$ to $\mathbb{B}$.

It is clear that under the group of transformations $\mathcal{G}$ the desired expression (3.55) remains unchanged.

3.90. Definition. We will call the group of transformations $\mathcal{G}$ defined in (3.57) the *beliefs-preferences gauge symmetry group for a market populace* or simply *beliefs-preferences gauge group* for $\mathbb{H}$.

3.91. Remark. We comment that, to the best of our knowledge, the existence of an interconnection between the beliefs and preferences of an investor was first noted by Samuelson and Merton (see, for example, [44]).

Let us show that $\mathcal{G}$ defined in (3.56) indeed forms a group of transformations of the market populace $\mathbb{H}$, in fact an abelian group of transformations.

3.92. Theorem. The set $\mathcal{G}$ of transformations of the market populace $\mathbb{H}$ is an abelian group with the group operation of composition.

Proof. We start by proving that the set $\mathcal{G}_{\mathcal{B}}$ of all transformations $g_{\mathcal{B}}$ is an abelian group with the group operation of composition.

Let $g_{\mathcal{B}}^{(1)}$ and $g_{\mathcal{B}}^{(2)}$ be generated by $\mathbf{u'}_1(t,T)$ and $\mathbf{u'}_2(t,T)$. For each $\boldsymbol{F}(t,T)$ in a belief $\mathcal{B}$ in the market populace belief $\mathbb{B}$ we have the following chain of equalities

$$
\begin{aligned}
&g_{\mathcal{B}}^{(2)}\big(g_{\mathcal{B}}^{(1)}\,\boldsymbol{F}(t,T)\big) = \\
&\qquad \frac{\mathbf{u'}_2^{-1}(t,t)\big(g_{\mathcal{B}}^{(1)}\,\boldsymbol{F}(t,T)\big)\mathbf{u'}_2(t,T)}{\mathbf{u'}_2^{-1}(t,t)\big(g_{\mathcal{B}}^{(1)}\,\boldsymbol{F}(t,T)\big)\mathbf{u'}_2(t,T)\mathbf{1}} = \\
&\qquad \frac{\mathbf{u'}_2{}^{-1}(t,t)\left(\frac{\mathbf{u'}_1{}^{-1}(t,t)\boldsymbol{F}(t,T)\mathbf{u'}_1(t,T)}{\mathbf{u'}_1{}^{-1}(t,t)\boldsymbol{F}(t,T)\mathbf{u'}_1(t,T)\mathbf{1}}\right)\mathbf{u'}_2(t,T)}{\mathbf{u'}_2{}^{-1}(t,t)\left(\frac{\mathbf{u'}_1{}^{-1}(t,t)\boldsymbol{F}(t,T)\mathbf{u'}_1(t,T)}{\mathbf{u'}_1{}^{-1}(t,t)\boldsymbol{F}(t,T)\mathbf{u'}_1(t,T)\mathbf{1}}\right)\mathbf{u'}_2(t,T)\mathbf{1}} = \\
&\qquad \frac{\mathbf{u'}_2^{-1}(t,t)\,\mathbf{u'}_1^{-1}(t,t)\,\boldsymbol{F}(t,T)\,\mathbf{u'}_1(t,T)\,\mathbf{u'}_2(t,T)}{\mathbf{u'}_2^{-1}(t,t)\,\mathbf{u'}_1^{-1}(t,t)\,\boldsymbol{F}(t,T)\,\mathbf{u'}_1(t,T)\,\mathbf{u'}_2(t,T)\,\mathbf{1}},
\end{aligned}
$$

where, for the sake of economy of space, we have used the fraction notation to denote inverse operators of the operators of multiplication by functions, and where for the same reason we have omitted the lines over the operators of multiplication by functions.

On the other hand, for each $\boldsymbol{F}(t,T)$ in a belief $\boldsymbol{\mathcal{B}}$ in the market populace belief $\mathbb{B}$ we have the following chain of equalities

$$g_{\boldsymbol{\mathcal{B}}}^{(1)}\left(g_{\boldsymbol{\mathcal{B}}}^{(2)}\,\boldsymbol{F}(t,T)\right) = \frac{\mathbf{u'}_1^{-1}(t,t)\left(g_{\boldsymbol{\mathcal{B}}}^{(2)}\,\boldsymbol{F}(t,T)\right)\mathbf{u'}_1(t,T)}{\mathbf{u'}_1^{-1}(t,t)\left(g_{\boldsymbol{\mathcal{B}}}^{(2)}\,\boldsymbol{F}(t,T)\right)\mathbf{u'}_1(t,T)\mathbf{1}} = \frac{\mathbf{u'}_1{}^{-1}(t,t)\left(\frac{\mathbf{u'}_2{}^{-1}(t,t)\boldsymbol{F}(t,T)\mathbf{u'}_2(t,T)}{\mathbf{u'}_2{}^{-1}(t,t)\boldsymbol{F}(t,T)\mathbf{u'}_2(t,T)\mathbf{1}}\right)\mathbf{u'}_1(t,T)}{\mathbf{u'}_1{}^{-1}(t,t)\left(\frac{\mathbf{u'}_2{}^{-1}(t,t)\boldsymbol{F}(t,T)\mathbf{u'}_2(t,T)}{\mathbf{u'}_2{}^{-1}(t,t)\boldsymbol{F}(t,T)\mathbf{u'}_2(t,T)\mathbf{1}}\right)\mathbf{u'}_1(t,T)\mathbf{1}} = \frac{\mathbf{u'}_1^{-1}(t,t)\,\mathbf{u'}_2^{-1}(t,t)\,\boldsymbol{F}(t,T)\,\mathbf{u'}_2(t,T)\,\mathbf{u'}_1(t,T)}{\mathbf{u'}_1^{-1}(t,t)\,\mathbf{u'}_2^{-1}(t,t)\,\boldsymbol{F}(t,T)\,\mathbf{u'}_2(t,T)\,\mathbf{u'}_1(t,T)\,\mathbf{1}}.$$

Since the operators $\mathbf{u'}_1(t,T)$ and $\mathbf{u'}_2(t,T)$ commute for each t and T in $\mathcal{T}$ with $t \leq T$ we have that

$$g_{\boldsymbol{\mathcal{B}}}^{(2)}\left(g_{\boldsymbol{\mathcal{B}}}^{(1)}\boldsymbol{F}(t,T)\right) = g_{\boldsymbol{\mathcal{B}}}^{(1)}\left(g_{\boldsymbol{\mathcal{B}}}^{(2)}\,\boldsymbol{F}(t,T)\right)$$

for each $\boldsymbol{F}(t,T)$ in a belief $\boldsymbol{\mathcal{B}}$ in the market populace belief $\mathbb{B}$.

Therefore, the composition $g_{\boldsymbol{\mathcal{B}}}^{(2)} \circ g_{\boldsymbol{\mathcal{B}}}^{(1)} = g_{\boldsymbol{\mathcal{B}}}^{(1)} \circ g_{\boldsymbol{\mathcal{B}}}^{(2)}$ given, for each $\boldsymbol{F}(t,T)$ in a belief $\boldsymbol{\mathcal{B}}$ in the market populace belief $\mathbb{B}$, by

$$\left(g_{\boldsymbol{\mathcal{B}}}^{(2)} \circ g_{\boldsymbol{\mathcal{B}}}^{(1)}\right)\boldsymbol{F}(t,T) = \left(g_{\boldsymbol{\mathcal{B}}}^{(1)} \circ g_{\boldsymbol{\mathcal{B}}}^{(2)}\right)\boldsymbol{F}(t,T) = \frac{\mathbf{u'}_2^{-1}(t,t)\,\mathbf{u'}_1^{-1}(t,t)\,\boldsymbol{F}(t,T)\,\mathbf{u'}_1(t,T)\,\mathbf{u'}_2(t,T)}{\mathbf{u'}_2^{-1}(t,t)\,\mathbf{u'}_1^{-1}(t,t)\,\boldsymbol{F}(t,T)\,\mathbf{u'}_1(t,T)\,\mathbf{u'}_2(t,T)\,\mathbf{1}},$$

defines a commutative binary operation on $\mathcal{G}_{\boldsymbol{\mathcal{B}}}$.

Moreover, it is clear that $\circ$ is an associative binary operation on $\mathcal{G}_{\mathcal{B}}$. Indeed, for each $\boldsymbol{F}(t,T)$ in a belief $\mathcal{B}$ in $\mathbb{B}$ we have

$$\left(g_{\mathcal{B}}^{(3)} \circ \left(g_{\mathcal{B}}^{(2)} \circ g_{\mathcal{B}}^{(1)}\right)\right)\boldsymbol{F}(t,T) = \left(\left(g_{\mathcal{B}}^{(3)} \circ g_{\mathcal{B}}^{(2)}\right) \circ g_{\mathcal{B}}^{(1)}\right)\boldsymbol{F}(t,T) = \frac{\mathbf{u'}_3^{-1}(t,t)\mathbf{u'}_2^{-1}(t,t)\,\mathbf{u'}_1^{-1}(t,t)\,\boldsymbol{F}(t,T)\,\mathbf{u'}_1(t,T)\,\mathbf{u'}_2(t,T)\,\mathbf{u'}_3(t,T)}{\mathbf{u'}_3(t,T)\,\mathbf{u'}_2^{-1}(t,t)\,\mathbf{u'}_1^{-1}(t,t)\,\boldsymbol{F}(t,T)\,\mathbf{u'}_1(t,T)\,\mathbf{u'}_2(t,T)\mathbf{u'}_3(t,T)\,\mathbf{1}},$$

where each $g_{\mathcal{B}}^{(i)}$ is generated by $\mathbf{u'}_i(t,T)$.

It is clear that $\mathcal{G}_{\mathcal{B}}$ contains the identity transformation $g_{\mathcal{B}}^e$ which is generated by the operators $\mathbf{u'}(t,T)$ of multiplication by the function $\mathbf{1}$. Indeed, for each $\boldsymbol{F}(t,T)$ in a belief $\mathcal{B}$ in $\mathbb{B}$ we have

$$g_{\mathcal{B}}^e\,\boldsymbol{F}(t,T) = \frac{\boldsymbol{F}(t,T)}{\boldsymbol{F}(t,T)\,\mathbf{1}} = \boldsymbol{F}(t,T),$$

where in the last equality we make use of the fact that, by the definition of a belief $\mathcal{B}$ in $\mathbb{B}$, the function $\mathbf{1}$ in Π is the fixed point of $\boldsymbol{F}(t,T)$, that is

$$\boldsymbol{F}(t,T)\,\mathbf{1} = \mathbf{1}$$

for each t and T in $\mathcal{T}$ with $t \leq T$.

Let $g_{\mathcal{B}}$ be an arbitrary transformation in $\mathcal{G}_{\mathcal{B}}$ and let $g_{\mathcal{B}}$ be generated by $\mathbf{u'}(t,T)$. It is clear that the inverse transformation $g_{\mathcal{B}}^{-1}$ is generated by $\mathbf{u'}^{-1}(t,T)$ and hence is also in $\mathcal{G}_{\mathcal{B}}$. Indeed, for each $\boldsymbol{F}(t,T)$ in $\mathcal{B}$ in $\mathbb{B}$ we have

$$\begin{aligned}\left(g_{\mathcal{B}} \circ g_{\mathcal{B}}^{-1}\right)\boldsymbol{F}(t,T) &= \left(g_{\mathcal{B}}^{-1} \circ g_{\mathcal{B}}\right)\boldsymbol{F}(t,T) = \\ &\frac{\left(\mathbf{u'}^{-1}\right)^{-1}(t,t)\,\mathbf{u'}^{-1}(t,t)\,\boldsymbol{F}(t,T)\,\mathbf{u'}(t,T)\,\mathbf{u'}^{-1}(t,T)}{\left(\mathbf{u'}^{-1}\right)^{-1}(t,t)\,\mathbf{u'}^{-1}(t,t)\,\boldsymbol{F}(t,T)\,\mathbf{u'}(t,T)\,\mathbf{u'}^{-1}(t,T)\,\mathbf{1}} = \\ &\frac{\boldsymbol{F}(t,T)}{\boldsymbol{F}(t,T)\,\mathbf{1}} = \\ &\boldsymbol{F}(t,T) = \\ &g_{\mathcal{B}}^e\,\boldsymbol{F}(t,T).\end{aligned}$$

Therefore, the set $\mathcal{G}_{\mathcal{B}}$ of all transformations $g_{\mathcal{B}}$ is an abelian group with the group operation $\circ$ of composition.

Now we prove that the composition of transformations in $\mathcal{G}$ defines a commutative binary operation on $\mathcal{G}$.

Let $g_1 = (g_{\mathcal{B}}^{(1)}, g_{\mathcal{U}}^{(1)})$ and $g_2 = (g_{\mathcal{B}}^{(2)}, g_{\mathcal{U}}^{(2)})$ in $\mathcal{G}$ be generated by $\mathbf{u}'_1(t,T)$ and $\mathbf{u}'_2(t,T)$. For each $(\boldsymbol{F}(t,T), \boldsymbol{u}'(t,T))$ in a market participant $\mathcal{H} = (\mathcal{B}, \mathcal{U})$ in $\mathbb{H}$ we have the following chain of equalities

$$g_2\Big(g_1\big(\boldsymbol{F}(t,T), \boldsymbol{u}'(t,T)\big)\Big) =$$
$$g_2\Big(g_{\mathcal{B}}^{(1)}\, \boldsymbol{F}(t,T), g_{\mathcal{U}}^{(1)}\big(\boldsymbol{F}(t,T), \boldsymbol{u}'(t,T)\big)\Big) =$$
$$\Big(g_{\mathcal{B}}^{(2)}\Big(g_{\mathcal{B}}^{(1)}\, \boldsymbol{F}(t,T)\Big), g_{\mathcal{U}}^{(2)}\Big(g_{\mathcal{B}}^{(1)}\, \boldsymbol{F}(t,T), g_{\mathcal{U}}^{(1)}\big(\boldsymbol{F}(t,T), \boldsymbol{u}'(t,T)\big)\Big)\Big)$$

where

$$g_{\mathcal{B}}^{(2)}\big(g_{\mathcal{B}}^{(1)}\, \boldsymbol{F}(t,T)\big) = \Big(g_{\mathcal{B}}^{(2)} \circ g_{\mathcal{B}}^{(1)}\Big)\boldsymbol{F}(t,T) =$$
$$\frac{\mathbf{u}'^{-1}_2(t,t)\,\mathbf{u}'^{-1}_1(t,t)\,\boldsymbol{F}(t,T)\,\mathbf{u}'_1(t,T)\,\mathbf{u}'_2(t,T)}{\mathbf{u}'^{-1}_2(t,t)\,\mathbf{u}'^{-1}_1(t,t)\,\boldsymbol{F}(t,T)\,\mathbf{u}'_1(t,T)\,\mathbf{u}'_2(t,T)\,\mathbf{1}},$$

and where

$$g_{\mathcal{U}}^{(2)}\Big(g_{\mathcal{B}}^{(1)}\, \boldsymbol{F}(t,T), g_{\mathcal{U}}^{(1)}\big(\boldsymbol{F}(t,T), \boldsymbol{u}'(t,T)\big)\Big) =$$
$$\hat{\mathbf{u}}'^{-1}_2(t,T)\hat{\mathbf{u}}'^{-1}_1(t,T)\,\boldsymbol{u}'(t,T) =$$
$$\left(\left(\frac{\mathbf{u}'_2(t,T)}{\big(\mathbf{u}'^{-1}_2(t,t)\big(\frac{\mathbf{u}'^{-1}_1(t,t)\boldsymbol{F}(t,T)\mathbf{u}'_1(t,T)}{\mathbf{u}'^{-1}_1(t,t)\boldsymbol{F}(t,T)\mathbf{u}'_1(t,T)\mathbf{1}}\big)\mathbf{u}'_2(t,T)\mathbf{1}\big)}\right)^{-1} \times\right.$$
$$\left.\left(\frac{\mathbf{u}'_1(t,T)}{\mathbf{u}'^{-1}_1(t,t)\boldsymbol{F}(t,T)\mathbf{u}'_1(t,T)\mathbf{1}}\right)^{-1}\right)\boldsymbol{u}'(t,T) =$$
$$\Big(\Big(\Big(\mathbf{u}'^{-1}_2(t,t)\Big(\frac{\mathbf{u}'^{-1}_1(t,t)\boldsymbol{F}(t,T)\mathbf{u}'_1(t,T)}{\mathbf{u}'^{-1}_1(t,t)\boldsymbol{F}(t,T)\mathbf{u}'_1(t,T)\mathbf{1}}\Big)\mathbf{u}'_2(t,T)\mathbf{1}\Big)\mathbf{u}'^{-1}_2(t,T)\Big) \times$$
$$\Big(\big(\mathbf{u}'^{-1}_1(t,t)\boldsymbol{F}(t,T)\mathbf{u}'_1(t,T)\mathbf{1}\big)\mathbf{u}'^{-1}_1(t,T)\Big)\,\boldsymbol{u}'(t,T) =$$
$$\big(\mathbf{u}'^{-1}_2(t,t)\mathbf{u}'^{-1}_1(t,t)\boldsymbol{F}(t,T)\mathbf{u}'_1(t,T)\mathbf{u}'_2(t,T)\mathbf{1}\big) \times$$
$$\big(\mathbf{u}'^{-1}_2(t,T)\,\mathbf{u}'^{-1}_1(t,T)\big)\,\boldsymbol{u}'(t,T).$$

On the other hand, for each $(\boldsymbol{F}(t,T), \boldsymbol{u}'(t,T))$ in a market participant $\mathcal{H} = (\mathcal{B},\mathcal{U})$ in $\mathbb{H}$ we have the following chain of equalities

$$\begin{aligned}
&g_1\Big(g_2(\boldsymbol{F}(t,T), \boldsymbol{u}'(t,T))\Big) = \\
&\quad g_1\Big(g^{(2)}_{\mathcal{B}}\, \boldsymbol{F}(t,T), g^{(2)}_{\mathcal{U}}(\boldsymbol{F}(t,T), \boldsymbol{u}'(t,T))\Big) = \\
&\quad \Big(g^{(1)}_{\mathcal{B}}\Big(g^{(2)}_{\mathcal{B}}\, \boldsymbol{F}(t,T)\Big), g^{(1)}_{\mathcal{U}}\Big(g^{(2)}_{\mathcal{B}}\, \boldsymbol{F}(t,T), g^{(2)}_{\mathcal{U}}(\boldsymbol{F}(t,T), \boldsymbol{u}'(t,T))\Big)\Big),
\end{aligned}$$

where

$$g^{(1)}_{\mathcal{B}}(g^{(2)}_{\mathcal{B}}\, \boldsymbol{F}(t,T)) = \Big(g^{(1)}_{\mathcal{B}} \circ g^{(2)}_{\mathcal{B}}\Big)\boldsymbol{F}(t,T) = \frac{\mathbf{u'}^{-1}_1(t,t)\, \mathbf{u'}^{-1}_2(t,t)\, \boldsymbol{F}(t,T)\, \mathbf{u'}_2(t,T)\, \mathbf{u'}_1(t,T)}{\mathbf{u'}^{-1}_1(t,t)\, \mathbf{u'}^{-1}_2(t,t)\, \boldsymbol{F}(t,T)\, \mathbf{u'}_2(t,T)\, \mathbf{u'}_1(t,T)\, \mathbf{1}},$$

and where

$$\begin{aligned}
&g^{(1)}_{\mathcal{U}}\Big(g^{(2)}_{\mathcal{B}}\, \boldsymbol{F}(t,T), g^{(2)}_{\mathcal{U}}(\boldsymbol{F}(t,T), \boldsymbol{u}'(t,T))\Big) = \\
&\hat{\mathbf{u}}'^{-1}_1(t,T)\hat{\mathbf{u}}'^{-1}_2(t,T)\, \boldsymbol{u}'(t,T) = \\
&\Bigg(\Bigg(\frac{\mathbf{u'}_1(t,T)}{\Big(\mathbf{u'}^{-1}_1(t,t)\Big(\frac{\mathbf{u'}_2{}^{-1}(t,t)\boldsymbol{F}(t,T)\mathbf{u'}_2(t,T)}{\mathbf{u'}_2{}^{-1}(t,t)\boldsymbol{F}(t,T)\mathbf{u'}_2(t,T)\mathbf{1}}\Big)\mathbf{u'}_1(t,T)\mathbf{1}\Big)}\Bigg)^{-1} \times \\
&\qquad \Bigg(\frac{\mathbf{u'}_2(t,T)}{\mathbf{u'}_2{}^{-1}(t,t)\boldsymbol{F}(t,T)\mathbf{u'}_2(t,T)\mathbf{1}}\Bigg)^{-1}\Bigg)\, \boldsymbol{u}'(t,T) = \\
&\Bigg(\Bigg(\Big(\mathbf{u'}^{-1}_1(t,t)\Big(\frac{\mathbf{u'}_2{}^{-1}(t,t)\boldsymbol{F}(t,T)\mathbf{u'}_2(t,T)}{\mathbf{u'}_2{}^{-1}(t,t)\boldsymbol{F}(t,T)\mathbf{u'}_2(t,T)\mathbf{1}}\Big)\mathbf{u'}_1(t,T)\mathbf{1}\Big)\mathbf{u'}^{-1}_1(t,T)\Bigg) \times \\
&\qquad \Big(\Big(\mathbf{u'}_2{}^{-1}(t,t)\boldsymbol{F}(t,T)\mathbf{u'}_2(t,T)\mathbf{1}\Big)\mathbf{u'}^{-1}_2(t,T)\Big)\, \boldsymbol{u}'(t,T) = \\
&\Big(\mathbf{u'}^{-1}_1(t,t)\mathbf{u'}^{-1}_2(t,t)\boldsymbol{F}(t,T)\mathbf{u'}_2(t,T)\mathbf{u'}_1(t,T)\mathbf{1}\Big) \times \\
&\qquad \Big(\mathbf{u'}^{-1}_1(t,T)\, \mathbf{u'}^{-1}_2(t,T)\Big)\, \boldsymbol{u}'(t,T).
\end{aligned}$$

Since the operators $\mathbf{u'}_1(t,T)$ and $\mathbf{u'}_2(t,T)$ commute for each t and T in $\mathcal{T}$ with $t \leq T$ we have that

$$g_2\Big(g_1(\boldsymbol{F}(t,T), \boldsymbol{u}'(t,T))\Big) = g_1\Big(g_2(\boldsymbol{F}(t,T), \boldsymbol{u}'(t,T))\Big)$$

for each $(\boldsymbol{F}(t,T), \boldsymbol{u}'(t,T)$ in a market participant $\mathcal{H} = (\mathcal{B}, \mathcal{U})$ in $\mathbb{H}$.

Therefore, the composition $\boldsymbol{g}_1 \bullet \boldsymbol{g}_2 = \boldsymbol{g}_2 \bullet \boldsymbol{g}_1$ given for each $\big(\boldsymbol{F}(t,T), \boldsymbol{u}'(t,T)\big)$ in a market participant $\mathcal{H} = (\mathcal{B}, \mathcal{U})$ in $\mathbb{H}$ by

$$\begin{aligned}
&(\boldsymbol{g}_1 \bullet \boldsymbol{g}_2)\,(\boldsymbol{F}(t,T), \boldsymbol{u}'(t,T)) = \\
&\quad (\boldsymbol{g}_2 \bullet \boldsymbol{g}_1)\,(\boldsymbol{F}(t,T), \boldsymbol{u}'(t,T)) = \\
&\quad \Big(\hat{\mathbf{u}}'^{-1}_2(t,t)\hat{\mathbf{u}}'^{-1}_1(t,t)\boldsymbol{F}(t,T)\hat{\mathbf{u}}'_1(t,T)\hat{\mathbf{u}}'_2(t,T), \\
&\qquad\qquad \hat{\mathbf{u}}'^{-1}_2(t,T)\hat{\mathbf{u}}'^{-1}_1(t,T)\,\boldsymbol{u}'(t,T)\Big),
\end{aligned}$$

defines a commutative binary operation on $\mathcal{G}$. We comment that here $\boldsymbol{g}_1$ and $\boldsymbol{g}_2$ in $\mathcal{G}$ are generated by $\mathbf{u}'_1(t,T)$ and $\mathbf{u}'_2(t,T)$.

Moreover, it is clear that $\bullet$ is an associative binary operation on $\mathcal{G}$. Indeed, for each $(\boldsymbol{F}(t,T), \boldsymbol{u}'(t,T))$ in a market participant $\mathcal{H} = (\mathcal{B}, \mathcal{U})$ in $\mathbb{H}$ we have

$$\begin{aligned}
&\Big(\boldsymbol{g}_3 \bullet \big(\boldsymbol{g}_2 \bullet \boldsymbol{g}_1\big)\Big)(\boldsymbol{F}(t,T), \boldsymbol{u}'(t,T)) = \\
&\quad \Big(\big(\boldsymbol{g}_3 \bullet \boldsymbol{g}_2\big) \bullet \boldsymbol{g}_1\Big)(\boldsymbol{F}(t,T), \boldsymbol{u}'(t,T)) = \\
&\quad \Big(\hat{\mathbf{u}}'^{-1}_3(t,t)\hat{\mathbf{u}}'^{-1}_2(t,t)\hat{\mathbf{u}}'^{-1}_1(t,t)\boldsymbol{F}(t,T)\hat{\mathbf{u}}'_1(t,T)\hat{\mathbf{u}}'_2(t,T)\hat{\mathbf{u}}'_3(t,T), \\
&\qquad\qquad \hat{\mathbf{u}}'^{-1}_3(t,T)\hat{\mathbf{u}}'^{-1}_2(t,T)\hat{\mathbf{u}}'^{-1}_1(t,T)\,\boldsymbol{u}'(t,T)\Big),
\end{aligned}$$

where each $\boldsymbol{g}_i$ in $\mathcal{G}$ is generated by $\mathbf{u}'_i(t,T)$.

We comment that

$$\begin{aligned}
&\hat{\mathbf{u}}'^{-1}_3(t,t)\hat{\mathbf{u}}'^{-1}_2(t,t)\hat{\mathbf{u}}'^{-1}_1(t,t)\boldsymbol{F}(t,T)\hat{\mathbf{u}}'_1(t,T)\hat{\mathbf{u}}'_2(t,T)\hat{\mathbf{u}}'_3(t,T) = \\
&\quad \frac{\mathbf{u}'^{-1}_3(t,t)\mathbf{u}'^{-1}_2(t,t)\,\mathbf{u}'^{-1}_1(t,t)\,\boldsymbol{F}(t,T)\,\mathbf{u}'_1(t,T)\,\mathbf{u}'_2(t,T)\,\mathbf{u}'_3(t,T)}{\mathbf{u}'_3(t,T)\,\mathbf{u}'^{-1}_2(t,t)\,\mathbf{u}'^{-1}_1(t,t)\,\boldsymbol{F}(t,T)\,\mathbf{u}'_1(t,T)\,\mathbf{u}'_2(t,T)\mathbf{u}'_3(t,T)\,\mathbf{1}},
\end{aligned}$$

and

$$\begin{aligned}
&\hat{\mathbf{u}}'^{-1}_3(t,T)\hat{\mathbf{u}}'^{-1}_2(t,T)\hat{\mathbf{u}}'^{-1}_1(t,T)\,\boldsymbol{u}'(t,T) = \\
&(\mathbf{u}'^{-1}_3(t,t)\mathbf{u}'^{-1}_2(t,t)\mathbf{u}'^{-1}_1(t,t)\boldsymbol{F}(t,T)\mathbf{u}'_1(t,T)\mathbf{u}'_2(t,T)\mathbf{u}'_3(t,T)\mathbf{1}) \times \\
&\qquad\qquad (\mathbf{u}'^{-1}_3(t,T)\mathbf{u}'^{-1}_2(t,T)\,\mathbf{u}'^{-1}_1(t,T))\,\boldsymbol{u}'(t,T).
\end{aligned}$$

It is clear that $\mathcal{G}$ contains the identity transformation $\boldsymbol{g}^e$ which is generated by the operators $\mathbf{u}'(t,T)$ of multiplication by the function $\mathbf{1}$. Indeed, for each $(\boldsymbol{F}(t,T), \boldsymbol{u}'(t,T))$ in a market participant $\mathcal{H} = (\mathcal{B}, \mathcal{U})$ in $\mathbb{H}$ we have

$$\boldsymbol{g}^e\left(\boldsymbol{F}(t,T), \boldsymbol{u}'(t,T)\right) = \left(\frac{\boldsymbol{F}(t,T)}{\boldsymbol{F}(t,T)\,\mathbf{1}}, \left(\boldsymbol{F}(t,T)\,\mathbf{1}\right)\boldsymbol{u}'(t,T)\right) = \left(\boldsymbol{F}(t,T), \boldsymbol{u}'(t,T)\right)$$

where again we make use of the fact that, by the definition of a belief $\mathbb{B}$, the function $\mathbf{1}$ in Π is the fixed point of $\boldsymbol{F}(t,T)$, that is

$$\boldsymbol{F}(t,T)\,\mathbf{1} = \mathbf{1}$$

for each t and T in $\mathcal{T}$ with $t \leq T$.

Let $\boldsymbol{g}$ be an arbitrary transformation in $\mathcal{G}$ and let $\boldsymbol{g}$ be generated by $\mathbf{u}'(t,T)$. It is clear that the inverse transformation $\boldsymbol{g}^{-1}$ is generated by $\mathbf{u}'^{-1}(t,T)$ and hence is also in $\mathcal{G}$. Indeed, for each $(\boldsymbol{F}(t,T), \boldsymbol{u}'(t,T))$ in a market participant $\mathcal{H} = (\mathcal{B}, \mathcal{U})$ in $\mathbb{H}$ we have

$$\begin{aligned}
&\left(\boldsymbol{g} \bullet \boldsymbol{g}^{-1}\right)\left(\boldsymbol{F}(t,T), \boldsymbol{u}'(t,T)\right) = \left(\boldsymbol{g}^{-1} \bullet \boldsymbol{g}\right)\left(\boldsymbol{F}(t,T), \boldsymbol{u}'(t,T)\right) = \\
&\quad\Bigg(\frac{\left(\mathbf{u}'^{-1}\right)^{-1}(t,t)\,\mathbf{u}'^{-1}(t,t)\,\boldsymbol{F}(t,T)\,\mathbf{u}'(t,T)\,\mathbf{u}'^{-1}(t,T)}{\left(\mathbf{u}'^{-1}\right)^{-1}(t,t)\,\mathbf{u}'^{-1}(t,t)\,\boldsymbol{F}(t,T)\,\mathbf{u}'(t,T)\,\mathbf{u}'^{-1}(t,T)\,\mathbf{1}}, \\
&\qquad\left(\left(\mathbf{u}'^{-1}\right)^{-1}(t,t)\,\mathbf{u}'^{-1}(t,t)\boldsymbol{F}(t,T)\mathbf{u}'(t,T)\mathbf{u}'^{-1}(t,T)\mathbf{1}\right) \times \\
&\qquad\left(\mathbf{u}'^{-1}(t,T)\,\mathbf{u}'(t,T)\right)\boldsymbol{u}'(t,T)\Bigg) = \\
&\quad\left(\boldsymbol{F}(t,T), \boldsymbol{u}'(t,T)\right) = \\
&\quad\boldsymbol{g}^e\left(\boldsymbol{F}(t,T), \boldsymbol{u}'(t,T)\right).
\end{aligned}$$

This completes the proof of the Theorem. □

3.93. Remark. It is clear that

$$\boldsymbol{g}_{\mathcal{B}}^{(2)} \circ \boldsymbol{g}_{\mathcal{B}}^{(1)} = \hat{\mathbf{u}}'^{-1}_2(t,t)\hat{\mathbf{u}}'^{-1}_1(t,t)\boldsymbol{F}(t,T)\hat{\mathbf{u}}'_1(t,T)\hat{\mathbf{u}}'_2(t,T),$$

where $\boldsymbol{g}_{\mathcal{B}}^{(1)}$ and $\boldsymbol{g}_{\mathcal{B}}^{(2)}$ in $\mathcal{G}_{\mathcal{B}}$ are generated by $\mathbf{u}'_1(t,T)$ and $\mathbf{u}'_2(t,T)$.

3.94. Remark. It is clear that if $\boldsymbol{g}_{\mathcal{B}}^{(1)}$ and $\boldsymbol{g}_{\mathcal{B}}^{(1)}$ in $\mathcal{G}_{\mathcal{B}}$ are generated by $\mathbf{u'}_1(t,T)$ and $\mathbf{u'}_2(t,T)$ then $\boldsymbol{g}_{\mathcal{B}}^{(2)} \circ \boldsymbol{g}_{\mathcal{B}}^{(1)}$ in $\mathcal{G}_{\mathcal{B}}$ is generated by $\mathbf{u'}_2(t,T)\,\mathbf{u'}_1(t,T)$.

3.95. Remark. Due to preceding Remark (3.94) and Remark (3.57) the groups $\mathcal{G}_{\mathcal{B}}$ and $\mathfrak{G}_{\mathfrak{B}}$ are isomorphic with the isomorphism defined as follows. Let $\boldsymbol{g}_{\mathcal{B}}$ in $\mathcal{G}_{\mathcal{B}}$ be arbitrary and let $\boldsymbol{g}_{\mathcal{B}}$ be generated by $\mathbf{u'}(t,T)$. Then the image of $\boldsymbol{g}_{\mathcal{B}}$ under the isomorphism is $\mathfrak{g}_{\mathfrak{B}}$ in $\mathfrak{G}_{\mathfrak{B}}$ generated by $\mathbf{u'}(t,T)$.

3.96. Remark. It is clear that if $\boldsymbol{g}_1$ and $\boldsymbol{g}_2$ in $\mathcal{G}$ are generated by $\mathbf{u'}_1(t,T)$ and $\mathbf{u'}_2(t,T)$ then $\boldsymbol{g}_2 \bullet \boldsymbol{g}_1$ in $\mathcal{G}$ is generated by $\mathbf{u'}_2(t,T)\,\mathbf{u'}_1(t,T)$.

3.97. Remark. Due to preceding Remark (3.96) and Remark (3.55) the groups $\mathcal{G}$ and $\mathfrak{G}$ are isomorphic with the isomorphism defined as follows. Let $\boldsymbol{g}$ in $\mathcal{G}$ be arbitrary and let $\boldsymbol{g}$ be generated by $\mathbf{u'}(t,T)$. Then the image of $\boldsymbol{g}$ under the isomorphism is $\mathfrak{g}$ in $\mathfrak{G}$ generated by $\mathbf{u'}(t,T)$.

3.4 The Local in Time Formulation of the Beliefs-Preferences Gauge Symmetry Group for a Generalized Market Populace

Now we are ready to present a local in time formulation of the beliefs-preferences gauge symmetry group for a generalized market populace defined in (3.49) and (3.50).

More precisely, suppose that a trading time set $\mathcal{T}$ contains t and a neighborhood of t. Assume that $\boldsymbol{D}(t,T)$ and $\mathbf{u'}(t,T)$ in the generalized belief $\mathfrak{B}$ and the generalized preference $\mathcal{U}$ of a generalized market participant $\mathfrak{H} = (\mathfrak{B},\mathcal{U})$ are, in an appropriate sense, differentiable with respect to the time variables at t for each generalized market participant $\mathcal{H} = (\mathfrak{B},\mathcal{U})$ in the market populace $\mathbb{H} = \mathbb{B} \times \mathbb{U}$. Our immediate goal is to obtain the explicit form of

$$\mathbf{u}'^{-1}(t-\Delta t, t-\Delta t)\boldsymbol{D}(t-\Delta t, t)\mathbf{u}'(t-\Delta t, t)$$

up to the terms of the first order in Δt:

$$\begin{aligned}
&\mathbf{u}'^{-1}(t-\Delta t, t-\Delta t)\boldsymbol{D}(t-\Delta t, t)\mathbf{u}'(t-\Delta t, t) = \\
&\quad \mathbf{u}'^{-1}(t-\Delta t, t-\Delta t)\big(\boldsymbol{I}+\Delta t\,\mathsf{L}(t)\big)\mathbf{u}'(t-\Delta t, t) + o(\Delta t) = \\
&\quad \mathbf{u}'^{-1}(t-\Delta t, t-\Delta t)\,\mathbf{u}'(t-\Delta t, t) + \\
&\qquad \Delta t\,\mathbf{u}'^{-1}(t-\Delta t, t-\Delta t)\,\mathsf{L}(t)\,\mathbf{u}'(t-\Delta t, t) + o(\Delta t) = \\
&\quad \frac{\mathbf{u}'(t,t) - \Delta t\,\frac{\partial}{\partial t}^{(1)}\mathbf{u}'(t,t)}{\mathbf{u}'(t,t) - \Delta t\left(\frac{\partial}{\partial t}^{(1)}\mathbf{u}'(t,t) + \frac{\partial}{\partial t}^{(2)}\mathbf{u}'(t,t)\right)} + \\
&\qquad \Delta t\,\mathbf{u}'^{-1}(t,t)\,\mathsf{L}(\overset{2}{t})\,\mathbf{u}'(\overset{3}{t},\overset{1}{t}) + o(\Delta t) = \\
&\quad \frac{\mathbf{u}'(t,t) - \Delta t\,\frac{\partial}{\partial t}^{(1)}\mathbf{u}'(t,t)}{\mathbf{u}'(t,t)} \times \\
&\qquad \left(\boldsymbol{I} + \Delta t \frac{\frac{\partial}{\partial t}^{(1)}\mathbf{u}'(t,t) + \frac{\partial}{\partial t}^{(2)}\mathbf{u}'(t,t)}{\mathbf{u}'(t,t)}\right) + \\
&\qquad \Delta t\,\mathbf{u}'^{-1}(t,t)\,\mathsf{L}(\overset{2}{t})\,\mathbf{u}'(\overset{3}{t},\overset{1}{t}) + o(\Delta t) = \\
&\quad \boldsymbol{I} - \Delta t\,\frac{\frac{\partial}{\partial t}^{(1)}\mathbf{u}'(t,t)}{\mathbf{u}'(t,t)} + \Delta t\,\frac{\frac{\partial}{\partial t}^{(1)}\mathbf{u}'(t,t)}{\mathbf{u}'(t,t)} + \Delta t\,\frac{\frac{\partial}{\partial t}^{(2)}\mathbf{u}'(t,t)}{\mathbf{u}'(t,t)} + \\
&\qquad \Delta t\,\mathbf{u}'^{-1}(t,t)\,\mathsf{L}(\overset{2}{t})\,\mathbf{u}'(\overset{3}{t},\overset{1}{t}) + o(\Delta t) = \\
&\quad \boldsymbol{I} + \Delta t\left(\mathbf{u}'^{-1}(t,t)\,\mathsf{L}(\overset{2}{t})\,\mathbf{u}'(\overset{3}{t},\overset{1}{t}) + \frac{\mathbf{u}'_t(t,t)}{\mathbf{u}'(t,t)}\right) + o(\Delta t),
\end{aligned} \tag{3.58}$$

where $\frac{\partial}{\partial t}^{(1)}\mathbf{u}'(t,t)$ and $\frac{\partial}{\partial t}^{(2)}\mathbf{u}'(t,t) = \mathbf{u}'_t(t,t)$ stand for the partial derivatives of $\mathbf{u}'(t,t)$ with respect to the first and second time variable, and where the indexes over the operators indicate the orders in which these operators act. For example, the operator

$\mathbf{u}'^{-1}(t,t)\,\mathsf{L}(\overset{2}{t})\,\mathbf{u}'(\overset{3}{t},\overset{1}{t})$ is understood in the following sense

$$\big(\mathbf{u}'^{-1}(t,t)\,\mathsf{L}(\overset{2}{t})\,\mathbf{u}'(\overset{3}{t},\overset{1}{t})\,h\big)(s_t) = \\ \mathrm{u}'^{-1}(t,t,s_t,s_t)\big(\mathsf{L}(t)\,\mathrm{u}'(t,t,s_t,\cdot)\,h(\cdot)\big)(s_t),$$

where h is an admissible function in Π.

3.98. Remark. For an introduction to noncommutative analysis in general and to the calculus of functions of noncommutative ordered linear operators in particular, see [42].

3.99. Remark. Whenever ambiguity is unlikely we will write $\mathbf{u}'^{-1}(t,t)\,\mathsf{L}(\overset{2}{t})\,\mathbf{u}'(\overset{3}{t},\overset{1}{t})$ simply as $\mathbf{u}'^{-1}(t,t)\,\mathsf{L}(t)\,\mathbf{u}'(t,t)$.

3.100. Remark. It is clear that

$$\mathbf{u}'^{-1}(t,t)\,\mathsf{L}(t)\,\mathbf{u}'(t,t) + \frac{\mathbf{u}'_t(t,t)}{\mathbf{u}'(t,t)}$$

is the derivative of $-\mathbf{u}'^{-1}(t,t)\boldsymbol{D}(t,T)\mathbf{u}'(t,T)$ with respect to t evaluated at t equal to T understood in an appropriate sense, for example in the sense of the operator norm or in the strong sense.

3.101. Remark. In the preceding chain of equalities (3.58) the operator $\mathsf{L}(t)$ stands for the derivative of $-\,\boldsymbol{D}(t,T)$ with respect to t evaluated at t equal to T understood in an appropriate sense. The reason we have used the notation for this derivative identical to that of the generator at time t of a Markovian generalized belief is that in the case when $\boldsymbol{D}(t,T)$ is contained in a Markovian generalized belief $\mathfrak{B}$ this derivative coincides with the generator at time t of the Markovian generalized belief $\mathfrak{B}$. In this regard, we stress again that in the preceding chain of equalities (3.58) we did not assume that the generalized belief $\mathfrak{B}$ that contains $\boldsymbol{D}(t,T)$ is Markovian.

3.102. Remark. It is clear that the operator $\mathsf{L}(t)$ is also the derivative of $\boldsymbol{D}(t,T)$ with respect to T evaluated at T equal to t understood in an appropriate sense, provided that $\boldsymbol{D}(t,T)$ is a sufficiently regular function of the time variables.

For $\boldsymbol{D}(t,T)$ in $\mathfrak{B}$, by the beliefs-preferences gauge symmetry group for the generalized market populace,

$$\mathfrak{u}'^{-1}(t,t)\boldsymbol{D}(t,T)\mathfrak{u}'(t,T)$$

represents another generalized belief which we denote by $\boldsymbol{D}'(t,T)$ in $\mathfrak{B}' = \mathfrak{g}_{\mathfrak{B}}\mathfrak{B}$ with $\mathfrak{g}_{\mathfrak{B}}$ being generated by $\mathfrak{u}'(t,T)$. Therefore the derivative $\mathsf{L}'(t)$ of $-\boldsymbol{D}'(t,T)$ with respect to t evaluated at t equal to T has to be equal to the derivative

$$\mathfrak{u}'^{-1}(t,t)\,\mathsf{L}(t)\,\mathfrak{u}'(t,t) + \frac{\mathfrak{u}'_t(t,t)}{\mathfrak{u}'(t,t)}$$

of $-\mathfrak{u}'^{-1}(t,t)\boldsymbol{D}(t,T)\mathfrak{u}'(t,T)$ with respect to t evaluated at t equal to T:

$$\mathsf{L}'(t) = \mathfrak{u}'^{-1}(t,t)\,\mathsf{L}(t)\,\mathfrak{u}'(t,t) + \frac{\mathfrak{u}'_t(t,t)}{\mathfrak{u}'(t,t)}. \tag{3.59}$$

Therefore the beliefs-preferences gauge symmetry group for a generalized market populace defined in (3.49) and (3.50) can be represented as follows:

$$\mathsf{L}(t) \xrightarrow{\hat{\mathfrak{g}}_{\mathfrak{B}}} \mathfrak{u}'^{-1}(t,t)\,\mathsf{L}(t)\,\mathfrak{u}'(t,t) + \frac{\mathfrak{u}'_t(t,t)}{\mathfrak{u}'(t,t)} \quad \text{and}$$

$$\boldsymbol{u}'(t,T) \xrightarrow{\hat{\mathfrak{g}}_{\mathcal{U}}} \mathfrak{u}'^{-1}(t,T)\boldsymbol{u}'(t,T). \tag{3.60}$$

Denote by $\hat{\mathfrak{G}}$ the set of all such transformations $\hat{\mathfrak{g}} = (\hat{\mathfrak{g}}_{\mathfrak{B}}, \hat{\mathfrak{g}}_{\mathcal{U}})$.

3.103. Theorem. The set of transformations $\hat{\mathfrak{G}}$ is an abelian group with the group operation of composition.

Proof. Directly follows from the definitions of $\hat{\mathfrak{G}}$ and an abelian group. □

3.104. Definition. We will call the group of transformations $\hat{\mathfrak{G}}$ *the dynamic beliefs-preferences gauge symmetry group for a generalized market populace* or simply *dynamic beliefs-preferences gauge group* for $\mathbb{H}$.

3.105. Remark. Since a market environment $\mathbf{V}$ is a particular case of a generalized belief for a generalized market participant with the preference consisting of the identity operators, relation (3.59) implies that

$$\boldsymbol{L}(t) = \boldsymbol{u}'^{-1}(t,t)\,\mathsf{L}(t)\,\boldsymbol{u}'(t,t) + \frac{\boldsymbol{u}'_t(t,t)}{\boldsymbol{u}'(t,t)}, \tag{3.61}$$

where $\boldsymbol{L}(t)$ and $\mathsf{L}(t)$ stand for the derivative of $-\mathbf{V}(t,T)$ and $-\boldsymbol{D}(t,T)$ with respect to t evaluated at t equal to T understood in an appropriate sense. We comment that $\boldsymbol{D}(t,T)$ and $\boldsymbol{u}'(t,T)$ are in the generalized belief $\mathfrak{B}$ and in the generalized preference $\mathcal{U}$ of a generalized market participant $\mathfrak{H} = (\mathfrak{B}, \mathcal{U})$.

3.106. Definition. We call a generalized market participant $\mathfrak{H} = (\mathfrak{B}, \mathcal{U})$ in the generalized market populace $\mathbb{H} = \mathbb{B} \times \mathbb{U}$ a *representative generalized market participant* if the generalized belief $\mathfrak{B}$ coincides with a market environment $\mathbf{V}$ and the generalized preference $\mathcal{U}$ consists of the identity operators.

3.107. Remark. The terminology introduced in the preceding Definition is justified as follows. It is clear that each generalized market generation of the generalized market populace $\mathbb{H} = \mathbb{B} \times \mathbb{U}$ contains one and only one representative generalized market participant and that each representative generalized market participant in $\mathbb{H} = \mathbb{B} \times \mathbb{U}$ is contained in one and only one generalized market generation. In this regard, each generalized market generation of the generalized market populace $\mathbb{H} = \mathbb{B} \times \mathbb{U}$ can be uniquely characterized by a corresponding representative generalized market participant in $\mathbb{H} = \mathbb{B} \times \mathbb{U}$.

3.108. Remark. We make the following crucial observation. In the derivation of expression (3.59) via the chain of equalities

(3.58) we have assumed the financial strategy of viewing the marginal utilities $\mathbf{u}'^{-1}(t,t)$ and $\mathbf{u}'(t,T)$ in the generalized belief $\mathbf{u}'^{-1}(t,t)\boldsymbol{D}(t,T)\mathbf{u}'(t,T)$ from the running time t, that is, the second time variable in $\mathbf{u}'^{-1}(t,t)$ was kept equal to the first time variable and to the first time variable in $\mathbf{u}'(t,T)$. However, there is an alternative financial strategy of viewing the marginal utility at a time τ in the future from a fixed present time t so that for the generalized belief as viewed from time t we have $\mathbf{u}'^{-1}(t,\tau)\boldsymbol{D}(\tau,T)\mathbf{u}'(t,T)$. It is financially reasonable to require that these two financial strategies are equivalent locally in time. That is, it is financially reasonable to require that the rate of change $\mathsf{L}'(t)$ of $-\mathbf{u}'^{-1}(t,t)\boldsymbol{D}(t,T)\mathbf{u}'(t,T)$ with respect to time t at time $t = T$ has to be equal to the rate of change $\mathsf{L}'(t,\tau)$ of $-\mathbf{u}'^{-1}(t,\tau)\boldsymbol{D}(\tau,T)\mathbf{u}'(t,T)$ with respect to τ at time $\tau = T$ for time τ equal to t, which is indeed the case. In order to see this, let $\mathsf{L}'(t)$ stand for the derivative of $-\mathbf{u}'^{-1}(t,t)\boldsymbol{D}(t,T)\mathbf{u}'(t,T)$ with respect to t evaluated at t equal to T and let $\mathsf{L}'(t,\tau)$ stand for the derivative of $-\mathbf{u}'^{-1}(t,\tau)\boldsymbol{D}(\tau,T)\mathbf{u}'(t,T)$ with respect to τ evaluated at τ equal to T. It is clear that

$$\mathsf{L}'(t,\tau) = \mathbf{u}'^{-1}(t,\tau)\,\mathsf{L}(\tau)\,\mathbf{u}'(t,\tau) + \frac{\mathbf{u}'_\tau(t,\tau)}{\mathbf{u}'(t,\tau)}$$

so that $\mathsf{L}'(t,\tau = t)$ is equal to $\mathsf{L}'(t)$.

3.5 The Local in Time Formulation of the Beliefs-Preferences Gauge Symmetry Group for a Market Populace

Now we are ready to present a local in time formulation of the beliefs-preferences gauge symmetry group for a market populace defined in (3.56) and (3.57).

More precisely, suppose that a trading time set $\mathcal{T}$ contains t and a neighborhood of t. Assume that $\boldsymbol{F}(t,T)$ and $\mathbf{u}'(t,T)$ in the belief $\boldsymbol{\mathcal{B}}$ and the preference $\boldsymbol{\mathcal{U}}$ of a market participant $\mathcal{H} = (\boldsymbol{\mathcal{B}},\boldsymbol{\mathcal{U}})$ are, in an appropriate sense, differentiable with respect to the time variables at t for each market participant $\mathcal{H} = (\mathcal{B}, \mathcal{U})$ in the market populace $\mathbb{H} = \mathbb{B} \times \mathbb{U}$. Our immediate goal is to obtain the explicit form of the expansion of

$$\hat{\mathbf{u}}'^{-1}(t-\Delta t, t-\Delta t)\boldsymbol{F}(t-\Delta t, t)\hat{\mathbf{u}}'(t-\Delta t, t)$$

in powers of Δt up to the terms of the first order:

$$\begin{aligned}
&\hat{\mathbf{u}}'^{-1}(t-\Delta t, t-\Delta t)\boldsymbol{F}(t-\Delta t, t)\hat{\mathbf{u}}'(t-\Delta t, t) = \\
&\frac{\mathbf{u}'^{-1}(t-\Delta t, t-\Delta t)\boldsymbol{F}(t-\Delta t, t)\mathbf{u}'(t-\Delta t, t)}{\mathbf{u}'^{-1}(t-\Delta t, t-\Delta t)\boldsymbol{F}(t-\Delta t, t)\mathbf{u}'(t-\Delta t, t)\mathbf{1}} = \\
&\frac{\boldsymbol{I} + \Delta t\left(\mathbf{u}'^{-1}(t,t)\,\mathfrak{L}(\overset{2}{t})\,\mathbf{u}'(\overset{3}{t},\overset{1}{t}) + \frac{\mathbf{u}'_t(t,t)}{\mathbf{u}'(t,t)}\right) + o(\Delta t)}{\boldsymbol{I} + \Delta t\left(\mathbf{u}'^{-1}(t,t)\,\mathfrak{L}(\overset{2}{t})\,\mathbf{u}'(\overset{3}{t},\overset{1}{t}) + \frac{\mathbf{u}'_t(t,t)}{\mathbf{u}'(t,t)}\right)\mathbf{1} + o(\Delta t)} = \\
&\boldsymbol{I} + \Delta t\left(\mathbf{u}'^{-1}(t,t)\,\mathfrak{L}(\overset{2}{t})\,\mathbf{u}'(\overset{3}{t},\overset{1}{t}) + \frac{\mathbf{u}'_t(t,t)}{\mathbf{u}'(t,t)}\right) - \\
&\qquad \Delta t\left(\mathbf{u}'^{-1}(t,t)\,\mathfrak{L}(\overset{2}{t})\,\mathbf{u}'(\overset{3}{t},\overset{1}{t}) + \frac{\mathbf{u}'_t(t,t)}{\mathbf{u}'(t,t)}\right)\mathbf{1} + o(\Delta t) = \\
&\boldsymbol{I} + \Delta t\left(\mathbf{u}'^{-1}(t,t)\,\mathfrak{L}(\overset{2}{t})\,\mathbf{u}'(\overset{3}{t},\overset{1}{t}) + \frac{\mathbf{u}'_t(t,t)}{\mathbf{u}'(t,t)} - \mathfrak{d}(t)\right) + o(\Delta t),
\end{aligned} \tag{3.62}$$

where $\mathfrak{d}(t)$ is the operator of multiplication by the function

$$\mathfrak{d}(t) = \left(\mathbf{u}'^{-1}(t,t)\,\mathfrak{L}(\overset{2}{t})\,\mathbf{u}'(\overset{3}{t},\overset{1}{t}) + \frac{\mathbf{u}'_t(t,t)}{\mathbf{u}'(t,t)}\right)\mathbf{1}, \tag{3.63}$$

with $\mathbf{1}$ being the function in Π identically equal to unity, and where we made use of the following relation

$$\begin{aligned}
&\mathbf{u}'^{-1}(t-\Delta t, t-\Delta t)\boldsymbol{F}(t-\Delta t, t)\mathbf{u}'(t-\Delta t, t) = \\
&\quad \boldsymbol{I} + \Delta t\left(\mathbf{u}'^{-1}(t,t)\,\mathfrak{L}(\overset{2}{t})\,\mathbf{u}'(\overset{3}{t},\overset{1}{t}) + \frac{\mathbf{u}'_t(t,t)}{\mathbf{u}'(t,t)}\right) + o(\Delta t)
\end{aligned} \tag{3.64}$$

whose derivation is completely analogous to that of relation (3.58).

3.109. Remark. Whenever ambiguity is unlikely we will write $\mathfrak{u}'^{-1}(t,t)\,\mathfrak{L}(\overset{2}{t})\,\mathfrak{u}'(\overset{3}{t},\overset{1}{t})$ simply as $\mathfrak{u}'^{-1}(t,t)\,\mathfrak{L}(t)\,\mathfrak{u}'(t,t)$

3.110. Remark. It is clear that

$$\mathfrak{u}'^{-1}(t,t)\,\mathfrak{L}(t)\,\mathfrak{u}'(t,t) + \frac{\mathfrak{u}'_t(t,t)}{\mathfrak{u}'(t,t)}$$

is the derivative of $-\,\mathfrak{u}'^{-1}(t,t)\boldsymbol{F}(t,T)\mathfrak{u}'(t,T)$ with respect to t evaluated at t equal to T understood in an appropriate sense, for example in the sense of the operator norm or in the strong sense.

3.111. Remark. It is clear that

$$\mathfrak{u}'^{-1}(t,t)\,\mathfrak{L}(t)\,\mathfrak{u}'(t,t) + \frac{\mathfrak{u}'_t(t,t)}{\mathfrak{u}'(t,t)} - \mathfrak{d}(t)$$

is the derivative of $-\,\hat{\mathfrak{u}}'^{-1}(t,t)\boldsymbol{F}(t,T)\hat{\mathfrak{u}}'(t,T)$ with respect to t evaluated at t equal to T understood in an appropriate sense, for example in the sense of the operator norm or in the strong sense.

3.112. Remark. In the preceding chain of equalities (3.62) the operator $\mathfrak{L}(t)$ stands for the derivative of $-\,\boldsymbol{F}(t,T)$ with respect to t evaluated at t equal to T understood in an appropriate sense. The reason we have used the notation for this derivative identical to that of the generator at time t of a Markovian belief is that in the case when $\boldsymbol{F}(t,T)$ is contained in a Markovian belief $\boldsymbol{\mathcal{B}}$ this derivative coincides with the generator at time t of the Markovian generalized belief $\boldsymbol{\mathcal{B}}$. In this regard, we stress again that in the preceding chain of equalities (3.62) we did not assume that the belief $\boldsymbol{\mathcal{B}}$ that contains $\boldsymbol{F}(t,T)$ is Markovian.

3.113. Remark. It is clear that the operator $\mathfrak{L}(t)$ is also the derivative of $\boldsymbol{F}(t,T)$ with respect to T evaluated at T equal to t understood in an appropriate sense, provided that $\boldsymbol{F}(t,T)$ is sufficiently regular function of the time variables.

For $\boldsymbol{F}(t,T)$ in $\boldsymbol{\mathcal{B}}$, by the beliefs-preferences gauge symmetry group for the market populace, $\hat{\mathbf{u}}'^{-1}(t,t)\boldsymbol{F}(t,T)\hat{\mathbf{u}}'(t,T)$ represents another belief which we denote by $\boldsymbol{F}'(t,T)$ in $\boldsymbol{\mathcal{B}}' = g_{\boldsymbol{\mathcal{B}}}\mathfrak{B}$ with $g_{\boldsymbol{\mathcal{B}}}$ being generated by $\mathbf{u}'(t,T)$. Therefore the derivative $\mathfrak{L}'(t)$ of $-\boldsymbol{F}'(t,T)$ with respect to t evaluated at t equal to T has to be equal to the derivative

$$\mathbf{u}'^{-1}(t,t)\,\mathfrak{L}(t)\,\mathbf{u}'(t,t) + \frac{\mathbf{u}'_t(t,t)}{\mathbf{u}'(t,t)} - \mathfrak{d}(t)$$

of $-\hat{\mathbf{u}}'^{-1}(t,t)\boldsymbol{F}(t,T)\hat{\mathbf{u}}'(t,T)$ with respect to t evaluated at t equal to T:

$$\mathfrak{L}'(t) = \mathbf{u}'^{-1}(t,t)\,\mathfrak{L}(t)\,\mathbf{u}'(t,t) + \frac{\mathbf{u}'_t(t,t)}{\mathbf{u}'(t,t)} - \mathfrak{d}(t). \tag{3.65}$$

Therefore, the beliefs-preferences gauge symmetry group for a market populace defined in (3.56) and (3.57) can be represented as follows:

$$\mathfrak{L}(t) \xrightarrow{\hat{g}_{\boldsymbol{\mathcal{B}}}} \mathbf{u}'^{-1}(t,t)\,\mathfrak{L}(t)\,\mathbf{u}'(t,t) + \frac{\mathbf{u}'_t(t,t)}{\mathbf{u}'(t,t)} - \mathfrak{d}(t) \quad \text{and}$$
$$\boldsymbol{u}'(t,T) \xrightarrow{\hat{g}_{\boldsymbol{\mathcal{U}}}} \hat{\mathbf{u}}'^{-1}(t,T)\boldsymbol{u}'(t,T). \tag{3.66}$$

Denote by $\hat{\boldsymbol{\mathcal{G}}}$ the set of all such transformations $\hat{g} = (\hat{g}_{\boldsymbol{\mathcal{B}}}, \hat{g}_{\boldsymbol{\mathcal{U}}})$.

3.114. Theorem. The set of transformations $\hat{\boldsymbol{\mathcal{G}}}$ is an abelian group with the group operation of composition.

Proof. Directly follows from the definition of $\hat{\mathfrak{G}}$ and Theorem (3.92). □

3.115. Definition. We will call the group of transformations $\hat{\boldsymbol{\mathcal{G}}}$ *the dynamic beliefs-preferences gauge symmetry group for a market populace* or simply *dynamic beliefs-preferences gauge group* for $\mathbb{H}$.

3.116. Remark. It is clear that in terms of preference $\hat{\mathbf{u}}'(t,T)$ we can rewrite the transformations from the dynamic beliefs-preferences gauge symmetry group for a market populace defined in (3.66) as follows

$$\mathfrak{L}(t) \xrightarrow{\hat{g}_{\mathcal{B}}} \hat{\mathbf{u}}'^{-1}(t,t)\,\mathfrak{L}(t)\,\hat{\mathbf{u}}'(t,t) + \frac{\hat{\mathbf{u}}'_t(t,t)}{\hat{\mathbf{u}}'(t,t)} \quad \text{and}$$
$$\boldsymbol{u}'(t,T) \xrightarrow{\hat{g}_{\mathcal{U}}} \hat{\mathbf{u}}'^{-1}(t,T)\boldsymbol{u}'(t,T). \tag{3.67}$$

3.117. Remark. The fact that $\boldsymbol{F}(t,T)$ is a belief, that is, that the function $\mathbf{1}$ in Π identically equal to unity is a fixed point of $\boldsymbol{F}(t,T)$:

$$\boldsymbol{F}(t,T)\,\mathbf{1} = \mathbf{1}$$

implies (see, for example, [18] page 55) that $\mathbf{1}$ is in the kernel of the derivative $\mathfrak{L}(t)$ of $-\boldsymbol{F}(t,T)$ with respect to t evaluated at t equal to T understood in an appropriate sense:

$$\mathfrak{L}(t)\,\mathbf{1} = \mathbf{0}, \tag{3.68}$$

where $\mathbf{0}$ stands for the zero function in Π. In this regard the meaning of the compensating term $\mathfrak{d}(t)$ is exactly to ensure that $\mathbf{1}$ is in the kernel of the derivative

$$\mathbf{u}'^{-1}(t,t)\,\mathfrak{L}(t)\,\mathbf{u}'(t,t) + \frac{\mathbf{u}'_t(t,t)}{\mathbf{u}'(t,t)} - \mathfrak{d}(t)$$

of $-\hat{\mathbf{u}}'^{-1}(t,t)\boldsymbol{F}(t,T)\hat{\mathbf{u}}'(t,T)$ with respect to t evaluated at t equal to T:

$$\left(\mathbf{u}'^{-1}(t,t)\,\mathfrak{L}(t)\,\mathbf{u}'(t,t) + \frac{\mathbf{u}'_t(t,t)}{\mathbf{u}'(t,t)} - \mathfrak{d}(t)\right)\mathbf{1} = \mathbf{0}.$$

3.118. Remark. In view of the preceding Remark (3.117) we can rewrite expression (3.63) for $\mathfrak{d}(t)$ as follows

$$\begin{aligned}\mathfrak{d}(t) &= \left(\mathbf{u}'^{-1}(t,t)\,\mathfrak{L}(t)\,\mathbf{u}'(t,t) + \frac{\mathbf{u}'_t(t,t)}{\mathbf{u}'(t,t)}\right)\mathbf{1} = \\ &\mathfrak{L}(t)\,\mathbf{1} + \mathbf{u}'^{-1}(t,t)[\mathfrak{L}(t),\mathbf{u}'(t,t)]\,\mathbf{1} + \frac{\mathbf{u}'_t(t,t)}{\mathbf{u}'(t,t)}\,\mathbf{1} = \\ &\mathbf{u}'^{-1}(t,t)\left([\mathfrak{L}(t),\mathbf{u}'(t,t)] + \mathbf{u}'_t(t,t)\right)\mathbf{1},\end{aligned} \tag{3.69}$$

where in the second equality we took into account equality (3.68), and where $[A, B] = A\,B - B\,A$ stands for the commutator of linear operators A and B. We comment that we have loosely used the same notation for the operators of multiplication by functions and for the functions themselves.

3.119. Remark. Since a market participant is a particular case of a generalized market participant, relation (3.59) implies that

$$\mathsf{L}(t) = \mathbf{u}'^{-1}(t,t)\,\mathfrak{L}(t)\,\mathbf{u}'(t,t) + \frac{\mathbf{u}'_t(t,t)}{\mathbf{u}'(t,t)}, \tag{3.70}$$

where $\mathsf{L}(t)$ and $\mathfrak{L}(t)$ stand for the derivatives of $-\boldsymbol{D}(t,T)$ and $-\boldsymbol{F}(t,T)$ with respect to t evaluated at t equal to T understood in an appropriate sense. We comment that in order to use relation (3.59) we treated the belief $\boldsymbol{F}$ as a particular case of a generalized belief $\boldsymbol{D}$.

3.120. Remark. Since a market environment $\mathbf{V}$ is a particular case of a generalized belief for a generalized market participant with the preference consisting of the identity operators, that is, of a representative generalized market participant, and since a market participant is a particular case of a generalized market participant, relation (3.59) implies that

$$\boldsymbol{L}(t) = \boldsymbol{u}'^{-1}(t,t)\,\mathfrak{L}(t)\,\boldsymbol{u}'(t,t) + \frac{\boldsymbol{u}'_t(t,t)}{\boldsymbol{u}'(t,t)}, \tag{3.71}$$

where $\boldsymbol{L}(t)$ and $\mathfrak{L}(t)$ stand for the derivatives of $-\mathbf{V}(t,T)$ and $-\boldsymbol{F}(t,T)$ with respect to t evaluated at t equal to T understood in an appropriate sense. We comment that $\boldsymbol{F}(t,T)$ and $\boldsymbol{u}'(t,T)$ are in the belief $\mathfrak{B}$ and in the preference $\boldsymbol{\mathcal{U}}$ of a generalized market participant $\boldsymbol{\mathcal{H}} = (\boldsymbol{\mathcal{B}}, \boldsymbol{\mathcal{U}})$. We also comment that in order to use relation (3.59) we treated the belief $\boldsymbol{\mathcal{B}}$ as a particular case of a generalized belief $\mathfrak{B}$.

3.121. Remark. We make the following crucial observation. In the derivation of relation (3.65) via the chain of equalities

(3.62) we have assumed the financial strategy of viewing the marginal utilities $\hat{\mathbf{u}}'^{-1}(t,t)$ and $\hat{\mathbf{u}}'(t,T)$ in the belief

$$\hat{\mathbf{u}}'^{-1}(t,t)\boldsymbol{F}(t,T)\hat{\mathbf{u}}'(t,T)$$

from the running time t, that is, the second time variable in $\hat{\mathbf{u}}'^{-1}(t,t)$ was kept equal to the first time variable and to the first time variable in $\hat{\mathbf{u}}'(t,T)$. However, there is an alternative financial strategy of viewing the marginal utility at a time τ in the future from a fixed present time t so that for the belief as viewed from time t we have $\hat{\mathbf{u}}'^{-1}(t,\tau)\boldsymbol{F}(\tau,T)\hat{\mathbf{u}}'(t,T)$. It is financially reasonable to require that these two financial strategies are equivalent locally in time. That is, it is financially reasonable to require that the rate of change $\mathfrak{L}'(t)$ of $-\hat{\mathbf{u}}'^{-1}(t,t)\boldsymbol{F}(t,T)\hat{\mathbf{u}}'(t,T)$ with respect to time t at time $t = T$ has to be equal to the rate of change $\mathfrak{L}'(t,\tau)$ of $-\hat{\mathbf{u}}'^{-1}(t,\tau)\boldsymbol{F}(\tau,T)\hat{\mathbf{u}}'(t,T)$ with respect to τ at time $\tau = T$ for time τ equal to t, which is indeed the case. In order to see this, let $\mathfrak{L}'(t)$ stand for the derivative of $-\hat{\mathbf{u}}'^{-1}(t,t)\boldsymbol{F}(t,T)\hat{\mathbf{u}}'(t,T)$ with respect to t evaluated at t equal to T and let $\mathfrak{L}'(t,\tau)$ stand for the derivative of $-\hat{\mathbf{u}}'^{-1}(t,\tau)\boldsymbol{F}(\tau,T)\hat{\mathbf{u}}'(t,T)$ with respect to τ evaluated at τ equal to T. It is clear that

$$\mathfrak{L}'(t,\tau) = \mathbf{u}'^{-1}(t,\tau)\,\mathfrak{L}(\tau)\,\mathbf{u}'(t,\tau) + \frac{\mathbf{u}'_\tau(t,\tau)}{\mathbf{u}'(t,\tau)} - \left(\mathbf{u}'^{-1}(t,\tau)\,\mathfrak{L}(\tau)\,\mathbf{u}'(t,\tau) + \frac{\mathbf{u}'_\tau(t,\tau)}{\mathbf{u}'(t,\tau)}\right)\mathbf{1}$$

so that $\mathfrak{L}'(t,\tau=t)$ is equal to $\mathfrak{L}'(t)$.

3.6 Beliefs-Preferences Gauge Symmetry Group for a Markovian Generalized Market Populace

Suppose that the trading time set $\mathcal{T}$ is an interval, either finite or infinite, of nonnegative real numbers. Consider a Markovian generalized market populace $\mathbb{H} = \mathbb{B} \times \mathbb{U}$ such that $\boldsymbol{D}(t,T)$

and $\mathbf{u}'(t,T)$ in each Markovian generalized belief $\mathfrak{B}$ and in each Markovian generalized preference $\mathcal{U}$ are differentiable, in an appropriate sense, with respect to time. This, in particular, implies that each Markovian generalized belief $\mathfrak{B}$ is generated by L. In this case each Markovian generalized market participant $\mathfrak{H} = (\mathfrak{B}, \mathcal{U})$ can be uniquely characterized as a pair $(\mathsf{L}, \mathcal{U})$ and, whenever ambiguity is unlikely, we will loosely say that a Markovian generalized market participant $\mathfrak{H}$ is a pair $(\mathsf{L}, \mathcal{U})$ and we will write $\mathfrak{H} = (\mathsf{L}, \mathcal{U})$. In the same way we will write $\mathbb{H} = \mathbb{L} \times \mathbb{U}$ where $\mathbb{L}$ stands for the set of all families L.

3.122. Remark. Since a market environment $\mathbf{V}$ that satisfies the intervention condition (2.4) is a particular case of a Markovian generalized belief $\mathfrak{B}$ we have, in the case under consideration, that $\mathbf{V}$ is generated by $\boldsymbol{L}$.

In the case under consideration, we show that the beliefs-preferences gauge symmetry group $\mathfrak{G}$ for $\mathbb{H} = \mathbb{B} \times \mathbb{U}$ can be represented as an abelian group of transformations of $\mathbb{L} \times \mathbb{U}$.

In relation (3.60), as we have indicated in Remark (3.101), the derivative $\mathsf{L}(t)$ of $-\boldsymbol{D}(t,T)$ with respect to t evaluated at t equal to T with $\boldsymbol{D}(t,T)$ in $\mathfrak{B}$ coincides with the generator at time t of $\mathfrak{B}$ in the case when a generalized belief $\mathfrak{B}$ is Markovian and generated by L. Therefore, taking into account relation (3.60) we have the representation of the beliefs-preferences gauge symmetry group $\mathfrak{G}$ of transformations of $\mathbb{H} = \mathbb{B} \times \mathbb{U}$ defined in (3.49) as the group $\hat{\mathfrak{G}}$ of transformations of $\mathbb{L} \times \mathbb{U}$ defined by

$$(\mathsf{L}, \mathcal{U}) \to \hat{\mathfrak{g}}\,(\mathsf{L}, \mathcal{U}) = (\hat{\mathfrak{g}}_{\mathsf{L}}\mathsf{L}, \hat{\mathfrak{g}}_{\mathcal{U}}\mathcal{U}), \quad \hat{\mathfrak{g}} \in \hat{\mathfrak{G}}. \tag{3.72}$$

Here each $\hat{\mathfrak{g}} = (\hat{\mathfrak{g}}_{\mathsf{L}}, \hat{\mathfrak{g}}_{\mathcal{U}})$ in $\hat{\mathfrak{G}}$ is defined by

$$\begin{gathered}\mathsf{L}(t) \xrightarrow{\hat{\mathfrak{g}}_{\mathsf{L}}} \mathbf{u}'^{-1}(t,t)\,\mathsf{L}(t)\,\mathbf{u}'(t,t) + \frac{\mathbf{u}'_t(t,t)}{\mathbf{u}'(t,t)} \quad \text{and} \\ \boldsymbol{u}'(t,T) \xrightarrow{\hat{\mathfrak{g}}_{\mathcal{U}}} \mathbf{u}'^{-1}(t,T)\boldsymbol{u}'(t,T),\end{gathered} \tag{3.73}$$

where $\mathsf{L}(t)$ is in L and

$$\mathfrak{u}'^{-1}(t,t)\,\mathsf{L}(t)\,\mathfrak{u}'(t,t) + \frac{\mathfrak{u}'_t(t,t)}{\mathfrak{u}'(t,t)}$$

is in $\hat{\mathfrak{g}}_{\mathsf{L}}\mathsf{L}$, and where $\boldsymbol{u}'(t,T)$ is in $\boldsymbol{\mathcal{U}}$ and $\mathfrak{u}'^{-1}(t,T)\boldsymbol{u}'(t,T)$ is in $\hat{\mathfrak{g}}_{\mathcal{U}}\boldsymbol{\mathcal{U}}$.

Now we show that $\hat{\mathfrak{G}}$ is indeed a group, in fact an abelian group.

3.123. Theorem. The set $\hat{\mathfrak{G}}$ of transformations of $\mathbb{L} \times \mathbb{U}$ is an abelian group with the group operation of composition.

Proof. Directly follows from the definition of $\hat{\mathfrak{G}}$ and the definition of an abelian group. □

3.124. Definition. We will call the group of transformations $\hat{\mathfrak{G}}$ the *beliefs-preferences gauge symmetry group for a Markovian generalized market populace* or simply the *beliefs-preferences gauge group for* $\mathbb{H} = \mathbb{L} \times \mathbb{U}$.

3.125. Remark. It is clear that the sets of all transformations $\hat{\mathfrak{g}}_{\mathsf{L}}$ and $\hat{\mathfrak{g}}_{\mathcal{U}}$ of $\mathbb{L}$ and $\mathbb{U}$ are abelian groups themselves with the group operation of composition. Denote these groups by $\hat{\mathfrak{G}}_{\mathsf{L}}$ and $\hat{\mathfrak{G}}_{\mathcal{U}}$

3.126. Remark. It is clear that the representation of the beliefs-preferences gauge symmetry group $\mathfrak{G}$ of transformations of $\mathbb{H} = \mathbb{B} \times \mathbb{U}$ as the group $\hat{\mathfrak{G}}$ of transformations of $\mathbb{L} \times \mathbb{U}$ is in fact an isomorphism so that the groups, or more precisely abelian groups $\mathfrak{G}$ and $\hat{\mathfrak{G}}$ are isomorphic.

3.127. Remark. Since a market environment $\mathbf{V}$ is a particular case of a generalized belief for a generalized market participant with the preference consisting of the identity operators, that is, for a representative generalized market participant, relation (3.73) implies that

$$\boldsymbol{L}(t) = \boldsymbol{u}'^{-1}(t,t)\,\mathsf{L}(t)\,\boldsymbol{u}'(t,t) + \frac{\boldsymbol{u}'_t(t,t)}{\boldsymbol{u}'(t,t)}, \tag{3.74}$$

where $\boldsymbol{L}(t)$ and $\mathsf{L}(t)$ are generators at time t of the market environment $\mathbf{V}$ and the generalized belief $\mathfrak{B}$ related via the transformation from the beliefs-preferences gauge symmetry for the Markovian generalized market populace defined in relation (3.72). We comment that $\boldsymbol{u}'(t,T)$ is in the generalized preference $\boldsymbol{\mathcal{U}}$ of a generalized market participant $\mathfrak{H} = (\mathfrak{B}, \boldsymbol{\mathcal{U}})$ with the generalized belief $\mathfrak{B}$.

We make the following observation. Consider a Markovian generalized market populace $\mathbb{H} = \mathbb{B} \times \mathbb{U}$ or more precisely $\mathbb{H} = \mathbb{L} \times \mathbb{U}$ under the assumption that the Markovian generalized market populace preference $\mathbb{U}$ is local. In this case the transformations from (3.73) from beliefs-preferences gauge symmetry group $\hat{\mathfrak{G}}$ of a Markovian generalized market populace $\mathbb{H} = \mathbb{B} \times \mathbb{U}$ or more precisely $\mathbb{H} = \mathbb{L} \times \mathbb{U}$ take the following form

$$\begin{aligned} &\mathsf{L}(t) \xrightarrow{\hat{\mathfrak{g}}_{\mathsf{L}}} \mathfrak{u}'^{-1}(t)\,\mathsf{L}(t)\,\mathfrak{u}'(t) + \frac{\mathfrak{u}'_t(t)}{\mathfrak{u}'(t)} \quad \text{and} \\ &\boldsymbol{u}'(t) \xrightarrow{\hat{\mathfrak{g}}_{\mathcal{U}}} \mathfrak{u}'^{-1}(t)\,\boldsymbol{u}'(t). \end{aligned} \tag{3.75}$$

In this case the generators $\mathsf{L}(t)$ in L of a Markovian generalized belief $\mathfrak{B}$ are nothing but the differential-geometric connection on the payoff bundle $\boldsymbol{\mathcal{P}}$ with the gauge group $\hat{\mathfrak{G}}$. The covariant derivative $\boldsymbol{\nabla}_t$ is given by $\frac{d}{dt} + \mathsf{L}(t)$ and the evolution equation in (3.6) states that its solution $v = v(t)$ is such a section on $\boldsymbol{\mathcal{P}}$, that is, such a vector field on $\mathcal{T}$ that it is parallel to itself. Therefore, the Cauchy problem (3.6) states that $v(t)$ in the fiber Π over t is the result of the parallel transport of $v(T)$ in the fiber Π over T determined by $\boldsymbol{D}(t,T)$ from $\mathfrak{B}$:

$$v(t) = \boldsymbol{D}(t,T)v(T).$$

Moreover, using the concept of the covariant derivative $\boldsymbol{\nabla}_t$, the evolution equation in (3.6) can be rewritten in the following covariant form

$$\boldsymbol{\nabla}_t v(t) = 0. \tag{3.76}$$

Moreover, again using the concept of the covariant derivative $\boldsymbol{\nabla}_t$, the evolution equation in (3.8) can be rewritten in the following covariant form

$$\boldsymbol{\nabla}_t \boldsymbol{D}(t, T) = 0. \tag{3.77}$$

This again implies that each $\boldsymbol{D}(t, T)$ in $\mathfrak{B}$ is nothing but a parallel transport from the fiber Π over T to the fiber Π over t and that $\mathfrak{B}$ itself is a connection on $\boldsymbol{\mathcal{P}}$.

3.128. Remark. Since a market environment $\mathbf{V}$ is a particular case of a generalized belief for a generalized market participant with the preference consisting of the identity operators, that is, for a representative generalized market participant, relation (3.61) implies that in the particular gauge associated with the representative generalized market participant the differential-geometric connection on $\boldsymbol{\mathcal{P}}$ is given by the generators $\boldsymbol{L}(t)$ in $\boldsymbol{L}$ of $\mathbf{V}$. In this gauge, the covariant derivative $\boldsymbol{\nabla}_t$ is given by $\frac{d}{dt} + \boldsymbol{L}(t)$ and the evolution equation in (2.6) states that the value v of a European contingent claim is such a section of $\boldsymbol{\mathcal{P}}$, that is, such a vector field on $\mathcal{T}$ with values $v(t)$ in the fiber Π over t that it is parallel to itself. Therefore the Cauchy problem (2.6) states that the value $v(t)$ in the fiber Π over t of a European contingent claim at time $t \leq T$ is a result of a parallel transport of the value $v(T)$ in the fiber Π over T of this European contingent claim at time T determined by $\mathbf{V}(t, T)$ from $\mathbf{V}$:

$$v(t) = \mathbf{V}(t, T) v(T).$$

Moreover, using the concept of the covariant derivative $\boldsymbol{\nabla}_t$, the evolution equation in (2.8) can be rewritten in the following covariant form

$$\boldsymbol{\nabla}_t v(t) = 0. \tag{3.78}$$

Moreover, again using the concept of the covariant derivative $\boldsymbol{\nabla}_t$, the evolution equation in (2.8) can be rewritten in the following covariant form

$$\boldsymbol{\nabla}_t \mathbf{V}(t, T) = 0. \tag{3.79}$$

This again indicates that each $\mathbf{V}(t,T)$ in $\mathbf{V}$ is nothing but a parallel transport from the fiber Π over T to the fiber Π over t and that $\mathbf{V}$ itself is a connection on $\boldsymbol{\mathcal{P}}$ in the gauge under consideration.

At this point we would like to illustrate the beliefs-preferences gauge symmetry group $\hat{\mathfrak{G}}$ of a Markovian generalized market populace $\mathbb{H} = \mathbb{B} \times \mathbb{U}$ or more precisely $\mathbb{H} = \mathbb{L} \times \mathbb{U}$ with local Markovian generalized market populace preference $\mathbb{U}$ using an example of the gauge group from nonrelativistic quantum mechanics.

Consider a spinless particle of electric charge q and mass m placed in the electromagnetic field with the vector potential $A(x,t)$ and the scalar potential $U(x,t)$. The dynamic of the state vector $\Psi(t) = \Psi(x,t)$ for such a particle is given by the Cauchy problem for the Schrödinger equation

$$\begin{aligned} i\hbar\frac{d}{dt}\Psi(t) &= \boldsymbol{H}(t)\Psi(t) \\ \Psi(t)|_{t=t_0} &= \Psi_{t_0} \end{aligned} \tag{3.80}$$

where the Hamiltonian $\boldsymbol{H}(t)$ is given by

$$\boldsymbol{H}(t) = \frac{1}{2m}\left(-i\hbar\nabla - q\boldsymbol{A}(x,t)\right)^2 + q\boldsymbol{U}(x,t), \tag{3.81}$$

where ∇ is the operator Nabla in $\mathbb{R}^3$ and where $\boldsymbol{A}(x,t)$ and $\boldsymbol{U}(x,t)$ are the operators of multiplication by the functions $A(x,t)$ and $U(x,t)$ (see, for example, [12] pages 222 and 224).

The evolution operator, or propagator $\mathsf{U}(t,t_0)$ for the Schrödinger equation (3.80) is given by

$$\mathsf{U}(t,t_0) = e^{-\frac{i}{\hbar}\int_{t_0}^{t}\boldsymbol{H}(\tau)d\tau},$$

where the order of Hamiltonians $\boldsymbol{H}(\tau)$ is that of τ (see, for example, [12] page 310).

Denote by $\boldsymbol{U}(1)$ the group of complex numbers with absolute values equal to unity and with the group operation of multiplication. It is well known (see, for example, [12] page 321) that the Schrödinger equation is invariant with respect to the gauge transformations with the gauge group $\boldsymbol{U}(1)$ defined by

$$\begin{aligned} &(A(x,t), U(x,t)) \to (A(x,t) - \nabla\lambda(x,t), U(x,t) + \frac{\partial}{\partial t}\lambda(x,t)) \\ &\Psi(x,t) \to e^{-i\frac{q}{\hbar}\lambda(x,t)}\,\Psi(x,t). \end{aligned} \tag{3.82}$$

Whenever ambiguity is unlikely we will denote the group of gauge transformations of $(A(x,t), U(x,t))$ and $\Psi(x,t)$ defined in (3.82) simply by $\boldsymbol{U}(1)$ and call it the gauge symmetry group, or simply the gauge group.

Now we rewrite the Schrödinger equation in (3.80) as follows

$$\frac{d}{dt}\Psi(t) + \frac{i}{\hbar}\boldsymbol{H}(t)\Psi(t) = 0, \tag{3.83}$$

so that we can rewrite the gauge transformations in (3.82) in terms of the operator $\frac{i}{\hbar}\boldsymbol{H}(t)$ and the state vector $\Psi(t)$:

$$\begin{aligned} &\frac{i}{\hbar}\boldsymbol{H}(t) \to \boldsymbol{u}^{-1}(t)\frac{i}{\hbar}\boldsymbol{H}(t)\boldsymbol{u}(t) + \frac{\boldsymbol{u}_t(t)}{\boldsymbol{u}(t)} \\ &\Psi(t) \to \boldsymbol{u}^{-1}(t)\,\Psi(t), \end{aligned} \tag{3.84}$$

where here $\boldsymbol{u}(t)$ is the operator of multiplication by the function

$$u(x,t) = e^{i\frac{q}{\hbar}\lambda(x,t)},$$

and where $\boldsymbol{u}_t(t)$ stands for the derivative of $\boldsymbol{u}(t)$ with respect to the time variable t.

3.129. Remark. It is clear that the set of all transformations of $\boldsymbol{H}(t)$ and $\Psi(t)$ defined in (3.84) is a group with the group operation of composition isomorphic to the gauge group $\boldsymbol{U}(1)$ of transformations of $\big(A(x,t), U(x,t)\big)$ and $\Psi(x,t)$ defined in (3.82).

Denote by $L_2(\mathbb{R}^3)$ the Hilbert space of all complex-valued Lebesgue measurable square integrable functions on $\mathbb{R}^3$ with the standard scalar product. It is well-known that for admissible $A(x,t)$ and $U(x,t)$, each evolution operator $\mathbf{U}(t_2,t_1)$ with t_1 and t_2 in $\mathbb{R}_+$ such that $t_1 \leq t_2$ is a unitary operator on $L_2(\mathbb{R}^3)$, with the inverse operator $\mathbf{U}^{-1}(t_2,t_1)$ given by

$$\mathbf{U}^{-1}(t_2,t_1) = e^{\frac{i}{\hbar}\int_{t_1}^{t_2} \boldsymbol{H}(\tau)d\tau},$$

where the order of the Hamiltonians $\boldsymbol{H}(\tau)$ is opposite to that of τ.

Denote by $\mathbf{U}$ the family of all the evolution operators $\mathbf{U}(t_2,t_1)$ with t_1 and t_2 in $\mathbb{R}_+$

$$\mathbf{U} = \{\mathbf{U}(t_2,t_1) : t_1,\, t_2 \in \mathbb{R}_+\},$$

where whenever $t_2 \leq t_1$ we understand $\mathbf{U}(t_2,t_1)$ as $\mathbf{U}^{-1}(t_1,t_2)$.

Denote by $\mathbb{S}$ the vector bundle with the fiber $L_2(\mathbb{R}^3)$ and the base space $\mathbb{R}_+$. It is clear that $\mathbf{U}$ is nothing but a connection on the vector bundle $\mathbb{S}$ and each $\mathbf{U}(t_2,t_1)$ in $\mathbf{U}$ is the parallel transport from the fiber $L_2(\mathbb{R}^3)$ over t_1 to the fiber $L_2(\mathbb{R}^3)$ over t_2. In this way the operator $\frac{i}{\hbar}\boldsymbol{H}(t)$ is nothing but the differential-geometric connection on $\mathbb{S}$ with the gauge group $\boldsymbol{U}(1)$. The covariant derivative $\boldsymbol{\nabla}_t$ is given by $\frac{d}{dt}+\frac{i}{\hbar}\boldsymbol{H}(t)$ and the Schrödinger equation in (3.80) in the form (3.83) states that the state vector Ψ is such a section of $\mathbb{S}$, that is, is such a vector field on $\mathbb{R}_+$ with values $\Psi(t)$ in the fiber $L_2(\mathbb{R}^3)$ over t that it is parallel to itself. Therefore, the Cauchy problem for the Schrödinger equation (3.80) states that the state vector $\Psi(t)$ at time t is a result of a parallel transport of the state vector $\Psi(t_0)$ at time t_0 determined by $\mathbf{U}(t,t_0)$ from $\mathbf{U}$:

$$\Psi(t) = \mathbf{U}(t,t_0)\Psi(t_0).$$

Moreover, using the concept of the covariant derivative $\boldsymbol{\nabla}_t$, the Schrödinger equation in (3.80) in the form (3.83) can be rewritten in the following covariant form

$$\boldsymbol{\nabla}_t\Psi(t) = 0. \tag{3.85}$$

In this regard we note that the Cauchy problem for the Schrödinger equation in (3.80) can be rewritten in terms of $\mathsf{U}(t, t_0)$ as follows

$$\begin{aligned} i\hbar\frac{d}{dt}\mathsf{U}(t, t_0) &= \boldsymbol{H}(t)\mathsf{U}(t, t_0), \quad t_0 < t, \\ \mathsf{U}(t, t_0)|_{t=t_0} &= \boldsymbol{I}, \end{aligned} \tag{3.86}$$

where $\boldsymbol{I}$ is the identity operator on $L_2(\mathbb{R}^3)$. Moreover, again using the concept of the covariant derivative $\boldsymbol{\nabla}_t$, the evolution equation in (3.86) can be rewritten in the following covariant form

$$\boldsymbol{\nabla}_t \mathsf{U}(t, t_0) = 0. \tag{3.87}$$

This again implies that each $\mathsf{U}(t_2, t_1)$ in U is nothing but a parallel transport from the fiber $L_2(\mathbb{R}^3)$ over t_1 to the fiber $L_2(\mathbb{R}^3)$ over t_2 and that U itself is a connection on $\mathbb{S}$.

3.130. Remark. We note that the gauge group $\boldsymbol{U}(1)$ represented as the group of transformations of $\boldsymbol{H}(t)$ and $\Psi(t)$ defined in (3.84) remains true not only for Hamiltonians of the form (3.81) but for arbitrary Hamiltonians as well.

3.131. Remark. We note that the analogy between the gauge symmetry group $\boldsymbol{U}(1)$ represented as the group of transformations of $\boldsymbol{H}(t)$ and $\Psi(t)$ given in (3.84) in nonrelativistic quantum mechanics and the beliefs-preferences gauge symmetry group $\hat{\mathfrak{G}}$ of a Markovian generalized market populace $\mathbb{H} = \mathbb{B} \times \mathbb{U}$ or more precisely $\mathbb{H} = \mathbb{L} \times \mathbb{U}$ with local Markovian generalized market populace preference $\mathbb{U}$ given in (3.75) is self-explanatory.

3.132. Remark. It is the differential-geometric connection $\frac{i}{\hbar}\boldsymbol{H}(t)$ on the vector bundle $\mathbb{S}$, or equivalently the Hamiltonian $\boldsymbol{H}(t)$ treated as a field over the time domain that is quantized in the second quantization of the Schrödinger equation in (3.80) that corresponds to the first quantization. (For an introduction to the concept of the second quantization see, for example, [24].)

It is this approach to treating the differential-geometric connections, or equivalently the generators of the market environment $\boldsymbol{L}(t)$ as a field, or more precisely as a gauge field over the trading time set $\mathcal{T}$ that we have demonstrated to be fruitful in the second quantization of the evolution equation (2.6) that corresponds to the first quantization. In this regard the field $\boldsymbol{L}(t)$ over the trading time set $\mathcal{T}$ is quantized in the second quantization as a bosonic field and the value of a European contingent claim $v = v(t)$, also treated as a field over the trading time set $\mathcal{T}$, is quantized as a fermionic field. In this way, for example, since after the second quantization the generators of the market environment $\boldsymbol{L}(t)$ are, roughly speaking, operator-valued random variables, it is possible to model the random character of the interest rates. Finally, we note that it is the second quantization of the fields $\boldsymbol{L}(t)$ and $v = v(t)$ over the trading time set $\mathcal{T}$ that is one of the main reasons to treat $\boldsymbol{L}(t)$ as a differential-geometric connection and $\frac{d}{dt} + \boldsymbol{L}(t)$ as a covariant derivative. Since the generator of the market environment $\boldsymbol{L}(t)$ is nothing but a generator of the generalized belief $\mathsf{L}(t)$ in the gauge associated with the representative market participant, what we said above about generators $\boldsymbol{L}(t)$ remains true for the generators $\mathsf{L}(t)$. The second quantization of the fields $\boldsymbol{L}(t)$ and $v = v(t)$ over the trading time set $\mathcal{T}$ and related supersymmetry linking, roughly speaking, the bosonic nature of money and the fermionic nature of a commodity along with the supersymmetry breaking will be presented in forthcoming articles. (For an introduction to the concept of supersymmetry see, for example, [46].)

3.133. Definition. We call a vector bundle P with the fiber $\Pi(\mathbb{R}^n_{++} \times \mathbb{R}^n_{++})$ and the base space

$$\Delta_{\mathcal{T}} = \{(t, T) \; : \; t, T \in \mathcal{T}, \, t \leq T\}$$

a *contingent payoff bundle.* We refer to the base space $\Delta_{\mathcal{T}}$ as a *triangle* and to the set $\{(t, T) \in \Delta_{\mathcal{T}} : t = T\}$ as the *hypotenuse.*

3.134. Remark. We note that in the case when the trading time set is a finite interval the base space $\Delta_{\mathcal{T}}$ is a right triangle with the hypotenuse $\{(t,T) \in \Delta_T : t = T\}$. This justifies the terminology introduced for Δ_T and $\{(t,T) \in \Delta_T : t = T\}$ in the preceding Definition.

3.135. Remark. We comment that each element $h = h(s_t, s_T)$ in the fiber $\Pi(\mathbb{R}^n_{++} \times \mathbb{R}^n_{++})$ over (t,T) in Δ_T financially represents a payoff in units of account at time T contingent on both the state of the market as expressed by the prices of the underlying securities s_T at time T and the state of the market as expressed by the prices of the underlying securities s_t at time t prior or equal to T. Equivalently, each element $h = h(s_t, s_T)$ in the fiber $\Pi(\mathbb{R}^n_{++} \times \mathbb{R}^n_{++})$ over (t,T) in Δ_T financially represents a payoff $h_{s_t} = h_{s_t}(s_T)$ in Π at time T contingent on the state of the market as expressed by the prices of the underlying securities s_t at time t prior or equal to T, where $h_{s_t} = h(s_t, \cdot)$.

3.136. Remark. Consider the case of a Markovian generalized market populace $\mathbb{H} = \mathbb{B} \times \mathbb{U}$ or more precisely $\mathbb{H} = \mathbb{L} \times \mathbb{U}$ without the assumption that the Markovian generalized market populace preference $\mathbb{U}$ is local. In this case the transformations in (3.73) from the beliefs-preferences gauge symmetry group $\hat{\mathfrak{G}}$ of a Markovian generalized market populace $\mathbb{H} = \mathbb{B} \times \mathbb{U}$ or more precisely $\mathbb{H} = \mathbb{L} \times \mathbb{U}$ admits the following interpretation. The generators $\mathsf{L}(t)$ in L of $\mathfrak{B}$ can be viewed as the restriction to the hypotenuse of Δ_T of a certain differential-geometric connection on P with the gauge group $\hat{\mathfrak{G}}$. The restriction to the hypotenuse of Δ_T of the covariant derivative in the t direction $\boldsymbol{\nabla}_t$ is given by $\frac{d}{dt} + \mathsf{L}(t)$. Moreover, due to Remark (3.108) the restriction to the hypotenuse of Δ_T of the covariant derivative in the direction of the hypotenuse is equal to the restriction to the hypotenuse of Δ_T of the covariant derivative $\boldsymbol{\nabla}_t$ in the t direction. Therefore the evolution equation in (3.6) states that its solution $v = v(t)$ is the restriction to the hypotenuse of Δ_T of such a section on P, that is, of such a vector field on Δ_T that it is parallel to itself along the hypotenuse of Δ_T. Therefore, the Cauchy problem (3.6) states that $v(t)$ in the fiber Π over (t,t) is the result of the parallel transport along the hypotenuse of Δ_T of $v(T)$ in the fiber Π over (T,T) determined by $\boldsymbol{D}(t,T)$ from $\mathfrak{B}$:

$$v(t) = \boldsymbol{D}(t,T)v(T),$$

where Π is viewed as a vector sublattice of $\Pi(\mathbb{R}^n_{++} \times \mathbb{R}^n_{++})$. This implies that each $\boldsymbol{D}(t,T)$ in $\mathfrak{B}$ is nothing but a parallel transport along the hypotenuse of Δ_T from the fiber Π over (T,T) to the fiber Π over (t,t) and that $\mathfrak{B}$ itself is a restriction to the hypotenuse of Δ_T of a connection on P, where again Π is viewed as a vector sublattice of $\Pi(\mathbb{R}^n_{++} \times \mathbb{R}^n_{++})$.

Since a market environment $\mathbf{V}$ is a particular case of a generalized belief for a generalized market participant with the preference consisting of the identity operators, that is, for a representative generalized market participant, relation (3.61) implies that, in the particular gauge associated with the representative generalized market participant, the restriction to the hypotenuse of Δ_T of the differential-geometric connection on P is given by the generators $\boldsymbol{L}(t)$ in $\boldsymbol{L}$ of $\mathbf{V}$. In this gauge, the restriction to the hypotenuse of Δ_T of the covariant derivative in the t direction $\boldsymbol{\nabla}_t$ is given by $\frac{d}{dt} + \boldsymbol{L}(t)$. Moreover, due to Remark (3.108) the restriction to the hypotenuse of Δ_T of the covariant derivative in the direction of the hypotenuse is equal to the restriction to the hypotenuse of Δ_T of the covariant derivative $\boldsymbol{\nabla}_t$ in the t direction. Therefore, the evolution equation in (2.6) states that the value v of a European contingent claim is the restriction to the hypotenuse of Δ_T of such a section of P, that is, of such a vector field on Δ_T that it is parallel to itself along the hypotenuse of Δ_T. Therefore, the Cauchy problem (2.6) states that the value $v(t)$ in the fiber Π over (t,t) of a European contingent claim at time $t \leq T$ is a result of a parallel transport of the value $v(T)$ in the fiber Π over (T,T) of this European contingent claim at time T determined by $\mathbf{V}(t,T)$ from $\mathbf{V}$:

$$v(t) = \mathbf{V}(t,T)v(T),$$

where Π is viewed as a vector sublattice of $\Pi(\mathbb{R}^n_{++} \times \mathbb{R}^n_{++})$. This implies that in the gauge associated with a representative generalized market participant each $\mathbf{V}(t,T)$ in $\mathbf{V}$ is nothing but a parallel transport along the hypotenuse of $\Delta_{\mathcal{T}}$ from the fiber Π over (T,T) to the fiber Π over (t,t) and that $\mathbf{V}$ itself is a restriction to the hypotenuse of $\Delta_{\mathcal{T}}$ of a connection on P, where again Π is viewed as a vector sublattice of $\Pi(\mathbb{R}^n_{++} \times \mathbb{R}^n_{++})$. This connection on P will be studied in more detail in forthcoming articles. This completes the Remark.

Now our goal is to present a simple method for converting the Cauchy problem (3.6) with generator $\mathsf{L}(t)$ to the Cauchy problem (3.6) with the generator $\mathsf{L}'(t)$ related to $\mathsf{L}(t)$ by the beliefs-preferences gauge symmetry group $\hat{\mathfrak{G}}$ defined in (3.73).

Let $\boldsymbol{D}(t,T)$ and $\boldsymbol{D}'(t,T)$ be in the generalized beliefs $\mathfrak{B}$ and $\mathfrak{B}'$ related via a transformation $\mathfrak{g}_{\mathfrak{B}}$ from $\mathfrak{G}_{\mathfrak{B}}$ defined in (3.50), that is

$$\boldsymbol{D}'(t,T) = \mathbf{u}'^{-1}(t,t)\boldsymbol{D}(t,T)\mathbf{u}'(t,T).$$

Therefore if

$$v'(t) = \boldsymbol{D}'(t,T)\, v'(T) \tag{3.88}$$

then

$$v'(t) = \mathbf{u}'^{-1}(t,t)\boldsymbol{D}(t,T)\mathbf{u}'(t,T)\, v'(T),$$

or equivalently

$$\mathbf{u}'(t,t)\, v'(t) = \boldsymbol{D}(t,T)\mathbf{u}'(t,T)\, v'(T). \tag{3.89}$$

Let $\mathfrak{B}$ and $\mathfrak{B}'$ be generated by L and L' so that $\mathsf{L}(t)$ and $\mathsf{L}'(t)$ in L and L' are related via a transformation $\hat{\mathfrak{g}}_{\mathsf{L}}$ from $\hat{\mathfrak{G}}_{\mathsf{L}}$ defined in (3.73), that is

$$\mathsf{L}'(t) = \mathbf{u}'^{-1}(t,t)\,\mathsf{L}(t)\,\mathbf{u}'(t,t) + \frac{\mathbf{u}'_t(t,t)}{\mathbf{u}'(t,t)}. \tag{3.90}$$

Then the function $v'(t)$ defined in (3.88) is the solution of the Cauchy problem (3.6) with a generator $\mathsf{L}'(t)$, that is

$$\begin{aligned} \frac{d}{dt}v' + \mathsf{L}'(t)v' = 0, \quad t < T, \\ v'(t)|_{t=T} = v'(T). \end{aligned} \tag{3.91}$$

Substituting relation (3.90) into (3.91) we obtain that $v'(t)$ is also the solution of the following Cauchy problem

$$\frac{d}{dt}v' + \mathbf{u}'^{-1}(t,t)\,\mathsf{L}(t)\,\mathbf{u}'(t,t)\,v' + \frac{\mathbf{u}'_t(t,t)}{\mathbf{u}'(t,t)}v' = 0, \quad t < T,$$
$$v'(t)|_{t=T} = v'(T). \qquad (3.92)$$

Inserting the identity operator $\mathbf{u}'^{-1}(t,t)\mathbf{u}'(t,t)$ between the time derivative and the function v' in the preceding evolution equation (3.92) we obtain that $v'(t)$ is also the solution of the following Cauchy problem

$$\frac{d}{dt}\mathbf{u}'^{-1}(t,t)\mathbf{u}'(t,t)\,v' + \mathbf{u}'^{-1}(t,t)\,\mathsf{L}(t)\,\mathbf{u}'(t,t)\,v' +$$
$$\frac{\mathbf{u}'_t(t,t)}{\mathbf{u}'(t,t)}v' = 0, \quad t < T, \qquad (3.93)$$
$$v'(t)|_{t=T} = v'(T).$$

Differentiating $\mathbf{u}'^{-1}(t,t)$ and $\mathbf{u}'(t,t)v'$ with respect to time t in the preceding evolution equation (3.93) and acting on both the left hand side and the right hand side of this equation by the operator $\mathbf{u}'(t,t)$ we obtain that $v'(t)$ is also the solution of the following Cauchy problem

$$\frac{d}{dt}\mathbf{u}'(t,t)\,v' - \frac{\partial}{\partial t}^{(1)}\mathbf{u}'(t,t)\,v' + \mathsf{L}(t)\,\mathbf{u}'(t,t)\,v' = 0, \quad t < T,$$
$$v'(t)|_{t=T} = v'(T), \qquad (3.94)$$

where we have taken into account that

$$\frac{d}{dt}\mathbf{u}'(t,t) = \frac{\partial}{\partial t}^{(1)}\mathbf{u}'(t,t) + \frac{\partial}{\partial t}^{(2)}\mathbf{u}'(t,t) \qquad (3.95)$$

with $\frac{\partial}{\partial t}^{(1)}$ and $\frac{\partial}{\partial t}^{(2)}$ standing again for the derivative with respect to the first and second time variable of $\mathbf{u}'(t,t)$.

Taking again into account relation (3.95) in the preceding evolution equation (3.94) we obtain that $v'(t)$ is also the solution of the following Cauchy problem

$$\overset{2}{\frac{d}{dt}}\mathbf{u}'(\overset{3}{t},\overset{1}{t})\,v' + \mathbf{L}(\overset{2}{t})\,\mathbf{u}'(\overset{3}{t},\overset{1}{t})\,v' = 0, \quad t < T,$$
$$v'(t)|_{t=T} = v'(T), \tag{3.96}$$

where again the numbers over the operators indicate the order in which these operators act.

3.137. Remark. We comment that the fact that $\mathbf{u}'(t,t)\,v'$ is the solution of the Cauchy problem (3.6) with a generator $\mathbf{L}(t)$ or, more precisely, of the Cauchy problem (3.96) also directly follows from relation (3.89).

3.138. Remark. We now arrive at the following conclusion. Given the Cauchy problem (3.6) with a generator $\mathbf{L}(t)$, in order to obtain the Cauchy problem (3.6) with a generator $\mathbf{L}'(t)$, that is, the Cauchy problem (3.91) it is enough to substitute $\mathbf{u}'(t,t)\,v'$ instead of v in the Cauchy problem (3.6) with a generator $\mathbf{L}(t)$ and after acting on both sides of the evolution equation in (3.6) with $\mathbf{u}'(t,t)$ the resulting Cauchy problem for v' will be the desired Cauchy problem (3.6) with a generator $\mathbf{L}'(t)$.

3.139. Remark. It is clear from relation (3.90) that

$$\mathbf{L}'(t) = \mathbf{L}(t) + \mathbf{u}'^{-1}(t,t)\,[\mathbf{L}(t), \mathbf{u}'(t,t)] + \frac{\mathbf{u}'_t(t,t)}{\mathbf{u}'(t,t)}. \tag{3.97}$$

We comment that the commutator $[\mathbf{L}(t), \mathbf{u}'(t,t)]$ in the preceding relation is understood as follows

$$[\mathbf{L}(t), \mathbf{u}'(t,t)] = \mathbf{L}(\overset{2}{t})\,\mathbf{u}'(\overset{3}{t},\overset{1}{t}) - \mathbf{u}'(\overset{3}{t},\overset{2}{t})\mathbf{L}(\overset{1}{t}).$$

3.7 Beliefs-Preferences Gauge Symmetry Group for a Markovian Market Populace

Suppose that the trading time set $\mathcal{T}$ is an interval, either finite or infinite, of nonnegative real numbers. Consider a Markovian market populace $\mathbb{H} = \mathbb{B} \times \mathbb{U}$ such that $\boldsymbol{F}(t,T)$ and $\mathbf{u}'(t,T)$ in each Markovian belief $\boldsymbol{\mathcal{B}}$ and in each Markovian preference $\boldsymbol{\mathcal{U}}$ are differentiable, in an appropriate sense, with respect to time. This, in particular, implies that each Markovian belief $\boldsymbol{\mathcal{B}}$ is generated by $\boldsymbol{\mathfrak{L}}$. In this case each Markovian market participant $\boldsymbol{\mathcal{H}} = (\boldsymbol{\mathcal{B}}, \boldsymbol{\mathcal{U}})$ can be uniquely characterized as a pair $(\boldsymbol{\mathfrak{L}}, \boldsymbol{\mathcal{U}})$ and, whenever ambiguity is unlikely, we will loosely say that a Markovian market participant $\boldsymbol{\mathcal{H}}$ is a pair $(\boldsymbol{\mathfrak{L}}, \boldsymbol{\mathcal{U}})$ and we will write $\boldsymbol{\mathcal{H}} = (\boldsymbol{\mathfrak{L}}, \boldsymbol{\mathcal{U}})$. In the same way we will write $\mathbb{H} = \mathbb{L} \times \mathbb{U}$ where $\mathbb{L}$ stands for the set of all families $\boldsymbol{\mathfrak{L}}$.

In the case under consideration, we show that the beliefs-preferences gauge symmetry group $\boldsymbol{\mathcal{G}}$ for $\mathbb{H} = \mathbb{B} \times \mathbb{U}$ can be represented as an abelian group of transformations of $\mathbb{L} \times \mathbb{U}$.

In relation (3.66), as we have indicated in Remark (3.112), the derivative $\boldsymbol{\mathfrak{L}}(t)$ of $-\boldsymbol{F}(t,T)$ with respect to t evaluated at t equal to T with $\boldsymbol{F}(t,T)$ in $\boldsymbol{\mathcal{B}}$ coincides with the generator at time t of $\boldsymbol{\mathcal{B}}$ in the case when the belief $\boldsymbol{\mathcal{B}}$ is Markovian and generated by $\boldsymbol{\mathfrak{L}}$. Therefore, taking into account relation (3.66) we have the representation of the beliefs-preferences gauge symmetry group $\boldsymbol{\mathcal{G}}$ of transformations of $\mathbb{H} = \mathbb{B} \times \mathbb{U}$ defined in (3.56) as the group $\hat{\boldsymbol{\mathcal{G}}}$ of transformations of $\mathbb{L} \times \mathbb{U}$ defined by

$$(\boldsymbol{\mathfrak{L}}, \boldsymbol{\mathcal{U}}) \to \hat{\boldsymbol{g}}\,(\boldsymbol{\mathfrak{L}}, \boldsymbol{\mathcal{U}}) = \big(\hat{\boldsymbol{g}}_{\boldsymbol{\mathfrak{L}}}(\boldsymbol{\mathfrak{L}}, \boldsymbol{\mathcal{U}}), \hat{\boldsymbol{g}}_{\boldsymbol{\mathcal{U}}}(\boldsymbol{\mathfrak{L}}, \boldsymbol{\mathcal{U}})\big), \quad \hat{\boldsymbol{g}} \in \hat{\boldsymbol{\mathcal{G}}}. \tag{3.98}$$

Here each $\hat{\boldsymbol{g}} = (\hat{\boldsymbol{g}}_{\boldsymbol{\mathfrak{L}}}, \hat{\boldsymbol{g}}_{\boldsymbol{\mathcal{U}}})$ in $\hat{\boldsymbol{\mathcal{G}}}$ is defined by

$$\begin{aligned} &\boldsymbol{\mathfrak{L}}(t) \xrightarrow{\hat{\boldsymbol{g}}_{\boldsymbol{\mathcal{B}}}} \mathbf{u}'^{-1}(t,t)\,\boldsymbol{\mathfrak{L}}(t)\,\mathbf{u}'(t,t) + \frac{\mathbf{u}'_t(t,t)}{\mathbf{u}'(t,t)} - \boldsymbol{\mathfrak{d}}(t) \quad \text{and} \\ &\boldsymbol{u}'(t,T) \xrightarrow{\hat{\boldsymbol{g}}_{\boldsymbol{\mathcal{U}}}} \big(e^{-\int_t^T \boldsymbol{\mathfrak{d}}(\overset{\tau}{\tau})d\tau}\,\mathbf{u}'(\overset{t}{t},\overset{T}{T})\big)^{-1}\boldsymbol{u}'(t,T), \end{aligned} \tag{3.99}$$

where $\boldsymbol{\mathfrak{d}}(t)$ is the operator of multiplication by the function

$$\boldsymbol{\mathfrak{d}}(t) = \Big(\mathbf{u}'^{-1}(t,t)\,\boldsymbol{\mathfrak{L}}(\overset{2}{t})\,\mathbf{u}'(\overset{3}{t},\overset{1}{t}) + \frac{\mathbf{u}'_t(t,t)}{\mathbf{u}'(t,t)}\Big)\mathbf{1}, \tag{3.100}$$

with $\mathbf{1}$ being the function in Π identically equal to unity, and where $\mathfrak{L}(t)$ is in $\mathfrak{L}$ and

$$\mathfrak{u}'^{-1}(t,t)\,\mathfrak{L}(t)\,\mathfrak{u}'(t,t) + \frac{\mathfrak{u}'_t(t,t)}{\mathfrak{u}'(t,t)} - \mathfrak{d}(t)$$

is in $\hat{g}_{\mathfrak{L}}(\mathfrak{L},\mathcal{U})$, and where $\boldsymbol{u}'(t,T)$ is in $\mathcal{U}$ and

$$\left(e^{-\int_t^T \mathfrak{d}(\overset{\tau}{\tau})d\tau}\mathfrak{u}'(\overset{t}{t},\overset{T}{T})\right)^{-1}\boldsymbol{u}'(t,T)$$

is in $\hat{g}_{\mathcal{U}}(\mathfrak{L},\mathcal{U})$.

We comment that $e^{-\int_t^T \mathfrak{d}(\overset{\tau}{\tau})d\tau}\mathfrak{u}'(\overset{t}{t},\overset{T}{T})$ is the operator on $\Pi(\mathbb{R}^n_{++}\times\mathbb{R}^n_{++})$ of multiplication by the function

$$e^{-\int_t^T \mathfrak{d}(\tau,s_t)d\tau}\mathfrak{u}'(t,T,s_t,s_T),$$

with the indexes over the operators indicating the order inverse to the order in which these operators act.

3.140. Remark. We comment that the preference $\hat{g}_{\mathcal{U}}(\mathfrak{L},\mathcal{U})$ is Markovian whenever the preference $\mathcal{U}$ is Markovian.

3.141. Remark. In view of relation (3.99) we will say that $\hat{g} = (\hat{g}_{\mathfrak{L}}, \hat{g}_{\mathcal{U}})$ in $\hat{\mathcal{G}}$ is generated by $\mathfrak{u}'(t,T)$.

3.142. Remark. We note that $\hat{g}_{\mathfrak{L}}$ is in fact a map from $\mathbb{L}$ to $\mathbb{L}$.

3.143. Remark. We comment that the reason we have used the same notation $\mathfrak{d}(t)$ for the operators defined in (3.100) and (3.63) is as follows. As we have indicated in Remark (3.112), the derivative $\mathfrak{L}(t)$ of $-\boldsymbol{F}(t,T)$, where $\boldsymbol{F}(t,T)$ is in $\mathcal{B}$, with respect to t evaluated at t equal to T coincides with the generator at time t of $\mathcal{B}$ in the case when the belief $\mathcal{B}$ is Markovian and generated by $\mathfrak{L}$. Therefore, in the case when the belief $\mathcal{B}$ is Markovian and is generated by $\mathfrak{L}$, the operator defined in (3.63) via the derivative $\mathfrak{L}(t)$ of $-\boldsymbol{F}(t,T)$, where $\boldsymbol{F}(t,T)$ is in $\mathcal{B}$, with respect to t evaluated at t equal to T coincides with the operator defined (3.100) via the generator at time t of $\mathcal{B}$.

Now we show that $\hat{\mathcal{G}}$ is indeed a group, in fact an abelian group.

3.144. Theorem. The set $\hat{\mathcal{G}}$ of transformations of $\mathbb{L} \times \mathbb{U}$ is an abelian group with the group operation of composition.

Proof. Directly follows from the definitions of $\hat{\mathcal{G}}$ and Theorem (3.92). □

3.145. Definition. We will call the group of transformations $\hat{\mathcal{G}}$ the *beliefs-preferences gauge symmetry group for a Markovian market populace* or simply the *beliefs-preferences gauge group for* $\mathbb{H} = \mathbb{L} \times \mathbb{U}$.

3.146. Remark. The fact that $\boldsymbol{F}(t, T)$ is in the belief $\boldsymbol{\mathcal{B}}$ generated by $\mathfrak{L}$, that is, that the function $\mathbf{1}$ in Π identically equal to unity is a fixed point of $\boldsymbol{F}(t, T)$:

$$\boldsymbol{F}(t, T)\, \mathbf{1} = \mathbf{1}$$

can be expressed solely in terms of the generators $\mathfrak{L}(t)$ in $\mathfrak{L}$ as the fact that the function $\mathbf{1}$ is in the kernel of each generator $\mathfrak{L}(t)$:

$$\mathfrak{L}(t)\, \mathbf{1} = \mathbf{0}, \quad t \in \mathcal{T}, \tag{3.101}$$

where $\mathbf{0}$ stands for the zero function in Π. In this regard the meaning of the compensating term $\mathfrak{d}(t)$ defined in (3.100) is exactly to ensure that the function $\mathbf{1}$ is in the kernel of the generator

$$\mathfrak{L}'(t) = \mathbf{u}'^{-1}(t, t)\, \mathfrak{L}(t)\, \mathbf{u}'(t, t) + \frac{\mathbf{u}'_t(t, t)}{\mathbf{u}'(t, t)} - \mathfrak{d}(t)$$

from $\mathfrak{L}' = \hat{g}_{\mathfrak{L}} \mathfrak{L}$:

$$\mathfrak{L}'(t)\, \mathbf{1} =$$

$$\Big(\mathbf{u}'^{-1}(t, t)\, \mathfrak{L}(t)\, \mathbf{u}'(t, t) + \frac{\mathbf{u}'_t(t, t)}{\mathbf{u}'(t, t)} - \mathfrak{d}(t)\Big)\mathbf{1} = \mathbf{0},$$

so that $\boldsymbol{\mathcal{B}}'$ generated by $\mathfrak{L}'$ is a belief.

3.147. Remark. In view of the preceding Remark (3.146) we can rewrite expression (3.100) for $\mathfrak{d}(t)$ as follows

$$\mathfrak{d}(t) = \left(\mathbf{u}'^{-1}(t,t)\,\mathfrak{L}(t)\,\mathbf{u}'(t,t) + \frac{\mathbf{u}'_t(t,t)}{\mathbf{u}'(t,t)}\right)\mathbf{1} = \\ \mathfrak{L}(t)\,\mathbf{1} + \mathbf{u}'^{-1}(t,t)[\mathfrak{L}(t), \mathbf{u}'(t,t)]\,\mathbf{1} + \frac{\mathbf{u}'_t(t,t)}{\mathbf{u}'(t,t)}\,\mathbf{1} = \\ \mathbf{u}'^{-1}(t,t)\left([\mathfrak{L}(t), \mathbf{u}'(t,t)] + \mathbf{u}'_t(t,t)\right)\mathbf{1}, \tag{3.102}$$

where in the second equality we took into account equality (3.101), and where $[A, B] = A\,B - B\,A$ stands for the commutator of linear operators A and B. We comment that we have loosely used the same notation for the operators of multiplication by functions and for the functions themselves.

3.148. Remark. Since a Markovian market participant is a particular case of a Markovian generalized market participant relation (3.73) implies that

$$\mathsf{L}(t) = \mathbf{u}'^{-1}(t,t)\,\mathfrak{L}(t)\,\mathbf{u}'(t,t) + \frac{\mathbf{u}'_t(t,t)}{\mathbf{u}'(t,t)}, \tag{3.103}$$

where $\mathfrak{L}(t)$ is in $\mathfrak{L}$ and $\mathsf{L}(t)$ is in L, and where $\mathfrak{L}$ and L are related via the transformation from the beliefs-preferences gauge symmetry group for a Markovian generalized market populace defined in (3.72). We comment that in order to use relation (3.73) we treated the generators $\mathfrak{L}(t)$ of the belief of a Markovian market participant as a particular case of the generators $\mathsf{L}(t)$ of the generalized belief of a Markovian generalized market participant.

3.149. Remark. Since a market environment $\mathbf{V}$ is a particular case of a generalized belief $\mathfrak{B}$ for a generalized market participant with the preference consisting of the identity operators, that is, for the representative generalized market participant, relation (3.73) implies that

$$\boldsymbol{L}(t) = \boldsymbol{u}'^{-1}(t,t)\, \mathfrak{L}(t)\, \boldsymbol{u}'(t,t) + \frac{\boldsymbol{u}'_t(t,t)}{\boldsymbol{u}'(t,t)}, \tag{3.104}$$

where $\boldsymbol{L}(t)$ and $\mathfrak{L}(t)$ are generators at time t of the market environment $\mathbf{V}$ and a belief $\boldsymbol{\mathcal{B}}$ related via the transformation from the beliefs-preferences gauge symmetry group for a Markovian generalized market populace defined in (3.72). We comment that $\boldsymbol{u}'(t,T)$ is in the preference $\boldsymbol{\mathcal{U}}$ of a market participant $\boldsymbol{\mathcal{H}} = (\boldsymbol{\mathcal{B}}, \boldsymbol{\mathcal{U}})$ with the belief $\boldsymbol{\mathcal{B}}$. We also comment that in order to use relation (3.73) we treated the belief $\boldsymbol{\mathcal{B}}$ as a particular case of a generalized belief.

3.150. Remark. In the previous Remark (3.149) we have implicitly made the crucial financial assumption that the market environment $\mathbf{V}$ satisfies the intervention condition (2.4) whenever the beliefs $\boldsymbol{\mathcal{B}}$ are Markovian.

Due to the explicit presence of the term $\mathfrak{d}(t)$ in the transformations (3.99) from the beliefs-preferences gauge symmetry group for a Markovian market populace defined in (3.98), the form of these transformations differs from the transformations (3.73) from the beliefs-preferences gauge symmetry group for a Markovian generalized market populace defined in (3.72). Now we show that, by incorporating the term $\mathfrak{d}(t)$ into $\mathbf{u}'(t,T)$, the transformations (3.99) can be rewritten in a form analogous to that of transformations (3.73).

For each $\hat{g} = (\hat{g}_{\mathfrak{L}}, \hat{g}_{\mathcal{U}})$ in $\hat{\mathcal{G}}$ generated by $\mathbf{u}'(t,T)$, or more precisely for each such $\mathbf{u}'(t,T)$ define $\hat{\mathbf{u}}'(t,T)$ by

$$\hat{\mathbf{u}}'(t,T) = e^{-\int_t^T \mathfrak{d}(\overset{T}{\tau})d\tau}\, \mathbf{u}'(\overset{t}{t}, \overset{T}{T}), \tag{3.105}$$

where the indexes over the operators indicate the order inverse to the order in which these operators act.

We comment that $\hat{\mathbf{u}}'(t,T)$ is the operator on $\Pi(\mathbb{R}^n_{++} \times \mathbb{R}^n_{++})$ of multiplication by the function $\hat{\mathrm{u}}' = \hat{\mathrm{u}}'(t,T,s_t,s_T)$ in $\Pi(\mathbb{R}^n_{++} \times \mathbb{R}^n_{++})$ defined by

$$\hat{\mathrm{u}}'(t,T,s_t,s_T) = e^{-\int_t^T \mathfrak{d}(\tau,s_t)d\tau}\mathrm{u}'(t,T,s_t,s_T) \tag{3.106}$$

Using the operators $\hat{\mathbf{u}}'(t,T)$ we can rewrite the transformations (3.99) from the beliefs-preferences gauge symmetry group for a Markovian market populace defined in (3.98) as follows

$$\begin{aligned} &\mathfrak{L}(t) \xrightarrow{\hat{g}_{\mathcal{B}}} \hat{\mathbf{u}}'^{-1}(t,t)\,\mathfrak{L}(t)\,\hat{\mathbf{u}}'(t,t) + \frac{\hat{\mathbf{u}}'_t(t,t)}{\hat{\mathbf{u}}'(t,t)} \quad \text{and} \\ &\boldsymbol{u}'(t,T) \xrightarrow{\hat{g}_{\mathcal{U}}} \hat{\mathbf{u}}'^{-1}(t,T)\boldsymbol{u}'(t,T). \end{aligned} \tag{3.107}$$

3.151. Remark. It is clear that the beliefs-preferences gauge symmetry group $\mathcal{G}$ defined in (3.56) for a market populace $\mathbb{H} = \mathbb{B} \times \mathbb{U}$ remains true for the case of a Markovian market populace $\mathbb{H} = \mathbb{L} \times \mathbb{U}$ if $\hat{\mathbf{u}}'(t,T)$ in (3.57) are defined as in (3.105).

Let $\boldsymbol{F}(t,T)$ and $\boldsymbol{F}'(t,T)$ be in the beliefs $\mathcal{B}$ and $\mathcal{B}'$ related via a transformation $g_{\mathcal{B}}$ in (3.57) with $\hat{\mathbf{u}}'(t,T)$ defined as in (3.105), that is

$$\boldsymbol{F}'(t,T) = \hat{\mathbf{u}}'^{-1}(t,t)\boldsymbol{F}(t,T)\hat{\mathbf{u}}'(t,T).$$

Moreover, let $\mathcal{B}$ and $\mathcal{B}'$ be generated by $\mathfrak{L}$ and $\mathfrak{L}'$ so that $\mathfrak{L}(t)$ and $\mathfrak{L}'(t)$ in $\mathfrak{L}$ and $\mathfrak{L}'$ are related via a transformation $\hat{\mathfrak{g}}_{\mathfrak{L}}$ defined in (3.99), or more precisely in (3.107), that is

$$\mathfrak{L}'(t) = \hat{\mathbf{u}}'^{-1}(t,t)\,\mathfrak{L}(t)\,\hat{\mathbf{u}}'(t,t) + \frac{\hat{\mathbf{u}}'_t(t,t)}{\hat{\mathbf{u}}'(t,t)}.$$

It is clear that

$$\hat{\mathbf{u}}'^{-1}(t,t)\boldsymbol{F}(t,T)\hat{\mathbf{u}}'(t,T) = e^{\int_t^T \left(\hat{\mathbf{u}}'^{-1}(\tau,\tau)\,\mathfrak{L}(\tau)\,\hat{\mathbf{u}}'(\tau,\tau) + \frac{\hat{\mathbf{u}}'_t(\tau,\tau)}{\hat{\mathbf{u}}'(\tau,\tau)}\right)d\tau}, \tag{3.108}$$

where the generator

$$\hat{\mathfrak{u}}'^{-1}(\tau,\tau)\,\mathfrak{L}(\tau)\,\hat{\mathfrak{u}}'(\tau,\tau)+\frac{\hat{\mathfrak{u}}'_t(\tau,\tau)}{\hat{\mathfrak{u}}'(\tau,\tau)}$$

at time τ acts in the order inverse to that of τ.

3.152. Remark. It is clear that the representation of the beliefs-preferences gauge symmetry group $\mathcal{G}$ of transformations of $\mathbb{H}=\mathbb{B}\times\mathbb{U}$ as the group $\hat{\mathcal{G}}$ of transformations of $\mathbb{L}\times\mathbb{U}$ is in fact an isomorphism so that the groups, or more precisely abelian groups $\mathcal{G}$ and $\hat{\mathcal{G}}$ are isomorphic.

3.153. Remark. The transformations (3.99) from the beliefs-preferences gauge symmetry group for a Markovian market populace $\hat{\mathcal{G}}$ admit the following interpretation. The generators $\mathfrak{L}(t)$ in $\mathfrak{L}$ of $\mathcal{B}$ can be viewed as the restriction to the hypotenuse of Δ_T of a certain differential-geometric connection on P with the gauge group $\hat{\mathcal{G}}$. The restriction to the hypotenuse of Δ_T of the covariant derivative in the t direction $\boldsymbol{\nabla}_t$ is given by $\frac{d}{dt}+\mathfrak{L}(t)$. Moreover, due to Remark (3.121) the restriction to the hypotenuse of Δ_T of the covariant derivative in the direction of the hypotenuse is equal to the restriction to the hypotenuse of Δ_T of the covariant derivative $\boldsymbol{\nabla}_t$ in the t direction. Therefore, the evolution equation in (3.3) states that its solution $v=v(t)$ is the restriction to the hypotenuse of Δ_T of such a section on P, that is, of such a vector field on Δ_T that it is parallel to itself along the hypotenuse. Therefore, the Cauchy problem (3.3) states that $v(t)$ in the fiber Π over (t,t) is the result of the parallel transport along the hypotenuse of Δ_T of $v(T)$ in the fiber Π over (T,T) determined by $\boldsymbol{F}(t,T)$ from $\mathcal{B}$:

$$v(t)=\boldsymbol{F}(t,T)v(T),$$

where Π is viewed as the vector sublattice of $\Pi(\mathbb{R}^n_{++}\times\mathbb{R}^n_{++})$. This implies that each $\boldsymbol{F}(t,T)$ in $\mathcal{B}$ is nothing but a parallel transport along the hypotenuse of Δ_T from the fiber Π over

(T, T) to the fiber Π over (t, t) and that $\mathcal{B}$ itself is a restriction to the hypotenuse of $\triangle_{\mathcal{T}}$ of a connection on P, where Π is viewed as the vector sublattice of $\Pi(\mathbb{R}^n_{++} \times \mathbb{R}^n_{++})$. This connection on P will be studied in more detail in forthcoming articles.

3.154. Remark. Similar to Remark (3.132), it is the approach to treating the differential-geometric connection, or equivalently the generators of the belief $\mathfrak{L}(t)$ as a field, or more precisely as a gauge field over the trading time set $\mathcal{T}$, that we have demonstrated to be fruitful in the second quantization of the evolution equation (3.3) that corresponds to the first quantization. In this regard the field $\mathfrak{L}(t)$ over the trading time set $\mathcal{T}$ is quantized in the second quantization as a bosonic field and $v = v(t)$, also treated as a field over the trading time set $\mathcal{T}$, is quantized as a fermionic field. Finally, we note that it is the second quantization of the fields $\mathfrak{L}(t)$ and $v = v(t)$ over the trading time set $\mathcal{T}$ that is one of the main reasons to treat $\mathfrak{L}(t)$ as a differential-geometric connection and $\frac{d}{dt} + \mathfrak{L}(t)$ as a covariant derivative. The second quantization of the fields $\mathfrak{L}(t)$ and $v = v(t)$ over the trading time set $\mathcal{T}$ and related supersymmetry along with supersymmetry breaking will be presented in forthcoming articles.

Now our goal is to present a simple method for converting the Cauchy problem (3.3) with a generator $\mathfrak{L}(t)$ to the Cauchy problem (3.3) with the generator $\mathfrak{L}'(t)$ related to $\mathfrak{L}(t)$ by the transformation from beliefs-preferences gauge symmetry group $\hat{\mathcal{G}}$ defined in (3.99).

Let $\boldsymbol{F}(t, T)$ and $\boldsymbol{F}'(t, T)$ be in the beliefs $\mathcal{B}$ and $\mathcal{B}'$ related via a transformation $g_{\mathcal{B}}$ in (3.57) with $\hat{\mathbf{u}}'(t, T)$ defined as in (3.105), that is

$$\boldsymbol{F}'(t, T) = \hat{\mathbf{u}}'^{-1}(t, t)\boldsymbol{F}(t, T)\hat{\mathbf{u}}'(t, T).$$

Therefore if

$$v'(t) = \boldsymbol{F}'(t, T)\, v'(T) \tag{3.109}$$

then

$$v'(t) = \hat{\mathfrak{u}}'^{-1}(t,t)\boldsymbol{F}(t,T)\hat{\mathfrak{u}}'(t,T)\,v'(T),$$

or equivalently

$$\hat{\mathfrak{u}}'(t,t)\,v'(t) = \boldsymbol{F}(t,T)\hat{\mathfrak{u}}'(t,T)\,v'(T). \tag{3.110}$$

Let $\boldsymbol{\mathcal{B}}$ and $\boldsymbol{\mathcal{B}}'$ be generated by $\mathfrak{L}$ and $\mathfrak{L}'$ so that $\mathfrak{L}(t)$ and $\mathfrak{L}'(t)$ in $\mathfrak{L}$ and $\mathfrak{L}'$ are related via a transformation $\hat{\mathfrak{g}}_{\mathfrak{L}}$ defined in (3.99), or more precisely in (3.107), that is

$$\mathfrak{L}'(t) = \hat{\mathfrak{u}}'^{-1}(t,t)\,\mathfrak{L}(t)\,\hat{\mathfrak{u}}'(t,t) + \frac{\hat{\mathfrak{u}}_t'(t,t)}{\hat{\mathfrak{u}}'(t,t)}. \tag{3.111}$$

Then the function $v'(t)$ defined in (3.109) is the solution of the Cauchy problem (3.3) with a generator $\mathfrak{L}'(t)$, that is

$$\begin{aligned} \frac{d}{dt}v' + \mathfrak{L}'(t)v' = 0, \quad t < T, \\ v'(t)|_{t=T} = v'(T). \end{aligned} \tag{3.112}$$

Substituting relation (3.111) into (3.112) we obtain that $v'(t)$ is also the solution of the following Cauchy problem

$$\begin{aligned} \frac{d}{dt}v' + \hat{\mathfrak{u}}'^{-1}(t,t)\,\mathfrak{L}(t)\,\hat{\mathfrak{u}}'(t,t)\,v' + \frac{\hat{\mathfrak{u}}_t'(t,t)}{\hat{\mathfrak{u}}'(t,t)}v' = 0, \quad t < T, \\ v'(t)|_{t=T} = v'(T). \end{aligned} \tag{3.113}$$

Inserting the identity operator $\hat{\mathfrak{u}}'^{-1}(t,t)\hat{\mathfrak{u}}'(t,t)$ between the time derivative and the function v' in the preceding evolution equation (3.113) we obtain that $v'(t)$ is also the solution of the following Cauchy problem

$$\begin{aligned} \frac{d}{dt}\hat{\mathfrak{u}}'^{-1}(t,t)\hat{\mathfrak{u}}'(t,t)\,v' + \hat{\mathfrak{u}}'^{-1}(t,t)\,\mathfrak{L}(t)\,\hat{\mathfrak{u}}'(t,t)\,v' + \\ \frac{\hat{\mathfrak{u}}_t'(t,t)}{\hat{\mathfrak{u}}'(t,t)}v' = 0, \quad t < T, \\ v'(t)|_{t=T} = v'(T). \end{aligned} \tag{3.114}$$

Differentiating $\hat{\mathbf{u}}'^{-1}(t,t)$ and $\hat{\mathbf{u}}'(t,t)v'$ with respect to time t in the preceding evolution equation (3.114) and acting on both the left hand side and the right hand side of this equation by the operator $\hat{\mathbf{u}}'(t,t)$ we obtain that $v'(t)$ is also the solution of the following Cauchy problem

$$\frac{d}{dt}\hat{\mathbf{u}}'(t,t)\,v' - \frac{\partial}{\partial t}^{(1)}\hat{\mathbf{u}}'(t,t)\,v' + \mathfrak{L}(t)\,\hat{\mathbf{u}}'(t,t)\,v' = 0, \quad t < T,$$
$$v'(t)|_{t=T} = v'(T), \quad (3.115)$$

where we have taken into account that

$$\frac{d}{dt}\hat{\mathbf{u}}'(t,t) = \frac{\partial}{\partial t}^{(1)}\hat{\mathbf{u}}'(t,t) + \frac{\partial}{\partial t}^{(2)}\hat{\mathbf{u}}'(t,t) \quad (3.116)$$

with $\frac{\partial}{\partial t}^{(1)}$ and $\frac{\partial}{\partial t}^{(2)}$ standing again for the derivative with respect to the first and second time variable of $\hat{\mathbf{u}}'(t,t)$.

Taking again into account the preceding relation (3.116) in the evolution equation (3.115) we obtain that $v'(t)$ is also the solution of the following Cauchy problem

$$\frac{\overset{2}{d}}{dt}\hat{\mathbf{u}}'(\overset{3}{t},\overset{1}{t})\,v' + \mathfrak{L}(\overset{2}{t})\,\hat{\mathbf{u}}'(\overset{3}{t},\overset{1}{t})\,v' = 0, \quad t < T,$$
$$v'(t)|_{t=T} = v'(T), \quad (3.117)$$

where again the numbers over the operators indicate the order in which these operators act.

3.155. Remark. We comment that the fact that $\hat{\mathbf{u}}'(t,t)\,v'$ is the solution of the Cauchy problem (3.3) with a generator $\mathfrak{L}(t)$ or, more precisely, of the Cauchy problem (3.117) also directly follows from relation (3.110).

3.156. Remark. With the help of Remark (3.149) and relation (3.117) we can rewrite the Cauchy problem (2.6) as follows

$$\frac{\overset{2}{d}}{dt}\boldsymbol{u}'(\overset{3}{t},\overset{1}{t})\,v + \mathfrak{L}(\overset{2}{t})\,\boldsymbol{u}'(\overset{3}{t},\overset{1}{t})\,v = 0, \quad t < T,$$
$$v(T) = v_T, \quad (3.118)$$

where $v = v(t)$ stands for the value at time t of the European contingent claim with inception time t, expiration time T and the payoff v_T.

3.157. Remark. We now arrive at the following conclusion. Given the Cauchy problem (3.3) with a generator $\mathfrak{L}(t)$, in order to obtain the Cauchy problem (3.3) with the generator $\mathfrak{L}'(t)$, that is, the Cauchy problem (3.112) it is enough to substitute $\hat{\mathbf{u}}'(t,t)\, v'$ instead of v in the Cauchy problem (3.3) with a generator $\mathfrak{L}(t)$ and, after acting on both sides of the evolution equation in (3.3) with $\hat{\mathbf{u}}'(t,t)$, the resulting Cauchy problem for v' will be the desired Cauchy problem (3.3) with a generator $\mathfrak{L}'(t)$.

3.158. Remark. It is clear from relation (3.111) that

$$\mathfrak{L}'(t) = \mathfrak{L}(t) + \hat{\mathbf{u}}'^{-1}(t,t)\,[\mathfrak{L}(t), \hat{\mathbf{u}}'(t,t)] + \frac{\hat{\mathbf{u}}'_t(t,t)}{\hat{\mathbf{u}}'(t,t)}. \tag{3.119}$$

We comment that the commutator $[\mathfrak{L}(t), \hat{\mathbf{u}}'(t,t)]$ in the preceding relation is understood as follows

$$[\mathfrak{L}(t), \hat{\mathbf{u}}'(t,t)] = \mathfrak{L}(\overset{2}{t})\,\hat{\mathbf{u}}'(\overset{3}{t},\overset{1}{t}) - \hat{\mathbf{u}}'(\overset{3}{t},\overset{2}{t})\mathfrak{L}(\overset{1}{t}).$$

4 Beliefs-Preferences Gauge Symmetry Group for a Markovian Generalized Market Populace with the Generalized Beliefs Determined by Diffusion Processes

We illustrate the beliefs-preferences gauge symmetry group $\hat{\mathfrak{G}}$ for the Markovian generalized market populace $\mathbb{H} = \mathbb{B} \times \mathbb{U}$, or more precisely $\mathbb{H} = \mathbb{L} \times \mathbb{U}$ which was defined in Section (3) in relation (3.72) in the particular case when each generalized belief $\mathfrak{B}$ in the generalized market populace belief $\mathbb{B}$ is determined by a diffusion process.

4.1 The Case of a Single Underlying Security

First we consider the beliefs-preferences gauge symmetry group $\hat{\mathfrak{G}}$ for a Markovian generalized market populace $\mathbb{H} = \mathbb{B} \times \mathbb{U}$, or more precisely $\mathbb{H} = \mathbb{L} \times \mathbb{U}$ in the particular case of a single underlying security and when each generalized belief $\mathfrak{B}$ in the generalized market populace belief $\mathbb{B}$ is generated by the family

$$\mathsf{L} = \{\mathsf{L}(t) : \Pi \to \Pi \,|\, t \in \mathcal{T}\},$$

in $\mathbb{L}$ with each generator $\mathsf{L}(t)$ at time t of the form

$$\mathsf{L}(t) = \frac{1}{2}\sigma^2(s,t)\frac{\partial^2}{\partial s^2} + \mu(s,t)\frac{\partial}{\partial s} + \rho(s,t), \qquad (4.1)$$

where $\sigma(s,t) > 0$, $\mu(s,t)$ and $\rho(s,t)$ are admissible real-valued functions on $\mathbb{R}_{++} \times \mathcal{T}$.

4.1. Remark. We comment that, for the sake of simplicity, in relation (4.1) we used the same notations for the operators of multiplication by the functions $\sigma(s,t)$, $\mu(s,t)$ and $\rho(s,t)$ and for the functions $\sigma(s,t)$, $\mu(s,t)$ and $\rho(s,t)$ themselves. Whenever we would like to distinguish the operators of multiplication by the functions $\sigma(s,t)$, $\mu(s,t)$ and $\rho(s,t)$ from the functions $\sigma(s,t)$, $\mu(s,t)$ and $\rho(s,t)$ themselves we will denote these operators by $\boldsymbol{\sigma}(s,t)$, $\boldsymbol{\mu}(s,t)$ and $\boldsymbol{\rho}(s,t)$.

Our goal is to establish the behavior of the generator $\mathbf{L}(t)$ in (4.1) under the transformations $\hat{\mathfrak{g}}_{\mathbf{L}}$ defined in (3.73) from the beliefs-preferences gauge symmetry group $\hat{\mathfrak{G}}$ for a Markovian generalized market populace $\mathbb{H} = \mathbb{B} \times \mathbb{U}$, or more precisely $\mathbb{H} = \mathbb{L} \times \mathbb{U}$. In other words, our goal is to find the explicit form of the operator

$$\mathbf{L}'(t) = \mathbf{u}'^{-1}(t,t)\,\mathbf{L}(t)\,\mathbf{u}'(t,t) + \frac{\mathbf{u}'_t(t,t)}{\mathbf{u}'(t,t)}, \tag{4.2}$$

where $\mathbf{L}(t)$ is defined in (4.1).

In order to do this, according to Remark (3.138) we use the following chain of equalities

$$\begin{aligned}
0 = {} & \frac{\overset{2}{d}}{dt}\mathbf{u}'(\overset{3}{t},\overset{1}{t})v' + \mathbf{L}(\overset{2}{t})\mathbf{u}'(\overset{3}{t},\overset{1}{t})v' = \\
& \frac{\overset{2}{d}}{dt}\mathbf{u}'(\overset{3}{t},\overset{1}{t})v' + \overbrace{\Big(\frac{1}{2}\sigma^2(s,t)\frac{\partial^2}{\partial s^2} + \mu(s,t)\frac{\partial}{\partial s} + \rho(s,t)\Big)}^{2}\mathbf{u}'(\overset{3}{t},\overset{1}{t})v' = \\
& \mathbf{u}'(t,t)\frac{d}{dt}v' + \mathbf{u}'_t(t,t)v' + \\
& \quad \mathbf{u}'(t,t)\Big(\frac{1}{2}\sigma^2(s,t)\frac{\partial^2}{\partial s^2} + \mu(s,t)\frac{\partial}{\partial s} + \rho(s,t)\Big)v' + \\
& \quad \Big(\frac{1}{2}\sigma^2(s,t)\mathbf{u}'_{ss}(t,t) + \sigma^2(s,t)\mathbf{u}'_s(t,t)\frac{\partial}{\partial s} + \mathbf{u}'_s(t,t)\mu(s,t)\Big)v' = \\
& \mathbf{u}'(t,t)\bigg(\frac{d}{dt}v' + \frac{\mathbf{u}'_t(t,t)}{\mathbf{u}'(t,t)}v' + \\
& \quad \Big(\frac{1}{2}\sigma^2(s,t)\frac{\partial^2}{\partial s^2} + \mu(s,t)\frac{\partial}{\partial s} + \rho(s,t)\Big)v' + \\
& \quad \Big(\frac{\sigma^2(s,t)\mathbf{u}'_s(t,t)}{\mathbf{u}'(t,t)}\frac{\partial}{\partial s} + \frac{\frac{1}{2}\sigma^2(s,t)\mathbf{u}'_{ss}(t,t) + \mathbf{u}'_s(t,t)\mu(s,t)}{\mathbf{u}'(t,t)}\Big)v'\bigg),
\end{aligned} \tag{4.3}$$

where $\mathbf{u}'_s(t,t)$ and $\mathbf{u}'_{ss}(t,t)$ stand for the operators of multiplication by the functions $\frac{\partial}{\partial s}\mathrm{u}'(t,t,s_t,s)|_{s=s_t}$ and $\frac{\partial^2}{\partial s^2}\mathrm{u}'(t,t,s_t,s)|_{s=s_t}$.

Therefore due to Remark (3.138) the desired generator $\mathbf{L}'(t)$ is given by

$$\mathbf{L}'(t) = \frac{1}{2}\sigma^2(s,t)\frac{\partial^2}{\partial s^2} + \mu(s,t)\frac{\partial}{\partial s} + \rho(s,t) + \frac{\mathbf{u}'_t(t,t)}{\mathbf{u}'(t,t)} + \frac{\sigma^2(s,t)\mathbf{u}'_s(t,t)}{\mathbf{u}'(t,t)}\frac{\partial}{\partial s} + \frac{\frac{1}{2}\sigma^2(s,t)\mathbf{u}'_{ss}(t,t) + \mathbf{u}'_s(t,t)\mu(s,t)}{\mathbf{u}'(t,t)}. \quad (4.4)$$

4.2. Remark. The relation (4.4) for the generator $\mathbf{L}'(t)$ can also be obtained from relation (3.97) with the help of the obvious identity

$$\mathbf{u}'^{-1}(t,t)[\mathbf{L}(t), \mathbf{u}'(t,t)] = \frac{\sigma^2(s,t)\mathbf{u}'_s(t,t)}{\mathbf{u}'(t,t)}\frac{\partial}{\partial s} + \frac{\frac{1}{2}\sigma^2(s,t)\mathbf{u}'_{ss}(t,t) + \mathbf{u}'_s(t,t)\mu(s,t)}{\mathbf{u}'(t,t)}$$

that directly follows from the chain of equalities (4.3).

It is clear from relation (4.4) that the generator $\mathbf{L}'(t)$ also is of the form (4.1), that is

$$\mathbf{L}'(t) = \frac{1}{2}\sigma^2(s,t)\frac{\partial^2}{\partial s^2} + \mu'(s,t)\frac{\partial}{\partial s} + \rho'(s,t), \quad (4.5)$$

where

$$\mu'(s,t) = \mu(s,t) + \sigma^2(s,t)\frac{\mathbf{u}'_s(t,t)}{\mathbf{u}'(t,t)}$$

and

$$\rho'(s,t) = \rho(s,t) + \frac{\mathbf{u}'_t(t,t)}{\mathbf{u}'(t,t)} + \frac{\frac{1}{2}\sigma^2(s,t)\mathbf{u}'_{ss}(t,t) + \mathbf{u}'_s(t,t)\mu(s,t)}{\mathbf{u}'(t,t)}.$$

Therefore, the behavior of the generator $\mathbf{L}(t)$ under the transformations $\hat{\mathfrak{g}}_{\mathbf{L}}$ defined in (3.73) from the beliefs-preferences gauge symmetry group $\hat{\mathfrak{G}}$ for a Markovian generalized market populace

$\mathbb{H} = \mathbb{B} \times \mathbb{U}$, or more precisely $\mathbb{H} = \mathbb{L} \times \mathbb{U}$ can be characterized solely in terms of $\mu(s,t)$ and $\rho(s,t)$ as follows

$$\mu(s,t) \to \mu(s,t) + \sigma^2(s,t)\frac{\mathbf{u}'_s(t,t)}{\mathbf{u}'(t,t)} \tag{4.6}$$

and

$$\rho(s,t) \to \rho(s,t) + \frac{\mathbf{u}'_t(t,t)}{\mathbf{u}'(t,t)} + \frac{\frac{1}{2}\sigma^2(s,t)\mathbf{u}'_{ss}(t,t) + \mathbf{u}'_s(t,t)\mu(s,t)}{\mathbf{u}'(t,t)}. \tag{4.7}$$

4.3. Remark. It is clear that the set of all transformations of $\big(\mu(s,t), \rho(s,t)\big)$ defined in (4.6) and (4.7) is a group with the group operation of composition isomorphic to the beliefs-preferences gauge symmetry group $\hat{\mathfrak{G}}$ for the Markovian generalized market populace $\mathbb{H} = \mathbb{B} \times \mathbb{U}$, or more precisely $\mathbb{H} = \mathbb{L} \times \mathbb{U}$ under consideration.

4.4. Remark. It is clear that the set of all transformations of $\mu(s,t)$ defined in (4.6) is a group with the group operation of composition which is a representation of the beliefs-preferences gauge symmetry group $\hat{\mathfrak{G}}$ for the Markovian generalized market populace $\mathbb{H} = \mathbb{B} \times \mathbb{U}$, or more precisely $\mathbb{H} = \mathbb{L} \times \mathbb{U}$ under consideration.

4.5. Remark. The representation of the transformations in (3.73) from the beliefs-preferences gauge symmetry group $\hat{\mathfrak{G}}$ for the generators $\mathsf{L}(t)$ of the form (4.1) as the transformations in (4.6) and (4.7) of $\mu(s,t)$ and $\rho(s,t)$ is analogous to the representation of the transformations in (3.84) of the Hamiltonian $\boldsymbol{H}(t)$ of the form (3.81) as the transformations in (3.82) from the gauge symmetry group $\boldsymbol{U}(1)$ of the vector potential $A(x,t)$ and the scalar potential $U(x,t)$.

4.6. Remark. In the terminology of this article, the behavior of the generator $\mathsf{L}(t)$ of the form (4.1) under the transformations in (3.73) from the beliefs-preferences gauge symmetry group $\hat{\mathfrak{G}}$

was established by the author in [34] in the case of the Markovian generalized market populace $\mathbb{H} = \mathbb{B} \times \mathbb{U}$, or more precisely $\mathbb{H} = \mathbb{L} \times \mathbb{U}$ with the local generalized market populace preference $\mathbb{U}$. In particular, relation (4.5), or equivalently the transformations in (4.6) and (4.7) were used in [34] to study solutions of the Cauchy problem for the Black and Scholes equation (5.50) in the financially natural weighted Sobolev spaces and weighted spaces of continuously differentiable functions. This was achieved by means of introduction of the Gauge spaces which, roughly speaking, are obtained in the same manner as the standard Sobolev spaces and the spaces of continuously differentiable functions with the derivatives replaced by the covariant derivatives. Finally, we note that it is the realization of the fact that the transformations of $\mu(s,t)$ in (4.6) form a group which is a representation of the beliefs-preferences gauge symmetry group $\hat{\mathfrak{G}}$ that was one of the main observations that led to this article.

Now our goal is to obtain the explicit form of the transformations $\hat{\mathfrak{g}}_{\mathsf{L}}$ from the beliefs-preferences gauge symmetry group $\hat{\mathfrak{G}}$ in (4.2), or equivalently in the representation given by relations (4.6) and (4.7) if the following change of variables takes place: $s \longrightarrow \exp x$.

Denote by $\Pi(\mathbb{R}^n)$ the vector space of all real-valued functions on the set $\mathbb{R}^n$. Let $\Pi_+(\mathbb{R}^n)$ be the nonnegative cone of $\Pi(\mathbb{R}^n)$, that is, the set of all nonnegative real-valued functions on the set $\mathbb{R}^n$.

We note that the vector space $\Pi(\mathbb{R}^n)$ with the partial order generated by the nonnegative cone $\Pi_+(\mathbb{R}^n)$ is a partially ordered vector space. Moreover, equipped with the lattice operation of supremum and infimum defined as pointwise maximum and minimum, $\Pi(\mathbb{R}^n)$ is a vector lattice.

Define the map $\Upsilon_{s\mapsto x} : \Pi \longrightarrow \Pi(\mathbb{R}^n)$ by

$$(\Upsilon_{s\mapsto x} f)(x) = f(\mathbf{exp}\, x), \quad f \in \Pi, \tag{4.8}$$

where x is in $\mathbb{R}^n$ and

$$\mathbf{exp}\, x = (\exp x_1, \exp x_2, \ldots, \exp x_n)$$

is in $\mathbb{R}^n_{++}$.

Define also the map $\Upsilon_{x\mapsto s} : \Pi(\mathbb{R}^n) \to \Pi$ by

$$(\Upsilon_{x\mapsto s} f)(s) = f(\mathbf{log}\, s), \quad f \in \Pi(\mathbb{R}^n), \tag{4.9}$$

where s is in $\mathbb{R}^n_{++}$ and

$$\mathbf{log}\, s = (\log s_1, \log s_2, \ldots, \log s_n)$$

is in $\mathbb{R}^n$.

4.7. Remark. We note that the maps $\mathbf{exp} : \mathbb{R}^n \to \mathbb{R}^n_{++}$ and $\mathbf{log} : \mathbb{R}^n_{++} \to \mathbb{R}^n$ are one-to-one and onto and that they are inverses of each other

$$\mathbf{exp} \circ \mathbf{log} = \boldsymbol{i}_s \quad \text{and} \quad \mathbf{log} \circ \mathbf{exp} = \boldsymbol{i}_x$$

where $\boldsymbol{i}_s$ and $\boldsymbol{i}_x$ are the identity maps on $\mathbb{R}^n_{++}$ and $\mathbb{R}^n$.

4.8. Remark. It is clear that $\Upsilon_{s\mapsto x}$ and $\Upsilon_{x\mapsto s}$ are substitution operators. It is also clear that $\Upsilon_{s\mapsto x}$ and $\Upsilon_{x\mapsto s}$ perform the change of variable $s \to \mathbf{exp}\, x$ and $x \to \mathbf{log}\, s$

4.9. Remark. It is clear that the maps $\Upsilon_{s\mapsto x}$ and $\Upsilon_{x\mapsto s}$ are inverses of each other

$$\Upsilon_{x\mapsto s}\Upsilon_{s\mapsto x} = \boldsymbol{I}_s \quad \text{and} \quad \Upsilon_{s\mapsto x}\Upsilon_{x\mapsto s} = \boldsymbol{I}_x$$

where $\boldsymbol{I}_s$ and $\boldsymbol{I}_x$ are the identity operators on Π and $\Pi(\mathbb{R}^n)$.

4.10. Remark. It is also clear that the maps $\Upsilon_{s\mapsto x}$ and $\Upsilon_{x\mapsto s}$ are isomorphisms between Π and $\Pi(\mathbb{R}^n)$ as vector spaces, and in fact, as vector lattices.

Following [33], we interpret $\Upsilon_{s\mapsto x}$ and $\Upsilon_{x\mapsto s}$ as the change-of-basis operators and the spaces Π and $\Pi(\mathbb{R}^n)$ as spaces of coordinates, or simply, coordinates in the bases called the *s-basis* and the *x-basis*.

In this regard, in the case under consideration of a single underlying security, the generator $\mathbf{L}(t)$ given in the s-basis by expression (4.1) takes the following form in the x-basis

$$\begin{aligned}\mathbf{L}_*(t) =&\Upsilon_{s\mapsto x}\mathbf{L}(t)\Upsilon_{x\mapsto s} = \\ &\frac{1}{2}\sigma_*^2(x,t)\frac{\partial^2}{\partial x^2} + \mu_*(x,t)\frac{\partial}{\partial x} + \rho_*(x,t),\end{aligned} \qquad (4.10)$$

where

$$\sigma_*(x,t) = \hat{\sigma}(\exp x, t),$$

$$\mu_*(x,t) = \hat{\mu}(\exp x, t) - \frac{1}{2}\sigma_*^2(x,t),$$

and

$$\rho_*(x,t) = \rho(\exp x, t)$$

with $\hat{\sigma}(s,t)$ and $\hat{\mu}(s,t)$ such that

$$\hat{\sigma}(s,t)s = \sigma(s,t)$$

and

$$\hat{\mu}(s,t)s = \mu(s,t).$$

4.11. Remark. We comment that in the derivation of relation (4.10) we have used the following chain of equalities

$$\begin{aligned}\mathbf{L}(t) =&\frac{1}{2}\sigma^2(s,t)\frac{\partial^2}{\partial s^2} + \mu(s,t)\frac{\partial}{\partial s} + \rho(s,t) = \\ &\frac{1}{2}\hat{\sigma}^2(s,t)s^2\frac{\partial^2}{\partial s^2} + \hat{\mu}(s,t)s\frac{\partial}{\partial s} + \rho(s,t) = \\ &\frac{1}{2}\hat{\sigma}^2(s,t)\big(s\frac{\partial}{\partial s}\big)^2 + \big(\hat{\mu}(s,t) - \frac{1}{2}\hat{\sigma}^2(s,t)\big)s\frac{\partial}{\partial s} + \rho(s,t)\end{aligned}$$

and the following identity

$$\Upsilon_{s\mapsto x}\big(s\frac{\partial}{\partial s}\big)\Upsilon_{x\mapsto s} = \frac{\partial}{\partial x}. \qquad (4.11)$$

Similarly, the generator $\mathbf{L}'(t)$ given in the s-basis by relation (4.5) takes the following form in the x-basis

$$\begin{aligned}\mathbf{L}'_*(t) =& \Upsilon_{s\mapsto x}\mathbf{L}'(t)\Upsilon_{x\mapsto s} = \\ & \frac{1}{2}\sigma_*^2(x,t)\frac{\partial^2}{\partial x^2} + \mu'_*(x,t)\frac{\partial}{\partial x} + \rho'_*(x,t),\end{aligned} \tag{4.12}$$

where

$$\mu'_*(x,t) = \hat{\mu}'(\exp x, t) - \frac{1}{2}\sigma_*^2(x,t),$$

and

$$\rho'_*(x,t) = \rho'(\exp x, t)$$

with $\hat{\mu}'(s,t)$ such that

$$\hat{\mu}'(s,t)s = \mu'(s,t).$$

Finally, we present the explicit form of the transformations (4.2) from the beliefs-preferences gauge symmetry group $\hat{\mathfrak{G}}$ for the Markovian generalized market populace $\mathbb{H} = \mathbb{B} \times \mathbb{U}$, or more precisely $\mathbb{H} = \mathbb{L} \times \mathbb{U}$ under consideration solely in the x-basis

$$\begin{aligned}&\mathbf{L}'_*(t) = \Upsilon_{s\mapsto x}\mathbf{L}'(t)\Upsilon_{x\mapsto s} = \\ &\Upsilon_{s\mapsto x}\,\mathbf{u}'^{-1}(t,t)\,\mathbf{L}(t)\,\mathbf{u}'(t,t)\Upsilon_{x\mapsto s} + \Upsilon_{s\mapsto x}\frac{\mathbf{u}'_t(t,t)}{\mathbf{u}'(t,t)}\Upsilon_{x\mapsto s} = \\ &\left(\Upsilon_{s\mapsto x}\,\mathbf{u}'^{-1}(t,t)\,\Upsilon_{x\mapsto s}\right)\left(\Upsilon_{s\mapsto x}\,\mathbf{L}(t)\,\Upsilon_{x\mapsto s}\right)\left(\Upsilon_{s\mapsto x}\,\mathbf{u}'(t,t)\,\Upsilon_{x\mapsto s}\right) + \\ &\qquad\left(\Upsilon_{s\mapsto x}\,\mathbf{u}'_t(t,t)\,\Upsilon_{x\mapsto s}\right)\left(\Upsilon_{s\mapsto x}\,\mathbf{u}'^{-1}(t,t)\,\Upsilon_{x\mapsto s}\right) = \\ &\mathbf{u}'^{-1}_*(t,t)\,\mathbf{L}_*(t)\,\mathbf{u}'_*(t,t) + \frac{\mathbf{u}'_{*t}(t,t)}{\mathbf{u}'_*(t,t)},\end{aligned} \tag{4.13}$$

where

$$\mathbf{u}'_*(t,t) = \Upsilon_{s\mapsto x}\,\mathbf{u}'(t,t)\,\Upsilon_{x\mapsto s},$$

and where we have made use of the following chain of equalities

$$\begin{aligned}\left(\Upsilon_{s\mapsto x}\,\mathbf{u}'(t,t)\,\Upsilon_{x\mapsto s}\right)^{-1} =& \Upsilon^{-1}_{x\mapsto s}\,\mathbf{u}'^{-1}(t,t)\,\Upsilon^{-1}_{s\mapsto x} = \\ & \Upsilon_{s\mapsto x}\,\mathbf{u}'^{-1}(t,t)\,\Upsilon_{x\mapsto s}.\end{aligned}$$

4.12. Remark. In this way, the transformations from the beliefs-preferences gauge symmetry group $\hat{\mathfrak{G}}$ in the case under consideration can be trivially reformulated in the case when $\mathsf{L}(t)$ is a general second order linear differential operator on $\Pi(\mathbb{R})$.

4.13. Remark. We comment that, as should be expected, for the transformations (4.2) from the beliefs-preferences gauge symmetry group $\hat{\mathfrak{G}}$ in the x-basis, $\mathbf{u'}_*(t,t)$, or more precisely $\mathbf{u'}_*(\overset{3}{t},\overset{1}{t})$ is the operator on $\Pi(\mathbb{R})$ of multiplication by the function

$$\mathrm{u'}_*(t,t,\overset{3}{x}_t,\overset{1}{x}_t) = \big(\Upsilon_{s\mapsto x}\,\mathrm{u'}(t,t,\cdot,\cdot)\big)(\overset{3}{x}_t,\overset{1}{x}_t) = \mathrm{u'}(t,t,\exp\overset{3}{x}_t,\exp\overset{1}{x}_t),$$

where the operator $\mathsf{L}_*(t)$, or more precisely $\mathsf{L}_*(\overset{2}{t})$ on $\Pi(\mathbb{R})$ acts second.

4.14. Remark. We comment that the preceding transformations in (4.13) from the beliefs-preferences gauge symmetry group $\hat{\mathfrak{G}}$ in the x-basis remain true in the general case of a Markovian generalized market populace $\mathbb{H} = \mathbb{B} \times \mathbb{U}$, or more precisely $\mathbb{H} = \mathbb{L} \times \mathbb{U}$.

4.2 The Case of a Multiple Underlying Security

Now we consider the beliefs-preferences gauge symmetry group $\hat{\mathfrak{G}}$ for a Markovian generalized market populace $\mathbb{H} = \mathbb{B} \times \mathbb{U}$, or more precisely $\mathbb{H} = \mathbb{L} \times \mathbb{U}$ in the general case of n underlying securities and when each generalized belief $\mathfrak{B}$ in the market populace belief $\mathbb{B}$ is generated by the family

$$\mathsf{L} = \{\mathsf{L}(t) : \Pi \to \Pi \,|\, t \in \mathcal{T}\},$$

in $\mathbb{L}$ with each generator $\mathsf{L}(t)$ at time t of the form

$$\mathsf{L}(t) = \frac{1}{2}\sum_{i,j=1}^{n} \sigma_{ij}^2(s,t)\frac{\partial^2}{\partial s_i \partial s_j} + \sum_{i=1}^{n} \mu_i(s,t)\frac{\partial}{\partial s_i} + \rho(s,t), \tag{4.14}$$

where $\sigma^2_{ij}(s,t)$ is the (i,j) entry of an $n \times n$ real matrix $\sigma^2(s,t)$ which is assumed to be symmetric and positively defined, and where $\sigma^2_{ij}(s,t)$, $\mu_i(s,t)$ and $\rho(s,t)$ are admissible real-valued functions on the set $\mathbb{R}^n_{++} \times \mathcal{T}$.

4.15. Remark. We comment that, for the sake of simplicity, in relation (4.14) we used the same notations for the operators of multiplication by functions $\sigma^2_{ij}(s,t)$, $\mu_i(s,t)$ and $\rho(s,t)$ and for the functions $\sigma^2_{ij}(s,t)$, $\mu_i(s,t)$ and $\rho(s,t)$ themselves. Whenever we would like to distinguish the operators of multiplication by the functions $\sigma^2_{ij}(s,t)$, $\mu_i(s,t)$ and $\rho(s,t)$ from the functions $\sigma^2_{ij}(s,t)$, $\mu_i(s,t)$ and $\rho(s,t)$ themselves we will denote these operators by $\boldsymbol{\sigma}^2_{ij}(s,t)$, $\boldsymbol{\mu}_i(s,t)$ and $\boldsymbol{\rho}(s,t)$.

Later in the article we will need the following well-known technical result that we state here for convenience of reference.

4.16. Theorem. Let a be an $n \times n$ real symmetric positively defined matrix. Then there exists a $n \times n$ real symmetric positively defined matrix b such that $b^2 = a$.

Proof. Let o be the $n \times n$ orthogonal matrix such that $a' = o^*\, a\, o$ is a diagonal matrix, where o^* is the matrix transposed to o. It is clear, that since a is symmetric, such an orthogonal matrix o exists. It is also clear that $o\, a'\, o^* = a$.

Since matrix a is positively defined each diagonal entry of the matrix a' is positive. Denote by b' the square root of the matrix a', that is, the diagonal matrix such that each of its diagonal elements i with $i = 1, \ldots, n$ is the square root of the diagonal element i with $i = 1, \ldots, n$ of a'. It is clear that $b'^2 = a'$. Therefore

$$
\begin{aligned}
a =& o\, a'\, o^* = \\
& o\, b'^2\, o^* = \\
& o\, b'\, o^* o\, b'\, o^* = \\
& b^2,
\end{aligned}
$$

where $b = o\,b'\,o^*$. It is clear that the $n \times n$ real matrix b is symmetric and positively defined. □

4.17. Remark. We comment that the reason for using the notation $\sigma^2(s,t)$ for the $n \times n$ real symmetric positively defined matrix with entries $\sigma^2_{ij}(s,t)$ in the expression (4.14) is as follows. By the preceding Theorem (4.16) there exists a $n \times n$ real symmetric positive matrix $\sigma(s,t)$ such that $\sigma^2(s,t) = \sigma(s,t)\,\sigma(s,t)$. That is why we can interpret $\sigma^2(s,t)$ not merely as a notation but as a statement that the matrix $\sigma^2(s,t)$ is equal to the square of the matrix $\sigma(s,t)$. Whenever ambiguity is unlikely we will adopt this interpretation from now on in this article.

Our goal is to establish the behavior of the generator $\mathsf{L}(t)$ under the transformations $\hat{\mathfrak{g}}_{\mathsf{L}}$ defined in (3.73) from the beliefs-preferences gauge symmetry group $\hat{\mathfrak{G}}$ for a Markovian generalized market populace $\mathbb{H} = \mathbb{B} \times \mathbb{U}$, or more precisely $\mathbb{H} = \mathbb{L} \times \mathbb{U}$. In other words, our goal is to find the explicit form of the operator

$$\mathsf{L}'(t) = \mathbf{u}'^{-1}(t,t)\,\mathsf{L}(t)\,\mathbf{u}'(t,t) + \frac{\mathbf{u}'_t(t,t)}{\mathbf{u}'(t,t)}, \tag{4.15}$$

where $\mathsf{L}(t)$ is defined in (4.14). In order to do this, according to Remark (3.138) we use the following chain of equalities

$$0 = \frac{\overset{2}{d}}{dt}\mathbf{u}'(\overset{3}{t},\overset{1}{t})v' + \mathsf{L}(\overset{2}{t})\mathbf{u}'(\overset{3}{t},\overset{1}{t})v' =$$

$$\frac{\overset{2}{d}}{dt}\mathbf{u}'(\overset{3}{t},\overset{1}{t})v' +$$

$$\overbrace{\Big(\frac{1}{2}\sum_{i,j=1}^{n}\sigma^2_{ij}(s,t)\frac{\partial^2}{\partial s_i \partial s_j} + \sum_{i=1}^{n}\mu_i(s,t)\frac{\partial}{\partial s_i} + \rho(s,t)\Big)}^{2}\mathbf{u}'(\overset{3}{t},\overset{1}{t})v' = \tag{4.16}$$

$$\mathbf{u}'(t,t)\frac{d}{dt}v' + \mathbf{u}'_t(t,t)v' +$$
$$\mathbf{u}'(t,t)\Big(\frac{1}{2}\sum_{i,j=1}^{n}\sigma^2_{ij}(s,t)\frac{\partial^2}{\partial s_i \partial s_j} + \sum_{i=1}^{n}\mu_i(s,t)\frac{\partial}{\partial s_i} + \rho(s,t)\Big)v' +$$
$$\Big(\frac{1}{2}\sum_{i,j=1}^{n}\sigma^2_{ij}(s,t)\mathbf{u}'_{s_i s_j}(t,t) +$$
$$\frac{1}{2}\sum_{i=1}^{n}\Big(\sum_{j=1}^{n}\sigma^2_{ij}(s,t)\mathbf{u}'_{s_j}(t,t)\Big)\frac{\partial}{\partial s_i} +$$
$$\frac{1}{2}\sum_{j=1}^{n}\Big(\sum_{i=1}^{n}\sigma^2_{ij}(s,t)\mathbf{u}'_{s_i}(t,t)\Big)\frac{\partial}{\partial s_j} +$$
$$\sum_{i=1}^{n}\mathbf{u}'_{s_i}(t,t)\mu_i(s,t)\Big)v' =$$
$$\mathbf{u}'(t,t)\left(\frac{d}{dt}v' + \frac{\mathbf{u}'_t(t,t)}{\mathbf{u}'(t,t)}v' +\right.$$
$$\Big(\frac{1}{2}\sum_{i,j=1}^{n}\sigma^2_{ij}(s,t)\frac{\partial^2}{\partial s_i \partial s_j} + \sum_{i=1}^{n}\mu_i(s,t)\frac{\partial}{\partial s_i} + \rho(s,t)\Big)v' +$$
$$\Big(\sum_{i=1}^{n}\frac{\sum_{j=1}^{n}\sigma^2_{ij}(s,t)\mathbf{u}'_{s_j}(t,t)}{\mathbf{u}'(t,t)}\frac{\partial}{\partial s_i} +$$
$$\left.\frac{\frac{1}{2}\sum_{i,j=1}^{n}\sigma^2_{ij}(s,t)\mathbf{u}'_{s_i s_j}(t,t) + \sum_{i=1}^{n}\mathbf{u}'_{s_i}(t,t)\mu_i(s,t)}{\mathbf{u}'(t,t)}\Big)v'\right),$$

where in the last equality we have used the symmetricity of the matrix $\sigma^2(s,t)$, and where $\mathbf{u}'_{s_i}(t,t)$ and $\mathbf{u}'_{s_i s_j}(t,t)$ stand for the operators of multiplications by the functions $\frac{\partial}{\partial s_i}\mathrm{u}'(t,t,s_t,s)|_{s=s_t}$ and $\frac{\partial^2}{\partial s_i \partial s_j}\mathrm{u}'(t,t,s_t,s)|_{s=s_t}$.

Therefore due to Remark (3.138) the desired generator $\mathbf{L}'(t)$

is given by

$$\mathbf{L}'(t) =$$
$$\frac{1}{2}\sum_{i,j=1}^{n}\sigma_{ij}^2(s,t)\frac{\partial^2}{\partial s_i\partial s_j}+\sum_{i=1}^{n}\mu_i(s,t)\frac{\partial}{\partial s_i}+\rho(s,t)+\frac{\mathbf{u}'_t(t,t)}{\mathbf{u}'(t,t)}+$$
$$\sum_{i=1}^{n}\frac{\sum_{j=1}^{n}\sigma_{ij}^2(s,t)\mathbf{u}'_{s_j}(t,t)}{\mathbf{u}'(t,t)}\frac{\partial}{\partial s_i}+ \tag{4.17}$$
$$\frac{\frac{1}{2}\sum_{i,j=1}^{n}\sigma_{ij}^2(s,t)\mathbf{u}'_{s_is_j}(t,t)+\sum_{i=1}^{n}\mathbf{u}'_{s_i}(t,t)\mu_i(s,t)}{\mathbf{u}'(t,t)}.$$

4.18. Remark. The relation (4.17) for the generator $\mathbf{L}'(t)$ can also be obtained from relation (3.97) with the help of the obvious identity

$$\mathbf{u}'^{-1}(t,t)[\mathbf{L}(t),\mathbf{u}'(t,t)] =$$
$$\sum_{i=1}^{n}\frac{\sum_{j=1}^{n}\sigma_{ij}^2(s,t)\mathbf{u}'_{s_j}(t,t)}{\mathbf{u}'(t,t)}\frac{\partial}{\partial s_i}+$$
$$\frac{\frac{1}{2}\sum_{i,j=1}^{n}\sigma_{ij}^2(s,t)\mathbf{u}'_{s_is_j}(t,t)+\sum_{i=1}^{n}\mathbf{u}'_{s_i}(t,t)\mu_i(s,t)}{\mathbf{u}'(t,t)}$$

that directly follows from the chain of equalities (4.16).

It is clear from relation (4.17) that the generator $\mathbf{L}'(t)$ also is of the form (4.14), that is

$$\mathbf{L}'(t)=\frac{1}{2}\sum_{i,j=1}^{n}\sigma_{ij}^2(s,t)\frac{\partial^2}{\partial s_i\partial s_j}+\sum_{i=1}^{n}\mu'_i(s,t)\frac{\partial}{\partial s_i}+\rho'(s,t), \tag{4.18}$$

where

$$\mu'(s,t)=\mu(s,t)+\sigma^2(s,t)\frac{\mathbf{u}'_s(t,t)}{\mathbf{u}'(t,t)}$$

and

$$\rho'(s,t)=\rho(s,t)+\frac{\mathbf{u}'_t(t,t)}{\mathbf{u}'(t,t)}+$$
$$\frac{\frac{1}{2}\sum_{i,j=1}^{n}\sigma_{ij}^2(s,t)\mathbf{u}'_{s_is_j}(t,t)+\sum_{i=1}^{n}\mathbf{u}'_{s_i}(t,t)\mu_i(s,t)}{\mathbf{u}'(t,t)},$$

with

$$\mu(s,t) = (\mu_1(s,t), \mu_2(s,t), \ldots, \mu_n(s,t)),$$

$$\mu'(s,t) = (\mu_1'(s,t), \mu_2'(s,t), \ldots, \mu_n'(s,t))$$

and

$$\mathbf{u}'_{\boldsymbol{s}}(t,t) = (\mathbf{u}'_{\boldsymbol{s}_1}(t,t), \mathbf{u}'_{\boldsymbol{s}_2}(t,t), \ldots, \mathbf{u}'_{\boldsymbol{s}_n}(t,t)).$$

Therefore, the behavior of the generator $\mathsf{L}(t)$ under the transformations $\hat{\mathfrak{g}}_{\mathsf{L}}$ defined in (3.73) from the beliefs-preferences gauge symmetry group $\hat{\mathfrak{G}}$ for a Markovian generalized market populace $\mathbb{H} = \mathbb{B} \times \mathbb{U}$, or more precisely $\mathbb{H} = \mathbb{L} \times \mathbb{U}$ can be characterized solely in terms of $\mu(s,t)$ and $\rho(s,t)$ as follows

$$\mu(s,t) \to \mu(s,t) + \sigma^2(s,t)\frac{\mathbf{u}'_{\boldsymbol{s}}(t,t)}{\mathbf{u}'(t,t)} \tag{4.19}$$

and

$$\rho(s,t) \to \rho(s,t) + \frac{\mathbf{u}'_{\boldsymbol{t}}(t,t)}{\mathbf{u}'(t,t)} + \frac{\frac{1}{2}\sum_{i,j=1}^{n}\sigma_{ij}^2(s,t)\mathbf{u}'_{\boldsymbol{s}_i\boldsymbol{s}_j}(t,t) + \sum_{i=1}^{n}\mathbf{u}'_{\boldsymbol{s}_i}(t,t)\mu_i(s,t)}{\mathbf{u}'(t,t)}. \tag{4.20}$$

4.19. Remark. It is clear that the set of all transformations of $\big(\mu(s,t), \rho(s,t)\big)$ defined in (4.19) and (4.20) is a group with the group operation of composition isomorphic to the beliefs-preferences gauge symmetry group $\hat{\mathfrak{G}}$ for the Markovian generalized market populace $\mathbb{H} = \mathbb{B} \times \mathbb{U}$, or more precisely $\mathbb{H} = \mathbb{L} \times \mathbb{U}$ under consideration.

4.20. Remark. It is clear that the set of all transformations of $\mu(s,t)$ defined in (4.19) is a group with the group operation of composition which is a representation of the beliefs-preferences gauge symmetry group $\hat{\mathfrak{G}}$ for the Markovian generalized market populace $\mathbb{H} = \mathbb{B} \times \mathbb{U}$, or more precisely $\mathbb{H} = \mathbb{L} \times \mathbb{U}$ under consideration.

4.21. Remark. The representation of the transformations in (3.73) from the beliefs-preferences gauge symmetry group $\hat{\mathfrak{G}}$ for the generators $\mathsf{L}(t)$ of the form (4.14) as the transformations in (4.19) and (4.20) of $\mu(s,t)$ and $\rho(s,t)$ is analogous to the representation of the transformations in (3.84) of the Hamiltonian $\boldsymbol{H}(t)$ of the form (3.81) as the transformations in (3.82) from the gauge symmetry group $\boldsymbol{U}(1)$ of the vector potential $A(x,t)$ and the scalar potential $U(x,t)$.

4.22. Remark. In the terminology of this article, the behavior of the generator $\mathsf{L}(t)$ of the form (4.14) under the transformations in (3.73) from the beliefs-preferences gauge symmetry group $\hat{\mathfrak{G}}$ was established by the author in [34] in the case of the Markovian generalized market populace $\mathbb{H} = \mathbb{B} \times \mathbb{U}$, or more precisely $\mathbb{H} = \mathbb{L} \times \mathbb{U}$ with the local market populace preference $\mathbb{U}$. In particular, relation (4.18), or equivalently the transformations in (4.19) and (4.20) were used in [34] to study solutions of the Cauchy problem for the Black and Scholes equation (5.100) in the financially natural weighted Sobolev spaces and weighted spaces of continuously differentiable functions. This was achieved by means of introduction of the Gauge spaces which, roughly speaking, are obtained in the same manner as the standard Sobolev spaces and the spaces of continuously differentiable functions with the derivatives replaced by the covariant derivatives. Finally, we note that it is the realization of the fact that the transformations of $\mu(s,t)$ in (4.19) form a group which is a representation of the beliefs-preferences gauge symmetry group $\hat{\mathfrak{G}}$ that was one of the main observations that led to this article.

Now our goal is to obtain the explicit form in the x-basis of the transformations $\hat{\mathfrak{g}}_{\mathsf{L}}$ from the beliefs-preferences gauge symmetry group $\hat{\mathfrak{G}}$ in (4.15), or equivalently in the representation given by relations (4.19) and (4.20).

The generator $\mathsf{L}(t)$ given in the s-basis by relation (4.14) takes the following form in the x-basis

$$\mathbf{L}(t) = \Upsilon_{s\mapsto x}\mathbf{L}(t)\Upsilon_{x\mapsto s} =$$

$$\frac{1}{2}\sum_{i,j=1}^{n}\sigma_{*ij}^2(x,t)\frac{\partial^2}{\partial x_i \partial x_j} + \sum_{i=1}^{n}\mu_{*i}(x,t)\frac{\partial}{\partial x_i} + \rho_*(x,t), \tag{4.21}$$

where

$$\sigma_{*ij}^2(x,t) = \hat{\sigma}_{ij}^2(\mathbf{exp}\, x, t),$$

$$\mu_{*i}(x,t) = \hat{\mu}_i(\mathbf{exp}\, x, t) - \frac{1}{2}\sigma_{*ii}^2(x,t),$$

and

$$\rho_*(x,t) = \rho(\mathbf{exp}\, x, t)$$

with $\hat{\sigma}_{ij}^2(s,t)$ and $\hat{\mu}_i(s,t)$ defined by

$$\hat{\sigma}_{ij}^2(s,t)s_i s_j = \sigma_{ij}^2(s,t) \tag{4.22}$$

and

$$\hat{\mu}_i(s,t)s_i = \mu_i(s,t). \tag{4.23}$$

4.23. Remark. We comment that in the derivation of relation (4.21) we have used the following chain of equalities

$$\mathbf{L}(t) = \frac{1}{2}\sum_{i,j=1}^{n}\sigma_{ij}^2(s,t)\frac{\partial^2}{\partial s_i \partial s_j} + \sum_{i=1}^{n}\mu_i(s,t)\frac{\partial}{\partial s_i} + \rho(s,t) =$$

$$\frac{1}{2}\sum_{i,j=1}^{n}\hat{\sigma}_{ij}^2(s,t)s_i s_j\frac{\partial^2}{\partial s_i \partial s_j} + \sum_{i=1}^{n}\hat{\mu}_i(s,t)s_i\frac{\partial}{\partial s_i} + \rho(s,t) =$$

$$\frac{1}{2}\sum_{i,j=1}^{n}\hat{\sigma}_{ij}^2(s,t)\big(s_i\frac{\partial}{\partial s_i}\big)\big(s_j\frac{\partial}{\partial s_j}\big) +$$

$$\sum_{i=1}^{n}\big(\hat{\mu}_i(s,t) - \frac{1}{2}\hat{\sigma}_{ii}^2(s,t)\big)s_i\frac{\partial}{\partial s_i} + \rho(s,t)$$

and the following identity

$$\Upsilon_{s\mapsto x}\big(s_i\frac{\partial}{\partial s_i}\big)\Upsilon_{x\mapsto s} = \frac{\partial}{\partial x_i}. \tag{4.24}$$

4.24. Remark. We comment that the reason for using the notation $\hat{\sigma}^2(s,t)$ for the $n \times n$ real symmetric positive matrix with entries $\hat{\sigma}^2_{ij}(s,t)$ in the expression (4.22) is as follows. By the Theorem (4.16) there exists a $n \times n$ real symmetric positive matrix $\hat{\sigma}(s,t)$ such that $\hat{\sigma}^2(s,t) = \hat{\sigma}(s,t)\,\hat{\sigma}(s,t)$. That is why we can interpret $\hat{\sigma}^2(s,t)$ not only as a notation but as a statement that the matrix $\hat{\sigma}^2(s,t)$ is equal to the square of the matrix $\hat{\sigma}(s,t)$. Whenever ambiguity is unlikely we will adopt this interpretation from now on in this article.

4.25. Remark. We note that expressions (4.22) and (4.23) can be rewritten as follows

$$s\,\hat{\sigma}^2(s,t)\,s = \sigma^2(s,t), \tag{4.25}$$

and

$$s\,\hat{\mu}(s,t) = \mu(s,t), \tag{4.26}$$

where the set $\mathbb{R}^n_{++}$ with members s is realized as the set of all $n \times n$ diagonal matrixes with positive entries, and where

$$\hat{\mu}(s,t) = (\hat{\mu}_1(s,t), \hat{\mu}_2(s,t), \cdots, \hat{\mu}_n(s,t)).$$

Similarly, the generator $\mathbf{L}'(t)$ given in the s-basis by relation (4.18) takes the following form in the x-basis

$$\mathbf{L}'_*(t) = \Upsilon_{s\mapsto x}\mathbf{L}'(t)\Upsilon_{x\mapsto s} =$$
$$\frac{1}{2}\sum_{i,j=1}^{n}\sigma^2_{*ij}(x,t)\frac{\partial^2}{\partial x_i \partial x_j} + \sum_{i=1}^{n}\mu'_{*i}(x,t)\frac{\partial}{\partial x} + \rho'_*(x,t), \tag{4.27}$$

where

$$\mu'_{*i}(x,t) = \hat{\mu}'_i(\mathbf{exp}\,x,t) - \frac{1}{2}\sigma^2_{*ii}(x,t),$$

and

$$\rho'_*(x,t) = \rho'(\mathbf{exp}\,x,t)$$

with $\hat{\mu}'_i(s,t)$ defined by

$$\hat{\mu}'_i(s,t)s_i = \mu'_i(s,t).$$

4.26. Remark. We note that

$$s\,\hat{\mu}'(s,t) = \mu'(s,t), \tag{4.28}$$

where the set $\mathbb{R}^n_{++}$ with members s is realized as the set of all $n \times n$ diagonal matrixes with positive entries, and where

$$\hat{\mu}'(s,t) = (\hat{\mu}'_1(s,t), \hat{\mu}'_2(s,t), \cdots, \hat{\mu}'_n(s,t)).$$

Finally, we present the explicit form of the transformations (4.15) from the beliefs-preferences gauge symmetry group $\hat{\mathfrak{G}}$ for the Markovian generalized market populace $\mathbb{H} = \mathbb{B} \times \mathbb{U}$, or more precisely $\mathbb{H} = \mathbb{L} \times \mathbb{U}$ under consideration solely in the x-basis

$$\begin{aligned}
&\mathsf{L}'_*(t) = \Upsilon_{s\mapsto x}\mathsf{L}'(t)\Upsilon_{x\mapsto s} = \\
&\quad \Upsilon_{s\mapsto x}\,\mathbf{u}'^{-1}(t,t)\,\mathsf{L}(t)\,\mathbf{u}'(t,t)\Upsilon_{x\mapsto s} + \Upsilon_{s\mapsto x}\frac{\mathbf{u}'_t(t,t)}{\mathbf{u}'(t,t)}\Upsilon_{x\mapsto s} = \\
&\quad \left(\Upsilon_{s\mapsto x}\,\mathbf{u}'^{-1}(t,t)\,\Upsilon_{x\mapsto s}\right)\left(\Upsilon_{s\mapsto x}\,\mathsf{L}(t)\,\Upsilon_{x\mapsto s}\right)\left(\Upsilon_{s\mapsto x}\,\mathbf{u}'(t,t)\,\Upsilon_{x\mapsto s}\right) + \\
&\qquad \left(\Upsilon_{s\mapsto x}\,\mathbf{u}'_t(t,t)\,\Upsilon_{x\mapsto s}\right)\left(\Upsilon_{s\mapsto x}\,\mathbf{u}'^{-1}(t,t)\,\Upsilon_{x\mapsto s}\right) = \\
&\quad \mathbf{u}'^{-1}_*(t,t)\,\mathsf{L}_*(t)\,\mathbf{u}'_*(t,t) + \frac{\mathbf{u}'_{*t}(t,t)}{\mathbf{u}'_*(t,t)},
\end{aligned} \tag{4.29}$$

where

$$\mathbf{u}'_*(t,t) = \Upsilon_{s\mapsto x}\,\mathbf{u}'(t,t)\,\Upsilon_{x\mapsto s},$$

and where we have made use of the following chain of equalities

$$\begin{aligned}
\left(\Upsilon_{s\mapsto x}\,\mathbf{u}'(t,t)\,\Upsilon_{x\mapsto s}\right)^{-1} &= \Upsilon^{-1}_{x\mapsto s}\,\mathbf{u}'^{-1}(t,t)\,\Upsilon^{-1}_{s\mapsto x} = \\
&\Upsilon_{s\mapsto x}\,\mathbf{u}'^{-1}(t,t)\,\Upsilon_{x\mapsto s}.
\end{aligned}$$

4.27. Remark. In this way, the transformations from the beliefs-preferences gauge symmetry group $\hat{\mathfrak{G}}$ in the case under consideration can be trivially reformulated in the case when $\mathsf{L}(t)$ is a general second order linear partial differential operator on $\Pi(\mathbb{R}^n)$.

4.28. Remark. We comment that, as should be expected, for the transformations (4.15) from the beliefs-preferences gauge symmetry group $\hat{\mathfrak{G}}$ in the x-basis, $\mathbf{u'}_*(t,t)$, or more precisely $\mathbf{u'}_*(\overset{3}{t},\overset{1}{t})$ is the operator on $\Pi(\mathbb{R}^n)$ of multiplication by the function

$$\mathrm{u'}_*(t,t,\overset{3}{x}_t,\overset{1}{x}_t) = \left(\Upsilon_{s\mapsto x}\mathrm{u}'(t,t,\cdot,\cdot)\right)(\overset{3}{x}_t,\overset{1}{x}_t) = \mathrm{u}'(t,t,\mathbf{exp}\,\overset{3}{x}_t,\mathbf{exp}\,\overset{1}{x}_t),$$

where the operator $\mathsf{L}_*(t)$, or more precisely $\mathsf{L}_*(\overset{2}{t})$ on $\Pi(\mathbb{R}^n)$ acts second.

4.29. Remark. We comment that the preceding transformations in (4.29) from the beliefs-preferences gauge symmetry group $\hat{\mathfrak{G}}$ in the x-basis remain true in the general case of a Markovian generalized market populace $\mathbb{H} = \mathbb{B} \times \mathbb{U}$, or more precisely $\mathbb{H} = \mathbb{L} \times \mathbb{U}$.

5 Beliefs-Preferences Gauge Symmetry Group for a Markovian Market Populace with the Beliefs Determined by Diffusion Processes

We illustrate the beliefs-preferences gauge symmetry group $\hat{\mathcal{G}}$ for a Markovian market populace $\mathbb{H} = \mathbb{B} \times \mathbb{U}$, or more precisely $\mathbb{H} = \mathbb{L} \times \mathbb{U}$ which was defined in Section (3) in relation (3.98) in the particular case when each belief $\boldsymbol{\mathcal{B}}$ in the market populace belief $\mathbb{B}$ is determined by a diffusion process.

5.1 The Case of a Single Underlying Security

First we consider the beliefs-preferences gauge symmetry group $\hat{\mathcal{G}}$ for the Markovian market populace $\mathbb{H} = \mathbb{B} \times \mathbb{U}$, or more precisely $\mathbb{H} = \mathbb{L} \times \mathbb{U}$ in the particular case of a single underlying security and when each belief $\boldsymbol{\mathcal{B}}$ in the market populace belief $\mathbb{B}$ is generated by the family

$$\mathfrak{L} = \{\mathfrak{L}(t) : \Pi \rightarrow \Pi \,|\, t \in \mathcal{T}\},$$

in $\mathbb{L}$ with each generator $\mathfrak{L}(t)$ at time t of the form

$$\mathfrak{L}(t) = \frac{1}{2}\sigma^2(s,t)\frac{\partial^2}{\partial s^2} + \mu(s,t)\frac{\partial}{\partial s}, \tag{5.1}$$

where $\sigma(s,t) > 0$ and $\mu(s,t)$ are admissible real-valued functions on $\mathbb{R}_{++} \times \mathcal{T}$.

5.1. Remark. We comment that for the sake of simplicity we used in the preceding expression (5.1) the same notations for the operators of multiplication by functions $\sigma(s,t)$ and $\mu(s,t)$ and for the functions $\sigma(s,t)$ and $\mu(s,t)$ themselves. Whenever we would like to distinguish the operators of multiplication by the functions $\sigma(s,t)$ and $\mu(s,t)$ from the functions $\sigma(s,t)$ and $\mu(s,t)$ themselves we will denote these operators by $\boldsymbol{\sigma}(s,t)$ and $\boldsymbol{\mu}(s,t)$.

5.2. Remark. We comment that financially $\sigma^2(s,t)$ and $\mu(s,t)$ are the variance per unit time and drift per unit time of the diffusion process for the price of the underlying security.

Our goal is to establish the behavior of the generator $\mathfrak{L}(t)$ of the form (5.1) under the transformations $\hat{\mathfrak{g}}$ defined in (3.99) in the form (3.107) from the beliefs-preferences gauge symmetry group $\hat{\mathfrak{G}}$ for the Markovian market populace $\mathbb{H} = \mathbb{B} \times \mathbb{U}$, or more precisely $\mathbb{H} = \mathbb{L} \times \mathbb{U}$. In other words, our goal is to find the explicit form of the operator

$$\mathfrak{L}'(t) = \hat{\mathbf{u}}'^{-1}(t,t)\,\mathfrak{L}(t)\,\hat{\mathbf{u}}'(t,t) + \frac{\hat{\mathbf{u}}'_t(t,t)}{\hat{\mathbf{u}}'(t,t)}, \tag{5.2}$$

where $\mathfrak{L}(t)$ is defined in (5.1). In order to do this, according to Remark (3.157) we use the following chain of equalities

$$\begin{aligned}
0 = {} & \overset{2}{\frac{d}{dt}}\hat{\mathbf{u}}'(\overset{3}{t},\overset{1}{t})v' + \mathfrak{L}(\overset{2}{t})\hat{\mathbf{u}}'(\overset{3}{t},\overset{1}{t})v' = \\
& \overset{2}{\frac{d}{dt}}\hat{\mathbf{u}}'(\overset{3}{t},\overset{1}{t})v' + \overbrace{\Big(\frac{1}{2}\sigma^2(s,t)\frac{\partial^2}{\partial s^2} + \mu(s,t)\frac{\partial}{\partial s}\Big)}^{2}\hat{\mathbf{u}}'(\overset{3}{t},\overset{1}{t})v' = \\
& \hat{\mathbf{u}}'(t,t)\frac{d}{dt}v' + \hat{\mathbf{u}}'_t(t,t)v' + \\
& \hat{\mathbf{u}}'(t,t)\Big(\frac{1}{2}\sigma^2(s,t)\frac{\partial^2}{\partial s^2} + \mu(s,t)\frac{\partial}{\partial s}\Big)v' + \\
& \Big(\frac{1}{2}\sigma^2(s,t)\hat{\mathbf{u}}'_{ss}(t,t) + \sigma^2(s,t)\hat{\mathbf{u}}'_s(t,t)\frac{\partial}{\partial s} + \hat{\mathbf{u}}'_s(t,t)\mu(s,t)\Big)v' = \\
& \hat{\mathbf{u}}'(t,t)\bigg(\frac{d}{dt}v' + \Big(\frac{1}{2}\sigma^2(s,t)\frac{\partial^2}{\partial s^2} + \mu(s,t)\frac{\partial}{\partial s}\Big)v' + \frac{\hat{\mathbf{u}}'_t(t,t)}{\hat{\mathbf{u}}'(t,t)}v' + \\
& \Big(\frac{\sigma^2(s,t)\hat{\mathbf{u}}'_s(t,t)}{\hat{\mathbf{u}}'(t,t)}\frac{\partial}{\partial s} + \frac{\frac{1}{2}\sigma^2(s,t)\hat{\mathbf{u}}'_{ss}(t,t) + \hat{\mathbf{u}}'_s(t,t)\mu(s,t)}{\hat{\mathbf{u}}'(t,t)}\Big)v'\bigg),
\end{aligned} \tag{5.3}$$

where $\hat{\mathbf{u}}'_s(t,t)$ and $\hat{\mathbf{u}}'_{ss}(t,t)$ stand for the operators of multiplication by the functions $\frac{\partial}{\partial s}\hat{\mathrm{u}}'(t,t,s_t,s)|_{s=s_t}$ and $\frac{\partial^2}{\partial s^2}\hat{\mathrm{u}}'(t,t,s_t,s)|_{s=s_t}$.

Therefore, due to Remark (3.157) the desired generator $\mathfrak{L}'(t)$ is given by

$$\mathfrak{L}'(t) = \frac{1}{2}\sigma^2(s,t)\frac{\partial^2}{\partial s^2} + \mu(s,t)\frac{\partial}{\partial s} + \frac{\hat{\mathbf{u}}'_t(t,t)}{\hat{\mathbf{u}}'(t,t)} + \frac{\sigma^2(s,t)\hat{\mathbf{u}}'_s(t,t)}{\hat{\mathbf{u}}'(t,t)}\frac{\partial}{\partial s} + \frac{\frac{1}{2}\sigma^2(s,t)\hat{\mathbf{u}}'_{ss}(t,t) + \hat{\mathbf{u}}'_s(t,t)\mu(s,t)}{\hat{\mathbf{u}}'(t,t)}. \tag{5.4}$$

5.3. Remark. The relation (5.4) for the generator $\mathfrak{L}'(t)$ can also be obtained from relation (3.119) with the help of the obvious identity

$$\hat{\mathbf{u}}'^{-1}(t,t)[\mathfrak{L}(t), \hat{\mathbf{u}}'(t,t)] = \frac{\sigma^2(s,t)\hat{\mathbf{u}}'_s(t,t)}{\hat{\mathbf{u}}'(t,t)}\frac{\partial}{\partial s} + \frac{\frac{1}{2}\sigma^2(s,t)\hat{\mathbf{u}}'_{ss}(t,t) + \hat{\mathbf{u}}'_s(t,t)\mu(s,t)}{\hat{\mathbf{u}}'(t,t)} \tag{5.5}$$

that directly follows from the chain of equalities (4.3).

Due to expression (3.100) we have the following expression for $\mathfrak{d}(t)$ in the case under consideration

$$\mathfrak{d}(t) = \frac{\mathbf{u}'_t(t,t)}{\mathbf{u}'(t,t)} + \frac{\frac{1}{2}\sigma^2(s,t)\mathbf{u}'_{ss}(t,t) + \mathbf{u}'_s(t,t)\mu(s,t)}{\mathbf{u}'(t,t)}. \tag{5.6}$$

5.4. Remark. We comment that in the preceding relation (5.6) we have taken into account the fact that, due to the definition of $\hat{\mathbf{u}}'(t,T)$ in expression (3.105) and due to the definitions of $\hat{\mathbf{u}}'_s(t,t)$ and $\hat{\mathbf{u}}'_{ss}(t,t)$ as the operators on Π of multiplication by the functions $\frac{\partial}{\partial s}\hat{\mathrm{u}}'(t,t,s_t,s)|_{s=s_t}$ and $\frac{\partial^2}{\partial s^2}\hat{\mathrm{u}}'(t,t,s_t,s)|_{s=s_t}$, the following equalities hold:

$$\hat{\mathbf{u}}'(t,t) = \mathbf{u}'(t,t), \tag{5.7}$$

$$\hat{\mathbf{u}}'_s(t,t) = \mathbf{u}'_s(t,t), \tag{5.8}$$

and

$$\hat{\mathbf{u}}'_{ss}(t,t) = \mathbf{u}'_{ss}(t,t), \tag{5.9}$$

where $\mathbf{u}'(t,t)$, $\mathbf{u}'_s(t,t)$ and $\mathbf{u}'_{ss}(t,t)$ are the operators on Π of multiplication by the functions $\mathrm{u}'(t,t,s_t,s_t)$, $\frac{\partial}{\partial s}\mathrm{u}'(t,t,s_t,s)|_{s=s_t}$ and $\frac{\partial^2}{\partial s^2}\mathrm{u}'(t,t,s_t,s)|_{s=s_t}$.

5.5. Remark. We comment that the expression for $\mathfrak{d}(t)$ in (5.6) also directly follows from expressions (5.5) and (3.102)

It is clear from relation (5.4) that the generator $\mathfrak{L}'(t)$ also is of the form (5.1), that is

$$\mathfrak{L}'(t) = \frac{1}{2}\sigma^2(s,t)\frac{\partial^2}{\partial s^2} + \mu'(s,t)\frac{\partial}{\partial s}, \tag{5.10}$$

where

$$\mu'(s,t) = \mu(s,t) + \sigma^2(s,t)\frac{\hat{\mathbf{u}}'_s(t,t)}{\hat{\mathbf{u}}'(t,t)}. \tag{5.11}$$

Therefore, the behavior of the generator $\mathfrak{L}(t)$ of the form (5.1) under the transformations $\hat{g}$ defined in (3.99) in the form (3.107) from the beliefs-preferences gauge symmetry group $\hat{\mathcal{G}}$ for a Markovian market populace $\mathbb{H} = \mathbb{B} \times \mathbb{U}$, or more precisely $\mathbb{H} = \mathbb{L} \times \mathbb{U}$ can be characterized solely in terms of the drift $\mu(s,t)$ as follows

$$\mu(s,t) \to \mu(s,t) + \sigma^2(s,t)\frac{\hat{\mathbf{u}}'_s(t,t)}{\hat{\mathbf{u}}'(t,t)}. \tag{5.12}$$

5.6. Remark. Due to relations (5.7) and (5.8) we can rewrite relation (5.11) as follows

$$\mu'(s,t) = \mu(s,t) + \sigma^2(s,t)\frac{\mathbf{u}'_s(t,t)}{\mathbf{u}'(t,t)}. \tag{5.13}$$

In this way we can also rewrite the transformation (5.12) as follows

$$\mu(s,t) \to \mu(s,t) + \sigma^2(s,t)\frac{\mathbf{u}'_s(t,t)}{\mathbf{u}'(t,t)}. \tag{5.14}$$

5.7. Remark. It is clear that the set of all transformations of the drift $\mu(s,t)$ defined in (5.12), or equivalently (5.14) is a group with the group operation of composition isomorphic to the beliefs-preferences gauge symmetry group $\hat{\mathcal{G}}$ for the Markovian market populace $\mathbb{H} = \mathbb{B} \times \mathbb{U}$, or more precisely $\mathbb{H} = \mathbb{L} \times \mathbb{U}$ under consideration.

5.8. Remark. The representation of the transformations in (3.99) or equivalently (3.107) from the beliefs-preferences gauge symmetry group $\hat{\mathfrak{G}}$ for the generators $\mathfrak{L}(t)$ of the form (5.1) as the transformations in (5.12), or equivalently (5.14) of the drift $\mu(s,t)$ is analogous to the representation of the transformations in (3.84) of the Hamiltonian $\boldsymbol{H}(t)$ of the form (3.81) as the transformations in (3.82) from the gauge symmetry group $\boldsymbol{U}(1)$ of the vector potential $A(x,t)$ and the scalar potential $U(x,t)$.

5.9. Remark. Using the operator $\boldsymbol{\Lambda}(t,T)$ defined according to (3.16) as

$$\mathbf{u}'(t,T) = e^{\boldsymbol{\Lambda}(t,T)} \tag{5.15}$$

we can rewrite expression (5.11) with the help of (5.13) as follows

$$\mu'(s,t) = \mu(s,t) + \sigma^2 \boldsymbol{\Lambda}_s(t,t), \tag{5.16}$$

where $\boldsymbol{\Lambda}_s(t,t)$ is the operator on Π of multiplication by the function $\frac{\partial}{\partial s}\Lambda(t,t,s_t,s)|_{s=s_t}$ with the function $\Lambda(t,T,s_t,s_T)$ defined according to (3.17) as

$$\mathrm{u}'(t,T,s_t,s_T) = e^{\Lambda(t,T,s_t,s_T)}. \tag{5.17}$$

In this way we can also rewrite the transformation (5.12) with the help of (5.14) as follows

$$\mu(s,t) \to \mu(s,t) + \sigma^2(s,t)\boldsymbol{\Lambda}_s(t,t). \tag{5.18}$$

5.10. Remark. It is clear, due to Remarks (5.4) and (5.9), that

$$\hat{\mathbf{u}}'(t,t) = e^{\boldsymbol{\Lambda}(t,t)}. \tag{5.19}$$

Now we pose a somewhat inverse problem, namely to find a transformation $\hat{\boldsymbol{g}}$ from the beliefs-preferences gauge symmetry group $\hat{\boldsymbol{\mathcal{G}}}$ such that it maps a given generator

$$\mathfrak{L}(t) = \frac{1}{2}\sigma^2(s,t)\frac{\partial^2}{\partial s^2} + \mu(s,t)\frac{\partial}{\partial s}$$

to a given generator

$$\mathfrak{L}'(t) = \frac{1}{2}\sigma^2(s,t)\frac{\partial^2}{\partial s^2} + \mu'(s,t)\frac{\partial}{\partial s}.$$

Due to relation (5.11) or more precisely (5.13) such a transformation $\hat{\boldsymbol{g}}$ must be generated by $\mathbf{u}'(t,t)$ such that

$$\frac{\mathbf{u}'_s(t,t)}{\mathbf{u}'(t,t)} = \frac{\mu'(s,t) - \mu(s,t)}{\sigma^2(s,t)} = \sigma^{-1}(s,t)\,\theta(s,t) \tag{5.20}$$

where

$$\theta(s,t) = \frac{\mu'(s,t) - \mu(s,t)}{\sigma(s,t)}. \tag{5.21}$$

5.11. Remark. We comment that in light of Remark (5.1) we used the same notation in the expressions (5.20) and (5.21) for the operators $\boldsymbol{\mu}'(s,t)$, $\boldsymbol{\mu}(s,t)$, $\boldsymbol{\sigma}(s,t)$ and $\boldsymbol{\theta}(s,t)$ of multiplication by the functions $\mu'(s,t)$, $\mu(s,t)$, $\sigma(s,t)$ and $\theta(s,t)$ and for the functions $\mu'(s,t)$, $\mu(s,t)$, $\sigma(s,t)$ and $\theta(s,t)$ themselves. In this regard it is clear that expressions (5.20) and (5.21) can be interpreted as either operator relations or function relations.

5.12. Definition. We call the function $\theta(s,t)$ the *price of risk relative to* $\mu'(s,t)$ *and* $\mu(s,t)$ or simply *relative price of risk.* Similarly, we call the operator $\boldsymbol{\theta}(s,t)$ the *price of risk operator relative to* $\boldsymbol{\mu}'(s,t)$ *and* $\boldsymbol{\mu}(s,t)$ or simply *relative price of risk operator.*

The terminology introduced in the preceding Definition will be justified later in this article.

5.13. Remark. In terms of the operator $\mathbf{\Lambda}(t,T)$ defined in (5.15) we can rewrite expression (5.20) as follows

$$\mathbf{\Lambda}_s(t,t) = \frac{\boldsymbol{\mu}'(s,t) - \boldsymbol{\mu}(s,t)}{\boldsymbol{\sigma}^2(s,t)} = \boldsymbol{\sigma}^{-1}(s,t)\,\boldsymbol{\theta}(s,t). \tag{5.22}$$

The preceding expression (5.22) provides the financial interpretation for the operator $\mathbf{\Lambda}(t,T)$ of the multiplication by the function $\Lambda(t,T,s_t,s_T)$ defined in (5.17) and for the function $\Lambda(t,T,s_t,s_T)$ itself in terms of the relative price of risk operator $\boldsymbol{\theta}(s,t)$ and the relative price of risk $\theta(s,t)$.

5.14. Definition. We call the operator $\mathbf{\Lambda}(t,T)$ the *relative price of risk potential operator.* Similarly, we call the function $\Lambda(t,T,s_t,s_T)$ the *relative price of risk potential.*

The terminology introduced in the preceding Definition will also be justified later in this article.

The fact that the behavior of the generators $\mathfrak{L}(t)$ of the form (5.1) under the transformations $\hat{\boldsymbol{g}}$ defined in (3.99) in the form (3.107) from the beliefs-preferences gauge symmetry group $\hat{\mathcal{G}}$ for a Markovian market populace $\mathbb{H} = \mathbb{B} \times \mathbb{U}$, or more precisely $\mathbb{H} = \mathbb{L} \times \mathbb{U}$ can be represented as the transformations (5.12), or equivalently (5.14) of the drift $\mu(s,t)$ naturally fits our financial intuition. More precisely the transformations $\hat{\boldsymbol{g}}$ from the beliefs-preferences gauge symmetry group $\hat{\mathcal{G}}$ for the generators $\mathfrak{L}(t)$ of the form (5.1) represented as transformations (5.12), or equivalently (5.14) of the drift $\mu(s,t)$ are equivalent to the changes of measure due to the Girsanov Theorem which we present here for convenience of reference (see, for example, [16] page 229).

5.15. Fact. Girsanov Theorem. Let $(\Omega, \mathcal{F}, F, P)$ be a filtered probability space for the time set $\mathcal{T} = [0,\infty)$, where $F = \{\mathcal{F}_t : t \geq 0\}$ is the standard filtration of a Standard Brownian Motion $B = \{B_1, B_2, \ldots B_n\}$ in $\mathbb{R}^n$.

Let $\theta = (\theta_1, \theta_2 \dots \theta_n)$ be in the vector space $\mathcal{L}$ of all predictable processes satisfying

$$\int_0^t \theta_s \theta_s ds < \infty$$

almost surely for all $t \geq 0$.

Suppose that

$$E\left[\exp(\frac{1}{2}\int_0^T \theta_s \theta_s ds)\right] < \infty.$$

Then the $\mathbb{R}^n$ valued Ito process $\hat{B}$ defined by

$$\hat{B}_t = B_t - \int_0^t \theta_s ds, \quad t \in [0, T],$$

is a Standard Brownian Motion in $\mathbb{R}^n$ for the filtered probability space $(\Omega, \mathcal{F}, F, Q^\theta)$ where the probability measure Q^θ on $(\Omega, \mathcal{F})$ is defined by

$$Q^\theta(A) = E[\mathbf{1}_A \xi_T(\theta)], \quad A \in \mathcal{F},$$

meaning that Q^θ has the Radon-Nikodym derivative $dQ^\theta/dP = \xi_T(\theta)$ with

$$\xi_t(\theta) = \exp\left(\int_0^t \theta_s dB_s - \frac{1}{2}\int_0^t \theta_s \theta_s ds\right), \quad t \in [0, T].$$

5.16. Definition. We will say that the change of measure in the Girsanov Theorem is *generated* by θ.

One of the main applications of the Girsanov Theorem (see, for example, [16] page 229) is that it allows one to change the drift of a given Ito process by changing the probability measure. Let X be the $\mathbb{R}^n$ valued Ito process on $(\Omega, \mathcal{F}, F, P)$ defined by some starting point x in $\mathbb{R}^n$ and the stochastic differential equation

$$dX_t = g(X_t, t)dt + \sigma(X_t, t)dB_t \tag{5.23}$$

where the drift g and the diffusion σ have the properties ensuring that X is well defined. If one wishes to represent X as an Ito process with a new drift vector $f(x,t)$ replacing $g(x,t)$ one can do this by altering the probability measure P with the help of the Girsanov Theorem as follows (see, for example, [16] page 229).

5.17. Fact. Suppose that g, f and σ are Borel measurable and satisfy the following Lipschitz condition: for all x and y in $\mathbb{R}^n$ and t in $[0,\infty)$ there exists $k>0$ such that

$$\|f(x,t)-f(y,t)\| \le k\|x-y\|, \quad \|g(x,t)-g(y,t)\| \le k\|x-y\|$$

and

$$\|\sigma(x,t)-\sigma(y,t)\|_{n\times n} \le k\|x-y\|$$

where $\|\cdot\|$ and $\|\cdot\|_{n\times n}$ are the standard Euclidean norms in $\mathbb{R}^n$ and in the vector space of all real $n\times n$ matrixes.

Suppose also that f, g and σ satisfy the following growth condition: for all x in $\mathbb{R}^n$ and t in $[0,\infty)$ there exists $k>0$ such that

$$\|f(x,t)\| \le k(1+\|x\|), \quad \|g(x,t)\| \le k(1+\|x\|)$$

and

$$\|\sigma(x,t)\|_{n\times n} \le k(1+\|x\|).$$

Suppose also that the $n\times n$ matrix $\sigma(x,t)$ is nonsingular and that there exists $k>0$ such that $\|\sigma^{-1}(x,t)\|_{n\times n} \le k$ for all x in $\mathbb{R}^n$ and t in $[0,T]$.

Then there exists a probability Q on $(\Omega,\mathcal{F})$ equivalent to P and a Standard Brownian Motion $\hat{B}$ in $\mathbb{R}^n$ for $(\Omega,\mathcal{F},F,Q)$ such that the Ito process X defined by (5.23) also obeys the stochastic differential equation

$$dX_t = f(X_t,t)dt + \sigma(X_t,t)d\hat{B}_t. \tag{5.24}$$

Moreover, the probability measure Q is explicitly given by Q^θ from the Girsanov Theorem with

$$\theta_t = \sigma^{-1}(X_t,t)(f(X_t,t)-g(X_t,t)), \quad t\in[0,T]. \tag{5.25}$$

We observe that the transformations of drift due to the changes of measure in the Girsanov Theorem form a group, in fact an abelian group.

5.18. Theorem. Suppose that the conditions of the Fact (5.17) are satisfied. Then the set of all transformations of drift

$$g(x,t) \to f(x,t)$$

from the Fact (5.17) due to the change of measure $P \to Q$ in the Girsanov Theorem generated by θ defined in (5.25) is an abelian group isomorphic to the abelian group of all Borel measurable real-valued functions on the set $\mathbb{R}^n \times [0,\infty)$ satisfying the Lipschitz and growth conditions from the Fact (5.17) with the group operation of addition.

Proof. Without loss of generality we chose the transformations of drift from the Fact (5.17) of the form

$$g(x,t) \to g(x,t) + f(x,t).$$

It is clear that these transformations of drift are due to the change of measure $P \to Q$ in the Girsanov Theorem generated by θ defined according to expression (5.25) by

$$\begin{aligned}\theta_t =& \sigma^{-1}(X_t,t)(f(X_t,t) + g(X_t,t) - g(X_t,t)) = \\ & \sigma^{-1}(X_t,t)\, f(X_t,t).\end{aligned}$$

Then, by the preceding Fact (5.17) the process X defined by (5.23) also obeys the stochastic differential equation

$$dX_t = \big(g(X_t,t) + f(X_t,t)\big)dt + \sigma(X_t,t)d\hat{B}_t. \tag{5.26}$$

□

5.19. Theorem. The set of all transformations or, equivalently, changes of measure $P \to Q$ in the Girsanov Theorem generated by θ in $\mathcal{L}$ is an abelian group isomorphic to the abelian group of all Borel measurable real-valued functions on the set $\mathbb{R}^n \times [0, \infty)$ satisfying the Lipschitz and growth conditions from the Fact (5.17) with the group operation of addition.

Proof. The proof directly follows from the definition of the changes of measure $P \to Q$ generated by θ in $\mathcal{L}$ in the Girsanov Theorem, from the Fact (5.17) and Theorem (5.18) □

Now our goal is to obtain in the x-basis the explicit form of the transformations $\hat{g}$ from the beliefs-preferences gauge symmetry group $\hat{\mathfrak{G}}$ in the representation given by relations (5.12), or equivalently (5.14) or (5.18).

In the case under consideration of a single underlying security, the generator $\mathfrak{L}(t)$ given in the s-basis by relation (5.1) takes the following form in the x-basis

$$\begin{aligned}\mathfrak{L}_*(t) = & \Upsilon_{s\mapsto x}\mathfrak{L}(t)\Upsilon_{x\mapsto s} = \\ & \frac{1}{2}\sigma_*^2(x,t)\frac{\partial^2}{\partial x^2} + \mu_*(x,t)\frac{\partial}{\partial x},\end{aligned} \tag{5.27}$$

where

$$\sigma_*(x,t) = \hat{\sigma}(\exp x, t),$$

and

$$\mu_*(x,t) = \hat{\mu}(\exp x, t) - \frac{1}{2}\sigma_*^2(x,t),$$

with $\hat{\sigma}(s,t)$ and $\hat{\mu}(s,t)$ defined by

$$\hat{\sigma}(s,t)s = \sigma(s,t)$$

and

$$\hat{\mu}(s,t)s = \mu(s,t).$$

5.20. Remark. We comment that in the derivation of relation

(5.27) we have used the following chain of equalities

$$\begin{aligned}\mathfrak{L}(t) =& \frac{1}{2}\sigma^2(s,t)\frac{\partial^2}{\partial s^2} + \mu(s,t)\frac{\partial}{\partial s} = \\ & \frac{1}{2}\hat{\sigma}^2(s,t)s^2\frac{\partial^2}{\partial s^2} + \hat{\mu}(s,t)s\frac{\partial}{\partial s} = \\ & \frac{1}{2}\hat{\sigma}^2(s,t)\Big(s\frac{\partial}{\partial s}\Big)^2 + \Big(\hat{\mu}(s,t) - \frac{1}{2}\hat{\sigma}^2(s,t)\Big)s\frac{\partial}{\partial s}\end{aligned}$$

and identity (4.11).

Similarly, the generator $\mathfrak{L}'(t)$ given in the s-basis by relation (5.10) takes the following form in the x-basis

$$\begin{aligned}\mathfrak{L}'_*(t) =& \Upsilon_{s\mapsto x}\mathfrak{L}'_*(t)\Upsilon_{x\mapsto s} = \\ & \frac{1}{2}\sigma_*^2(x,t)\frac{\partial^2}{\partial x^2} + \mu'_*(x,t)\frac{\partial}{\partial x},\end{aligned} \tag{5.28}$$

where

$$\mu'_*(x,t) = \hat{\mu}'(\exp x, t) - \frac{1}{2}\sigma_*^2(x,t),$$

with $\hat{\mu}'(s,t)$ defined by

$$\hat{\mu}'(s,t)s = \mu'(s,t).$$

Finally, we present the explicit form of the transformations (5.2) from the beliefs-preferences gauge symmetry group $\hat{\mathcal{G}}$ for the Markovian market populace $\mathbb{H} = \mathbb{B} \times \mathbb{U}$ or more precisely $\mathbb{H} = \mathbb{B} \times \mathbb{U}$ under consideration solely in the x-basis

$$\begin{aligned}&\mathfrak{L}'_*(t) = \Upsilon_{s\mapsto x}\mathfrak{L}'(t)\Upsilon_{x\mapsto s} = \\ &\Upsilon_{s\mapsto x}\,\hat{\mathbf{u}}'^{-1}(t,t)\,\mathfrak{L}(t)\,\hat{\mathbf{u}}'(t,t)\Upsilon_{x\mapsto s} + \Upsilon_{s\mapsto x}\frac{\hat{\mathbf{u}}'_t(t,t)}{\hat{\mathbf{u}}'(t,t)}\Upsilon_{x\mapsto s} = \\ &\big(\Upsilon_{s\mapsto x}\,\hat{\mathbf{u}}'^{-1}(t,t)\,\Upsilon_{x\mapsto s}\big)\big(\Upsilon_{s\mapsto x}\,\mathfrak{L}(t)\,\Upsilon_{x\mapsto s}\big)\big(\Upsilon_{s\mapsto x}\,\hat{\mathbf{u}}'(t,t)\,\Upsilon_{x\mapsto s}\big) + \\ &\quad\big(\Upsilon_{s\mapsto x}\,\hat{\mathbf{u}}'_t(t,t)\,\Upsilon_{x\mapsto s}\big)\,\big(\Upsilon_{s\mapsto x}\,\hat{\mathbf{u}}'^{-1}(t,t)\,\Upsilon_{x\mapsto s}\big) = \\ &\hat{\mathbf{u}}'^{-1}_*(t,t)\,\mathfrak{L}_*(t)\,\hat{\mathbf{u}}'_*(t,t) + \frac{\hat{\mathbf{u}}'_{*t}(t,t)}{\hat{\mathbf{u}}'_*(t,t)},\end{aligned} \tag{5.29}$$

where

$$\hat{\mathbf{u}}'_*(t,t) = \Upsilon_{s\mapsto x}\, \hat{\mathbf{u}}'(t,t)\, \Upsilon_{x\mapsto s},$$

and where we have made use of the following chain of equalities

$$\left(\Upsilon_{s\mapsto x}\, \hat{\mathbf{u}}'(t,t)\, \Upsilon_{x\mapsto s}\right)^{-1} = \Upsilon^{-1}_{x\mapsto s}\, \hat{\mathbf{u}}'^{-1}(t,t)\, \Upsilon^{-1}_{s\mapsto x} = \Upsilon_{s\mapsto x}\, \hat{\mathbf{u}}'^{-1}(t,t)\, \Upsilon_{x\mapsto s}.$$

5.21. Remark. In this way, the transformations from beliefs-preferences gauge symmetry group $\hat{\mathcal{G}}$ in the case under consideration can be trivially reformulated in the case when $\mathfrak{L}(t)$ is a general second order linear differential operator on $\Pi(\mathbb{R})$ with the free coefficient being zero.

5.22. Remark. We comment that, as should be expected, for the transformations (5.2) from the beliefs-preferences gauge symmetry group $\hat{\mathcal{G}}$ in the x-basis, $\hat{\mathbf{u}}'_*(t,t)$, or more precisely $\hat{\mathbf{u}}'_*(\overset{3}{t},\overset{1}{t})$ is the operator on $\Pi(\mathbb{R})$ of multiplication by the function

$$\hat{\mathrm{u}}'_*(t,t,\overset{3}{x}_t,\overset{1}{x}_t) = \left(\Upsilon_{s\mapsto x}\hat{\mathrm{u}}'(t,t,\cdot,\cdot)\right)(\overset{3}{x}_t,\overset{1}{x}_t) = \hat{\mathrm{u}}'(t,t,\exp\overset{3}{x}_t,\exp\overset{1}{x}_t),$$

where the operator $\mathfrak{L}_*(t)$, or more precisely $\mathfrak{L}_*(\overset{2}{t})$ on $\Pi(\mathbb{R})$ acts second.

5.23. Remark. We comment that the preceding transformations in (5.29) from the beliefs-preferences gauge symmetry group $\hat{\mathcal{G}}$ in the x-basis remain true in the general case of a Markovian market populace $\mathbb{H} = \mathbb{B} \times \mathbb{U}$, or more precisely $\mathbb{H} = \mathbb{L} \times \mathbb{U}$.

In the x-basis relation (5.11) takes the following form

$$\mu'_*(x,t) = \mu_*(x,t) + \sigma^2_*(x,t)\frac{\hat{\mathbf{u}}'_{*x}(t,t)}{\hat{\mathbf{u}}'_*(t,t)}, \tag{5.30}$$

where $\hat{\mathbf{u}}'_{*x}(t,t)$ is the operator on $\Pi(\mathbb{R})$ of multiplication by the function $\frac{\partial}{\partial x}\hat{\mathrm{u}}'_*(t,t,x_t,x)|_{x=x_t}$.

5.24. Remark. We comment that in the derivation of relation (5.30) we have made use of the following obvious relation

$$\hat{\mu}'(s,t)\, s = \hat{\mu}(s,t)\, s + \hat{\sigma}^2(s,t)\, s^2 \frac{\hat{\mathbf{u}}'_s(t,t)}{\hat{\mathbf{u}}'(t,t)}, \tag{5.31}$$

or equivalently

$$\hat{\mu}'(s,t) = \hat{\mu}(s,t) + \hat{\sigma}^2(s,t) \frac{s\,\hat{\mathbf{u}}'_s(t,t)}{\hat{\mathbf{u}}'(t,t)}, \tag{5.32}$$

and identity (4.11).

Therefore, the representation of the transformations $\hat{g}$ from the beliefs-preferences gauge symmetry group $\hat{\mathcal{G}}$ as the transformations of the drift $\mu(s,t)$ given in the s-basis by (5.12) takes the following form in the x-basis

$$\mu'_*(x,t) \to \mu_*(x,t) + \sigma^2_*(x,t) \frac{\hat{\mathbf{u}}'_{*x}(t,t)}{\hat{\mathbf{u}}'_*(t,t)}. \tag{5.33}$$

5.25. Remark. It is clear that due to Remark (5.4) the following relations hold

$$\hat{\mathbf{u}}'_*(t,t) = \mathbf{u}'_*(t,t), \tag{5.34}$$

$$\hat{\mathbf{u}}'_{*x}(t,t) = \mathbf{u}'_{*x}(t,t), \tag{5.35}$$

and

$$\hat{\mathbf{u}}'_{*xx}(t,t) = \mathbf{u}'_{*xx}(t,t), \tag{5.36}$$

where

$$\mathbf{u}'_*(t,t) = \Upsilon_{s\mapsto x}\, \mathbf{u}'^{-1}(t,t)\, \Upsilon_{x\mapsto s}$$

with $\hat{\mathbf{u}}'(t,T)$ defined in (3.105). We comment that $\mathbf{u}'_*(t,t)$, $\mathbf{u}'_{*x}(t,t)$ and $\mathbf{u}'_{*xx}(t,t)$ are the operators on Π of multiplication by the functions $\mathrm{u}'_*(t,t,x_t,x_t)$, $\frac{\partial}{\partial x}\mathrm{u}'_*(t,t,x_t,x)|_{x=x_t}$ and $\frac{\partial^2}{\partial x^2}\mathrm{u}'_*(t,t,x_t,x)|_{x=x_t}$.

5.26. Remark. Due to relations (5.34) and (5.35) we can rewrite relation (5.30) as follows

$$\mu'_*(x,t) = \mu_*(x,t) + \sigma_*^2(x,t)\frac{\mathbf{u}'_{*x}(t,t)}{\mathbf{u}'_*(t,t)}. \tag{5.37}$$

In this way we can also rewrite the transformation (5.33) as follows

$$\mu'_*(x,t) \to \mu_*(x,t) + \sigma_*^2(x,t)\frac{\mathbf{u}'_{*x}(t,t)}{\mathbf{u}'_*(t,t)}. \tag{5.38}$$

5.27. Remark. According to Remark (5.24) relation (5.16) takes the following form in the x-basis

$$\mu'_*(x,t) = \mu_*(x,t) + \sigma_*^2(x,t)\boldsymbol{\Lambda}_{*x}(t,t), \tag{5.39}$$

where

$$\boldsymbol{\Lambda}_*(t,t) = \Upsilon_{s\mapsto x}\,\boldsymbol{\Lambda}(t,t)\,\Upsilon_{x\mapsto s}$$

with $\boldsymbol{\Lambda}(t,t)$ defined in (5.15).

In this way the transformation (5.18) takes the following form in the x-basis

$$\mu'_*(x,t) \to \mu_*(x,t) + \sigma_*^2(x,t)\boldsymbol{\Lambda}_{*x}(t,t). \tag{5.40}$$

We comment that $\boldsymbol{\Lambda}_*(t,t)$, or more precisely $\boldsymbol{\Lambda}_*(\overset{3}{t},\overset{1}{t})$ is the operator on $\Pi(\mathbb{R})$ of multiplication by the function

$$\Lambda_*(t,t,\overset{3}{x}_t,\overset{1}{x}_t) = \left(\Upsilon_{s\mapsto x}\,\Lambda(t,t,\cdot,\cdot)\right)(\overset{3}{x}_t,\overset{1}{x}_t) = \\ \Lambda_*(t,t,\exp\overset{3}{x}_t,\exp\overset{1}{x}_t),$$

where the operator $\mathfrak{L}_*(t)$, or more precisely $\mathfrak{L}_*(\overset{2}{t})$ on $\Pi(\mathbb{R})$ acts second.

We also comment that $\boldsymbol{\Lambda}_{*x}(t,t)$, or more precisely $\boldsymbol{\Lambda}_{*x}(\overset{3}{t},\overset{1}{t})$ is the operator on $\Pi(\mathbb{R})$ of multiplication by the function $\Lambda_{*x}(t,t,x_t,x_t)$ or more precisely $\Lambda_{*x}(t,t,\overset{3}{x}_t,\overset{1}{x}_t)$ where

$$\Lambda_{*x}(t,t,x_t,x_t) = \frac{\partial}{\partial x}\Lambda_*(t,t,x_t,x)|_{x=x_t}.$$

It is also clear that

$$\mathbf{u}'_*(t,t) = e^{\mathbf{\Lambda}_*(t,t)} \tag{5.41}$$

and

$$\mathbf{u}'_*(t,t,\overset{3}{x}_t,\overset{1}{x}_t) = e^{\Lambda_*(t,t,\overset{3}{x}_t,\overset{1}{x}_t)}. \tag{5.42}$$

This completes the Remark.

5.28. Remark. It is clear, due to Remarks (5.25) and (5.27), that

$$\hat{\mathbf{u}}'_*(t,t) = e^{\mathbf{\Lambda}_*(t,t)}. \tag{5.43}$$

Now we pose a somewhat inverse problem, namely to find a transformation $\hat{g}$ from the beliefs-preferences gauge symmetry group $\hat{\mathcal{G}}$ such that it maps a given generator $\mathfrak{L}(t)$ defined in the x-basis by

$$\mathfrak{L}_*(t) = \frac{1}{2}\sigma_*^2(x,t)\frac{\partial^2}{\partial x^2} + \mu_*(x,t)\frac{\partial}{\partial x}$$

to a given generator $\mathfrak{L}'(t)$ defined in the x-basis by

$$\mathfrak{L}'_*(t) = \frac{1}{2}\sigma_*^2(x,t)\frac{\partial^2}{\partial x^2} + \mu'_*(x,t)\frac{\partial}{\partial x}.$$

Due to relation (5.30) or more precisely (5.37) such a transformation $\hat{g}$ must be generated by $\mathbf{u}'(t,t)$ such that

$$\frac{\mathbf{u}'_{*x}(t,t)}{\mathbf{u}'_*(t,t)} = \frac{\mu'_*(x,t) - \mu_*(x,t)}{\sigma_*^2(x,t)} = \sigma_*^{-1}(x,t)\,\theta_*(x,t) \tag{5.44}$$

where

$$\theta_*(x,t) = \frac{\mu'_*(x,t) - \mu_*(x,t)}{\sigma_*(x,t)}. \tag{5.45}$$

5.29. Remark. We comment that in light of Remark (5.1) we used the same notation in relations (5.44) and (5.45) for the operators $\boldsymbol{\mu}'_*(x,t)$, $\boldsymbol{\mu}_*(x,t)$, $\boldsymbol{\sigma}_*(x,t)$ and $\boldsymbol{\theta}_*(x,t)$ of multiplication by the functions $\mu'_*(x,t)$, $\mu_*(x,t)$, $\sigma_*(x,t)$ and $\theta_*(x,t)$ and for the functions $\mu'_*(x,t)$, $\mu_*(x,t)$, $\sigma_*(x,t)$ and $\theta_*(x,t)$ themselves. In this regard it is clear that expressions (5.44) and (5.45) can be interpreted as either operator relations or function relations.

5.30. Remark. Expression (5.44) can also be obtained from expression (5.20) in the form

$$\frac{s\,\mathbf{u}'_s(t,t)}{\mathbf{u}'(t,t)} = \frac{\hat{\mu}'(s,t) - \hat{\mu}(s,t)}{\hat{\sigma}^2(s,t)} = \hat{\sigma}^{-1}(s,t)\,\theta(s,t) \tag{5.46}$$

expressed in the x-basis with the help of identity (4.11).

5.31. Remark. It is clear that the operator $\boldsymbol{\theta}_*(x,t)$ and the function $\theta_*(x,t)$ are the expressions in the x-basis of the operator $\boldsymbol{\theta}(s,t)$ and the function $\theta(s,t)$ defined in (5.21), that is:

$$\boldsymbol{\theta}_*(x,t) = \Upsilon_{s\mapsto x}\,\boldsymbol{\theta}(s,t)\,\Upsilon_{x\mapsto s} \tag{5.47}$$

and

$$\theta_*(x,t) = \big(\Upsilon_{s\mapsto x}\,\theta(\cdot,t)\big)(x). \tag{5.48}$$

5.32. Remark. In terms of the operator $\boldsymbol{\Lambda}_*(t,t)$ defined in (5.41) we can rewrite expression (5.44) as follows

$$\boldsymbol{\Lambda}_{*x}(t,t) = \frac{\boldsymbol{\mu}'_*(x,t) - \boldsymbol{\mu}_*(x,t)}{\boldsymbol{\sigma}^2_*(x,t)} = \boldsymbol{\sigma}^{-1}_*(x,t)\,\boldsymbol{\theta}_*(x,t). \tag{5.49}$$

Now we are ready to present the following Theorems on the equivalence of transformations of the drift of the generators $\mathfrak{L}(t)$ due to the beliefs-preferences gauge symmetry group $\hat{\mathcal{G}}$ for the Markovian market populace $\mathbb{H} = \mathbb{B} \times \mathbb{U}$, or more precisely $\mathbb{H} = \mathbb{L} \times \mathbb{U}$ under consideration with the transformations of the drift due to the changes of measure in the Girsanov Theorem.

5.33. Theorem. Let $\mu_*(x,t)$, $\mu'_*(x,t)$ and $\sigma_*(x,t)$ satisfy the conditions for g, f and σ in the Fact (5.17). Then the transformation of the drift

$$g(x,t) \to f(x,t)$$

in the Fact (5.17) due to the change of measure in the Girsanov Theorem generated by $\theta = \theta(x,t)$ coincides with the transformation of the drift

$$\mu_*(x,t) \to \mu'_*(x,t)$$

in (5.33) due to the transformation $\hat{\boldsymbol{g}}$ from the beliefs-preferences gauge symmetry group $\hat{\boldsymbol{\mathcal{G}}}$ defined in (3.107) of the generator $\mathfrak{L}(t)$ defined in the x-basis by (5.27) whenever $\hat{\boldsymbol{g}}$ is generated by $\mathfrak{u}'(t,T)$ defined in the x-basis in (5.44) and whenever $\theta(x,t) = \theta_*(x,t)$ and $\sigma(x,t) = \sigma_*(x,t)$.

Proof. The proof directly follows from the explicit expressions of the transformations of the drift in the Fact (5.17) and in relation (5.33). □

5.34. Theorem. The representation of the beliefs-preferences gauge symmetry group $\hat{\boldsymbol{\mathcal{G}}}$ defined in (3.107) for the generators $\mathfrak{L}(t)$ of the form (5.27) in the x-basis as the group of transformations of the drift

$$\mu_*(x,t) \to \mu'_*(x,t)$$

defined in (5.33) is isomorphic to the abelian group of transformations of the drift

$$g(x,t) \to f(x,t)$$

defined in the Fact (5.17) and Theorem (5.18) due to the changes of measure in the Girsanov Theorem generated by $\theta = \theta(x,t)$ in $\mathcal{L}$.

Proof. Directly follows from Theorems (5.33) and (5.18). □

5.35. Theorem. The representation of the beliefs-preferences gauge symmetry group $\hat{\mathcal{G}}$ given in (3.107) of the generators $\mathfrak{L}(t)$ of the form (5.27) in the x-basis as the group of transformations of the drift

$$\mu_*(x,t) \to \mu'_*(x,t)$$

defined in (5.33) is isomorphic to the abelian group of transformations or, equivalently, of changes of measure $P \to Q$ in the Girsanov Theorem generated by θ in $\mathcal{L}$.

Proof. The proof directly follows from Theorems (5.34) and (5.19). □

5.36. Remark. We established in the preceding Theorems (5.33), (5.34) and (5.35) the equivalence of the transformations of the drift $\mu(s,t)$ of the generators $\mathfrak{L}(t)$ due to the beliefs-preferences gauge symmetry group $\hat{\mathcal{G}}$ for the Markovian market populace $\mathbb{H} = \mathbb{B} \times \mathbb{U}$, or more precisely $\mathbb{H} = \mathbb{L} \times \mathbb{U}$ under consideration with the transformations of the drift due to the changes of measure in the Girsanov Theorem by means of expressing the generator $\mathfrak{L}(t)$ and drift $\mu(s,t)$ in the x-basis. The same results can be achieved directly for the transformations of the drift $\mu(s,t)$ of the generators $\mathfrak{L}(t)$ in the s-basis due to the beliefs-preferences gauge symmetry group $\hat{\mathcal{G}}$ by means of Ito processes obeying the following stochastic differential equation

$$dS_t = \mu(S_t,t)dt + \sigma(S_t,t)dB_t, \quad S_0 > 0,$$

with almost surely positive solutions.

5.37. Remark. In view of Theorems (5.33), (5.34) and (5.35) we can consider the transformations

$$\boldsymbol{F}(t,T) \xrightarrow{g_{\boldsymbol{\mathcal{B}}}} \hat{\mathbf{u}}'^{-1}(t,t)\boldsymbol{F}(t,T)\hat{\mathbf{u}}'(t,T), \quad g = (g_{\boldsymbol{\mathcal{B}}}, g_{\boldsymbol{\mathcal{U}}}) \in \mathcal{G}$$

of the probability measures determined by $\boldsymbol{F}(t,T)$ associated with the transformation

$$\mathfrak{L}(t) \xrightarrow{\hat{g}_{\mathfrak{L}}} \hat{\mathbf{u}}'^{-1}(t,t)\,\mathfrak{L}(t)\,\hat{\mathbf{u}}'(t,t) + \frac{\hat{\mathbf{u}}'_t(t,t)}{\hat{\mathbf{u}}'(t,t)}, \quad \hat{g} = (\hat{g}_{\mathfrak{L}}, \hat{g}_{\boldsymbol{\mathcal{U}}}) \in \hat{\mathcal{G}}$$

in both s-basis and x-basis as a natural extension of the changes of measure due to the Girsanov Theorem. It is clear that $\boldsymbol{F}(t,T)$ is in $\boldsymbol{\mathcal{B}}$ with generators $\mathfrak{L}(t)$ and $\hat{\mathbf{u}}'^{-1}(t,t)\boldsymbol{F}(t,T)\hat{\mathbf{u}}'(t,T)$ is in $g_{\boldsymbol{\mathcal{B}}}\boldsymbol{\mathcal{B}}$ with generators

$$\hat{\mathbf{u}}'^{-1}(t,t)\,\mathfrak{L}(t)\,\hat{\mathbf{u}}'(t,t) + \frac{\hat{\mathbf{u}}'_t(t,t)}{\hat{\mathbf{u}}'(t,t)}.$$

We comment that we have made use of Remark (3.151).

It is well known [7] that in the case of the Markovian market populace $\mathbb{H} = \mathbb{B} \times \mathbb{U}$, or more precisely $\mathbb{H} = \mathbb{L} \times \mathbb{U}$ under consideration the value $v = v(t)$ in Π of a European contingent claim with inception time t, expiration time T and payoff v_T in Π is a possibly generalized solution of the Cauchy problem for the Black and Scholes equation

$$\begin{aligned} &\frac{\partial}{\partial t}v + \frac{1}{2}\hat{\sigma}^2(s,t)\,s^2\frac{\partial^2}{\partial s^2}v + \\ &\qquad \big(r(s,t) - d(s,t)\big)\,s\frac{\partial}{\partial s}v - r(s,t)v = 0, \quad t < T, \\ &\qquad\qquad v(T) = v_T, \end{aligned} \tag{5.50}$$

where $\hat{\sigma}^2(s,t)$ is the variance of return per unit time, $r(s,t)$ is the continuously compounded interest rate, and $d(s,t)$ is the continuously compounded dividend yield in terms of the underlying security being a stock.

5.38. Remark. We recall that the case under consideration is that of the Markovian market populace $\mathbb{H} = \mathbb{B} \times \mathbb{U}$, or more precisely $\mathbb{H} = \mathbb{L} \times \mathbb{U}$ in the particular case of a single underlying security and when each belief $\boldsymbol{\mathcal{B}}$ in the market populace belief $\mathbb{B}$ is generated by the family

$$\mathfrak{L} = \{\mathfrak{L}(t) : \Pi \to \Pi \,|\, t \in \mathcal{T}\},$$

in $\mathbb{L}$ with each generator $\mathfrak{L}(t)$ at time t of the form (5.1).

5.39. Remark. We comment that in order to derive the Black and Scholes equation (5.50) one has to assume that the pure discount bonds with all maturity times and the underlying security itself are traded at any time from the trading time set.

Following [33] we call a market environment

$$\mathbf{V}^{BS} = \{\mathbf{V}^{BS}(t,T) : \Pi \to \Pi \,|\, t,T \in \mathcal{T}, t \leq T\}$$

generated by the family

$$\boldsymbol{L}^{BS} = \{\boldsymbol{L}^{BS}(t) : \Pi \to \Pi \,|\, t \in \mathcal{T}\}$$

with the generator $\boldsymbol{L}^{BS}(t)$ at time t defined by

$$\boldsymbol{L}^{BS}(t) = \frac{1}{2}\hat{\sigma}^2(s,t)\, s^2 \frac{\partial^2}{\partial s^2} + \big(r(s,t) - d(s,t)\big)\, s\frac{\partial}{\partial s} - r(s,t)$$

a *Black and Scholes* market environment.

5.40. Remark. We comment that for the sake of simplicity we have used the same notations for the operators of multiplication by the functions $r(s,t)$ and $d(s,t)$ and for the functions $r(s,t)$ and $d(s,t)$ themselves. Whenever we would like to distinguish the operators of multiplication by the functions $r(s,t)$ and $d(s,t)$ from the functions $r(s,t)$ and $d(s,t)$ themselves we will denote these operators by $\boldsymbol{r}(s,t)$ and $\mathbf{d}(s,t)$.

5.41. Definition. We call a market participant $\mathcal{H} = (\mathcal{B},\mathcal{U})$ in $\mathbb{H} = \mathbb{B} \times \mathbb{U}$ a *risk-neutral market participant* if:

(i) the belief $\mathcal{B}$ is generated by

$$\mathfrak{L} = \{\mathfrak{L}(t) : \Pi \to \Pi \,|\, t \in \mathcal{T}\}$$

with the generator $\mathfrak{L}(t)$ at time t defined by

$$\mathfrak{L}(t) = \frac{1}{2}\hat{\sigma}^2(s,t)\, s^2 \frac{\partial^2}{\partial s^2} + \big(r(s,t) - d(s,t)\big)\, s\frac{\partial}{\partial s},$$

and

(ii) the preference

$$\boldsymbol{\mathcal{U}} = \{\boldsymbol{u}'(t,T) : \Pi(\mathbb{R}^2_{++}) \to \Pi(\mathbb{R}^2_{++}) \,|\, t,T \in \mathcal{T}, t \leq T\}$$

is such that each $\boldsymbol{u}'(t,T)$ is given by

$$\boldsymbol{u}'(t,T) = e^{-\int_t^T \overset{T}{\boldsymbol{r}}(s,\tau)d\tau},$$

where the index over the operator $\boldsymbol{r}(s,\tau)$ indicates its order which is assumed to be inverse to that of τ.

We call the belief $\boldsymbol{\mathcal{B}}$ and preference $\boldsymbol{\mathcal{U}}$ of the risk-neutral market participant $\boldsymbol{\mathcal{H}} = (\boldsymbol{\mathcal{B}}, \boldsymbol{\mathcal{U}})$ a *risk-neutral belief* and a *risk-neutral preference.* Moreover, we call the family $\boldsymbol{\mathfrak{L}}$ of generators $\boldsymbol{\mathfrak{L}}(t)$ a *risk-neutral family of generators* and the generators $\boldsymbol{\mathfrak{L}}(t)$ themselves *risk-neutral generators.*

5.42. Remark. It is clear that risk-neutral market participants exist due to Remark (3.149).

5.43. Remark. In the case of Markovian market populace $\mathbb{H} = \mathbb{B} \times \mathbb{U}$, or more precisely $\mathbb{H} = \mathbb{B} \times \mathbb{U}$ under consideration, a market generation, that is, an orbit of the group $\boldsymbol{\mathcal{G}}$ in $\mathbb{H} = \mathbb{B} \times \mathbb{U}$, or equivalently due to Remark (3.151), an orbit of the group $\hat{\boldsymbol{\mathcal{G}}}$ in $\mathbb{H} = \mathbb{L} \times \mathbb{U}$ admits the following description. Due to the fact that transformations in (3.99) or equivalently (3.107) from the beliefs-preferences gauge symmetry group $\hat{\boldsymbol{\mathfrak{G}}}$ for the generators $\boldsymbol{\mathfrak{L}}(t)$ of the form (5.1) can be represented as the transformations in (5.12), or equivalently (5.14) of the drift $\mu(s,t)$ leaving the variance $\sigma^2(s,t)$ unchanged, each such orbit can be uniquely characterized by $\sigma(s,t)$ as a function on the set $\mathbb{R}_{++} \times \mathcal{T}$. Moreover, each market participant $\boldsymbol{\mathcal{H}} = (\boldsymbol{\mathcal{B}}, \boldsymbol{\mathcal{U}})$ in such an orbit can be uniquely characterized by a drift $\mu(s,t)$ as a function on the set $\mathbb{R}_{++} \times \mathcal{T}$. We comment that each market participant in such an orbit can be uniquely characterized by a drift up to an equivalence class of indistinguishable market participants with indistinguishable preferences. In addition we note that each such orbit in the Markovian market populace $\mathbb{H} = \mathbb{B} \times \mathbb{U}$, or more precisely $\mathbb{H} = \mathbb{B} \times \mathbb{U}$ under consideration contains one and only one risk-neutral market participant and that each risk neutral market participant in the Markovian market populace $\mathbb{H} = \mathbb{B} \times \mathbb{U}$, or more precisely $\mathbb{H} = \mathbb{B} \times \mathbb{U}$ under consideration is contained in one and only one such orbit.

Finally, we recall that the case of the Markovian market populace $\mathbb{H} = \mathbb{B} \times \mathbb{U}$, or more precisely $\mathbb{H} = \mathbb{L} \times \mathbb{U}$ under consideration is that of a single underlying security and when each belief $\mathcal{B}$ in the market populace belief $\mathbb{B}$ is generated by the family

$$\mathfrak{L} = \{\mathfrak{L}(t) : \Pi \to \Pi \,|\, t \in \mathcal{T}\},$$

in $\mathbb{L}$ with each generator $\mathfrak{L}(t)$ at time t of the form (5.1). This completes the Remark.

Due to relation (5.20), or more precisely (5.46) the transformation $\hat{g}$ from the beliefs-preferences gauge symmetry group $\hat{\mathcal{G}}$ that maps a risk-neutral generator

$$\mathfrak{L}(t) = \frac{1}{2}\hat{\sigma}^2(s,t)\, s^2 \frac{\partial^2}{\partial s^2} + \big(r(s,t) - d(s,t)\big)\, s\frac{\partial}{\partial s}$$

to a given generator

$$\mathfrak{L}'(t) = \frac{1}{2}\hat{\sigma}^2(s,t)\, s^2 \frac{\partial^2}{\partial s^2} + \hat{\mu}(s,t)\, s\frac{\partial}{\partial s}$$

is generated by $\mathbf{u}'(t,t)$ such that

$$\frac{s\,\mathbf{u}'_s(t,t)}{\mathbf{u}'(t,t)} = \frac{\hat{\mu}'(s,t) - \big(r(s,t) - d(s,t)\big)}{\hat{\sigma}^2(s,t)} = \hat{\sigma}^{-1}(s,t)\,\theta(s,t) \tag{5.51}$$

where

$$\theta(s,t) = \frac{\hat{\mu}'(s,t) - \big(r(s,t) - d(s,t)\big)}{\hat{\sigma}(s,t)}. \tag{5.52}$$

5.44. Remark. We comment that in light of Remark (5.1) we used the same notation in relations (5.51) and (5.52) for the operators $\hat{\boldsymbol{\mu}}'(s,t)$, $\boldsymbol{r}(s,t)$, $\boldsymbol{d}(s,t)$, $\hat{\boldsymbol{\sigma}}(s,t)$ and $\boldsymbol{\theta}(s,t)$ of multiplication by the functions $\hat{\mu}'(s,t)$, $r(s,t)$, $d(s,t)$, $\hat{\sigma}(s,t)$ and $\theta(s,t)$ and for the functions $\hat{\mu}'(s,t)$, $r(s,t)$, $d(s,t)$, $\hat{\sigma}(s,t)$ and $\theta(s,t)$ themselves. In this regard it is clear that relations (5.51) and (5.52) can be interpreted as either operator relations or function relations.

It is clear from the financial standpoint that $\theta(s,t)$ defined in (5.52) is nothing but the *market price of risk*. This justifies the following definition.

5.45. Definition. We call the operator $\boldsymbol{\theta}(s,t)$ of multiplication by the market price of risk $\theta(s,t)$ defined in (5.52) a *market price of risk operator.*

5.46. Remark. The preceding Definition justifies the terminology we have introduced in Definition (5.12) for the operator $\boldsymbol{\theta}(s,t)$ of multiplication by the function $\theta(s,t)$ defined in relation (5.21) and for the function $\theta(s,t)$ itself.

5.47. Remark. In terms of the operator $\boldsymbol{\Lambda}(t,T)$ defined in (5.15) we can rewrite expression (5.51) as follows

$$s\,\boldsymbol{\Lambda}_{\boldsymbol{s}}(t,t) = \frac{\hat{\boldsymbol{\mu}}'(s,t) - (\boldsymbol{r}(s,t) - \boldsymbol{d}(s,t))}{\hat{\boldsymbol{\sigma}}^2(s,t)} = \hat{\boldsymbol{\sigma}}^{-1}(s,t)\,\boldsymbol{\theta}(s,t). \tag{5.53}$$

5.48. Definition. We call the operator $\boldsymbol{\Lambda}(t,T)$ obeying the identity (5.53) the *market price of risk potential operator.* Similarly we call the function $\Lambda(t,T,s_t,s_T)$ the *market price of risk potential.*

We make the following crucial observation. In the case of the Markovian market populace $\mathbb{H} = \mathbb{B} \times \mathbb{U}$, or more precisely $\mathbb{H} = \mathbb{L} \times \mathbb{U}$ under consideration the values of European contingent claims are determined by the Cauchy problem for the

Black and Scholes equation (5.50) which, in turn, is determined by a risk-neutral market participant, or more precisely by the belief and preference of a risk-neutral market participant, and this risk-neutral market participant is determined by the particular choice of gauge. Therefore, it might seem that valuation of European contingent claims, at least in a Black and Scholes market environment, is based on the particular choice of gauge, that is, on the breaking of the beliefs-preferences gauge symmetry for a Markovian market populace $\mathbb{H} = \mathbb{B} \times \mathbb{U}$, or more precisely $\mathbb{H} = \mathbb{L} \times \mathbb{U}$ in general. However, this is not the case and in fact, as we will show in the next Section (6), valuation of European contingent claims in a general market environment, valuation that is independent of the beliefs and preferences of market participants is based not on the breaking of the beliefs-preferences gauge symmetry for a Markovian market populace $\mathbb{H} = \mathbb{B} \times \mathbb{U}$, or more precisely $\mathbb{H} = \mathbb{L} \times \mathbb{U}$ but on the contrary, is based on promoting the beliefs-preferences gauge symmetry to a certain larger symmetry.

5.2 The Case of a Multiple Underlying Security

Now we consider the beliefs-preferences gauge symmetry group $\hat{\mathcal{G}}$ for the Markovian market populace $\mathbb{H} = \mathbb{B} \times \mathbb{U}$, or more precisely $\mathbb{H} = \mathbb{L} \times \mathbb{U}$ in the general case of n underlying securities and when each belief $\boldsymbol{\mathcal{B}}$ in the market populace belief $\mathbb{B}$ is generated by the family

$$\mathfrak{L} = \{\mathfrak{L}(t) : \Pi \to \Pi \,|\, t \in \mathcal{T}\},$$

in $\mathbb{L}$ with each generator $\mathfrak{L}(t)$ at time t of the form

$$\mathfrak{L}(t) = \frac{1}{2}\sum_{i,j=1}^{n} \sigma_{ij}^2(s,t)\frac{\partial^2}{\partial s_i \partial s_j} + \sum_{i=1}^{n} \mu_i(s,t)\frac{\partial}{\partial s_i}, \tag{5.54}$$

where $\sigma_{ij}^2(s,t)$ is the (i,j) entry of an $n \times n$ real matrix $\sigma^2(s,t)$ which is assumed to be symmetric and positively defined, and where $\sigma_{ij}^2(s,t)$ and $\mu_i(s,t)$ are admissible real-valued functions on the set $\mathbb{R}_{++}^n \times \mathcal{T}$.

5.49. Remark. We comment that for the sake of simplicity we used in relation (5.54) the same notations for the operators of multiplication by the functions $\sigma_{ij}^2(s,t)$ and $\mu_i(s,t)$ and for the functions $\sigma_{ij}^2(s,t)$ and $\mu_i(s,t)$ themselves. Whenever we would like to distinguish the operators of multiplication by the functions $\sigma_{ij}^2(s,t)$ and $\mu_i(s,t)$ from the functions $\sigma_{ij}^2(s,t)$ and $\mu_i(s,t)$ themselves we will denote these operators by $\boldsymbol{\sigma}_{ij}^2(s,t)$ and $\boldsymbol{\mu}_i(s,t)$.

Denote by $\mu(s,t)$ the n-dimensional real vector function defined by

$$\mu(s,t) = (\mu_1(s,t), \mu_2(s,t), \ldots, \mu_n(s,t)).$$

5.50. Remark. We comment that financially $\sigma^2(s,t)$ and $\mu(s,t)$ are the variance-covariance matrix per unit time and drift per unit time of the diffusion process for the prices of the underlying securities.

5.51. Remark. We comment that the reason for using the notation $\sigma^2(s,t)$ for the $n \times n$ real symmetric positively defined matrix with entries $\sigma_{ij}^2(s,t)$ in expression (5.54) is as follows. By Theorem (4.16) there exists a $n \times n$ real symmetric positive matrix $\sigma(s,t)$ such that $\sigma^2(s,t) = \sigma(s,t)\,\sigma(s,t)$. That is why we can interpret $\sigma^2(s,t)$ not merely as a notation but as a statement that the matrix $\sigma^2(s,t)$ is equal to the square of the matrix $\sigma(s,t)$. Whenever ambiguity is unlikely we will adopt this interpretation from now on in this article.

Our goal is to establish the behavior of the generator $\mathfrak{L}(t)$ of the form (5.54) under the transformations $\hat{\boldsymbol{g}}$ defined in (3.99) in the form (3.107) from the beliefs-preferences gauge symmetry group $\hat{\mathcal{G}}$ for a Markovian market populace $\mathbb{H} = \mathbb{B} \times \mathbb{U}$, or more precisely $\mathbb{H} = \mathbb{L} \times \mathbb{U}$. In other words, our goal is to find the explicit form for the operator

$$\mathfrak{L}'(t) = \hat{\mathbf{u}}'^{-1}(t,t)\,\mathfrak{L}(t)\,\hat{\mathbf{u}}'(t,t) + \frac{\hat{\mathbf{u}}'_t(t,t)}{\hat{\mathbf{u}}'(t,t)}, \tag{5.55}$$

where $\mathfrak{L}(t)$ is defined in (5.54). In order to do this, according to Remark (3.157) we use the following chain of equalities

$$\begin{aligned}
0 = {} & \overset{2}{\frac{d}{dt}} \hat{\mathbf{u}}'(\overset{3}{t},\overset{1}{t})v' + \mathfrak{L}(\overset{2}{t})\hat{\mathbf{u}}'(\overset{3}{t},\overset{1}{t})v' = \\
& \overset{2}{\frac{d}{dt}} \hat{\mathbf{u}}'(\overset{3}{t},\overset{1}{t})v' + \\
& \overbrace{\Big(\frac{1}{2}\sum_{i,j=1}^{n} \sigma_{ij}^2(s,t)\frac{\partial^2}{\partial s_i \partial s_j} + \sum_{i=1}^{n} \mu_i(s,t)\frac{\partial}{\partial s_i}\Big)}^{2} \hat{\mathbf{u}}'(\overset{3}{t},\overset{1}{t})v' = \\
& \hat{\mathbf{u}}'(t,t)\frac{d}{dt}v' + \hat{\mathbf{u}}'_t(t,t)v' + \\
& \quad \hat{\mathbf{u}}'(t,t)\Big(\frac{1}{2}\sum_{i,j=1}^{n} \sigma_{ij}^2(s,t)\frac{\partial^2}{\partial s_i \partial s_j} + \sum_{i=1}^{n} \mu_i(s,t)\frac{\partial}{\partial s_i}\Big)v' + \\
& \quad \Big(\frac{1}{2}\sum_{i,j=1}^{n} \sigma_{ij}^2(s,t)\hat{\mathbf{u}}'_{s_i s_j}(t,t) + \\
& \quad \frac{1}{2}\sum_{i=1}^{n}\Big(\sum_{j=1}^{n} \sigma_{ij}^2(s,t)\hat{\mathbf{u}}'_{s_j}(t,t)\Big)\frac{\partial}{\partial s_i} + \\
& \quad \frac{1}{2}\sum_{j=1}^{n}\Big(\sum_{i=1}^{n} \sigma_{ij}^2(s,t)\hat{\mathbf{u}}'_{s_i}(t,t)\Big)\frac{\partial}{\partial s_j} + \\
& \quad \sum_{i=1}^{n} \hat{\mathbf{u}}'_{s_i}(t,t)\mu_i(s,t)\Big)v' =
\end{aligned} \tag{5.56}$$

$$\hat{\mathbf{u}}'(t,t)\Bigg(\frac{d}{dt}v' + \frac{\hat{\mathbf{u}}_t'(t,t)}{\hat{\mathbf{u}}'(t,t)}v' +$$
$$\Big(\frac{1}{2}\sum_{i,j=1}^{n}\sigma_{ij}^2(s,t)\frac{\partial^2}{\partial s_i \partial s_j} + \sum_{i=1}^{n}\mu_i(s,t)\frac{\partial}{\partial s_i}\Big)v' +$$
$$\Big(\sum_{i=1}^{n}\frac{\sum_{j=1}^{n}\sigma_{ij}^2(s,t)\hat{\mathbf{u}}_{s_j}'(t,t)}{\hat{\mathbf{u}}'(t,t)}\frac{\partial}{\partial s_i} +$$
$$\frac{\frac{1}{2}\sum_{i,j=1}^{n}\sigma_{ij}^2(s,t)\hat{\mathbf{u}}_{s_i s_j}'(t,t) + \sum_{i=1}^{n}\hat{\mathbf{u}}_{s_i}'(t,t)\mu_i(s,t)}{\hat{\mathbf{u}}'(t,t)}\Big)v'\Bigg),$$

where in the last equality we have used the symmetricity of the matrix $\sigma^2(s,t)$, and where $\hat{\mathbf{u}}_{s_i}'(t,t)$ and $\hat{\mathbf{u}}_{s_i s_j}'(t,t)$ stand for the operators of multiplication by the functions $\frac{\partial}{\partial s_i}\hat{\mathrm{u}}'(t,t,s_t,s)|_{s=s_t}$ and $\frac{\partial^2}{\partial s_i \partial s_j}\hat{\mathrm{u}}'(t,t,s_t,s)|_{s=s_t}$.

Therefore, due to Remark (3.157) the desired generator $\mathfrak{L}'(t)$ is given by

$$\mathfrak{L}'(t) = \frac{1}{2}\sum_{i,j=1}^{n}\sigma_{ij}^2(s,t)\frac{\partial^2}{\partial s_i \partial s_j} + \sum_{i=1}^{n}\mu_i(s,t)\frac{\partial}{\partial s_i} + \frac{\hat{\mathbf{u}}_t'(t,t)}{\hat{\mathbf{u}}'(t,t)} +$$
$$\sum_{i=1}^{n}\frac{\sum_{j=1}^{n}\sigma_{ij}^2(s,t)\hat{\mathbf{u}}_{s_j}'(t,t)}{\hat{\mathbf{u}}'(t,t)}\frac{\partial}{\partial s_i} + \tag{5.57}$$
$$\frac{\frac{1}{2}\sum_{i,j=1}^{n}\sigma_{ij}^2(s,t)\hat{\mathbf{u}}_{s_i s_j}'(t,t) + \sum_{i=1}^{n}\hat{\mathbf{u}}_{s_i}'(t,t)\mu_i(s,t)}{\hat{\mathbf{u}}'(t,t)}.$$

5.52. Remark. The relation (5.57) for the generator $\mathfrak{L}'(t)$ can also be obtained from relation (3.119) with the help of the obvious identity

$$\hat{\mathbf{u}}'^{-1}(t,t)[\mathfrak{L}(t),\hat{\mathbf{u}}'(t,t)] = \sum_{i=1}^{n} \frac{\sum_{j=1}^{n} \sigma_{ij}^2(s,t)\hat{\mathbf{u}}'_{s_j}(t,t)}{\hat{\mathbf{u}}'(t,t)} \frac{\partial}{\partial s_i} + \frac{\frac{1}{2}\sum_{i,j=1}^{n} \sigma_{ij}^2(s,t)\hat{\mathbf{u}}'_{s_i s_j}(t,t) + \sum_{i=1}^{n} \hat{\mathbf{u}}'_{s_i}(t,t)\mu_i(s,t)}{\hat{\mathbf{u}}'(t,t)} \tag{5.58}$$

that directly follows from the chain of equalities (5.56).

Due to expression (3.100) we have the following expression for $\mathfrak{d}(t)$ in the case under consideration

$$\mathfrak{d}(t) = \frac{\mathbf{u}'_t(t,t)}{\mathbf{u}'(t,t)} + \frac{\frac{1}{2}\sum_{i,j=1}^{n} \sigma_{ij}^2(s,t)\mathbf{u}'_{s_i s_j}(t,t) + \sum_{i=1}^{n} \mathbf{u}'_{s_i}(t,t)\mu_i(s,t)}{\mathbf{u}'(t,t)}. \tag{5.59}$$

5.53. Remark. We comment that in the preceding relation (5.59) we have taken into account the fact that due to the definition of $\hat{\mathbf{u}}'(t,T)$ in expression (3.105) and due to the definitions of $\hat{\mathbf{u}}'_{s_i}(t,t)$ and $\hat{\mathbf{u}}'_{s_i s_j}(t,t)$ as the operators on Π of multiplication by the functions $\frac{\partial}{\partial s_i}\hat{\mathrm{u}}'(t,t,s_t,s)|_{s=s_t}$ and $\frac{\partial^2}{\partial s_i \partial s_j}\hat{\mathrm{u}}'(t,t,s_t,s)|_{s=s_t}$ the following equalities hold:

$$\hat{\mathbf{u}}'(t,t) = \mathbf{u}'(t,t), \tag{5.60}$$

$$\hat{\mathbf{u}}'_{s_i}(t,t) = \mathbf{u}'_{s_i}(t,t), \tag{5.61}$$

and

$$\hat{\mathbf{u}}'_{s_i s_j}(t,t) = \mathbf{u}'_{s_i s_j}(t,t), \tag{5.62}$$

where $\mathbf{u}'(t,t)$, $\mathbf{u}'_{s_i}(t,t)$ and $\mathbf{u}'_{s_i s_j}(t,t)$ are the operators on Π of multiplication by the functions $\mathrm{u}'(t,t,s_t,s_t)$, $\frac{\partial}{\partial s_i}\mathrm{u}'(t,t,s_t,s)|_{s=s_t}$ and $\frac{\partial^2}{\partial s_i \partial s_j}\mathrm{u}'(t,t,s_t,s)|_{s=s_t}$.

5.54. Remark. We comment that the expression for $\mathfrak{d}(t)$ in (5.59) also directly follows from expressions (5.58) and (3.102)

It is clear from relation (5.57) that the generator $\mathfrak{L}'(t)$ is also of the form (5.54), that is

$$\mathfrak{L}'(t) = \frac{1}{2}\sum_{i,j=1}^{n} \sigma_{ij}^2(s,t)\frac{\partial^2}{\partial s_i \partial s_j} + \sum_{i=1}^{n} \mu_i'(s,t)\frac{\partial}{\partial s_i}, \tag{5.63}$$

where

$$\mu'(s,t) = \mu(s,t) + \sigma^2(s,t)\frac{\hat{\mathbf{u}}_{\boldsymbol{s}}'(t,t)}{\hat{\mathbf{u}}'(t,t)}. \tag{5.64}$$

with

$$\mu'(s,t) = (\mu_1'(s,t), \mu_2'(s,t), \ldots, \mu_n'(s,t))$$

and

$$\hat{\mathbf{u}}_{\boldsymbol{s}}'(t,t) = (\hat{\mathbf{u}}_{\boldsymbol{s_1}}'(t,t), \hat{\mathbf{u}}_{\boldsymbol{s_2}}'(t,t), \ldots, \hat{\mathbf{u}}_{\boldsymbol{s_n}}'(t,t)).$$

Therefore, the behavior of the generator $\mathfrak{L}(t)$ of the form (5.54) under the transformations $\hat{\mathcal{g}}$ defined in (3.99) in the form (3.107) from the beliefs-preferences gauge symmetry group $\hat{\mathcal{G}}$ for a Markovian market populace $\mathbb{H} = \mathbb{B} \times \mathbb{U}$, or more precisely $\mathbb{H} = \mathbb{L} \times \mathbb{U}$ can be characterized solely in terms of the drift $\mu(s,t)$ as follows

$$\mu(s,t) \to \mu(s,t) + \sigma^2(s,t)\frac{\hat{\mathbf{u}}_{\boldsymbol{s}}'(t,t)}{\hat{\mathbf{u}}'(t,t)}. \tag{5.65}$$

5.55. Remark. Due to relations (5.60) and (5.61) we can rewrite relation (5.64) as follows

$$\mu'(s,t) = \mu(s,t) + \sigma^2(s,t)\frac{\mathbf{u}_{\boldsymbol{s}}'(t,t)}{\mathbf{u}'(t,t)}. \tag{5.66}$$

In this way we can also rewrite the transformation (5.65) as follows

$$\mu(s,t) \to \mu(s,t) + \sigma^2(s,t)\frac{\mathbf{u}_{\boldsymbol{s}}'(t,t)}{\mathbf{u}'(t,t)}. \tag{5.67}$$

5.56. Remark. Using the operator $\mathbf{\Lambda}(t,T)$ defined according to (3.16) as

$$\mathbf{u}'(t,T) = e^{\mathbf{\Lambda}(t,T)} \tag{5.68}$$

we can rewrite expression (5.64) with the help of (5.66) as follows

$$\mu'(s,t) = \mu(s,t) + \sigma^2 \mathbf{\Lambda}_{\boldsymbol{s}}(t,t), \tag{5.69}$$

where

$$\mathbf{\Lambda}_{\boldsymbol{s}}(t,t) = (\mathbf{\Lambda}_{\boldsymbol{s_1}}(t,t), \mathbf{\Lambda}_{\boldsymbol{s_2}}(t,t), \ldots, \mathbf{\Lambda}_{\boldsymbol{s_n}}(t,t))$$

with each $\mathbf{\Lambda}_{\boldsymbol{s_i}}(t,t)$ being the operator on Π of multiplication by the function $\frac{\partial}{\partial s_i}\Lambda(t,t,s_t,s)|_{s=s_t}$ with the function $\Lambda(t,T,s_t,s_T)$ defined according to (3.17) as

$$\mathrm{u}'(t,T,s_t,s_T) = e^{\Lambda(t,T,s_t,s_T)}. \tag{5.70}$$

In this way we can also rewrite the transformation (5.65) with the help of (5.67) as follows

$$\mu(s,t) \to \mu(s,t) + \sigma^2(s,t)\mathbf{\Lambda}_{\boldsymbol{s}}(t,t). \tag{5.71}$$

5.57. Remark. It is clear due to Remarks (5.53) and (5.56) that

$$\hat{\mathbf{u}}'(t,t) = e^{\mathbf{\Lambda}(t,t)}. \tag{5.72}$$

Now we pose a somewhat inverse problem, namely to find a transformation $\hat{\boldsymbol{g}}$ from the beliefs-preferences gauge symmetry group $\hat{\boldsymbol{\mathcal{G}}}$ such that it maps a given generator

$$\mathfrak{L}(t) = \frac{1}{2}\sum_{i,j=1}^{n} \sigma_{ij}^2(s,t)\frac{\partial^2}{\partial s_i \partial s_j} + \sum_{i=1}^{n} \mu_i(s,t)\frac{\partial}{\partial s_i}$$

to a given generator

$$\mathfrak{L}'(t) = \frac{1}{2}\sum_{i,j=1}^{n} \sigma_{ij}^2(s,t)\frac{\partial^2}{\partial s_i \partial s_j} + \sum_{i=1}^{n} \mu_i'(s,t)\frac{\partial}{\partial s_i}.$$

Due to relation (5.64) or more precisely (5.66) such a transformation $\hat{\boldsymbol{g}}$ must be generated by $\mathbf{u}'(t,t)$ such that

$$\begin{aligned}\frac{\mathbf{u}'_{\boldsymbol{s}}(t,t)}{\mathbf{u}'(t,t)} =&\sigma^{-2}(s,t)\big(\mu'(s,t) - \mu(s,t)\big) = \\ &\sigma^{-1}(s,t)\,\theta(s,t)\end{aligned} \tag{5.73}$$

where

$$\theta(s,t) = \sigma^{-1}(s,t)\big(\mu'(s,t) - \mu(s,t)\big). \tag{5.74}$$

5.58. Remark. We comment that in light of Remark (5.49) we used the same notation in the expressions (5.73) and (5.74) for the vector operator $\boldsymbol{\mu}'(s,t)$, the vector operator $\boldsymbol{\mu}(s,t)$, the matrix operator $\boldsymbol{\sigma}(s,t)$ and the vector operator $\boldsymbol{\theta}(s,t)$ with the entries being the operators $\boldsymbol{\mu}'_i(s,t)$, $\boldsymbol{\mu}_i(s,t)$, $\boldsymbol{\sigma}_{ij}(s,t)$ and $\boldsymbol{\theta}_i(s,t)$ of multiplication by the functions $\mu'_i(s,t)$, $\mu_i(s,t)$, $\sigma_{ij}(s,t)$ and $\theta_i(s,t)$ and for the vector function $\mu'(s,t)$, vector function $\mu(s,t)$, matrix function $\sigma(s,t)$ and vector function $\theta(s,t)$ with the entries $\mu'_i(s,t)$, $\mu_i(s,t)$, $\sigma_{ij}(s,t)$ and $\theta_i(s,t)$ themselves. In this regard it is clear that expressions (5.73) and (5.74) can be interpreted as either operator relations or function relations.

5.59. Definition. We call the vector function $\theta(s,t)$ the *price of risk relative to* $\mu'(s,t)$ *and* $\mu(s,t)$ or simply *relative price of risk*. Similarly, we call the vector operator $\boldsymbol{\theta}(s,t)$ the *price of risk operator relative to* $\boldsymbol{\mu}'(s,t)$ *and* $\boldsymbol{\mu}(s,t)$ or simply *relative price of risk operator*.

The terminology introduced in the preceding Definition will be justified later in this article.

5.60. Remark. In terms of the operator $\boldsymbol{\Lambda}(t,T)$ defined in (5.68) we can rewrite expression (5.73) as follows

$$\begin{aligned}\boldsymbol{\Lambda}_{\boldsymbol{s}}(t,t) =&\boldsymbol{\sigma}^{-2}(s,t)\big(\boldsymbol{\mu}'(s,t) - \boldsymbol{\mu}(s,t)\big) = \\ &\boldsymbol{\sigma}^{-1}(s,t)\,\boldsymbol{\theta}(s,t).\end{aligned} \tag{5.75}$$

The preceding expression (5.75) provides the financial interpretation for the operator $\mathbf{\Lambda}(t,T)$ of the multiplication by the function $\Lambda(t,T,s_t,s_T)$ defined in (5.70) and for the function $\Lambda(t,T,s_t,s_T)$ itself in terms of the relative price of risk operator $\boldsymbol{\theta}(s,t)$ and the relative price of risk $\theta(s,t)$.

5.61. Definition. We call the operator $\mathbf{\Lambda}(t,T)$ the *relative price of risk potential operator.* Similarly we call the function $\Lambda(t,T,s_t,s_T)$ the *relative price of risk potential.*

The terminology introduced in the preceding Definition will also be justified later in this article.

The fact that the behavior of the generators $\mathfrak{L}(t)$ of the form (5.54) under the transformations $\hat{\boldsymbol{g}}$ defined in (3.99) in the form (3.107) from the beliefs-preferences gauge symmetry group $\hat{\boldsymbol{\mathcal{G}}}$ for a Markovian market populace $\mathbb{H} = \mathbb{B} \times \mathbb{U}$, or more precisely $\mathbb{H} = \mathbb{L} \times \mathbb{U}$ can be represented as the transformations (5.65) or equivalently (5.67) of the drift $\mu(s,t)$ naturally fits our financial intuition. More precisely the transformations $\hat{\boldsymbol{g}}$ from the beliefs-preferences gauge symmetry group $\hat{\boldsymbol{\mathcal{G}}}$ for the generators $\mathfrak{L}(t)$ represented as transformations (5.65) or equivalently (5.67) of the drifts $\mu(s,t)$ are equivalent to the changes of measure due to the Girsanov Theorem.

In order to show this equivalence we obtain in the x-basis the explicit form of the transformations $\hat{\boldsymbol{g}}$ from the beliefs-preferences gauge symmetry group $\hat{\mathfrak{G}}$ in the representation given by relations (5.65), or equivalently (5.67) or (5.14).

The generator $\mathfrak{L}(t)$ given in the s-basis by relation (5.54) takes the following form in the x-basis

$$\begin{aligned}\mathfrak{L}_*(t) =& \Upsilon_{s\mapsto x}\mathfrak{L}(t)\Upsilon_{x\mapsto s} = \\ & \frac{1}{2}\sum_{i,j=1}^{n}\sigma^2_{*ij}(x,t)\frac{\partial^2}{\partial x_i \partial x_j} + \sum_{i=1}^{n}\mu_{*i}(x,t)\frac{\partial}{\partial x_i},\end{aligned} \quad (5.76)$$

where

$$\sigma^2_{*ij}(x,t) = \hat{\sigma}^2_{ij}(\mathbf{exp}\, x, t),$$

$$\mu_{*i}(x,t) = \hat{\mu}_i(\mathbf{exp}\, x, t) - \frac{1}{2}\sigma^2_{*ii}(x,t),$$

with $\hat{\sigma}^2_{ij}(s,t)$ and $\hat{\mu}_i(s,t)$ defined in relations (4.22) and (4.23).

5.62. Remark. We comment that in the derivation of relation (5.76) we have used the following chain of equalities

$$\begin{aligned}\mathfrak{L}(t) = \frac{1}{2}\sum_{i,j=1}^{n}\sigma^2_{ij}(s,t)\frac{\partial^2}{\partial s_i \partial s_j} + \sum_{i=1}^{n}\mu_i(s,t)\frac{\partial}{\partial s_i} = \\ \frac{1}{2}\sum_{i,j=1}^{n}\hat{\sigma}^2_{ij}(s,t)s_i s_j\frac{\partial^2}{\partial s_i \partial s_j} + \sum_{i=1}^{n}\hat{\mu}_i(s,t)s_i\frac{\partial}{\partial s_i} = \\ \frac{1}{2}\sum_{i,j=1}^{n}\hat{\sigma}^2_{ij}(s,t)\big(s_i\frac{\partial}{\partial s_i}\big)\big(s_j\frac{\partial}{\partial s_j}\big) + \\ \sum_{i=1}^{n}\big(\hat{\mu}_i(s,t) - \frac{1}{2}\hat{\sigma}^2_{ii}(s,t)\big)s_i\frac{\partial}{\partial s_i}\end{aligned} \tag{5.77}$$

and identity (4.24).

Similarly, the generator $\mathfrak{L}'(t)$ given in the s-basis by relation (5.63) takes the following form in the x-basis

$$\begin{aligned}\mathfrak{L}'_*(t) =& \Upsilon_{s\mapsto x}\mathfrak{L}'_*(t)\Upsilon_{x\mapsto s} = \\ & \frac{1}{2}\sum_{i,j=1}^{n}\sigma^2_{*ij}(x,t)\frac{\partial^2}{\partial x_i \partial x_j} + \sum_{i=1}^{n}\mu'_{*i}(x,t)\frac{\partial}{\partial x_i},\end{aligned} \tag{5.78}$$

where

$$\mu'_{*i}(x,t) = \hat{\mu}'_i(\mathbf{exp}\, x, t) - \frac{1}{2}\sigma^2_{*ii}(x,t),$$

with $\hat{\mu}'_i(s,t)$ defined by

$$\hat{\mu}'_i(s,t)s_i = \mu'_i(s,t).$$

Finally, we present the explicit form of the transformations (5.55) from the beliefs-preferences gauge symmetry group $\hat{\mathcal{G}}$ for the Markovian market populace $\mathbb{H} = \mathbb{B} \times \mathbb{U}$, or more precisely $\mathbb{H} = \mathbb{L} \times \mathbb{U}$ under consideration solely in the x-basis

$$\begin{aligned}
&\mathfrak{L}'_*(t) = \Upsilon_{s\mapsto x}\mathfrak{L}'(t)\Upsilon_{x\mapsto s} = \\
&\Upsilon_{s\mapsto x}\,\hat{\mathfrak{u}}'^{-1}(t,t)\,\mathfrak{L}(t)\,\hat{\mathfrak{u}}'(t,t)\Upsilon_{x\mapsto s} + \Upsilon_{s\mapsto x}\frac{\hat{\mathfrak{u}}'_t(t,t)}{\hat{\mathfrak{u}}'(t,t)}\Upsilon_{x\mapsto s} = \\
&\big(\Upsilon_{s\mapsto x}\,\hat{\mathfrak{u}}'^{-1}(t,t)\,\Upsilon_{x\mapsto s}\big)\big(\Upsilon_{s\mapsto x}\,\mathfrak{L}(t)\,\Upsilon_{x\mapsto s}\big)\big(\Upsilon_{s\mapsto x}\,\hat{\mathfrak{u}}'(t,t)\,\Upsilon_{x\mapsto s}\big) + \\
&\qquad\big(\Upsilon_{s\mapsto x}\,\hat{\mathfrak{u}}'_t(t,t)\,\Upsilon_{x\mapsto s}\big)\,\big(\Upsilon_{s\mapsto x}\,\hat{\mathfrak{u}}'^{-1}(t,t)\,\Upsilon_{x\mapsto s}\big) = \\
&\hat{\mathfrak{u}}'^{-1}_*(t,t)\,\mathfrak{L}_*(t)\,\hat{\mathfrak{u}}'_*(t,t) + \frac{\hat{\mathfrak{u}}'_{*t}(t,t)}{\hat{\mathfrak{u}}'_*(t,t)},
\end{aligned} \tag{5.79}$$

where

$$\hat{\mathfrak{u}}'_*(t,t) = \Upsilon_{s\mapsto x}\,\hat{\mathfrak{u}}'(t,t)\,\Upsilon_{x\mapsto s},$$

and where we have made use of the following chain of equalities

$$\begin{aligned}
\big(\Upsilon_{s\mapsto x}\,\hat{\mathfrak{u}}'(t,t)\,\Upsilon_{x\mapsto s}\big)^{-1} =& \Upsilon^{-1}_{x\mapsto s}\,\hat{\mathfrak{u}}'^{-1}(t,t)\,\Upsilon^{-1}_{s\mapsto x} = \\
& \Upsilon_{s\mapsto x}\,\hat{\mathfrak{u}}'^{-1}(t,t)\,\Upsilon_{x\mapsto s}.
\end{aligned}$$

5.63. Remark. In this way, the transformations from the beliefs-preferences gauge symmetry group $\hat{\mathcal{G}}$ in the case under consideration can be trivially reformulated in the case when $\mathfrak{L}(t)$ is a general second order linear partial differential operator on $\Pi(\mathbb{R}^n)$ with the free coefficient being zero.

5.64. Remark. We comment that, as should be expected, for the transformations (5.55) from the beliefs-preferences gauge symmetry group $\hat{\mathcal{G}}$ in the x-basis, $\hat{\mathfrak{u}}'_*(t,t)$, or more precisely $\hat{\mathfrak{u}}'_*(\overset{3}{t},\overset{1}{t})$ is the operator on $\Pi(\mathbb{R}^n)$ of multiplication by the function

$$\begin{aligned}
\hat{\mathfrak{u}}'_*(t,t,\overset{3}{x}_t,\overset{1}{x}_t) =& \big(\Upsilon_{s\mapsto x}\hat{\mathfrak{u}}'(t,t,\cdot,\cdot)\big)(\overset{3}{x}_t,\overset{1}{x}_t) = \\
& \hat{\mathfrak{u}}'(t,t,\mathbf{exp}\,\overset{3}{x}_t,\mathbf{exp}\,\overset{1}{x}_t),
\end{aligned}$$

where the operator $\mathfrak{L}_*(t)$, or more precisely $\mathfrak{L}_*(\overset{2}{t})$ on $\Pi(\mathbb{R}^n)$ acts second.

5.65. Remark. We comment that the preceding transformations in (5.79) from the beliefs-preferences gauge symmetry group $\hat{\mathcal{G}}$ in the x-basis remain true in the general case of a Markovian market populace $\mathbb{H} = \mathbb{B} \times \mathbb{U}$, or more precisely $\mathbb{H} = \mathbb{L} \times \mathbb{U}$.

In the x-basis relation (5.64) takes he following form

$$\mu'_*(x,t) = \mu_*(x,t) + \sigma_*^2(x,t)\frac{\hat{\mathbf{u}}'_{*\boldsymbol{x}}(t,t)}{\hat{\mathbf{u}}'_*(t,t)}, \tag{5.80}$$

where

$$\hat{\mathbf{u}}'_{*\boldsymbol{x}}(t,t) = (\hat{\mathbf{u}}'_{*\boldsymbol{x_1}}(t,t), \hat{\mathbf{u}}'_{*\boldsymbol{x_2}}(t,t), \ldots, \hat{\mathbf{u}}'_{*\boldsymbol{x_n}}(t,t))$$

with each $\hat{\mathbf{u}}'_{*\boldsymbol{x_i}}(t,t)$ being the operator on $\Pi(\mathbb{R}^n)$ of multiplication by the function $\frac{\partial}{\partial x_i}\hat{\mathrm{u}}'_*(t,t,x_t,x)|_{x=x_t}$. We comment that

$$\mu_*(x,t) = (\mu_{*1}(x,t), \mu_{*2}(x,t), \ldots, \mu_{*n}(x,t))$$

and

$$\mu'_*(x,t) = (\mu'_{*1}(x,t), \mu'_{*2}(x,t), \ldots, \mu'_{*n}(x,t)).$$

5.66. Remark. We comment that in the derivation of relation (5.80) we have made use of the following obvious relation

$$s\,\hat{\mu}'(s,t) = s\,\hat{\mu}(s,t) + s\,\hat{\sigma}^2(s,t)\,s\,\frac{\hat{\mathbf{u}}'_{\boldsymbol{s}}(t,t)}{\hat{\mathbf{u}}'(t,t)}, \tag{5.81}$$

or equivalently

$$\hat{\mu}'(s,t) = \hat{\mu}(s,t) + \hat{\sigma}^2(s,t)\frac{s\,\hat{\mathbf{u}}'_{\boldsymbol{s}}(t,t)}{\hat{\mathbf{u}}'(t,t)}, \tag{5.82}$$

and identity (4.11). We note that in the preceding relations (5.81) and (5.82) the set $\mathbb{R}^n_{++}$ with members s is realized as the set of all $n \times n$ diagonal matrixes with positive entries.

Therefore, the representation of the transformations $\hat{g}$ from the beliefs-preferences gauge symmetry group $\hat{\mathcal{G}}$ as the transformations of the drift $\mu(s,t)$ given in the s-basis by (5.65) takes the following form in the x-basis

$$\mu'_*(x,t) \rightarrow \mu_*(x,t) + \sigma_*^2(x,t)\frac{\hat{\mathbf{u}}'_{*\boldsymbol{x}}(t,t)}{\hat{\mathbf{u}}'_*(t,t)}. \tag{5.83}$$

5.67. Remark. It is clear that due to Remark (5.53) the following equalities hold:

$$\hat{\mathbf{u}}'_*(t,t) = \mathbf{u}'_*(t,t), \tag{5.84}$$

$$\hat{\mathbf{u}}'_{*\boldsymbol{x}_i}(t,t) = \mathbf{u}'_{*\boldsymbol{x}_i}(t,t), \tag{5.85}$$

and

$$\hat{\mathbf{u}}'_{*\boldsymbol{x}_i\boldsymbol{x}_j}(t,t) = \mathbf{u}'_{*\boldsymbol{x}_i\boldsymbol{x}_j}(t,t), \tag{5.86}$$

where

$$\mathbf{u}'_*(t,t) = \Upsilon_{s\mapsto x}\,\mathbf{u}'^{-1}(t,t)\,\Upsilon_{x\mapsto s}$$

with $\hat{\mathbf{u}}'(t,T)$ defined in (3.106).

We comment that $\hat{\mathbf{u}}'_{*\boldsymbol{x}_i\boldsymbol{x}_j}(t,t)$ is the operator on Π of multiplication by the function $\frac{\partial^2}{\partial x_i \partial x_j}\hat{\mathrm{u}}'_*(t,t,x_t,x)|_{x=x_t}$.

We also comment that $\mathbf{u}'_*(t,t)$, $\mathbf{u}'_{*\boldsymbol{x}_i}(t,t)$ and $\mathbf{u}'_{*\boldsymbol{x}_i\boldsymbol{x}_j}(t,t)$ are the operators on Π of multiplication by the functions $\mathrm{u}'_*(t,t,x_t,x_t)$, $\frac{\partial}{\partial x_i}\mathrm{u}'_*(t,t,x_t,x)|_{x=x_t}$ and $\frac{\partial^2}{\partial x_i \partial x_j}\mathrm{u}'_*(t,t,x_t,x)|_{x=x_t}$.

5.68. Remark. Due to relations (5.84) and (5.85) we can rewrite relation (5.80) as follows

$$\mu'_*(x,t) = \mu_*(x,t) + \sigma_*^2(x,t)\frac{\mathbf{u}'_{*\boldsymbol{x}}(t,t)}{\mathbf{u}'_*(t,t)}, \tag{5.87}$$

where

$$\mathbf{u}'_{*\boldsymbol{x}}(t,t) = (\mathbf{u}'_{*\boldsymbol{x}_1}(t,t), \mathbf{u}'_{*\boldsymbol{x}_2}(t,t), \ldots, \mathbf{u}'_{*\boldsymbol{x}_n}(t,t)).$$

In this way we can also rewrite the transformation (5.83) as follows

$$\mu'_*(x,t) \to \mu_*(x,t) + \sigma_*^2(x,t)\frac{\mathbf{u}'_{*\boldsymbol{x}}(t,t)}{\mathbf{u}'_*(t,t)}. \tag{5.88}$$

5.69. Remark. According to Remark (5.66) relation (5.69) takes the following form in the x-basis

$$\mu'_*(x,t) = \mu_*(x,t) + \sigma_*^2(x,t)\boldsymbol{\Lambda}_{*\boldsymbol{x}}(t,t), \tag{5.89}$$

where

$$\boldsymbol{\Lambda}_*(t,t) = \Upsilon_{s\mapsto x}\,\boldsymbol{\Lambda}(t,t)\,\Upsilon_{x\mapsto s}$$

with $\boldsymbol{\Lambda}(t,t)$ defined in (5.68).

In this way the transformation (5.71) takes the following form in the x-basis

$$\mu'_*(x,t) \to \mu_*(x,t) + \sigma_*^2\boldsymbol{\Lambda}_{*\boldsymbol{x}}(t,t). \tag{5.90}$$

We comment that $\boldsymbol{\Lambda}_*(t,t)$, or more precisely $\boldsymbol{\Lambda}_*(\overset{3}{t},\overset{1}{t})$ is the operator on $\Pi(\mathbb{R}^n)$ of multiplication by the function

$$\Lambda_*(t,t,\overset{3}{x}_t,\overset{1}{x}_t) = \left(\Upsilon_{s\mapsto x}\,\Lambda_*(t,t,\cdot,\cdot)\right)(\overset{3}{x}_t,\overset{1}{x}_t) = \Lambda_*(t,t,\mathbf{exp}\,\overset{3}{x}_t,\mathbf{exp}\,\overset{1}{x}_t),$$

where the operator $\mathfrak{L}_*(t)$, or more precisely $\mathfrak{L}_*(\overset{2}{t})$ on $\Pi(\mathbb{R}^n)$ acts second.

We also comment that

$$\boldsymbol{\Lambda}_{*\boldsymbol{x}}(t,t) = (\boldsymbol{\Lambda}_{*\boldsymbol{x}_1}(t,t), \boldsymbol{\Lambda}_{*\boldsymbol{x}_2}(t,t), \ldots, \boldsymbol{\Lambda}_{*\boldsymbol{x}_n}(t,t))$$

with each $\boldsymbol{\Lambda}_{*\boldsymbol{x}_i}(t,t)$, or more precisely $\boldsymbol{\Lambda}_{*\boldsymbol{x}_i}(\overset{3}{t},\overset{1}{t})$ being the operator on $\Pi(\mathbb{R}^n)$ of multiplication by the function $\Lambda_{*x_i}(t,t,x_t,x_t)$ or more precisely $\Lambda_{*x_i}(t,t,\overset{3}{x}_t,\overset{1}{x}_t)$ where

$$\Lambda_{*x_i}(t,t,x_t,x_t) = \frac{\partial}{\partial x_i}\Lambda_*(t,t,x_t,x)|_{x=x_t}.$$

It is also clear that

$$\mathbf{u}'_*(t,t) = e^{\mathbf{\Lambda}_*(t,t)} \tag{5.91}$$

and

$$\mathbf{u}'_*(t,t,\overset{3}{x}_t,\overset{1}{x}_t) = e^{\Lambda_*(t,t,\overset{3}{x}_t,\overset{1}{x}_t)}. \tag{5.92}$$

This completes the Remark.

5.70. Remark. It is clear due to Remarks (5.67) and (5.69) that

$$\hat{\mathbf{u}}'_*(t,t) = e^{\mathbf{\Lambda}_*(t,t)}. \tag{5.93}$$

Now we pose a somewhat inverse problem, namely to find a transformation $\hat{\boldsymbol{g}}$ from the beliefs-preferences gauge symmetry group $\hat{\boldsymbol{\mathcal{G}}}$ such that it maps a given generator $\mathfrak{L}(t)$ defined in the x-basis by

$$\mathfrak{L}_*(t) = \frac{1}{2}\sum_{i,j=1}^{n} \sigma^2_{*ij}(x,t)\frac{\partial^2}{\partial x_i \partial x_j} + \sum_{i=1}^{n} \mu_{*i}(x,t)\frac{\partial}{\partial x_i}$$

to a given generator $\mathfrak{L}'(t)$ defined in the x-basis by

$$\mathfrak{L}'_*(t) = \frac{1}{2}\sum_{i,j=1}^{n} \sigma^2_{*ij}(x,t)\frac{\partial^2}{\partial x_i \partial x_j} + \sum_{i=1}^{n} \mu_{*i}(x,t)\frac{\partial}{\partial x_i}.$$

Due to relation (5.80) or more precisely (5.87) such a transformation $\hat{\boldsymbol{g}}$ must be generated by $\hat{\mathbf{u}}'(t,t)$ such that

$$\frac{\mathbf{u}'_{*x}(t,t)}{\mathbf{u}'_*(t,t)} = \frac{\mu'_*(x,t) - \mu_*(x,t)}{\sigma^2_*(x,t)} = \sigma_*^{-1}(x,t)\,\theta_*(x,t) \tag{5.94}$$

where

$$\theta_*(x,t) = \frac{\mu'_*(x,t) - \mu_*(x,t)}{\sigma_*(x,t)}. \tag{5.95}$$

5.71. Remark. We comment that in light of Remark (5.49) we used the same notation in relations (5.94) and (5.95) for the vector operator $\boldsymbol{\mu}'_*(x,t)$, the vector operator $\boldsymbol{\mu}_*(x,t)$, the matrix operator $\boldsymbol{\sigma}_*(x,t)$ and the vector operator $\boldsymbol{\theta}_*(x,t)$ with the entries being the operators $\boldsymbol{\mu}'_{*i}(x,t)$, $\boldsymbol{\mu}_{*i}(x,t)$, $\boldsymbol{\sigma}_{*ij}(x,t)$ and $\boldsymbol{\theta}_{*i}(x,t)$ of multiplication by the functions $\mu'_{*i}(x,t)$, $\mu_{*i}(x,t)$, $\sigma_{*ij}(x,t)$ and $\theta_{*i}(x,t)$ and for the vector function $\mu'_*(x,t)$, vector function $\mu_*(x,t)$, matrix function $\sigma_*(x,t)$ and vector function $\theta_*(x,t)$ with the entries being the functions $\mu'_{*i}(x,t)$, $\mu_{*i}(x,t)$, $\sigma_{*ij}(x,t)$ and $\theta_{*i}(x,t)$ themselves. In this regard it is clear that expressions (5.94) and (5.95) can be interpreted as either operator relations or function relations.

5.72. Remark. Relation (5.94) can also be obtained from relation (5.73) in the form

$$\frac{s\,\mathbf{u}'_s(t,t)}{\mathbf{u}'(t,t)} = \hat{\sigma}^{-2}(s,t)\big(\hat{\mu}'(s,t) - \hat{\mu}(s,t)\big) = \hat{\sigma}^{-1}(s,t)\,\theta(s,t) \tag{5.96}$$

expressed in the x-basis with the help of identity (4.24). We comment that, in the preceding relation (5.96), the set $\mathbb{R}^n_{++}$ with members s was realized as the set of all $n \times n$ diagonal matrixes with positive entries.

5.73. Remark. It is clear that the vector operator $\boldsymbol{\theta}_*(x,t)$ and the vector function $\theta_*(x,t)$ are the expressions in the x-basis of the vector operator $\boldsymbol{\theta}(s,t)$ and the vector function $\theta(s,t)$ defined in (5.74), that is

$$\boldsymbol{\theta}_{*i}(x,t) = \Upsilon_{s\mapsto x}\,\boldsymbol{\theta}_i(s,t)\,\Upsilon_{x\mapsto s} \tag{5.97}$$

and

$$\theta_{*i}(x,t) = \big(\Upsilon_{s\mapsto x}\,\theta_i(\cdot,t)\big)(x). \tag{5.98}$$

5.74. Remark. In terms of the operator $\boldsymbol{\Lambda}_*(t,t)$ defined in (5.91) we can rewrite expression (5.94) as follows

$$\begin{aligned}\boldsymbol{\Lambda}_{*x}(t,t) =&\boldsymbol{\sigma}_*^{-2}(x,t)\big(\boldsymbol{\mu}'_*(x,t) - \boldsymbol{\mu}_*(x,t)\big) = \\ &\boldsymbol{\sigma}_*^{-1}(x,t)\,\boldsymbol{\theta}_*(x,t).\end{aligned} \tag{5.99}$$

Now we are ready to present the generalizations of Theorems (5.33), (5.34) and (5.35) on the equivalence of transformations of the drift of the generators $\mathfrak{L}(t)$ due to the beliefs-preferences gauge symmetry group $\hat{\mathcal{G}}$ for the Markovian market populace $\mathbb{H} = \mathbb{B}\times\mathbb{U}$, or more precisely $\mathbb{H} = \mathbb{L}\times\mathbb{U}$ under consideration with the transformations of the drift due to the changes of measure in the Girsanov Theorem to the case of n underlying securities.

5.75. Theorem. Let $\mu_*(x,t)$, $\mu'_*(x,t)$ and $\sigma_*(x,t)$ satisfy the conditions for g, f and σ in the Fact (5.17). Then the transformation of the drift

$$g(x,t) \to f(x,t)$$

in the Fact (5.17) due to the change of measure in the Girsanov Theorem generated by $\theta = \theta(x,t)$ coincides with the transformation of the drift

$$\mu_*(x,t) \to \mu'_*(x,t)$$

in (5.83) due to the transformation $\hat{\boldsymbol{g}}$ from the beliefs-preferences gauge symmetry group $\hat{\mathcal{G}}$ defined in (3.107) for the generators $\mathfrak{L}(t)$ defined in the x-basis by (5.76) whenever $\hat{\boldsymbol{g}}$ is generated by $\hat{\mathbf{u}}'(t,T)$ defined in the x-basis in (5.94) and whenever $\theta(x,t) = \theta_*(x,t)$ and $\sigma(x,t) = \sigma_*(x,t)$.

Proof. The proof directly follows from the explicit expressions of the transformations of the drifts in the Fact (5.17) and in relation (5.83). □

5.76. Theorem. The representation of the beliefs-preferences gauge symmetry group $\hat{\mathcal{G}}$ defined in (3.107) for the generators

$\mathfrak{L}(t)$ of the form (5.76) in the x-basis as the group of transformations of the drift

$$\mu_*(x,t) \to \mu'_*(x,t)$$

defined in (5.83) is isomorphic to the group of transformations of the drift

$$g(x,t) \to f(x,t)$$

in the Fact (5.17) and the Theorem (5.18) due to the changes of measure in the Girsanov Theorem generated by $\theta = \theta(x,t)$ in $\mathcal{L}$.

Proof. Directly follows from Theorems (5.75) and (5.18). □

5.77. Theorem. The representation of the beliefs-preferences gauge symmetry group $\hat{\mathcal{G}}$ defined in (3.107) for the generators $\mathfrak{L}(t)$ of the form (5.76) in the x-basis as the group of transformations of the drift

$$\mu_*(x,t) \to \mu'_*(x,t)$$

defined in (5.83) is isomorphic to the abelian group of transformations or, equivalently, of changes of measure $P \to Q$ in the Girsanov Theorem generated by θ in $\mathcal{L}$.

Proof. The proof directly follows from Theorems (5.76) and (5.19). □

5.78. Remark. We established in the preceding Theorems (5.75), (5.76) and (5.77) the equivalence of transformations of the drift $\mu(s,t)$ of the generators $\mathfrak{L}(t)$ due to the beliefs-preferences gauge symmetry group $\hat{\mathcal{G}}$ for the Markovian market populace $\mathbb{H} = \mathbb{B} \times \mathbb{U}$, or more precisely $\mathbb{H} = \mathbb{L} \times \mathbb{U}$ under consideration with the transformations of the drift due to the changes of measure in the Girsanov Theorem by means of expressing the generator $\mathfrak{L}(t)$ and drift $\mu(s,t)$ in the x-basis. The same results can be achieved directly for the transformations of the drift $\mu(s,t)$ of the generators $\mathfrak{L}(t)$ in the s-basis by means of Ito processes obeying the following stochastic differential equation

$$dS_t = \mu(S_t,t)dt + \sigma(S_t,t)dB_t, \quad S_0 \in \mathbb{R}^n_{++},$$

with almost surely positive solutions.

5.79. Remark. In view of Theorems (5.75), (5.76) and (5.77) we can consider the transformations

$$\boldsymbol{F}(t,T) \xrightarrow{g_{\mathcal{B}}} \hat{\mathbf{u}}'^{-1}(t,t)\boldsymbol{F}(t,T)\hat{\mathbf{u}}'(t,T), \quad g = (g_{\mathcal{B}}, g_{\mathcal{U}}) \in \mathcal{G}$$

of the probability measures determined by $\boldsymbol{F}(t,T)$ associated with the transformation

$$\mathfrak{L}(t) \xrightarrow{\hat{g}_{\mathfrak{L}}} \hat{\mathbf{u}}'^{-1}(t,t)\,\mathfrak{L}(t)\,\hat{\mathbf{u}}'(t,t) + \frac{\hat{\mathbf{u}}'_t(t,t)}{\hat{\mathbf{u}}'(t,t)}, \quad \hat{g} = (\hat{g}_{\mathfrak{L}}, \hat{g}_{\mathcal{U}}) \in \hat{\mathcal{G}}$$

in both s-basis and x-basis as a natural extension of the changes of measure due to the Girsanov Theorem. It is clear that $\boldsymbol{F}(t,T)$ is in $\mathcal{B}$ with generators $\mathfrak{L}(t)$ and $\hat{\mathbf{u}}'^{-1}(t,t)\boldsymbol{F}(t,T)\hat{\mathbf{u}}'(t,T)$ is in $g_{\mathcal{B}}\mathcal{B}$ with generators

$$\hat{\mathbf{u}}'^{-1}(t,t)\,\mathfrak{L}(t)\,\hat{\mathbf{u}}'(t,t) + \frac{\hat{\mathbf{u}}'_t(t,t)}{\hat{\mathbf{u}}'(t,t)}.$$

We comment that we have made use of Remark (3.151).

It is well known [44] that in the case of the Markovian market populace $\mathbb{H} = \mathbb{B} \times \mathbb{U}$, or more precisely $\mathbb{H} = \mathbb{L} \times \mathbb{U}$ under consideration the value $v = v(t)$ in Π of a European contingent claim with inception time t, expiration time T and payoff v_T in Π is a possibly generalized solution of the Cauchy problem for the Black and Scholes equation

$$\begin{aligned}\frac{\partial}{\partial t}v + \frac{1}{2}\sum_{i,j=1}^{n} \hat{\sigma}^2_{ij}(s,t)\, s_i s_j \frac{\partial^2}{\partial s_i \partial s_j}v + \\ \sum_{i=1}^{n}\big(r(s,t) - d_i(s,t)\big)\, s_i \frac{\partial}{\partial s_i}v - \\ r(s,t)v = 0, \quad t < T, \\ v(T) = v_T,\end{aligned} \tag{5.100}$$

where $\hat{\sigma}^2_{ij}(s,t)$ is the variance-covariance matrix of returns per unit time, $r(s,t)$ is the continuously compounded interest rate and $d_i(s,t)$ is the continuously compounded dividend yield of the i-th stock with $i = 1, \ldots, n$ in terms of the underlying securities being stocks.

5.80. Remark. We recall that the case under consideration is that of the Markovian market populace $\mathbb{H} = \mathbb{B} \times \mathbb{U}$, or more precisely $\mathbb{H} = \mathbb{L} \times \mathbb{U}$ in the general case of n underlying securities and when each belief $\boldsymbol{\mathcal{B}}$ in the market populace belief $\mathbb{B}$ is generated by the family

$$\mathfrak{L} = \{\mathfrak{L}(t) : \Pi \to \Pi \,|\, t \in \mathcal{T}\},$$

in $\mathbb{L}$ with each generator $\mathfrak{L}(t)$ at time t of the form (5.54)

5.81. Remark. We comment that in order to derive the Black and Scholes equation (5.100) one has to assume that the pure discount bonds with all maturity times and the underlying securities themselves are traded at any time from the trading time set.

Following [33] we call a market environment

$$\mathbf{V}^{BS} = \{\mathbf{V}^{BS}(t,T) : \Pi \to \Pi \,|\, t, T \in \mathcal{T}, t \le T\}$$

generated by the family

$$\boldsymbol{L}^{BS} = \{\boldsymbol{L}^{BS}(t) : \Pi \to \Pi \,|\, t \in \mathcal{T}\}$$

with the generator $\boldsymbol{L}^{BS}(t)$ at time t defined by

$$\begin{aligned}\boldsymbol{L}^{BS}(t) = \frac{1}{2} \sum_{i,j=1}^{n} \hat{\sigma}^2_{ij}(s,t)\, s_i s_j \frac{\partial^2}{\partial s_i \partial s_j} + \\ \sum_{i=1}^{n} \big(r(s,t) - d_i(s,t)\big)\, s_i \frac{\partial}{\partial s_i} - r(s,t)\end{aligned}$$

a *Black and Scholes* market environment.

5.82. Remark. We comment that for the sake of simplicity we have used the same notations for the operators of multiplication by the functions $r(s,t)$ and $d_i(s,t)$ and for the functions $r(s,t)$ and $d_i(s,t)$ themselves. Whenever we would like to distinguish the operators of multiplication by the functions $r(s,t)$ and $d_i(s,t)$ from the functions $r(s,t)$ and $d_i(s,t)$ themselves we will denote these operators by $\boldsymbol{r}(s,t)$ and $\boldsymbol{d}_i(s,t)$.

5.83. Definition. We call a market participant $\mathcal{H} = (\mathcal{B},\mathcal{U})$ in $\mathbb{H} = \mathbb{B} \times \mathbb{U}$ a *risk-neutral market participant* if:

(i) the belief $\mathcal{B}$ is generated by

$$\mathfrak{L} = \{\mathfrak{L}(t) : \Pi \to \Pi \,|\, t \in \mathcal{T}\}$$

with the generator $\mathfrak{L}(t)$ at time t defined by

$$\mathfrak{L}(t) = \frac{1}{2}\sum_{i,j=1}^{n} \hat{\sigma}_{ij}^2(s,t)\, s_i s_j \frac{\partial^2}{\partial s_i \partial s_j} + \sum_{i=1}^{n}\big(r(s,t) - d_i(s,t)\big)\, s_i \frac{\partial}{\partial s_i},$$

and

(ii) the preference

$$\mathcal{U} = \{\boldsymbol{u}'(t,T) : \Pi(\mathbb{R}^{2n}_{++}) \to \Pi(\mathbb{R}^{2n}_{++}) \,|\, t,T \in \mathcal{T}, t \le T\}$$

is such that each $\boldsymbol{u}'(t,T)$ is given by

$$\boldsymbol{u}'(t,T) = e^{-\int_t^T \overset{\tau}{\boldsymbol{r}}(s,\tau)d\tau},$$

where the index over the operator $\boldsymbol{r}(s,\tau)$ indicates its order which is assumed to be inverse to that of τ.

We call the belief $\mathcal{B}$ and preference $\mathcal{U}$ of the risk-neutral market participant $\mathcal{H} = (\mathcal{B},\mathcal{U})$ a *risk-neutral belief* and a *risk-neutral preference.* Moreover, we call the family $\mathfrak{L}$ of generators $\mathfrak{L}(t)$ a *risk-neutral family of generators* and the generators $\mathfrak{L}(t)$ themselves *risk-neutral generators.*

5.84. Remark. It is clear that risk-neutral market participants exist due to Remark (3.149).

5.85. Remark. In the case of Markovian market populace $\mathbb{H} = \mathbb{B} \times \mathbb{U}$, or more precisely $\mathbb{H} = \mathbb{B} \times \mathbb{U}$ under consideration, a market generation, that is, an orbit of the group $\mathcal{G}$ in $\mathbb{H} = \mathbb{B} \times \mathbb{U}$, or equivalently due to Remark (3.151), an orbit of the group $\hat{\mathcal{G}}$ in $\mathbb{H} = \mathbb{L} \times \mathbb{U}$ admits the following description. Due to the fact that transformations in (3.99) or equivalently (3.107) from the beliefs-preferences gauge symmetry group $\hat{\mathfrak{G}}$ for the generators $\mathfrak{L}(t)$ of the form (5.54) can be represented as the transformations in (5.65), or equivalently (5.67) of the drift $\mu(s,t)$ leaving the variance-covariance matrix $\sigma^2(s,t)$ unchanged, each such orbit can be uniquely characterized by $\sigma(s,t)$ as a matrix function on the set $\mathbb{R}^n_{++} \times \mathcal{T}$. Moreover, each market participant $\mathcal{H} = (\mathcal{B}, \mathcal{U})$ in such an orbit can be uniquely characterized by a drift $\mu(s,t)$ as a vector function on the set $\mathbb{R}^n_{++} \times \mathcal{T}$. We comment that each market participant in such an orbit can be uniquely characterized by a drift up to an equivalence class of indistinguishable market participants with indistinguishable preferences. In addition we note that each such orbit in the Markovian market populace $\mathbb{H} = \mathbb{B} \times \mathbb{U}$, or more precisely $\mathbb{H} = \mathbb{B} \times \mathbb{U}$ under consideration contains one and only one risk-neutral market participant and that each risk-neutral market participant in the Markovian market populace $\mathbb{H} = \mathbb{B} \times \mathbb{U}$, or more precisely $\mathbb{H} = \mathbb{B} \times \mathbb{U}$ under consideration is contained in one and only one such orbit.

Finally, we recall that the case of the Markovian market populace $\mathbb{H} = \mathbb{B} \times \mathbb{U}$, or more precisely $\mathbb{H} = \mathbb{L} \times \mathbb{U}$ under consideration is that of n underlying securities and when each belief $\mathcal{B}$ in the market populace belief $\mathbb{B}$ is generated by the family

$$\mathfrak{L} = \{\mathfrak{L}(t) : \Pi \to \Pi \,|\, t \in \mathcal{T}\},$$

in $\mathbb{L}$ with each generator $\mathfrak{L}(t)$ at time t of the form (5.54). This completes the Remark.

Due to relation (5.73), or more precisely (5.96) the transformation $\hat{g}$ from the beliefs-preferences gauge symmetry group $\hat{\mathcal{G}}$

that maps a risk-neutral generator

$$\mathfrak{L}(t) = \frac{1}{2}\sum_{i,j=1}^{n} \hat{\sigma}_{ij}^2(s,t)\, s_i s_j \frac{\partial^2}{\partial s_i \partial s_j} + \sum_{i=1}^{n}\big(r(s,t) - d_i(s,t)\big)\, s_i \frac{\partial}{\partial s_i}$$

to a given generator

$$\mathfrak{L}'(t) = \frac{1}{2}\sum_{i,j=1}^{n} \hat{\sigma}_{ij}^2(s,t)\, s_i s_j \frac{\partial^2}{\partial s_i \partial s_j} + \sum_{i=1}^{n} \hat{\mu}_i(s,t)\, s_i \frac{\partial}{\partial s_i}$$

is generated by $\mathbf{u}'(t,t)$ such that

$$\frac{s\,\mathbf{u}'_s(t,t)}{\mathbf{u}'(t,t)} = \frac{\hat{\mu}'(s,t) - \big(\mathfrak{r}(s,t) - d(s,t)\big)}{\hat{\sigma}^2(s,t)} = \hat{\sigma}^{-1}(s,t)\,\theta(s,t) \tag{5.101}$$

where

$$\theta(s,t) = \hat{\sigma}^{-1}(s,t)\big(\hat{\mu}'(s,t) - \big(\mathfrak{r}(s,t) - d(s,t)\big)\big), \tag{5.102}$$

and where

$$\mathfrak{r}(s,t) = (\underbrace{r(s,t), r(s,t), \ldots, r(s,t)}_{n}),$$

and

$$d(s,t) = (d_1(s,t), d_2(s,t), \ldots, d_n(s,t)).$$

We comment that in relation (5.101) the set $\mathbb{R}^n_{++}$ with members s was realized as the set of all $n \times n$ diagonal matrixes with positive entries.

5.86. Remark. We comment that in light of Remark (5.49) we used the same notation in relations (5.101) and (5.102) for the vector operator $\hat{\boldsymbol{\mu}}'(s,t)$, the vector operator $\mathfrak{r}(s,t) - \boldsymbol{d}(s,t)$, the matrix operator $\hat{\boldsymbol{\sigma}}(s,t)$ and the vector operator $\boldsymbol{\theta}(s,t)$ with the entries being the operators $\hat{\boldsymbol{\mu}}_i'(s,t)$, $\boldsymbol{r}(s,t)-\boldsymbol{d}_i(s,t)$, $\hat{\boldsymbol{\sigma}}_{ij}(s,t)$ and $\boldsymbol{\theta}_i(s,t)$ of multiplication by the functions $\hat{\mu}_i'(s,t)$, $r(s,t)-d_i(s,t)$, $\hat{\sigma}_{ij}(s,t)$ and $\theta_i(s,t)$ and for the vector function $\hat{\mu}'(s,t)$, vector function $\mathfrak{r}(s,t) - d(s,t)$, matrix function $\hat{\sigma}(s,t)$ and vector function $\theta(s,t)$ with the entries being the functions $\hat{\mu}_i'(s,t)$, $r(s,t) - d_i(s,t)$, $\hat{\sigma}_{ij}(s,t)$ and $\theta_i(s,t)$ themselves. In this regard it is clear that relations (5.101) and (5.102) can be interpreted as either operator relations or function relations.

It is clear from the financial standpoint that $\theta(s,t)$ is nothing but the *market price of risk.* This justifies the following definition.

5.87. Definition. We call the vector operator $\boldsymbol{\theta}(s,t)$ defined in the preceding Remark (5.86) a *market price of risk operator.*

5.88. Remark. The preceding Definition justifies the terminology we have introduced in Definition (5.59) for the vector operator $\boldsymbol{\theta}(s,t)$ and the vector function $\theta(s,t)$ defined in relation (5.74).

5.89. Remark. In terms of the operator $\boldsymbol{\Lambda}(t,T)$ defined in (5.68) we can rewrite expression (5.101) as follows

$$\begin{aligned} s\,\boldsymbol{\Lambda}_{\boldsymbol{s}}(t,t) =& \hat{\boldsymbol{\sigma}}^{-2}(s,t)\big(\hat{\boldsymbol{\mu}}'(s,t) - \big(r(s,t) - d(s,t)\big)\big) = \\ & \hat{\boldsymbol{\sigma}}^{-1}(s,t)\,\boldsymbol{\theta}(s,t), \end{aligned} \tag{5.103}$$

where the set $\mathbb{R}^n_{++}$ with members s is realized as the set of all $n \times n$ diagonal matrixes with positive entries.

5.90. Definition. We call the operator $\boldsymbol{\Lambda}(t,T)$ obeying the identity (5.103) the *market price of risk potential operator.* Similarly we call the vector function $\Lambda(t,T,s_t,s_T)$ the *market price of risk potential.*

We make the following crucial observation. In the case of the Markovian market populace $\mathbb{H} = \mathbb{B} \times \mathbb{U}$, or more precisely $\mathbb{H} = \mathbb{L} \times \mathbb{U}$ under consideration the values of European contingent claims are determined by the Cauchy problem for the Black and Scholes equation (5.100) which, in turn, is determined by a risk-neutral market participant, or more precisely by the belief and preference of a risk-neutral market participant, and this risk-neutral market participant is determined by the particular choice of gauge. Therefore, it might seem that valuation of European contingent claims, at least in a Black and Scholes market environment, is based on the particular choice of gauge, that is, on the breaking of the beliefs-preferences gauge symmetry for a general Markovian market populace $\mathbb{H} = \mathbb{B} \times \mathbb{U}$, or more precisely $\mathbb{H} = \mathbb{L} \times \mathbb{U}$. However, this is not the case and in fact, as we will show in the next Section (6), valuation of European contingent claims in a general market environment, valuation that is independent of the beliefs and preferences of market participants is based not on the breaking of the beliefs-preferences gauge symmetry for a general Markovian market populace $\mathbb{H} = \mathbb{B} \times \mathbb{U}$, or more precisely $\mathbb{H} = \mathbb{L} \times \mathbb{U}$ but on the contrary, is based on promoting the beliefs-preferences gauge symmetry to a certain larger symmetry.

6 Application of the Beliefs-Preferences Gauge Symmetry Group to the Dynamic Replication of European Contingent Claims

First we consider the general case of a nonnecessarily Markovian market populace.

6.1 The General Case of a Market Populace

Suppose that a trading time set $\mathcal{T}$ contains t and an open neighborhood $\mathcal{N}_t(\mathcal{T})$ of t. Assume that $\boldsymbol{F}(t,T)$ and $\mathbf{u}'(t,T)$ in the belief $\boldsymbol{\mathcal{B}}$ and the preference $\boldsymbol{\mathcal{U}}$ of a market participant $\boldsymbol{\mathcal{H}} = (\boldsymbol{\mathcal{B}}, \boldsymbol{\mathcal{U}})$ are, in an appropriate sense, differentiable with respect to the time variables at t for each market participant $\boldsymbol{\mathcal{H}} = (\boldsymbol{\mathcal{B}}, \boldsymbol{\mathcal{U}})$ in the market populace $\mathbb{H} = \mathbb{B} \times \mathbb{U}$.

As we have seen in Subsection (3.5) of Section (3) the values v of European contingent claims remain unchanged under the action of dynamic beliefs-preferences gauge symmetry group $\hat{\boldsymbol{\mathcal{G}}}$ for a market populace $\mathbb{H} = \mathbb{B} \times \mathbb{U}$ defined in (3.66), or equivalently (3.67). In this way, the dynamic beliefs-preferences gauge symmetry group $\hat{\boldsymbol{\mathcal{G}}}$ provides us with the complete description of the degrees of freedom that market participants $\boldsymbol{\mathcal{H}} = (\boldsymbol{\mathcal{B}}, \boldsymbol{\mathcal{U}})$ in $\mathbb{H} = \mathbb{B} \times \mathbb{U}$ that populate a marketplace at the time t in $\mathcal{T}$ have in terms of their beliefs $\boldsymbol{\mathcal{B}}$ in $\mathbb{B}$ and preferences $\boldsymbol{\mathcal{U}}$ in $\mathbb{U}$. That is, the set of all market participants $\boldsymbol{\mathcal{H}} = (\boldsymbol{\mathcal{B}}, \boldsymbol{\mathcal{U}})$ in $\mathbb{H} = \mathbb{B} \times \mathbb{U}$ that agree at time t in $\mathcal{T}$ upon the values at the time t of a set of European contingent claims with inception time t and expiration time T for all T in the chosen open neighborhood $\mathcal{N}_t(\mathcal{T})$ of t with $t \leq T$ whose payoffs form a dense set is nothing but an orbit of the group $\hat{\boldsymbol{\mathcal{G}}}$. We comment that the interpretation of the action of $\hat{\boldsymbol{\mathcal{G}}}$ on $\mathbb{H} = \mathbb{B} \times \mathbb{U}$ is straightforward.

However, now our goal is to determine under what conditions European contingent claims in a general market environment $\mathbf{V}$

incepted at time t and expiring the next instant can be valued *independently* of the beliefs $\mathcal{B}$ in $\mathbb{B}$ and preferences $\mathcal{U}$ in $\mathbb{U}$ of market participants $\mathcal{H} = (\mathcal{B}, \mathcal{U})$ in an orbit of the group $\hat{\mathcal{G}}$ in $\mathbb{H} = \mathbb{B} \times \mathbb{U}$. The degrees of freedom that market participants $\mathcal{H} = (\mathcal{B}, \mathcal{U})$ in an orbit of the group $\hat{\mathcal{G}}$ in $\mathbb{H} = \mathbb{B} \times \mathbb{U}$ have in terms of their beliefs $\mathcal{B}$ in $\mathbb{B}$ and preferences $\mathcal{U}$ in $\mathbb{U}$ given by the dynamic beliefs-preferences gauge symmetry group $\hat{\mathcal{G}}$ allows us to formulate this problem rigorously. Indeed, the dynamic beliefs-preferences gauge symmetry group $\hat{\mathcal{G}}$ states that the values v of European contingent claims incepted at time t and expiring the next instant remain unchanged if the beliefs and preferences are both transformed in the consistent manner as indicated in (3.67). In order to have the desired independence of the values of European contingent claims of the beliefs $\mathcal{B}$ in $\mathbb{B}$ and preferences $\mathcal{U}$ in $\mathbb{U}$ of market participants $\mathcal{H} = (\mathcal{B}, \mathcal{U})$ in an orbit of the group $\hat{\mathcal{G}}$ in $\mathbb{H} = \mathbb{B} \times \mathbb{U}$, we have to require that these values v remain unchanged under the following *independent* transformations of the beliefs $\mathcal{B}$ in $\mathbb{B}$ and preferences $\mathcal{U}$ in $\mathbb{U}$:

$$
\begin{aligned}
&\mathfrak{L}(t) \xrightarrow{\hat{g}_{\mathcal{B}}^{(1)}} \hat{\mathbf{u}}_1'^{\,-1}(t,t)\,\mathfrak{L}(t)\,\hat{\mathbf{u}}_1'(t,t) + \frac{\hat{\mathbf{u}}_{1t}'(t,t)}{\hat{\mathbf{u}}_1'(t,t)} \quad \text{and} \\
&\boldsymbol{u}'(t,T) \xrightarrow{\hat{g}_{\mathcal{U}}^{(2)}} \hat{\mathbf{u}}_2'^{\,-1}(t,T)\boldsymbol{u}'(t,T),
\end{aligned}
\tag{6.1}
$$

where $\hat{\mathbf{u}}_1'(t,T)$ and $\hat{\mathbf{u}}_2'(t,T)$ are generated by $\mathbf{u}_1'(t,T)$ and $\mathbf{u}_2'(t,T)$.

Now the desired independence of the values of European contingent claims of the beliefs $\mathcal{B}$ in $\mathbb{B}$ and preferences $\mathcal{U}$ in $\mathbb{U}$ of market participants $\mathcal{H} = (\mathcal{B}, \mathcal{U})$ in an orbit of the group $\hat{\mathcal{G}}$ in $\mathbb{H} = \mathbb{B} \times \mathbb{U}$ can be restated as follows. The values v of European contingent claims incepted at time t and expiring the next instant in a general market environment $\mathbf{V}$ have to remain unchanged under the action of the group $G \times H$

$$
\begin{aligned}
(\mathfrak{L}(t), \boldsymbol{u}'(t,T)) &\xrightarrow{g} \left(\hat{\mathbf{u}}_1'^{-1}(t,t)\, \mathfrak{L}(t)\, \hat{\mathbf{u}}_1'(t,t) + \frac{\hat{\mathbf{u}}_{1t}'(t,t)}{\hat{\mathbf{u}}_1'(t,t)}, \boldsymbol{u}'(t,T)\right) \\
(\mathfrak{L}(t), \boldsymbol{u}'(t,T)) &\xrightarrow{h} (\mathfrak{L}(t), \hat{\mathbf{u}}_2'^{-1}(t,T)\boldsymbol{u}'(t,T)),
\end{aligned} \tag{6.2}
$$

where g is in G and h is in H, and where $\hat{\mathbf{u}}_1'(t,T)$ and $\hat{\mathbf{u}}_2'(t,T)$ are generated by $\mathbf{u}_1'(t,T)$ and $\mathbf{u}_2'(t,T)$.

6.1. Remark. We comment that the groups G and H are in fact defined as the sets of all transformations g and h in (6.2) with the group operations of composition.

6.2. Remark. Since the groups G and H defined in the preceding relation (6.2) are abelian groups, $G \times H$ is also an abelian group.

6.3. Remark. Denote the element (g,h) in $G \times H$ defined in (6.42) by $(\hat{\mathbf{u}}_1'(t,T), \hat{\mathbf{u}}_2'(t,T))$. It is clear that the beliefs-preferences gauge symmetry group $\hat{\mathcal{G}}$ of transformations of the market populace $\mathbb{H} = \mathbb{B} \times \mathbb{U}$ is the diagonal subgroup of the group $G \times H$ of transformations of the market populace $\mathbb{H} = \mathbb{B} \times \mathbb{U}$. That is, the group $\hat{\mathcal{G}}$ is a subgroup of the group $G \times H$ consisting of the elements of $G \times H$ of the form $(\hat{\mathbf{u}}'(t,T), \hat{\mathbf{u}}'(t,T))$. In this regard the desired independence of the values of European contingent claims incepted at time t and expiring the next instant of the beliefs $\mathcal{B}$ in $\mathbb{B}$ and preferences $\mathcal{U}$ in $\mathbb{U}$ of market participants $\mathcal{H} = (\mathcal{B}, \mathcal{U})$ in an orbit of the group $\hat{\mathcal{G}}$ in $\mathbb{H} = \mathbb{B} \times \mathbb{U}$ is equivalent to promoting the dynamic beliefs-preferences gauge symmetry group $\hat{\mathcal{G}}$ viewed as the diagonal subgroup of the group $G \times H$ to the group $G \times H$ itself.

Now we make the following crucial observation. Suppose that the values v of European contingent claims incepted at time t and expiring the next instant remain unchanged under the action of the dynamic beliefs-preferences gauge symmetry group $\hat{\mathcal{G}}$. Then, in order for the values v of such European contingent claims in a general market environment $\mathbf{V}$ to remain unchanged under the action of the group $G \times H$ it is enough to require that these values v remain unchanged under the actions of the groups G and H separately, where we have identified the groups G and H with the subgroups (G, e_H) and (e_G, H) of the group $G \times H$, with e_G and e_H being the identity elements of G and H. Indeed, denote by $G \times H/\hat{\mathcal{G}}$ the factor group of $G \times H$ relative to $\hat{\mathcal{G}}$ where $\hat{\mathcal{G}}$ is identified with the diagonal subgroup of $G \times H$ as in Remark (6.3). For any $[(\hat{\mathbf{u}}'_1(t,T), \hat{\mathbf{u}}'_2(t,T))]$ in $G \times H/\hat{\mathcal{G}}$ where $[(\hat{\mathbf{u}}'_1(t,T), \hat{\mathbf{u}}'_2(t,T))]$ stands for the coset of $(\hat{\mathbf{u}}'_1(t,T), \hat{\mathbf{u}}'_2(t,T))$ in $G \times H$ we have the following chain of equalities

$$\begin{aligned}
&[(\hat{\mathbf{u}}'_1(t,T), \hat{\mathbf{u}}'_2(t,T))] = \\
&\quad [(\hat{\mathbf{u}}'^{-1}_2(t,T), \hat{\mathbf{u}}'^{-1}_2(t,T)) \cdot (\hat{\mathbf{u}}'_1(t,T), \hat{\mathbf{u}}'_2(t,T))] = \\
&\quad [(\hat{\mathbf{u}}'^{-1}_2(t,T)\, \hat{\mathbf{u}}'_1(t,T), \hat{\mathbf{u}}'^{-1}_2(t,T)\, \hat{\mathbf{u}}'_2(t,T))] = \\
&\quad [(\hat{\mathbf{u}}'^{-1}_2(t,T)\, \hat{\mathbf{u}}'_1(t,T), \mathbf{1}_H)],
\end{aligned}$$

where $\mathbf{1}_H$ is the identity operator on $\Pi(\mathbb{R}^n_{++} \times \mathbb{R}^n_{++})$ so that $(\hat{\mathbf{u}}'(t,T), \mathbf{1}_H)$ is in G, or more precisely in (G, e_H).

On the other hand, for any $[(\hat{\mathbf{u}}'_1(t,T), \hat{\mathbf{u}}'_2(t,T))]$ in $G \times H/\hat{\mathcal{G}}$ where $[(\hat{\mathbf{u}}'_1(t,T), \hat{\mathbf{u}}'_2(t,T))]$ again stands for the coset of $(\hat{\mathbf{u}}'_1(t,T), \hat{\mathbf{u}}'_2(t,T))$ in $G \times H$ we have the following chain of equalities

$$\begin{aligned}
&[(\hat{\mathbf{u}}'_1(t,T), \hat{\mathbf{u}}'_2(t,T))] = \\
&\quad [(\hat{\mathbf{u}}'^{-1}_1(t,T), \hat{\mathbf{u}}'^{-1}_1(t,T)) \cdot (\hat{\mathbf{u}}'_1(t,T), \hat{\mathbf{u}}'_2(t,T))] = \\
&\quad [(\hat{\mathbf{u}}'^{-1}_1(t,T)\, \hat{\mathbf{u}}'_1(t,T), \hat{\mathbf{u}}'^{-1}_1(t,T)\, \hat{\mathbf{u}}'_2(t,T))] = \\
&\quad [(\mathbf{1}_G, \hat{\mathbf{u}}'^{-1}_1(t,T)\, \hat{\mathbf{u}}'_2(t,T))],
\end{aligned}$$

where $\mathbf{1}_G$ is the identity operator on $\Pi(\mathbb{R}^n_{++} \times \mathbb{R}^n_{++})$ so that $(\mathbf{1}_G, \hat{\mathbf{u}}'(t,T))$ is in H, or more precisely in (e_G, H).

Since $(\hat{\mathbf{u}}'^{-1}_2(t,T)\, \hat{\mathbf{u}}'_1(t,T), \mathbf{1}_H)$ and $(\mathbf{1}_G, \hat{\mathbf{u}}'^{-1}_1(t,T)\, \hat{\mathbf{u}}'_2(t,T))$ are arbitrary elements of G and H, or more precisely (G, e_H) and (e_G, H), we arrive at the desired result. In light of Remark

(6.3) this result can also be stated as follows. In order to promote the dynamic beliefs-preferences gauge symmetry group $\hat{\mathcal{G}}$ viewed as the diagonal subgroup of the group $G \times H$ to the group $G \times H$ itself so that the values v of European contingent claims incepted at time t and expiring the next instant in a general market environment $\mathbf{V}$ remain unchanged under the action of the group $G \times H$ it is enough to require that these values v remain unchanged under the action of the group G or H separately, where we again have identified the groups G and H with the subgroups (G, e_H) and (e_G, H) of the group $G \times H$ with e_G and e_H being the identity elements of G and H.

Taking advantage of this result with the group H, or more precisely (e_G, H), the requirement that the values v of European contingent claims incepted at time t and expiring the next instant in a general market environment $\mathbf{V}$ have to remain unchanged under the action of the group $G \times H$ can be restated as follows.

For a fixed market participant $\boldsymbol{\mathcal{H}} = (\boldsymbol{\mathcal{B}}, \boldsymbol{\mathcal{U}})$ in $\mathbb{H} = \mathbb{B} \times \mathbb{U}$ with

$$\boldsymbol{\mathcal{B}} = \{\boldsymbol{F}(t,T) : \Pi \to \Pi \,|\, t, T \in \mathcal{T}, t \leq T\}$$

and

$$\boldsymbol{\mathcal{U}} = \{\boldsymbol{u}'(t,T) : \Pi(\mathbb{R}^{2n}_{++}) \to \Pi(\mathbb{R}^{2n}_{++}) \,|\, t,\, T \in \mathcal{T}, t \leq T\}$$

the value $v = v(t)$ of the European contingent claim with inception time t, expiration time T in $\boldsymbol{\mathcal{N}}_t(\mathcal{T})$ and payoff v_T has to remain unchanged under the action of the group H, or more precisely (e_G, H) despite the fact that $v = v(t)$ obeys the following identity

$$\frac{\overset{2}{d}}{dt}\boldsymbol{u}'(\overset{3}{t},\overset{1}{t})\,v + \boldsymbol{\mathfrak{L}}(\overset{2}{t})\boldsymbol{u}'(\overset{3}{t},\overset{1}{t})\,v = 0, \quad t = T, \tag{6.3}$$

where the operator $\boldsymbol{\mathfrak{L}}(t)$ stands for the derivative of $-\boldsymbol{F}(t,T)$ with respect to t evaluated at t equal to T understood in an appropriate sense with $\boldsymbol{F}(t,T)$ in $\boldsymbol{\mathcal{B}}$.

6.4. Remark. We comment that the derivation of identity (6.3) is completely analogous to that of the evolution equation in the Cauchy problem (3.118) with the help of relation (3.71).

However, it is clear that this is not the case, that is, that value $v = v(t)$ of a European contingent claim with inception time t, expiration time T in $\mathcal{N}_t(\mathcal{T})$ and payoff v_T such that it obeys the identity (6.3) does not in general remain unchanged under the action of the group H, or more precisely (e_G, H).

6.5. Remark. Under each transformation $(\mathbf{1}_G, \hat{\mathbf{u}}'(t,T))$ from the group H, or more precisely (e_G, H) the preference $\boldsymbol{u}'(t,T)$ from $\boldsymbol{\mathcal{U}}$ in identity (6.3) are transformed to the preference $\hat{\mathbf{u}}'^{-1}(t,T)\, \boldsymbol{u}'(t,T)$ from

$$\hat{\mathbf{u}}'^{-1}\boldsymbol{\mathcal{U}} = \{\hat{\mathbf{u}}'^{-1}(t,T)\, \boldsymbol{u}'(t,T) : \Pi(\mathbb{R}^{2n}_{++}) \to \Pi(\mathbb{R}^{2n}_{++}) \,|\, t,\, T \in \mathcal{T}, t \le T\}.$$

Therefore, in order for the value $v = v(t)$ of the European contingent claim with inception time t, expiration time T in $\mathcal{N}_t(\mathcal{T})$ and payoff v_T that obeys identity (6.3) to remain unchanged under the action of the group H, or more precisely (e_G, H) it is enough to require that the value $v = v(t)$ of the European contingent claim with inception time t, expiration time T in $\mathcal{N}_t(\mathcal{T})$ and payoff v_T such that it obeys identity (6.3) remains unchanged for all preferences $\boldsymbol{u}'(t,T)$, that is, does not depend on the preference $\boldsymbol{u}'(t,T)$.

In order to achieve the goal of finding the values v of European contingent claims in a general market environment $\mathbf{V}$ that remain unchanged under the action of the group $G \times H$ of transformations of the market populace $\mathbb{H} = \mathbb{B} \times \mathbb{U}$ we choose an alternative route.

Denote by Ω an index set which is assumed to be a measurable space, that is, to be equipped with a sigma algebra. For t in $\mathcal{T}$ and for each s_t in $\mathbb{R}^n_{++}$ let $\pi(t, s_t, d\omega)$ be a signed measure on Ω. Denote by $\boldsymbol{\pi}(t, d\omega)$ the operator-valued measure on Ω defined by

$$(\boldsymbol{\pi}(t, d\omega)\, h)(s_t) = \pi(t, s_t, d\omega) h(s_t), \qquad h \in \Pi.$$

6.6. Remark. It is clear that $\pi(t, d\omega) = \pi(t, \cdot, d\omega)$ is a Π-valued measure on Ω. In this regard the relation between the Π-valued measure $\pi(t, d\omega)$ on Ω and the operator-valued measure $\boldsymbol{\pi}(t, d\omega)$ on Ω is self-explanatory.

6.7. Definition. Let $\{\mathfrak{v}_\omega : \omega \in \Omega\}$ be a set of traded European contingent claims with inception time t, expiration time T in some $\mathcal{N}_t(\mathcal{T})$, payoffs $\{v_T^\omega : \omega \in \Omega\}$ and values $\{v_\omega : \omega \in \Omega\}$ with the following property. For a European contingent claim $\mathfrak{v}$ with inception time t, expiration time T in $\mathcal{N}_t(\mathcal{T})$, payoff v_T and value v there exists an operator-valued measure $\boldsymbol{\pi}(t, d\omega)$ on Ω denoted by $\boldsymbol{\pi}_v(t, d\omega)$ such that

$$\begin{aligned}&\overset{2}{\frac{d}{dt}}\boldsymbol{u}'(\overset{3}{t},\overset{1}{t})\, v + \mathfrak{L}(\overset{2}{t})\, \boldsymbol{u}'(\overset{3}{t},\overset{1}{t})\, v = \\ &\int_\Omega \boldsymbol{\pi}_v(t, d\omega)\Big(\overset{2}{\frac{d}{dt}}\boldsymbol{u}'(\overset{3}{t},\overset{1}{t})\, v_\omega + \mathfrak{L}(\overset{2}{t})\, \boldsymbol{u}'(\overset{3}{t},\overset{1}{t})\, v_\omega\Big), \quad t = T,\end{aligned} \tag{6.4}$$

for any preference $\boldsymbol{u}'(t, T)$.

If in addition

$$v(t) = \int_\Omega \boldsymbol{\pi}_v(t, d\omega)\, v_\omega(t), \tag{6.5}$$

we will say that the set $\{\mathfrak{v}_\omega : \omega \in \Omega\}$ of European contingent claims *dynamically replicates* the European contingent claim $\mathfrak{v}$ at this time t in $\mathcal{T}$. We will call the portfolio of European contingent claims $\{\mathfrak{v}_\omega : \omega \in \Omega\}$ with *operator weights* $\boldsymbol{\pi}_v(t, d\omega)$ a *dynamically replicating portfolio* at this time t in $\mathcal{T}$.

6.8. Remark. We comment that a portfolio of European contingent claims $\{\mathfrak{v}_\omega : \omega \in \Omega\}$ with operator weights $\boldsymbol{\pi}(t, d\omega)$ is understood as a portfolio of European contingent claims $\{\mathfrak{v}_\omega : \omega \in \Omega\}$ with weights $\pi(t, s_t, d\omega)$ for t in $\mathcal{T}$ and for s_t in $\mathbb{R}^n_{++}$. In this regard, a portfolio of European contingent claims $\{\mathfrak{v}_\omega : \omega \in \Omega\}$ with operator weights $\boldsymbol{\pi}(t, d\omega)$ is, from the financial standpoint, nothing but a portfolio of European contingent claims $\{\mathfrak{v}_\omega : \omega \in \Omega\}$ with weights that depend on time t and the state of the market as expressed by the prices of the underlying securities s_t at this time t.

6.9. Remark. We comment that, due to Remark (3.119), Definition (6.7) is not affected if the derivative $\mathfrak{L}(t)$ of $-\boldsymbol{F}(t,T)$ with respect to t evaluated at t equal to T understood in an appropriate sense is replaced by the derivative $\mathsf{L}(t)$ of $-\boldsymbol{D}(t,T)$ with respect to t evaluated at t equal to T understood in an appropriate sense, where $\boldsymbol{F}(t,T)$ is in the belief $\boldsymbol{\mathcal{B}}$ of a market participant $\boldsymbol{\mathcal{H}} = (\boldsymbol{\mathcal{B}}, \boldsymbol{\mathcal{U}})$ in $\mathbb{H} = \mathbb{B} \times \mathbb{U}$ and where $\boldsymbol{D}(t,T)$ is in the generalized belief of a generalized market participant $\mathfrak{H} = (\mathfrak{B}, \boldsymbol{\mathcal{U}})$ in $\mathbf{H} = \mathbf{B} \times \mathbb{U}$.

6.10. Definition. We call a market environment $\mathbf{V}$, or simply a market *dynamically complete* at the time t in $\mathcal{T}$ if for each T in some $\mathcal{N}_t(\mathcal{T})$ with $t \leq T$ there exists a set $\{\mathfrak{v}_\omega : \omega \in \Omega\}$ of European contingent claims with inception time t, expiration time T and payoffs $\{\mathfrak{v}^\omega_T : \omega \in \Omega\}$ that dynamically replicates at this time t in $\mathcal{T}$ each European contingent claim with inception time t, expiration time T and payoff v_T in some dense set of payoffs. In this case the set $\{\mathfrak{v}_\omega : \omega \in \Omega\}$ for T in $\mathcal{N}_t(\mathcal{T})$ with $t \leq T$ of European contingent claims is said to *dynamically span* the market environment $\mathbf{V}$ at this time t in $\mathcal{T}$, or simply the market and we will call the set $\{\mathfrak{v}_\omega : \omega \in \Omega\}$ of European contingent claims itself *dynamically spanning* at this time t in $\mathcal{T}$.

6.11. Definition. We call the cardinality of a minimal dynamically spanning set $\{\mathfrak{v}_\omega : \omega \in \Omega\}$ of European contingent claims for a market environment $\mathbf{V}$ at time t in $\mathcal{T}$ a *stochastic dimension* of the generator $\mathfrak{L}(t)$.

6.12. Remark. We comment that in the preceding Definitions (6.7), (6.10) and (6.11) the derivative of $\mathfrak{L}(t)$ of $-\boldsymbol{F}(t,T)$ with respect to t evaluated at t equal to T understood in the appropriate sense, with $\boldsymbol{F}(t,T)$ in the belief $\boldsymbol{\mathcal{B}}$ of a market participant $\boldsymbol{\mathcal{H}} = (\boldsymbol{\mathcal{B}},\boldsymbol{\mathcal{U}})$ in $\mathbb{H} = \mathbb{B}\times\mathbb{U}$, is related to the market environment $\mathbf{V}$, or more precisely to the derivative $\boldsymbol{L}(t)$ of $-\mathbf{V}(t,T)$ with respect to t evaluated at t equal to T understood in the appropriate sense, with $\mathbf{V}(t,T)$ in $\mathbf{V}$, by means of equality (3.71).

6.13. Remark. The stochastic dimension of the derivative of $\mathfrak{L}(t)$ of $-\boldsymbol{F}(t,T)$ with respect to t evaluated at t equal to T understood in the appropriate sense, with $\boldsymbol{F}(t,T)$ in the belief $\boldsymbol{\mathcal{B}}$ of a market participant $\boldsymbol{\mathcal{H}} = (\boldsymbol{\mathcal{B}},\boldsymbol{\mathcal{U}})$ in $\mathbb{H} = \mathbb{B}\times\mathbb{U}$, is a certain measure of randomness associated with $\mathfrak{L}(t)$.

6.14. Remark. It is clear that in a similar way the concept of stochastic dimension can be defined for an arbitrary linear operator on a space of either real-valued or complex-valued functions defined on a domain in $\mathbb{R}^n$.

Now we present financial justification for the terminology introduced in Definitions (6.7) and (6.10).

Since European contingent claims $\{\mathfrak{v}_\omega : \omega \in \Omega\}$ and $\mathfrak{v}$ are traded their values $\{v_\omega : \omega \in \Omega\}$ and v obey identity (6.3), that is

$$\overset{2}{\frac{d}{dt}}\boldsymbol{u}'(\overset{3}{t},\overset{1}{t})\, v_\omega + \mathfrak{L}(\overset{2}{t})\, \boldsymbol{u}'(\overset{3}{t},\overset{1}{t})\, v_\omega = 0, \quad t = T, \quad \omega \in \Omega, \tag{6.6}$$

and

$$\overset{2}{\frac{d}{dt}}\boldsymbol{u}'(\overset{3}{t},\overset{1}{t})\, v + \mathfrak{L}(\overset{2}{t})\, \boldsymbol{u}'(\overset{3}{t},\overset{1}{t})\, v = 0, \quad t = T. \tag{6.7}$$

It is clear that the values v_ω with ω in Ω and v of European contingent claims $\{\mathfrak{v}_\omega : \omega \in \Omega\}$ and $\mathfrak{v}$ which obey the preceding identities (6.6) and (6.7) do not separately remain unchanged under the action of the group H, or more precisely (e_G, H). However, if for a European contingent claim $\mathfrak{v}$ there exists a set $\{\mathfrak{v}_\omega : \omega \in \Omega\}$ of European contingent claims that dynamically replicates $\mathfrak{v}$ at time t in $\mathcal{T}$ then the value

$$v - \int_\Omega \boldsymbol{\pi}_v(t, d\omega) v_\omega$$

of the portfolio consisting of a long position on the European contingent claim $\mathfrak{v}$ and a short position on the dynamically replicating portfolio of European contingent claims $\{\mathfrak{v}_\omega : \omega \in \Omega\}$ with the operator weights $\boldsymbol{\pi}_v(t, d\omega)$ with the value $\int_\Omega \boldsymbol{\pi}_v(t, d\omega) v_\omega$ obeys identity (6.3) and at the same time remains unchanged under the action of the group H, or more precisely (e_G, H). In order to see this it is enough to rewrite identity (6.4) as follows

$$\Big(\overset{2}{\frac{d}{dt}} + \mathfrak{L}(\overset{2}{t})\Big) \left(\boldsymbol{u}'(\overset{3}{t}, \overset{1}{t})\Big(v - \int_\Omega \overset{3}{\boldsymbol{\pi}}_v(t, d\omega) v_\omega\Big)\right) = 0, \quad t = T, \tag{6.8}$$

for any preference $\boldsymbol{u}'(t, T)$.

Since $\mathfrak{L}(t)$ is the derivative of $-\boldsymbol{F}(t, T)$ with respect to t evaluated at t equal to T understood in an appropriate sense with $\boldsymbol{F}(t, T)$ in the belief $\boldsymbol{\mathcal{B}}$ of the market participant $\boldsymbol{\mathcal{H}} = (\boldsymbol{\mathcal{B}}, \boldsymbol{\mathcal{U}})$ in the market populace $\mathbb{H} = \mathbb{B} \times \mathbb{U}$, identity (6.8) and hence identity (6.4) mean that the value

$$v - \int_\Omega \boldsymbol{\pi}_v(t, d\omega) v_\omega$$

at time t of the portfolio consisting of a long position on the European contingent claim $\mathfrak{v}$ and a short position on the dynamically replicating portfolio of European contingent claims $\{\mathfrak{v}_\omega : \omega \in \Omega\}$ with the operator weights $\boldsymbol{\pi}_v(t, d\omega)$ is nothing but the expected value of the value

$$v_T - \int_\Omega \boldsymbol{\pi}_v(T, d\omega) v_T^\omega$$

of this portfolio at time T an instant later with respect to the probability measures generated by $\boldsymbol{F}(t,T)$ in $\boldsymbol{\mathcal{B}}$.

Due to the fact that $v - \int_\Omega \boldsymbol{\pi}_v(t,d\omega)v_\omega$ obeys identity (6.8) and hence (6.4) and at the same time remains unchanged under the action of the group H, or more precisely (e_G, H) the results of this Subsection imply that $v - \int_\Omega \boldsymbol{\pi}_v(t,d\omega)v_\omega$ remains unchanged under the action of the group $G \times H$ defined in (6.2). Therefore $v - \int_\Omega \boldsymbol{\pi}_v(t,d\omega)v_\omega$ is independent of the choice of $\boldsymbol{\mathfrak{L}}(t)$ in the orbit of the group G, or more precisely (G, e_H), that is, $v - \int_\Omega \boldsymbol{\pi}_v(t,d\omega)v_\omega$ is independent of the choice of the belief $\boldsymbol{\mathcal{B}}$ of the market participant $\boldsymbol{\mathcal{H}} = (\boldsymbol{\mathcal{B}},\boldsymbol{\mathcal{U}})$ in the market populace $\mathbb{H} = \mathbb{B} \times \mathbb{U}$ such that the derivative $\boldsymbol{\mathfrak{L}}(t)$ of $-\boldsymbol{F}(t,T)$ with respect to t evaluated at t equal to T understood in an appropriate sense with $\boldsymbol{F}(t,T)$ in $\boldsymbol{\mathcal{B}}$ is in the orbit of the group G, or more precisely (G, e_H). From the financial standpoint this means that the value

$$v - \int_\Omega \boldsymbol{\pi}_v(t,d\omega)v_\omega$$

at time t of the portfolio consisting of a long position on the European contingent claim $\mathfrak{v}$ and a short position on the dynamically replicating portfolio of European contingent claims $\{\mathfrak{v}_\omega : \omega \in \Omega\}$ with the operator weights $\boldsymbol{\pi}_v(t,d\omega)$ is nothing but the expected value of the value

$$v_T - \int_\Omega \boldsymbol{\pi}_v(T,d\omega)v_T^\omega$$

of this portfolio at time T an instant later with respect to the probability measures generated by $\boldsymbol{F}(t,T)$ in the belief $\boldsymbol{\mathcal{B}}$ for any market participant $\boldsymbol{\mathcal{H}} = (\boldsymbol{\mathcal{B}},\boldsymbol{\mathcal{U}})$ in the orbit of the group $\hat{\boldsymbol{\mathcal{G}}}$ in $\mathbb{H} = \mathbb{B} \times \mathbb{U}$, that is, for any market participant $\boldsymbol{\mathcal{H}} = (\boldsymbol{\mathcal{B}},\boldsymbol{\mathcal{U}})$ in $\mathbb{H} = \mathbb{B} \times \mathbb{U}$ such that the pair $(\boldsymbol{\mathfrak{L}}(t),\boldsymbol{\mathcal{U}})$ of the derivative $\boldsymbol{\mathfrak{L}}(t)$ of $-\boldsymbol{F}(t,T)$ with respect to t evaluated at t equal to T understood in an appropriate sense with $\boldsymbol{F}(t,T)$ in $\boldsymbol{\mathcal{B}}$ and the preference $\boldsymbol{\mathcal{U}}$ is in the orbit of the group $\hat{\boldsymbol{\mathcal{G}}}$. We recall that such an orbit of the group $\hat{\boldsymbol{\mathcal{G}}}$ determines the set of all market participants $\mathcal{H} = (\mathcal{B}, \mathcal{U})$ in $\mathbb{H} = \mathbb{B} \times \mathbb{U}$ that agree at the time t in $\mathcal{T}$ upon the values of a set of European contingent claims with inception time t, expiration time T for all T in some $\mathcal{N}_t(\mathcal{T})$ with $t \leq T$ whose payoffs form a dense set. It is clear that by the no-arbitrage argument only such market participants are actually allowed to populate a marketplace at this time t in $\mathcal{T}$.

Finally due to relation (6.5) in Definition (6.7) the value

$$v - \int_{\Omega} \boldsymbol{\pi}_v(t, d\omega) v_\omega$$

at time t of the portfolio consisting of a long position on the European contingent claim $\mathfrak{v}$ and a short position on the dynamically replicating portfolio of European contingent claims $\{\mathfrak{v}_\omega : \omega \in \Omega\}$ with the operator weights $\boldsymbol{\pi}_v(t, d\omega)$ which is the expected value of the value

$$v_T - \int_{\Omega} \boldsymbol{\pi}_v(T, d\omega) v_T^\omega$$

of this portfolio at time T an instant later with respect to the probability measures generated by $\boldsymbol{F}(t, T)$ from the belief $\mathcal{B}$ is zero for this time t in $\mathcal{T}$ and for each state of the market as expressed by the prices of the underlying securities s_t at this time t for any market participant $\mathcal{H} = (\mathcal{B}, \mathcal{U})$ in the orbit of the group $\hat{\mathcal{G}}$ in $\mathbb{H} = \mathbb{B} \times \mathbb{U}$, that is, for any market participant $\mathcal{H} = (\mathcal{B}, \mathcal{U})$ in $\mathbb{H} = \mathbb{B} \times \mathbb{U}$ such that the pair $(\mathfrak{L}(t), \mathcal{U})$ of the derivative $\mathfrak{L}(t)$ of $-\boldsymbol{F}(t, T)$ with respect to t evaluated at t equal to T understood in an appropriate sense with $\boldsymbol{F}(t, T)$ in $\mathcal{B}$ and the preference $\mathcal{U}$ is in the orbit of the group $\hat{\mathcal{G}}$.

6.15. Remark. Due to Definition (6.7) if the set $\{\mathfrak{v}_\omega : \omega \in \Omega\}$ of European contingent claims dynamically replicates at a time t in $\mathcal{T}$ a European contingent claim $\mathfrak{v}$ then its value v such that it obeys identity (6.4) is independent of the preference $\boldsymbol{u}'(t, T)$, or equivalently remains unchanged under the action of the group H or more precisely (e_G, H) and hence under the action of the group $G \times H$. Therefore in order to find the value v of the European contingent claim $\mathfrak{v}$ in a general market environment $\mathbf{V}$ independent of the beliefs and preferences of market participants $\mathcal{H} = (\mathcal{B}, \mathcal{U})$ in the orbit of the group $\hat{\mathcal{G}}$ in $\mathbb{H} = \mathbb{B} \times \mathbb{U}$ it is enough to use relation (6.5).

Now, motivated by the fact that the value v of the European contingent claim $\mathfrak{v}$ in identity (6.4) is independent of the preference $\boldsymbol{u}'(t,T)$, we represent identity (6.4) in such a way that the preference $\boldsymbol{u}'(t,T)$ does not enter it explicitly, that is, solely in terms of $\mathfrak{L}(t)$. In order to do this we rewrite identity (6.4) as follows

$$\Big(\overset{2}{\frac{d}{dt}} + \mathfrak{L}(\overset{2}{t})\Big)\, \boldsymbol{u}'(\overset{3}{t},\overset{1}{t})\, \boldsymbol{v}\, \mathbf{1} =$$

$$\int_\Omega \Big(\boldsymbol{\pi}_v(t,d\omega)\Big(\overset{2}{\frac{d}{dt}} + \mathfrak{L}(\overset{2}{t})\Big)\, \boldsymbol{u}'(\overset{3}{t},\overset{1}{t})\, \boldsymbol{v}_\omega\, \mathbf{1}\Big) \quad t = T, \tag{6.9}$$

where $\boldsymbol{v} = \boldsymbol{v}(t)$ and $\boldsymbol{v}_\omega = \boldsymbol{v}_\omega(t)$ stand for the operators on Π of multiplication by the functions $v = v(t)$ and $v_\omega = v_\omega(t)$, and where $\mathbf{1}$ is the function in Π identically equal to unity.

Denote by $\Pi(\mathbb{R}^n_{++} \times \mathcal{N}_t(\mathcal{T}))$ the vector space of all real-valued functions on the set $\mathbb{R}^n_{++} \times \mathcal{N}_t(\mathcal{T})$. Let $\Pi_+(\mathbb{R}^n_{++} \times \mathcal{N}_t(\mathcal{T}))$ be the nonnegative cone of $\Pi(\mathbb{R}^n_{++} \times \mathcal{N}_t(\mathcal{T}))$, that is, the set of all nonnegative real-valued functions on the set $\mathbb{R}^n_{++} \times \mathcal{N}_t(\mathcal{T})$.

We note that the vector space $\Pi(\mathbb{R}^n_{++} \times \mathcal{N}_t(\mathcal{T}))$ with the partial order generated by the nonnegative cone $\Pi_+(\mathbb{R}^n_{++} \times \mathcal{N}_t(\mathcal{T}))$ is a partially ordered vector space. Moreover, equipped with the lattice operations of supremum and infimum defined as pointwise maximum and minimum $\Pi(\mathbb{R}^n_{++} \times \mathcal{N}_t(\mathcal{T}))$ is a vector lattice.

6.16. Remark. We comment that in the preceding identity (6.9) the operators $\frac{d}{dt} + \mathfrak{L}(t)$, $\boldsymbol{v} = \boldsymbol{v}(t)$, $\boldsymbol{v}_\omega = \boldsymbol{v}_\omega(t)$, $\boldsymbol{\pi}_v(t, d\omega)$ and $\boldsymbol{u}'(t,t)$ can also be interpreted as operators on $\Pi(\mathbb{R}^n_{++} \times \mathcal{N}_t(\mathcal{T}))$ with $\mathbf{1}$ being the function in $\Pi(\mathbb{R}^n_{++} \times \mathcal{N}_t(\mathcal{T}))$ identically equal to unity. Whenever ambiguity is unlikely we will assume this interpretation of these operators.

Consider the operators

$$\Big(\overset{2}{\frac{d}{dt}} + \mathfrak{L}(\overset{2}{t})\Big)\, \boldsymbol{u}'(\overset{3}{t},\overset{1}{t})\, \boldsymbol{v}$$

and

$$\Big(\overset{2}{\frac{d}{dt}} + \mathfrak{L}(\overset{2}{t})\Big)\, \boldsymbol{u}'(\overset{3}{t},\overset{1}{t})\, \boldsymbol{v}_{\hat{\omega}}$$

with ω in Ω from the preceding identity (6.9) separately.

For the operator $\big(\overset{2}{\frac{d}{dt}} + \mathfrak{L}(\overset{2}{t})\big)\, \boldsymbol{u}'(\overset{3}{t},\overset{1}{t})\, \boldsymbol{v}$ we have the following chain of equalities

$$\begin{aligned}
&\Big(\overset{2}{\frac{d}{dt}} + \mathfrak{L}(\overset{2}{t})\Big)\, \boldsymbol{u}'(\overset{3}{t},\overset{1}{t})\, \boldsymbol{v} = \\
&\quad \boldsymbol{v}\,\Big(\overset{2}{\frac{d}{dt}} + \mathfrak{L}(\overset{2}{t})\Big)\, \boldsymbol{u}'(\overset{3}{t},\overset{1}{t}) + \Big[\Big(\overset{2}{\frac{d}{dt}} + \mathfrak{L}(\overset{2}{t})\Big), \boldsymbol{v}\Big]\, \boldsymbol{u}'(\overset{3}{t},\overset{1}{t}) = \\
&\quad \boldsymbol{v}\,\boldsymbol{u}'(t,t)\,\Big(\frac{d}{dt} + \mathfrak{L}(t)\Big) + \boldsymbol{v}\,\Big[\Big(\overset{2}{\frac{d}{dt}} + \mathfrak{L}(\overset{2}{t})\Big), \boldsymbol{u}'(\overset{3}{t},\overset{1}{t})\Big] + \\
&\quad \boldsymbol{u}'(t,t)\,\Big[\Big(\frac{d}{dt} + \mathfrak{L}(t)\Big), \boldsymbol{v}\Big] + \Big[\Big[\Big(\overset{2}{\frac{d}{dt}} + \mathfrak{L}(\overset{2}{t})\Big), \boldsymbol{v}\Big], \boldsymbol{u}'(\overset{3}{t},\overset{1}{t})\Big] \overset{(6.10)}{=} \\
&\quad \boldsymbol{v}\,\Big(\frac{d}{dt} + \mathfrak{L}(t)\Big) + \boldsymbol{v}\,\Big[\Big(\overset{2}{\frac{d}{dt}} + \mathfrak{L}(\overset{2}{t})\Big), \boldsymbol{u}'(\overset{3}{t},\overset{1}{t})\Big] + \\
&\quad \Big[\Big(\frac{d}{dt} + \mathfrak{L}(t)\Big), \boldsymbol{v}\Big] + \Big[\Big[\Big(\overset{2}{\frac{d}{dt}} + \mathfrak{L}(\overset{2}{t})\Big), \boldsymbol{v}\Big], \boldsymbol{u}'(\overset{3}{t},\overset{1}{t})\Big],
\end{aligned}$$

where in the last equality we have taken into account the fact that due to Theorem (3.81) for each time t in $\mathcal{T}$ and each state of the market as expressed by the prices of the underlying securities s'_t at this time t there exists a global transformation from the beliefs-preferences gauge symmetry group $\hat{\mathcal{G}}$ such that the marginal utility $\boldsymbol{u}'(t,t)$ is the operator of multiplication by the function $u'(t,t,s_t,s_t)$ with the following property

$$u'(t,t,s_t = s'_t, s_t = s'_t) = 1.$$

For the operator $(\overset{2}{\tfrac{d}{dt}} + \mathfrak{L}(\overset{2}{t}))\, \boldsymbol{u}'(\overset{3}{t}, \overset{1}{t})\, \boldsymbol{v}_\omega$ with ω in Ω we have the following chain of equalities

$$
\begin{aligned}
&(\overset{2}{\frac{d}{dt}} + \mathfrak{L}(\overset{2}{t}))\, \boldsymbol{u}'(\overset{3}{t}, \overset{1}{t})\, \boldsymbol{v}_\omega = \\
&\boldsymbol{v}_\omega\, (\overset{2}{\frac{d}{dt}} + \mathfrak{L}(\overset{2}{t}))\, \boldsymbol{u}'(\overset{3}{t}, \overset{1}{t}) + [(\overset{2}{\frac{d}{dt}} + \mathfrak{L}(\overset{2}{t})), \boldsymbol{v}_\omega]\, \boldsymbol{u}'(\overset{3}{t}, \overset{1}{t}) = \\
&\boldsymbol{v}_\omega\, \boldsymbol{u}'(t,t)\, (\frac{d}{dt} + \mathfrak{L}(t)) + \boldsymbol{v}_\omega\, [(\overset{2}{\frac{d}{dt}} + \mathfrak{L}(\overset{2}{t})), \boldsymbol{u}'(\overset{3}{t}, \overset{1}{t})] + \\
&\quad \boldsymbol{u}'(t,t)\, [(\frac{d}{dt} + \mathfrak{L}(t)), \boldsymbol{v}_\omega] + [[(\overset{2}{\frac{d}{dt}} + \mathfrak{L}(\overset{2}{t})), \boldsymbol{v}_\omega], \boldsymbol{u}'(\overset{3}{t}, \overset{1}{t})] = \qquad (6.11) \\
&\boldsymbol{v}_\omega\, (\frac{d}{dt} + \mathfrak{L}(t)) + \boldsymbol{v}_\omega\, [(\overset{2}{\frac{d}{dt}} + \mathfrak{L}(\overset{2}{t})), \boldsymbol{u}'(\overset{3}{t}, \overset{1}{t})] + \\
&\quad [(\frac{d}{dt} + \mathfrak{L}(t)), \boldsymbol{v}_\omega] + [[(\overset{2}{\frac{d}{dt}} + \mathfrak{L}(\overset{2}{t})), \boldsymbol{v}_\omega], \boldsymbol{u}'(\overset{3}{t}, \overset{1}{t})],
\end{aligned}
$$

where again in the last equality we have taken into account the fact that due to Theorem (3.81) for each time t in $\mathcal{T}$ and each state of the market as expressed by the prices of the underlying securities s'_t at this time t there exists a global transformation from the beliefs-preferences gauge symmetry group $\hat{\mathcal{G}}$ such that the marginal utility $\boldsymbol{u}'(t,t)$ is the operator of multiplication by the function $u'(t, t, s_t, s_t)$ with the following property

$$u'(t, t, s_t = s'_t, s_t = s'_t) = 1.$$

Now we need the following assumption, which is natural from the financial standpoint, about the nature of the set $\{\mathfrak{v}_\omega : \omega \in \Omega\}$ of European contingent claims that dynamically replicates a European contingent claim $\mathfrak{v}$ at time t in $\mathcal{T}$. We suppose that for each T in some $\mathcal{N}_t(\mathcal{T})$ with $t \leq T$ the pure discount bond with inception time t, maturity time T and with the face value of one unit of account is traded. Let the pure discount bond be in the set $\{\mathfrak{v}_\omega : \omega \in \Omega\}$, that is, let there exist ω_B in Ω such that the European contingent claim $\mathfrak{v}_{\omega_B}$ has inception time t, expiration time T in $\mathcal{N}_t(\mathcal{T})$ and the payoff $\mathbf{1}$, where $\mathbf{1}$ is the function in Π identically equal to unity. The value v_{ω_B} of the pure discount bond $\mathfrak{v}_{\omega_B}$ obeys identity (6.6) that is

$$\overset{2}{\frac{d}{dt}} \boldsymbol{u}'(\overset{3}{t}, \overset{1}{t})\, v_{\omega_B} + \boldsymbol{\mathfrak{L}}(\overset{2}{t})\, \boldsymbol{u}'(\overset{3}{t}, \overset{1}{t})\, v_{\omega_B} = 0, \quad t = T. \tag{6.12}$$

In terms of the continuously compounded interest rate $r(s_t, t)$ the value v_{ω_B} of the pure discount bond incepted at time t and maturing at time T an instant later is formally given by

$$v_{\omega_B} = e^{-\int_{\overset{1}{(t)}}^{\overset{3}{(t)}} r(s_t, \tau) d\tau}$$

so that identity (6.12) can be rewritten as follows

$$\Big(\overset{2}{\frac{d}{dt}} + \boldsymbol{\mathfrak{L}}(\overset{2}{t})\Big)\, \boldsymbol{u}'(\overset{3}{t}, \overset{1}{t})\, e^{-\int_{\overset{1}{(t)}}^{\overset{3}{(t)}} \boldsymbol{r}(\overset{3}{s}, \tau) d\tau}\, \mathbf{1} = 0,$$

or equivalently

$$\Big(\overset{2}{\frac{d}{dt}} + \boldsymbol{\mathfrak{L}}(\overset{2}{t})\Big)\, \boldsymbol{u}'(\overset{3}{t}, \overset{1}{t})\, \mathbf{1} + r(s, t) = 0, \quad t = T, \tag{6.13}$$

where $\boldsymbol{r}(s, \tau)$ is the operator of multiplication by the function $r(s, t)$, and where the indexes over the operators indicate the order in which these operators act. We comment that $\mathbf{1}$ is the function in $\Pi(\mathbb{R}^n_{++} \times \mathcal{N}_t(\mathcal{T}))$ identically equal to unity.

With the help of identity (6.13), identity (6.9) can be rewritten as follows

$$
\begin{aligned}
&\Big(\overset{2}{\frac{d}{dt}} + \boldsymbol{\mathfrak{L}}(\overset{2}{t})\Big)\, \boldsymbol{u}'(\overset{3}{t},\overset{1}{t})\, \boldsymbol{v}\, \mathbf{1} = \\
&\qquad \int_{\Omega\setminus\omega_B} \Big(\boldsymbol{\pi}_v(t,d\omega)\Big(\overset{2}{\frac{d}{dt}} + \boldsymbol{\mathfrak{L}}(\overset{2}{t})\Big)\, \boldsymbol{u}'(\overset{3}{t},\overset{1}{t})\, \boldsymbol{v}_\omega\, \mathbf{1}\Big) + \\
&\qquad\qquad \boldsymbol{\pi}_v(t,B)\Big(\Big(\overset{2}{\frac{d}{dt}} + \boldsymbol{\mathfrak{L}}(\overset{2}{t})\Big)\, \boldsymbol{u}'(\overset{3}{t},\overset{1}{t})\, \mathbf{1} + r(s,t)\Big), \quad t = T,
\end{aligned}
\tag{6.14}
$$

where $\boldsymbol{\pi}_v(t,B) = \boldsymbol{\pi}_v(t,\omega_B)$ is the operator weight of the pure discount bond in the dynamically replicating portfolio at the time t for the European contingent claim $\mathfrak{v}$.

6.17. Remark. It is clear that $\boldsymbol{\pi}_v(t,B) = \boldsymbol{\pi}_v(t,\omega_B)$ is nothing but the operator-valued measure of ω_B in Ω.

Consider the operators

$$
\Big(\overset{2}{\frac{d}{dt}} + \boldsymbol{\mathfrak{L}}(\overset{2}{t})\Big)\, \boldsymbol{u}'(\overset{3}{t},\overset{1}{t})\, \boldsymbol{v}
$$

and

$$
\Big(\overset{2}{\frac{d}{dt}} + \boldsymbol{\mathfrak{L}}(\overset{2}{t})\Big)\, \boldsymbol{u}'(\overset{3}{t},\overset{1}{t})\, \boldsymbol{v}_\omega
$$

with ω in $\Omega \setminus \omega_B$ from the preceding identity (6.14) separately.

With the help of the chain of equalities (6.10) for the operator $\Big(\overset{2}{\frac{d}{dt}} + \boldsymbol{\mathfrak{L}}(\overset{2}{t})\Big)\, \boldsymbol{u}'(\overset{3}{t},\overset{1}{t})\, \boldsymbol{v}$ we have the following equality

$$
\begin{aligned}
&\Big(\overset{2}{\frac{d}{dt}} + \boldsymbol{\mathfrak{L}}(\overset{2}{t})\Big)\, \boldsymbol{u}'(\overset{3}{t},\overset{1}{t})\, \boldsymbol{v} = \\
&\qquad \boldsymbol{v}\, \Big(\overset{2}{\frac{d}{dt}} + \boldsymbol{\mathfrak{L}}(\overset{2}{t})\Big)\, \boldsymbol{u}'(\overset{3}{t},\overset{1}{t}) + \\
&\qquad\qquad \Big[\Big(\frac{d}{dt} + \boldsymbol{\mathfrak{L}}(t)\Big), \boldsymbol{v}\Big] + \Big[\Big[\Big(\overset{2}{\frac{d}{dt}} + \boldsymbol{\mathfrak{L}}(\overset{2}{t})\Big), \boldsymbol{v}\Big], \boldsymbol{u}'(\overset{3}{t},\overset{1}{t})\Big],
\end{aligned}
\tag{6.15}
$$

where again we have taken into account the fact that due to Theorem (3.81) for each time t in $\mathcal{T}$ and each state of the market as expressed by the prices of the underlying securities s'_t at this time t there exists a global transformation from the beliefs-preferences gauge symmetry group $\hat{\mathcal{G}}$ such that the marginal utility $\boldsymbol{u}'(t,t)$ is the operator of multiplication by the function $u'(t,t,s_t,s_t)$ with the following property

$$u'(t,t,s_t = s'_t, s_t = s'_t) = 1.$$

With the help of the chain of equalities (6.11) for the operator $(\overset{2}{\frac{d}{dt}} + \boldsymbol{\mathfrak{L}}(\overset{2}{t}))\, \boldsymbol{u}'(\overset{3}{t},\overset{1}{t})\, \boldsymbol{v}_\omega$ with ω in $\Omega \setminus \omega_B$ we have the following equality

$$\begin{aligned}
&(\overset{2}{\frac{d}{dt}} + \boldsymbol{\mathfrak{L}}(\overset{2}{t}))\, \boldsymbol{u}'(\overset{3}{t},\overset{1}{t})\, \boldsymbol{v}_\omega = \\
&\quad \boldsymbol{v}_\omega\, (\overset{2}{\frac{d}{dt}} + \boldsymbol{\mathfrak{L}}(\overset{2}{t}))\, \boldsymbol{u}'(\overset{3}{t},\overset{1}{t}) + \\
&\qquad [(\frac{d}{dt} + \boldsymbol{\mathfrak{L}}(t)), \boldsymbol{v}_\omega] + [[(\overset{2}{\frac{d}{dt}} + \boldsymbol{\mathfrak{L}}(\overset{2}{t})), \boldsymbol{v}_\omega], \boldsymbol{u}'(\overset{3}{t},\overset{1}{t})],
\end{aligned} \tag{6.16}$$

where again we have taken into account the fact that due to Theorem (3.81) for each time t in $\mathcal{T}$ and each state of the market as expressed by the prices of the underlying securities s'_t at this time t there exists a global transformation from the beliefs-preferences gauge symmetry group $\hat{\mathcal{G}}$ such that the marginal utility $\boldsymbol{u}'(t,t)$ is the operator of multiplication by the function $u'(t,t,s_t,s_t)$ with the following property

$$u'(t,t,s_t = s'_t, s_t = s'_t) = 1.$$

With the help of the preceding equalities (6.15) and (6.16)

we can rewrite identity (6.14) as follows

$$
\begin{aligned}
&\Big(\boldsymbol{v}\,\big(\overset{2}{\frac{d}{dt}} + \mathfrak{L}(\overset{2}{t})\big)\,\boldsymbol{u}'(\overset{3}{t},\overset{1}{t}) + \\
&\qquad [(\frac{d}{dt} + \mathfrak{L}(t)), \boldsymbol{v}] + [[(\overset{2}{\frac{d}{dt}} + \mathfrak{L}(\overset{2}{t})), \boldsymbol{v}], \boldsymbol{u}'(\overset{3}{t},\overset{1}{t})]\Big)\mathbf{1} = \\
&\int_{\Omega\setminus\omega_B} \Big(\boldsymbol{\pi}_v(t, d\omega)\Big(\boldsymbol{v}_\omega\,\big(\overset{2}{\frac{d}{dt}} + \mathfrak{L}(\overset{2}{t})\big)\,\boldsymbol{u}'(\overset{3}{t},\overset{1}{t}) + \\
&\qquad [(\frac{d}{dt} + \mathfrak{L}(t)), \boldsymbol{v}_\omega] + [[(\overset{2}{\frac{d}{dt}} + \mathfrak{L}(\overset{2}{t})), \boldsymbol{v}_\omega], \boldsymbol{u}'(\overset{3}{t},\overset{1}{t})]\Big)\mathbf{1}\Big) + \\
&\qquad \boldsymbol{\pi}_v(t, B)\Big(\big(\overset{2}{\frac{d}{dt}} + \mathfrak{L}(\overset{2}{t})\big)\,\boldsymbol{u}'(\overset{3}{t},\overset{1}{t})\,\mathbf{1} + r(s,t)\Big), \quad t = T,
\end{aligned}
\tag{6.17}
$$

where $\mathbf{1}$ is the function in $\Pi(\mathbb{R}^n_{++} \times \mathcal{N}_t(\mathcal{T}))$ identically equal to unity.

Let the operator weight $\boldsymbol{\pi}_v(t, B)$ of the pure discount bond in the dynamically replicating portfolio at time t in $\mathcal{T}$ for the European contingent claim $\mathfrak{v}$ be chosen according to relation (6.5), that is:

$$
\boldsymbol{\pi}_v(t, B) = \boldsymbol{v} - \int_{\Omega\setminus\omega_B} \boldsymbol{\pi}_v(t, d\omega)\,\boldsymbol{v}_\omega. \tag{6.18}
$$

With operator weight $\boldsymbol{\pi}_v(t, B)$ of the pure discount bond in the dynamically replicating portfolio at time t in $\mathcal{T}$ for the European contingent claim $\mathfrak{v}$ chosen as in the preceding relation

(6.18) we can rewrite identity (6.17) as follows

$$\begin{aligned}&\Big([(\frac{d}{dt}+\mathfrak{L}(t)),\boldsymbol{v}] + [[(\overset{2}{\frac{d}{dt}}+\mathfrak{L}(\overset{2}{t})),\boldsymbol{v}],\boldsymbol{u}'(\overset{3}{t},\overset{1}{t})]\Big)\mathbf{1} = \\ &\int_{\Omega\setminus\omega_B}\Big(\boldsymbol{\pi}_v(t,d\omega)\Big([(\frac{d}{dt}+\mathfrak{L}(t)),\boldsymbol{v}_\omega] + \\ &\qquad\qquad [[(\overset{2}{\frac{d}{dt}}+\mathfrak{L}(\overset{2}{t})),\boldsymbol{v}_\omega],\boldsymbol{u}'(\overset{3}{t},\overset{1}{t})]\Big)\mathbf{1}\Big) + \\ &\boldsymbol{\pi}_v(t,B)\,r(s,t), \quad t=T,\end{aligned} \tag{6.19}$$

where $\mathbf{1}$ is the function in $\Pi(\mathbb{R}^n_{++}\times\mathcal{N}_t(\mathcal{T}))$ identically equal to unity.

Since the operator $\boldsymbol{v}$ of multiplication by the value v of the European contingent claim $\mathfrak{v}$ in the preceding identity (6.19) has to remain unchanged under the action of the group H or more precisely (e_G, H), that is, has to be independent of preference $\boldsymbol{u}'(t,T)$, then the terms in this identity that possess the explicit dependence of $\boldsymbol{u}'(t,T)$ must be equal separately for any $\boldsymbol{u}'(t,T)$:

$$\begin{aligned}&[[(\overset{2}{\frac{d}{dt}}+\mathfrak{L}(\overset{2}{t})),\boldsymbol{v}],\boldsymbol{u}'(\overset{3}{t},\overset{1}{t})]\,\mathbf{1} = \\ &\int_{\Omega\setminus\omega_B}\Big(\boldsymbol{\pi}_v(t,d\omega)[[(\overset{2}{\frac{d}{dt}}+\mathfrak{L}(\overset{2}{t})),\boldsymbol{v}_\omega],\boldsymbol{u}'(\overset{3}{t},\overset{1}{t})]\,\mathbf{1}\Big),\end{aligned} \tag{6.20}$$

where $t = T$, and where $\mathbf{1}$ is the function in $\Pi(\mathbb{R}^n_{++}\times\mathcal{N}_t(\mathcal{T}))$ identically equal to unity.

It is this equation (6.20) that determines the operator weights $\boldsymbol{\pi}_v(t,d\omega)$ of the European contingent claims $\{\mathfrak{v}_\omega : \omega\in\Omega\}$ in the dynamically replicating portfolio at time t in $\mathcal{T}$ for a given European contingent claim $\mathfrak{v}$. More precisely, the preceding identity (6.20) determines the operator weights $\boldsymbol{\pi}_v(t,d\omega)$ of the European contingent claims $\{\mathfrak{v}_\omega : \omega\in\Omega\setminus\omega_B\}$ in the dynamically replicating portfolio at time t in $\mathcal{T}$ for the European contingent claim $\mathfrak{v}$ not including the pure discount bond $\mathfrak{v}_{\omega_B}$. After these operator weights are determined then the operator weight $\boldsymbol{\pi}_v(t, B)$ of the pure discount bond $\mathfrak{v}_{\omega_B}$ in the dynamically replicating portfolio at time t in $\mathcal{T}$ for the European contingent claim $\mathfrak{v}$ can be found from relation (6.18).

6.18. Remark. More precisely, equation (6.20) determines the map $\boldsymbol{\pi}_{(\cdot)}(t, d\omega)$ defined on Π.

Before we represent identity (6.19) in such a way that it does not possess explicit dependence on the preference $\boldsymbol{u}'(t, T)$, we analyze equation (6.20) for the operator weights $\boldsymbol{\pi}_v(t, d\omega)$ of the European contingent claims in the dynamically replicating portfolio at time t in $\mathcal{T}$ for the European contingent claim $\mathfrak{v}$ in more detail.

It is clear from the financial standpoint that, since equation (6.20) determines all the operator weights $\boldsymbol{\pi}_v(t, d\omega)$ of the European contingent claims $\{\mathfrak{v}_\omega : \omega \in \Omega \setminus \omega_B\}$ in the dynamically replicating portfolio at time t in $\mathcal{T}$ for the European contingent claim $\mathfrak{v}$ except for the operator weight $\boldsymbol{\pi}_v(t, B)$ of the pure discount bond $\mathfrak{v}_{\omega_B}$, and since the operator weight $\boldsymbol{\pi}_v(t, B)$ of the pure discount bond $\mathfrak{v}_{\omega_B}$ does not enter this equation, then the operator weights $\boldsymbol{\pi}_v(t, d\omega)$ of the European contingent claims $\{\mathfrak{v}_\omega : \omega \in \Omega \setminus \omega_B\}$ must depend only on the "random" component of $\mathfrak{L}(t)$. More precisely, the operator weights $\boldsymbol{\pi}_v(t, d\omega)$ of the European contingent claims $\{\mathfrak{v}_\omega : \omega \in \Omega \setminus \omega_B\}$ must remain unchanged under the following group $\mathcal{R}$ of transformations of the set $\mathsf{L}_t(\mathcal{T})$ of the derivatives $\mathsf{L}(t)$ of $-\boldsymbol{D}(t, T)$ with respect to t evaluated at t equal to T understood in an appropriate sense with $\boldsymbol{D}(t, T)$ in the generalized belief $\mathfrak{B}$ for all generalized market participants $\mathfrak{H} = (\mathfrak{B}, \mathcal{U})$ in the generalized market populace $\mathbb{H} = \mathbb{B} \times \mathbb{U}$:

$$\mathsf{L}(t) \xrightarrow{\mathfrak{r}} \mathsf{L}(t) + \sum_{i=1}^{n} a_i(s, t) \frac{\partial}{\partial s_i} + b(s, t), \quad \mathfrak{r} \in \mathcal{R},$$

where $a_i(s, t)$ and $b(s, t)$ are admissible functions in Π with t in $\mathcal{T}$.

6.19. Remark. We comment that for simplicity we have used the same notations for the operators of multiplication by the functions $a_i(s,t)$ and $b(s,t)$ and for the functions $a_i(s,t)$ and $b(s,t)$ themselves.

6.20. Remark. It is clear that $\mathcal{R}$ is an abelian group isomorphic to the direct product, or more precisely direct sum of $n+1$ abelian groups of functions in Π with the group operation of addition.

6.21. Remark. We comment that we have treated the set $\mathfrak{L}_t(\mathcal{T})$ of the derivatives $\mathfrak{L}(t)$ of $-\boldsymbol{F}(t,T)$ with respect to t evaluated at t equal to T understood in an appropriate sense with $\boldsymbol{F}(t,T)$ in the belief $\boldsymbol{\mathcal{B}}$ for all market participants $\boldsymbol{\mathcal{H}} = (\boldsymbol{\mathcal{B}}, \boldsymbol{\mathcal{U}})$ in the market populace $\mathbb{H} = \mathbb{B} \times \mathbb{U}$ as a subset of $\mathbf{L}_t(\mathcal{T})$. In order to restrict the group $\mathcal{R}$ to $\mathfrak{L}_t(\mathcal{T})$ it is enough to consider its subgroup of transformations $\mathfrak{r}$ of the form

$$\mathbf{L}(t) \xrightarrow{\mathfrak{r}} \mathbf{L}(t) + \sum_{i=1}^{n} a_i(s,t)\frac{\partial}{\partial s_i}.$$

It is clear that this subgroup is an abelian group isomorphic to the direct product, or more precisely direct sum of n abelian groups of functions in Π with the group operation of addition.

The fact that the operator weights $\boldsymbol{\pi}_v(t, d\omega)$ of the European contingent claims $\{\mathfrak{v}_\omega : \omega \in \Omega \setminus \omega_B\}$ remain unchanged under the group $\mathcal{R}$ of transformations of $\mathbf{L}_t(\mathcal{T})$ directly follows from the fact that each linear partial differential operator of the first order

$$\sum_{i=1}^{n} a_i(s,t)\frac{\partial}{\partial s_i} + b(s,t)$$

on Π is in the kernel subspace of the double commutator with operators $\boldsymbol{\alpha}(s,t)$ and $\boldsymbol{\beta}(s,t)$ of multiplication by arbitrary admissible real-valued functions $\alpha(s,t)$ and $\beta(s,t)$ in Π with t in $\mathcal{T}$:

$$[[\sum_{i=1}^{n} a_i(s,t)\frac{\partial}{\partial s_i} + b(s,t), \boldsymbol{\alpha}(s,t)], \boldsymbol{\beta}(s,t)] = \mathbf{0},$$

where $\mathbf{0}$ is the zero operator on Π.

6.22. Remark. The fact that the operator weights $\boldsymbol{\pi}_{\mathfrak{v}}(t, d\omega)$ of the European contingent claims $\{\mathfrak{v}_\omega : \omega \in \Omega \setminus \omega_B\}$ remain unchanged under the group $\mathcal{R}$ of transformations of $\mathbf{L}_t(\mathcal{T})$ can be restated as the fact that these operator weights can be defined on the orbits of the group $\mathcal{R}$.

Now our goal is to express equation (6.20) for the operator weights $\boldsymbol{\pi}_{\mathfrak{v}}(t, d\omega)$ of the European contingent claims in the dynamically replicating portfolio at time t in $\mathcal{T}$ for the European contingent claim $\mathfrak{v}$ solely in terms of $\mathfrak{L}(t)$ without the operator of differentiation with respect to time.

Denote by $\mathbf{D}_t(\mathcal{T})$ the set of all linear operators

$$\mathbf{D}(t) : \Pi(\mathbb{R}^n_{++} \times \mathcal{N}_t(\mathcal{T})) \to \Pi(\mathbb{R}^n_{++} \times \mathcal{N}_t(\mathcal{T}))$$

defined by

$$\mathbf{D}(t) = d(s,t)\frac{d}{dt} + \mathbf{L}(t),$$

where $d(s,t)$ is in Π with t in $\mathcal{T}$, and where $\mathbf{L}(t)$ is in $\mathbf{L}_t(\mathcal{T})$.

6.23. Remark. We comment that for simplicity we have used the same notations for the operator of multiplication by the function $d(s,t)$ and for the function $d(s,t)$ itself.

The operator weights $\boldsymbol{\pi}_{\mathfrak{v}}(t, d\omega)$ of the European contingent claims $\{\mathfrak{v}_\omega : \omega \in \Omega \setminus \omega_B\}$ remain unchanged under the following group $\hat{\mathcal{R}}$ of transformations of the set $\mathbf{D}_t(\mathcal{T})$:

$$\mathbf{D}(t) \xrightarrow{\hat{\mathfrak{r}}} \mathbf{D}(t) + c(s,t)\frac{d}{dt} + \sum_{i=1}^{n} a_i(s,t)\frac{\partial}{\partial s_i} + b(s,t), \quad \hat{\mathfrak{r}} \in \hat{\mathcal{R}},$$

where $a_i(s,t)$, $b(s,t)$ and $c(s,t)$ are admissible functions in Π for t in $\mathcal{T}$.

6.24. Remark. We comment that again for simplicity we have used the same notations for the operators of multiplication by the functions $a_i(s,t)$, $b(s,t)$ and $c(s,t)$ and for the functions $a_i(s,t)$, $b(s,t)$ and $c(s,t)$ themselves.

6.25. Remark. It is clear that $\hat{\mathcal{R}}$ is an abelian group isomorphic to the direct product, or more precisely direct sum of $n+2$ abelian groups of functions in Π with the group operation of addition.

6.26. Remark. We comment that we have treated the set $\mathfrak{D}_t(\mathcal{T})$ of all operators

$$\mathfrak{D}(t) : \Pi(\mathbb{R}^n_{++} \times \mathcal{N}_t(\mathcal{T})) \to \Pi(\mathbb{R}^n_{++} \times \mathcal{N}_t(\mathcal{T}))$$

of the form

$$\mathfrak{D}(t) = d(s,t)\frac{d}{dt} + \mathfrak{L}(t)$$

with $\mathfrak{L}(t)$ in $\mathfrak{L}_t(\mathcal{T})$ as a subset of $\mathbf{D}_t(\mathcal{T})$. In order to restrict the group $\hat{\mathcal{R}}$ to $\mathfrak{D}_t(\mathcal{T})$ it is enough to consider its subgroup of transformations $\hat{\mathfrak{r}}$ of the form

$$\mathbf{D} \xrightarrow{\hat{\mathfrak{r}}} \mathbf{D} + c(s,t)\frac{d}{dt} + \sum_{i=1}^{n} a_i(s,t)\frac{\partial}{\partial s_i}.$$

It is clear that this subgroup is an abelian group isomorphic to the direct product, or more precisely direct sum of $n+1$ abelian groups of functions in Π with the group operation of addition.

The fact that the operator weights $\boldsymbol{\pi}_v(t, d\omega)$ of the European contingent claims $\{\mathfrak{v}_\omega : \omega \in \Omega \setminus \omega_B\}$ remain unchanged under the group $\hat{\mathcal{R}}$ of transformations of $\mathbf{D}_t(\mathcal{T})$ directly follows from the fact that each linear partial differential operator of the first order

$$c(s,t)\frac{d}{dt} + \sum_{i=1}^{n} a_i(s,t)\frac{\partial}{\partial s_i} + b(s,t)$$

on $\Pi(\mathbb{R}^n_{++} \times \mathcal{N}_t(\mathcal{T}))$ is in the kernel subspace of the double commutator with operators $\boldsymbol{\alpha}(s,t)$ and $\boldsymbol{\beta}(s,t)$ of multiplication by arbitrary admissible functions $\alpha(s,t)$ and $\beta(s,t)$ in $\Pi(\mathbb{R}^n_{++} \times \mathcal{N}_t(\mathcal{T}))$:

$$[[c(s,t)\frac{d}{dt} + \sum_{i=1}^{n} a_i(s,t)\frac{\partial}{\partial s_i} + b(s,t), \boldsymbol{\alpha}(s,t)], \boldsymbol{\beta}(s,t)] = \mathbf{0},$$

where $\mathbf{0}$ is the zero operator on $\Pi(\mathbb{R}^n_{++} \times \mathcal{N}_t(\mathcal{T}))$.

6.27. Remark. The fact that the operator weights $\boldsymbol{\pi}_v(t, d\omega)$ of the European contingent claims $\{\mathfrak{v}_\omega : \omega \in \Omega \setminus \omega_B\}$ remain unchanged under the group $\hat{\mathcal{R}}$ of transformations of $\mathbf{D}_t(\mathcal{T})$ can be restated as the fact that these operator weights can be defined on the orbits of the group $\hat{\mathcal{R}}$.

Finally, for the operator

$$\mathfrak{D}(t) = d(s,t)\frac{d}{dt} + \mathfrak{L}(t)$$

in $\mathbf{D}_t(\mathcal{T})$, or more precisely in $\mathfrak{D}_t(\mathcal{T})$ with $d(s,t)$ identically equal to unity and for the transformation $\hat{\mathfrak{r}}$ from the group $\hat{\mathcal{R}}$ with $c(s,t) = -d(s,t)$ we can rewrite equation (6.20) for the operator weights $\boldsymbol{\pi}_v(t, d\omega)$ of the European contingent claims $\{\mathfrak{v}_\omega : \omega \in \Omega \setminus \omega_B\}$ in the dynamically replicating portfolio at time t in $\mathcal{T}$ for the European contingent claim $\mathfrak{v}$ solely in terms of $\mathfrak{L}(t)$ without the operator of differentiation with respect to time:

$$[[\mathfrak{L}(\overset{2}{t}), \boldsymbol{v}], \boldsymbol{u}'(\overset{3}{t}, \overset{1}{t})]\, \mathbf{1} = \int_{\Omega\setminus\omega_B} \left(\boldsymbol{\pi}_v(t, d\omega)[[\mathfrak{L}(\overset{2}{t}), \boldsymbol{v}_\omega], \boldsymbol{u}'(\overset{3}{t}, \overset{1}{t})]\, \mathbf{1}\right), \tag{6.21}$$

for any preference $\boldsymbol{u}'(t, T)$. We comment that $\mathbf{1}$ is the function in Π identically equal to unity.

Now with the help of equation (6.20), or equivalently (6.21) we represent identity (6.19) in such a way that it does not possess explicit dependence on the preference $\boldsymbol{u}'(t, T)$:

$$\begin{aligned} [(\frac{d}{dt} + \mathfrak{L}(t)), \boldsymbol{v}]\mathbf{1} = & \\ & \int_{\Omega\setminus\omega_B} \left(\boldsymbol{\pi}_v(t, d\omega)[(\frac{d}{dt} + \mathfrak{L}(t)), \boldsymbol{v}_\omega]\mathbf{1}\right) + \\ & (\boldsymbol{v} - \int_{\Omega\setminus\omega_B} \boldsymbol{\pi}_v(t, d\omega)\, \boldsymbol{v}_\omega) r(s,t), \quad t = T, \end{aligned} \tag{6.22}$$

where we have made use of relation (6.18), and where $\mathbf{1}$ is the function in $\Pi(\mathbb{R}^n_{++} \times \mathcal{N}_t(\mathcal{T}))$ identically equal to unity.

We note that relation (3.68) implies that the function $\mathbf{1}$ in $\Pi(\mathbb{R}^n_{++} \times \mathcal{N}_t(\mathcal{T}))$ identically equal to unity is in the kernel subspace of the operator $\frac{d}{dt} + \mathfrak{L}(t)$, that is:

$$(\frac{d}{dt} + \mathfrak{L}(t))\mathbf{1} = \mathbf{0}, \tag{6.23}$$

where $\mathbf{0}$ is the function in $\Pi(\mathbb{R}^n_{++} \times \mathcal{N}_t(\mathcal{T}))$ identically equal to zero.

Therefore identity (6.22) can be rewritten as follows

$$\begin{aligned}(\frac{d}{dt} + \mathfrak{L}(t))\, v = \\ \int_{\Omega\backslash\omega_B} \Big(\boldsymbol{\pi}_v(t, d\omega)(\frac{d}{dt} + \mathfrak{L}(t))\, v_\omega\Big) + \\ (v - \int_{\Omega\backslash\omega_B} \boldsymbol{\pi}_v(t, d\omega)\, v_\omega) r(s,t), \quad t = T.\end{aligned} \tag{6.24}$$

We rewrite the preceding identity (6.24) as follows

$$\begin{aligned}(\frac{d}{dt} + \mathfrak{L}(t))\, (v - \int_{\Omega\backslash\omega_B} \boldsymbol{\pi}_v(t, d\omega)\, v_\omega) = \\ (v - \int_{\Omega\backslash\omega_B} \boldsymbol{\pi}_v(t, d\omega)\, v_\omega) r(s,t), \quad t = T.\end{aligned} \tag{6.25}$$

Since $\mathfrak{L}(t)$ is the derivative of $-\boldsymbol{F}(t,T)$ with respect to t evaluated at t equal to T understood in an appropriate sense with $\boldsymbol{F}(t,T)$ in the belief $\boldsymbol{\mathcal{B}}$ of a market participant $\boldsymbol{\mathcal{H}} = (\boldsymbol{\mathcal{B}}, \boldsymbol{\mathcal{U}})$ in the market populace $\mathbb{H} = \mathbb{B} \times \mathbb{U}$, the preceding identity (6.25) financially means that the instantaneous return on the portfolio consisting of a long position on the European contingent claim $\mathfrak{v}$ and a short position on the dynamically replicating portfolio at time t in $\mathcal{T}$ of European contingent claims $\{\mathfrak{v}_\omega : \omega \in \Omega\backslash\omega_B\}$ with the operator weights $\boldsymbol{\pi}_v(t, d\omega)$ not including the pure discount bond $\mathfrak{v}_{\omega_B}$ is equal to the instantaneous return on the portfolio consisting of $\boldsymbol{v} - \int_{\Omega\backslash\omega_B} \boldsymbol{\pi}_v(t, d\omega)\boldsymbol{v}_\omega$ units, or more precisely operator units of pure discount bond. In order to see this more clearly we can formally rewrite identity (6.25) as follows

$$\Big(\overset{2}{\frac{d}{dt}} + \mathfrak{L}(\overset{2}{t})\Big)\Big(\big(v - \int_{\Omega\backslash\omega_B} \overset{3}{\boldsymbol{\pi}}_v(t, d\omega)\, v_\omega\big) - \overbrace{\big(\boldsymbol{v} - \int_{\Omega\backslash\omega_B} \boldsymbol{\pi}_v(t, d\omega)\, \boldsymbol{v}_\omega\big)}^{3} e^{-\int_{\overset{1}{(t)}}^{\overset{3}{(t)}} r(\overset{3}{s},\tau)d\tau}\Big) = 0, \quad t = T. \tag{6.26}$$

Since the preceding identity (6.26) is a particular case of identity (6.8) and hence of (6.4), the financial interpretation given for identity (6.8) and hence for (6.4) can be repeated verbatim for identity (6.26) and hence (6.25) and (6.24).

6.28. Remark. Let $\boldsymbol{L}(t)$ be the derivative of $-\mathbf{V}(t,T)$ with respect to t evaluated at t equal to T understood in an appropriate sense, where $\mathbf{V}(t,T)$ is an evolution operator in a market environment $\mathbf{V}$. It is clear that $\boldsymbol{L}(t)$ is also equal to the derivative of $\mathbf{V}(t,T)$ with respect to T evaluated at T equal to t understood in an appropriate sense. Assume that all market participants that populate a marketplace at time t in $\mathcal{T}$ have agreed upon the values at the time t of a set of European contingent claims with inception time t and the expiration time T for all T in some $\mathcal{N}_t(\mathcal{T})$ with $t \leq T$ whose payoffs form a dense set. In this case it is possible to observe the derivative $\boldsymbol{L}(t)$, or more precisely the image $\big(\boldsymbol{L}(t)\, h\big)(s_t)$ of any h in the dense set evaluated at the state of the market as expressed by the prices of the underlying securities s_t at the time t, directly from the market data. Indeed

$$\big(\boldsymbol{L}(t)\, h\big)(s_t) = \Big(\lim_{\Delta t \downarrow 0} \frac{\mathbf{V}(t, t+\Delta t) - \boldsymbol{I}}{\Delta t} h\Big)(s_t) = \Big(\lim_{\Delta t \downarrow 0} \frac{\big(\mathbf{V}(t, t+\Delta t)\, h\big)(s_t) - h(s_t)}{\Delta t}\Big),$$

where $\boldsymbol{I}$ is the identity operator on Π. We recall that $\mathbf{V}(t, t+\triangle t)\, h$ is the value in Π at the inception time t of the European contingent claim with expiration time $t+\triangle t$ and the payoff h in Π, so that $\big(\mathbf{V}(t, t+\triangle t)\, h\big)(s_t)$ is the value in units of account at the inception time t of this European contingent claim, when the state of the market as expressed by the prices of the underlying securities is s_t at this time t.

Now let $\mathfrak{L}(t)$ be the derivative of $-\boldsymbol{F}(t, T)$ with respect to t evaluated at t equal to T understood in an appropriate sense with $\boldsymbol{F}(t, T)$ in the belief $\boldsymbol{\mathcal{B}}$ of a market participant $\boldsymbol{\mathcal{H}} = (\boldsymbol{\mathcal{B}}, \boldsymbol{\mathcal{U}})$ that populates the marketplace at time t in $\boldsymbol{\mathcal{T}}$. Due to relations (3.71) and (3.63) the transformation of $\mathfrak{L}(t)$ from the dynamic beliefs-preferences gauge symmetry group $\hat{\boldsymbol{\mathcal{G}}}$ defined in (3.67) with $\hat{\mathbf{u}}'(t, T)$ generated by $\boldsymbol{u}'(t, T)$ in the preference $\boldsymbol{\mathcal{U}}$ takes the following form

$$
\begin{aligned}
\mathfrak{L}(t) \xrightarrow{\hat{g}_{\boldsymbol{\mathcal{B}}}} & \hat{\mathbf{u}}'^{-1}(t,t)\, \mathfrak{L}(t)\, \hat{\mathbf{u}}'(t,t) + \frac{\hat{\mathbf{u}}'_t(t,t)}{\hat{\mathbf{u}}'(t,t)} = \\
& \boldsymbol{u}'^{-1}(t,t)\, \mathfrak{L}(t)\, \boldsymbol{u}'(t,t) + \frac{\boldsymbol{u}'_t(t,t)}{\boldsymbol{u}'(t,t)} - \mathfrak{d}(t) = \\
& \boldsymbol{u}'^{-1}(t,t)\, \mathfrak{L}(t)\, \boldsymbol{u}'(t,t) + \frac{\boldsymbol{u}'_t(t,t)}{\boldsymbol{u}'(t,t)} - \\
& \qquad \Big(\boldsymbol{u}'^{-1}(t,t)\, \mathfrak{L}(t)\, \boldsymbol{u}'(t,t) + \frac{\boldsymbol{u}'_t(t,t)}{\boldsymbol{u}'(t,t)}\Big)\, \mathbf{1} = \\
& \boldsymbol{L}(t) + r(s,t),
\end{aligned} \tag{6.27}
$$

where

$$
r(s,t) = -\boldsymbol{L}(t)\, \mathbf{1},
$$

with $\mathbf{1}$ being the function in Π identically equal to unity, is the continuously compounded interest rate, and where we have used the same notation for the operator $\boldsymbol{r}(s,t)$ on Π of multiplication by the function $r(s,t)$ in Π and for the function $r(s,t)$ itself. Therefore due to Remark (3.113) the operator

$$
\mathfrak{L}'(t) = \boldsymbol{L}(t) + r(s,t)
$$

on Π is a derivative of $-\boldsymbol{F}'(t,T)$ with respect to t evaluated at t equal to T understood in an appropriate sense with $\boldsymbol{F}'(t,T)$ in the belief $\boldsymbol{\mathcal{B}}'$ of a market participant $\boldsymbol{\mathcal{H}}' = (\boldsymbol{\mathcal{B}}', \boldsymbol{\mathcal{U}}')$ in the same orbit of the group $\hat{\boldsymbol{\mathcal{G}}}$ in $\mathbb{H} = \mathbb{B} \times \mathbb{U}$ as the market participant $\boldsymbol{\mathcal{H}} = (\boldsymbol{\mathcal{B}}, \boldsymbol{\mathcal{U}})$. Therefore in the case under consideration it is possible to observe $\boldsymbol{\mathfrak{L}}'(t)$, or more precisely the image $\big(\boldsymbol{\mathfrak{L}}'(t)\, h\big)(s_t)$ of any h in the dense set evaluated at the state of the market as expressed by the prices of the underlying securities s_t at the time t in $\mathcal{T}$, directly from the market data, at least for some market participant $\boldsymbol{\mathcal{H}}' = (\boldsymbol{\mathcal{B}}', \boldsymbol{\mathcal{U}}')$ that populates the marketplace at time t, that is, is in the orbit of the group $\hat{\boldsymbol{\mathcal{G}}}$:

$$\big(\boldsymbol{\mathfrak{L}}'(t)\, h\big)(s_t) = \big(\boldsymbol{L}(t)\, h\big)(s_t) + r(s_t, t)\, h(s_t).$$

We comment that to be able to observe $\boldsymbol{\mathfrak{L}}'(t)$ for at least one market participant $\boldsymbol{\mathcal{H}}' = (\boldsymbol{\mathcal{B}}', \boldsymbol{\mathcal{U}}')$ that populates the marketplace at time t in $\mathcal{T}$ is enough for the dynamic replication at the time t of European contingent claims. Finally we note that in order to determine the continuously compounded interest rate $r(s,t)$ it is enough to assume that the pure discount bond with inception time t, maturity time T in $\boldsymbol{\mathcal{N}}_t(\mathcal{T})$ and with the face value of one unit of account is traded only effectively, that is, that the function $\mathbf{1}$ in Π identically equal to unity is in the dense set. This completes the Remark.

6.29. Remark. We make the following observation, which is crucial for practical applications of the results on the dynamic replication of European contingent claims in a general market environment $\mathbf{V}$ in the general case of a nonnecessarily Markovian market populace $\mathbb{H} = \mathbb{B} \times \mathbb{U}$. Assume that all market participants that populate a marketplace at time t in $\mathcal{T}$ have agreed upon the values at the inception time t of a set of European contingent claims whose payoffs at the expiration time T in $\boldsymbol{\mathcal{N}}_t(\mathcal{T})$ form a dense set. In this case, due to the preceding Remark (6.28), it is possible to observe the operator $\boldsymbol{\mathfrak{L}}(t)$, or more precisely the image $\big(\boldsymbol{\mathfrak{L}}(t)\, h\big)(s_t)$ of any h in the dense set evaluated at the state of the market as expressed by the prices of the underlying securities s_t at the time t, directly from the market data. Then in order to determine the operator weights $\boldsymbol{\pi}_v(t, d\omega)$, or more precisely the weights $\pi_v(t, s_t, d\omega)$ of the European contingent claims $\{\mathfrak{v}_\omega : \omega \in \Omega\}$ in the dynamically replicating portfolio at time t in $\mathcal{T}$ for the European contingent claim $\mathfrak{v}$ with the help of equation (6.20), or equivalently (6.21) and relation (6.18), we need to be able to evaluate the double commutator of the operator $\mathfrak{L}(t)$ with operators $\boldsymbol{\alpha}(s,t)$ and $\boldsymbol{\beta}(s,t)$ of multiplication by arbitrary admissible real-valued functions $\alpha(s,t)$ and $\beta(s,t)$ in Π:

$$[[\mathfrak{L}(t), \boldsymbol{\alpha}(s,t)], \boldsymbol{\beta}(s,t)],$$

or more precisely the image

$$\big([[\mathfrak{L}(t), \boldsymbol{\alpha}(s,t)], \boldsymbol{\beta}(s,t)]\, h\big)(s_t) \tag{6.28}$$

of any h in the dense set evaluated at the state of the market as expressed by the prices of the underlying securities s_t at the time t. This is indeed possible since what we need in order to evaluate the image of the double commutator in (6.28) is only the image $\big(\mathfrak{L}(t)\, h\big)(s_t)$ of any h in the dense set evaluated at the state of the market as expressed by the prices of the underlying securities s_t at the time t, which is directly observable from the market data. This completes the Remark.

Now we consider the general case when the set $\{\mathfrak{v}_\omega : \omega \in \Omega\}$ of European contingent claims dynamically replicates at time t in $\mathcal{T}$ a European contingent claim $\mathfrak{v}$ without the assumption that the pure discount bond is traded.

Instead of the European contingent claims $\{\mathfrak{v}_\omega : \omega \in \Omega\}$ and $\mathfrak{v}$ with values $\{v_\omega : \omega \in \Omega\}$ and v we consider portfolios of $\prod_{\omega' \in \Omega \cup \omega_0 \setminus \omega} \boldsymbol{v}_{\omega'}$ units of $\mathfrak{v}_\omega$ with ω in Ω and of $\prod_{\omega \in \Omega} \boldsymbol{v}_\omega$ units of $\mathfrak{v}$ with values

$$\{\Big(\prod_{\omega' \in \Omega \cup \omega_0 \setminus \omega} \boldsymbol{v}_{\omega'}\Big)\, v_\omega : \omega \in \Omega\} \quad \text{and} \quad \Big(\prod_{\omega \in \Omega} \boldsymbol{v}_\omega\Big)\, v$$

where $\boldsymbol{v}_\omega$ and $\boldsymbol{v}$ again stand for the operators of multiplication by the functions v_ω and v, and where the products are understood formally in the case when the set Ω is uncountable. We comment that ω_0, or more precisely $\mathfrak{v}_{\omega_0}$ denotes the European contingent claim $\mathfrak{v}$.

6.30. Remark. We comment that a portfolio of $\prod_{\omega' \in \Omega \cup \omega_0 \setminus \omega} \boldsymbol{v}_{\omega'}$ units of $\mathfrak{v}_\omega$ with ω in Ω and of $\prod_{\omega \in \Omega} \boldsymbol{v}_\omega$ units of $\mathfrak{v}$, or more precisely of $\prod_{\omega' \in \Omega \cup \omega_0 \setminus \omega} \boldsymbol{v}_{\omega'}$ operator units of $\mathfrak{v}_\omega$ with ω in Ω and of $\prod_{\omega \in \Omega} \boldsymbol{v}_\omega$ operator units of $\mathfrak{v}$, are financially understood as portfolios of $\prod_{\omega' \in \Omega \cup \omega_0 \setminus \omega} v_{\omega'}(t, s_t)$ units of $\mathfrak{v}_\omega$ with ω in Ω and of $\prod_{\omega \in \Omega} v_\omega(t, s_t)$ units of $\mathfrak{v}$ when the state of the market as expressed by the prices of the underlying securities is s_t in $\mathbb{R}^n_{++}$ at time t in $\mathcal{T}$. In other words, the portfolios of $\prod_{\omega' \in \Omega \cup \omega_0 \setminus \omega} \boldsymbol{v}_{\omega'}$ operator units of $\mathfrak{v}_\omega$ with ω in Ω and of $\prod_{\omega \in \Omega} \boldsymbol{v}_\omega$ operator units of $\mathfrak{v}$ are portfolios with amounts of units that depend on the time t and the state of the market as expressed by the prices of the underlying securities s_t at the time t.

It is clear that the values of all the portfolios of $\prod_{\omega' \in \Omega \cup \omega_0 \setminus \omega} \boldsymbol{v}_{\omega'}$ units of $\mathfrak{v}_\omega$ with ω in Ω and of $\prod_{\omega \in \Omega} \boldsymbol{v}_\omega$ units of $\mathfrak{v}$ are equal to each other, that is

$$\Big(\prod_{\omega' \in \Omega \cup \omega_0 \setminus \omega} \boldsymbol{v}_{\omega'} \Big) \, v_\omega = \Big(\prod_{\omega \in \Omega} \boldsymbol{v}_\omega \Big) \, v, \quad \omega \in \Omega. \tag{6.29}$$

For the portfolios of $\prod_{\omega' \in \Omega \cup \omega_0 \setminus \omega} \boldsymbol{v}_{\omega'}$ units of $\mathfrak{v}_\omega$ with ω in Ω and of $\prod_{\omega \in \Omega} \boldsymbol{v}_\omega$ units of $\mathfrak{v}$ we can rewrite identity (6.9) as follows

$$\Big(\prod_{\omega \in \Omega} \boldsymbol{v}_\omega\Big) \Big(\overset{2}{\frac{d}{dt}} + \overset{2}{\mathfrak{L}}(\overset{\ }{t}) \Big) \, \boldsymbol{u}'(\overset{3}{t}, \overset{1}{t}) \, \boldsymbol{v} \, \mathbf{1} =$$

$$\int_\Omega \Big(\boldsymbol{\pi}_v(t, d\omega) \Big(\prod_{\omega' \in \Omega \cup \omega_0 \setminus \omega} \boldsymbol{v}_{\omega'} \Big) \Big(\overset{2}{\frac{d}{dt}} + \overset{2}{\mathfrak{L}}(t) \Big) \, \boldsymbol{u}'(\overset{3}{t}, \overset{1}{t}) \, \boldsymbol{v}_\omega \, \mathbf{1} \Big), \tag{6.30}$$

where $t = T$, and where $\boldsymbol{\pi}_v(t, d\omega)$ is the operator weight of the portfolio of $\prod_{\omega' \in \Omega \cup \omega_0 \backslash \omega} \boldsymbol{v}_{\omega'}$ units of $\mathfrak{v}_\omega$ with ω in Ω in the dynamically replicating portfolio at time t in $\mathcal{T}$ for the portfolio of $\prod_{\omega \in \Omega} \boldsymbol{v}_\omega$ units of $\mathfrak{v}$.

With the help of equalities (6.15) and (6.16) we can rewrite the preceding identity (6.30) as follows

$$\begin{aligned}
&\Big(\prod_{\omega \in \Omega} \boldsymbol{v}_\omega\Big) \Big(\boldsymbol{v} \,\big(\overset{2}{\frac{d}{dt}} + \boldsymbol{\mathfrak{L}}(\overset{2}{t})\big)\, \boldsymbol{u}'(\overset{3}{t}, \overset{1}{t}) + \\
&\quad [(\frac{d}{dt} + \boldsymbol{\mathfrak{L}}(t)), \boldsymbol{v}] + [[(\overset{2}{\frac{d}{dt}} + \boldsymbol{\mathfrak{L}}(\overset{2}{t})), \boldsymbol{v}], \boldsymbol{u}'(\overset{3}{t}, \overset{1}{t})]\Big)\, \mathbf{1} = \\
&\int_\Omega \Big(\boldsymbol{\pi}_v(t, d\omega) \Big(\prod_{\omega' \in \Omega \cup \omega_0 \backslash \omega} \boldsymbol{v}_{\omega'}\Big) \Big(\boldsymbol{v}_\omega \,\big(\overset{2}{\frac{d}{dt}} + \boldsymbol{\mathfrak{L}}(\overset{2}{t})\big)\, \boldsymbol{u}'(\overset{3}{t}, \overset{1}{t}) + \\
&\quad [(\frac{d}{dt} + \boldsymbol{\mathfrak{L}}(t)), \boldsymbol{v}_\omega] + [[(\overset{2}{\frac{d}{dt}} + \boldsymbol{\mathfrak{L}}(\overset{2}{t})), \boldsymbol{v}_\omega], \boldsymbol{u}'(\overset{3}{t}, \overset{1}{t})]\Big)\, \mathbf{1}\Big), \quad t = T.
\end{aligned} \tag{6.31}$$

Without loss of generality we choose the total operator-valued measure, or equivalently the total operator weight for the portfolios of $\prod_{\omega' \in \Omega \cup \omega_0 \backslash \omega} \boldsymbol{v}_{\omega'}$ units of $\mathfrak{v}_\omega$ with ω in Ω in the dynamically replicating portfolio at time t in $\mathcal{T}$ for the portfolio of $\prod_{\omega \in \Omega} \boldsymbol{v}_\omega$ units of $\mathfrak{v}$ equal to the identity operator $\boldsymbol{I}$ on Π, that is

$$\int_\Omega \boldsymbol{\pi}_v(t, d\omega) = \boldsymbol{I}. \tag{6.32}$$

Indeed, if this is not the case we can formally choose the operator weight $\boldsymbol{\pi}_v(t, \omega_*)$ for one of the portfolios of $\prod_{\omega' \in \Omega \cup \omega_0 \backslash \omega_*} \boldsymbol{v}_{\omega'}$ units of $\mathfrak{v}_{\omega_*}$ with ω_* in Ω in the dynamically replicating portfolio at time t in $\mathcal{T}$ for the portfolio of $\prod_{\omega \in \Omega} \boldsymbol{v}_\omega$ units of $\mathfrak{v}$ as follows

$$\boldsymbol{\pi}_v(t, \omega_*) = \boldsymbol{I} - \int_{\Omega \backslash \omega_*} \boldsymbol{\pi}_v(t, d\omega). \tag{6.33}$$

6.31. Remark. Due to equality (6.29) the choice of the operator weights $\boldsymbol{\pi}_v(t, d\omega)$ of the portfolios of $\prod_{\omega' \in \Omega \cup \omega_0 \backslash \omega} \boldsymbol{v}_{\omega'}$ units of $\mathfrak{v}_\omega$ with ω in Ω in the dynamically replicating portfolio at time t in $\mathcal{T}$ for the portfolio of $\prod_{\omega \in \Omega} \boldsymbol{v}_\omega$ units of $\mathfrak{v}$ as given in (6.32) is consistent with equality (6.5). Indeed

$$\begin{aligned} &\int_\Omega \Big(\boldsymbol{\pi}_v(t, d\omega) \big(\prod_{\omega' \in \Omega \cup \omega_0 \backslash \omega} \boldsymbol{v}_{\omega'} \big) \, v_\omega \Big) = \\ &\int_\Omega \Big(\boldsymbol{\pi}_v(t, d\omega) \big(\prod_{\omega \in \Omega} \boldsymbol{v}_\omega \big) \, v \Big) = \\ &\Big(\int_\Omega \boldsymbol{\pi}_v(t, d\omega) \Big) \Big(\big(\prod_{\omega \in \Omega} \boldsymbol{v}_\omega \big) \, v \Big) = \\ &\big(\prod_{\omega \in \Omega} \boldsymbol{v}_\omega \big) \, v. \end{aligned} \tag{6.34}$$

With the choice of the operator weights $\boldsymbol{\pi}_v(t, d\omega)$ of the portfolios of $\prod_{\omega' \in \Omega \cup \omega_0 \backslash \omega} \boldsymbol{v}_{\omega'}$ units of $\mathfrak{v}_\omega$ with ω in Ω in the dynamically replicating portfolio at time t in $\mathcal{T}$ for the portfolio of $\prod_{\omega \in \Omega} \boldsymbol{v}_\omega$ units of $\mathfrak{v}$ as given in (6.32) and with the help of equality (6.29) we rewrite identity (6.31) as follows

$$\begin{aligned} &\big(\prod_{\omega \in \Omega} \boldsymbol{v}_\omega \big) \Big(([(\frac{d}{dt} + \mathfrak{L}(t)), \boldsymbol{v}] + [[(\frac{\overset{2}{d}}{dt} + \mathfrak{L}(\overset{2}{t})), \boldsymbol{v}], \boldsymbol{u}'(\overset{3}{t}, \overset{1}{t})] \Big) \mathbf{1} = \\ &\int_\Omega \Big(\boldsymbol{\pi}_v(t, d\omega) \big(\prod_{\omega' \in \Omega \cup \omega_0 \backslash \omega} \boldsymbol{v}_{\omega'} \big) \Big([(\frac{d}{dt} + \mathfrak{L}(t)), \boldsymbol{v}_\omega] + \\ &[[(\frac{\overset{2}{d}}{dt} + \mathfrak{L}(\overset{2}{t})), \boldsymbol{v}_\omega], \boldsymbol{u}'(\overset{3}{t}, \overset{1}{t})] \Big) \mathbf{1} \Big), \quad t = T. \end{aligned} \tag{6.35}$$

Since the operator $\boldsymbol{v}$ of the multiplication by the value v of the European contingent claim $\mathfrak{v}$ in the preceding identity (6.35) has to remain unchanged under the action of the group H or more precisely (e_G, H), that is, has to be independent of preference $\boldsymbol{u}'(t, T)$, then the terms in this equation that possess the explicit dependence of $\boldsymbol{u}'(t,T)$ must be equal separately for any $\boldsymbol{u}'(t,T)$:

$$
\begin{aligned}
&\Big(\prod_{\omega\in\Omega} \boldsymbol{v}_\omega\Big) \Big([[(\overset{2}{\frac{d}{dt}} + \mathfrak{L}(\overset{2}{t})), \boldsymbol{v}], \boldsymbol{u}'(\overset{3}{t}, \overset{1}{t})] \Big)\, \mathbf{1} = \\
&\qquad \int_\Omega \Big(\boldsymbol{\pi}_v(t, d\omega) \Big(\prod_{\omega'\in\Omega\cup\omega_0\backslash\omega} \boldsymbol{v}_{\omega'} \Big) \times \\
&\qquad\qquad [[(\overset{2}{\frac{d}{dt}} + \mathfrak{L}(\overset{2}{t})), \boldsymbol{v}_\omega], \boldsymbol{u}'(\overset{3}{t}, \overset{1}{t})] \Big)\, \mathbf{1} \Big), \quad t = T,
\end{aligned}
\tag{6.36}
$$

where $\mathbf{1}$ is the function in $\Pi(\mathbb{R}^n_{++} \times \mathcal{N}_t(\mathcal{T}))$ identically equal to unity.

It is this equation (6.36) that determines the operator weights $\boldsymbol{\pi}_v(t, d\omega)$ of the portfolios of $\prod_{\omega'\in\Omega\cup\omega_0\backslash\omega} \boldsymbol{v}_{\omega'}$ units of $\mathfrak{v}_\omega$ with ω in Ω in the dynamically replicating portfolio at time t in $\mathcal{T}$ for the portfolio of $\prod_{\omega\in\Omega} \boldsymbol{v}_\omega$ units of $\mathfrak{v}$.

6.32. Remark. More precisely, equation (6.36) determines the map $\boldsymbol{\pi}_{(\cdot)}(t, d\omega)$ defined on Π.

Before we represent identity (6.35) in such a way that it does not possess explicit dependence on the preference $\boldsymbol{u}'(t,T)$ we analyze the equation (6.36) for the operator weights $\boldsymbol{\pi}_v(t, d\omega)$ in more detail.

It is clear that the operator weights $\boldsymbol{\pi}_v(t, d\omega)$ of the portfolios of $\prod_{\omega'\in\Omega\cup\omega_0\backslash\omega} \boldsymbol{v}_{\omega'}$ units of $\mathfrak{v}_\omega$ with ω in Ω in the dynamically replicating portfolio for the portfolio of $\prod_{\omega\in\Omega} \boldsymbol{v}_\omega$ units of $\mathfrak{v}$ remain unchanged under the group $\mathcal{R}$ of transformations of $\mathsf{L}_t(\mathcal{T})$.

6.33. Remark. As we commented in Remark (6.21) we have treated $\mathfrak{L}_t(\mathcal{T})$ as a subset of $\mathsf{L}_t(\mathcal{T})$.

6.34. Remark. The fact that the operator weights $\boldsymbol{\pi}_v(t, d\omega)$ of the portfolios of $\prod_{\omega'\in\Omega\cup\omega_0\backslash\omega} \boldsymbol{v}_{\omega'}$ units of $\mathfrak{v}_\omega$ with ω in Ω in the dynamically replicating portfolio at time t in $\mathcal{T}$ for the portfolio of $\prod_{\omega\in\Omega} \boldsymbol{v}_\omega$ units of $\mathfrak{v}$ remain unchanged under the group $\boldsymbol{\mathcal{R}}$ of transformations of $\mathsf{L}_t(\mathcal{T})$ can be restated as the fact that these operator weights can be defined on the orbits of the group $\boldsymbol{\mathcal{R}}$.

Now our goal is to express equation (6.36) for the operator weights $\boldsymbol{\pi}_v(t, d\omega)$ of the portfolios of $\prod_{\omega'\in\Omega\cup\omega_0\setminus\omega} \boldsymbol{v}_{\omega'}$ units of $\mathfrak{v}_\omega$ with ω in Ω in the dynamically replicating portfolio at time t in $\mathcal{T}$ for the portfolio of $\prod_{\omega\in\Omega} \boldsymbol{v}_\omega$ units of $\mathfrak{v}$ solely in terms of the generator $\mathfrak{L}(t)$ without the operator of differentiation with respect to time.

It is clear that the operator weights $\boldsymbol{\pi}_v(t, d\omega)$ of the portfolios of $\prod_{\omega'\in\Omega\cup\omega_0\setminus\omega} \boldsymbol{v}_{\omega'}$ units of $\mathfrak{v}_\omega$ with ω in Ω in the dynamically replicating portfolio for the portfolio of $\prod_{\omega\in\Omega} \boldsymbol{v}_\omega$ units of $\mathfrak{v}$ remain unchanged under the group $\hat{\boldsymbol{\mathcal{R}}}$ of transformations of $\mathsf{D}_t(\mathcal{T})$.

6.35. Remark. The fact that the operator weights $\boldsymbol{\pi}_v(t, d\omega)$ of the portfolios of $\prod_{\omega'\in\Omega\cup\omega_0\setminus\omega} \boldsymbol{v}_{\omega'}$ units of $\mathfrak{v}_\omega$ with ω in Ω in the dynamically replicating portfolio at time t in $\mathcal{T}$ for the portfolio of $\prod_{\omega\in\Omega} \boldsymbol{v}_\omega$ units of $\mathfrak{v}$ remain unchanged under the group $\hat{\boldsymbol{\mathcal{R}}}$ of transformations of $\mathsf{D}_t(\mathcal{T})$ can be restated as the fact that these operator weights can be defined on the orbits of the group $\hat{\boldsymbol{\mathcal{R}}}$.

Finally, for the operator

$$\mathsf{D}(t) = d(s,t)\frac{d}{dt} + \mathfrak{L}(t)$$

in $\mathsf{D}_t(\mathcal{T})$, or more precisely in $\mathfrak{D}_t(\mathcal{T})$ with $d(s,t)$ identically equal to unity and for the transformation $\hat{\mathfrak{r}}$ from the group $\hat{\boldsymbol{\mathcal{R}}}$ with $c(s,t) = -d(s,t)$ we can rewrite equation (6.36) for the operator weights $\boldsymbol{\pi}_v(t, d\omega)$ of the portfolios of $\prod_{\omega'\in\Omega\cup\omega_0\setminus\omega} \boldsymbol{v}_{\omega'}$ units of $\mathfrak{v}_\omega$ with ω in Ω in the dynamically replicating portfolio at time t in $\mathcal{T}$ for the portfolio of $\prod_{\omega\in\Omega} \boldsymbol{v}_\omega$ units of $\mathfrak{v}$ solely in terms of $\mathfrak{L}(t)$ without the operator of differentiation with respect to time:

$$
\begin{aligned}
&(\prod_{\omega\in\Omega} \boldsymbol{v}_\omega)\left([[(\boldsymbol{\mathfrak{L}}(\overset{2}{t})), \boldsymbol{v}], \boldsymbol{u}'(\overset{3}{t}, \overset{1}{t})]\right)\mathbf{1} = \\
&\quad\int_\Omega \Bigg(\boldsymbol{\pi}_v(t, d\omega)(\prod_{\omega'\in\Omega\cup\omega_0\backslash\omega} \boldsymbol{v}_{\omega'}) \times \\
&\qquad [[(\boldsymbol{\mathfrak{L}}(\overset{2}{t})), \boldsymbol{v}_\omega], \boldsymbol{u}'(\overset{3}{t}, \overset{1}{t})]\Big)\,\mathbf{1}\Bigg), \quad t = T,
\end{aligned}
\tag{6.37}
$$

for any preference $\boldsymbol{u}'(t,T)$. We comment that $\mathbf{1}$ is the function in Π identically equal to unity.

Now with the help of equation (6.36), or equivalently (6.37) we represent identity (6.35) in such a way that it does not possess explicit dependence on the preference $\boldsymbol{u}'(t,T)$:

$$
\begin{aligned}
&(\prod_{\omega\in\Omega} \boldsymbol{v}_\omega)\,[(\frac{d}{dt} + \boldsymbol{\mathfrak{L}}(t)), \boldsymbol{v}]\,\mathbf{1} = \\
&\quad\int_\Omega \Bigg(\boldsymbol{\pi}_v(t, d\omega)(\prod_{\omega'\in\Omega\cup\omega_0\backslash\omega} \boldsymbol{v}_{\omega'})[(\frac{d}{dt} + \boldsymbol{\mathfrak{L}}(t)), \boldsymbol{v}_\omega]\,\mathbf{1}\Bigg),
\end{aligned}
\tag{6.38}
$$

where $t = T$.

Due to relation (6.23), identity (6.38) can be rewritten as follows

$$
\begin{aligned}
&(\prod_{\omega\in\Omega} \boldsymbol{v}_\omega)\,(\frac{d}{dt} + \boldsymbol{\mathfrak{L}}(t))\,v = \\
&\quad\int_\Omega \Bigg(\boldsymbol{\pi}_v(t, d\omega)(\prod_{\omega'\in\Omega\cup\omega_0\backslash\omega} \boldsymbol{v}_{\omega'})\,(\frac{d}{dt} + \boldsymbol{\mathfrak{L}}(t))\,v_\omega\Bigg),
\end{aligned}
\tag{6.39}
$$

where $t = T$.

Since $\boldsymbol{\mathfrak{L}}(t)$ is the derivative of $-\boldsymbol{F}(t,T)$ with respect to t evaluated at t equal to T with $\boldsymbol{F}(t,T)$ in the belief $\boldsymbol{\mathcal{B}}$ of the market participant $\boldsymbol{\mathcal{H}} = (\boldsymbol{\mathcal{B}}, \boldsymbol{\mathcal{U}})$ in the market populace $\mathbb{H} = \mathbb{B} \times \mathbb{U}$, the preceding identity (6.39) financially means that the instantaneous return on the portfolio consisting of the portfolio of $\prod_{\omega\in\Omega} \boldsymbol{v}_\omega$ units of the European contingent claim $\mathfrak{v}$ is equal to the instantaneous return on the portfolio consisting of the portfolios of $\prod_{\omega'\in\Omega\cup\omega_0\setminus\omega} \boldsymbol{v}_{\omega'}$ units of the European contingent claims $\mathfrak{v}_\omega$ with ω in Ω with the operator weights $\boldsymbol{\pi}_v(t, d\omega)$. In order to see this more clearly we can rewrite identity (6.39) as follows

$$\Big(\overset{1}{\frac{d}{dt}} + \mathfrak{L}(\overset{1}{t})\Big)\Bigg(\Big(\prod_{\omega\in\Omega} \overset{2}{\boldsymbol{v}}_\omega\Big)v - \int_\Omega \Big(\overset{2}{\boldsymbol{\pi}}_v(t, d\omega)\Big(\prod_{\omega'\in\Omega\cup\omega_0\setminus\omega} \overset{2}{\boldsymbol{v}}_{\omega'}\Big)\, v_\omega\Big)\Bigg) = 0, \quad t = T. \tag{6.40}$$

Since the preceding identity (6.40) is a particular case of identity (6.8) and hence of (6.4) the financial interpretation given for identity (6.8) and hence for (6.4) can be repeated verbatim for identity (6.40) and hence (6.39).

6.36. Remark. Let the map $\hat{\pi}(t, d\omega) : \Pi \to \Pi$ for each ω in Ω be formally defined by

$$\hat{\pi}(t, d\omega)\, v = \pi_v(t, d\omega),$$

where $\pi_v(t, d\omega)$ is the Π-valued measure on Ω associated as in Remark (6.6) with the operator-valued measure, or equivalently operator weights $\boldsymbol{\pi}_v(t, d\omega)$ of the European contingent claims $\{\mathfrak{v}_\omega : \omega \in \Omega\}$ in the dynamically replicating portfolio at time t in $\mathcal{T}$ for the European contingent claim $\mathfrak{v}$ with the value $v = v(t)$.

It is clear that by the no-arbitrage argument the map $\hat{\pi}(t, d\omega)$ is linear for each ω in Ω. We will refer to each linear operator $\hat{\pi}(t, d\omega)$ as a *portfolio operator*. It is also clear that in general the linear operators $\hat{\pi}(t, d\omega)$ on Π and linear operators on Π of multiplication by arbitrary admissible functions in Π do not commute. It is this noncommutativity of the linear operators $\hat{\pi}(t, d\omega)$ on Π and linear operators on Π of multiplication by arbitrary admissible functions in Π that is, in the essence, financially responsible for the randomness of the prices of the underlying securities, that is, for the first quantization in finance. This issue will be presented in detail in forthcoming articles.

6.2 The Case of a Markovian Market Populace

As we have seen in Subsection (3.7) of Section (3) the values v of European contingent claims remain unchanged under the action of beliefs-preferences gauge symmetry group $\hat{\mathcal{G}}$ for Markovian market populace $\mathbb{H} = \mathbb{B} \times \mathbb{U}$, or more precisely $\mathbb{H} = \mathbb{L} \times \mathbb{U}$ defined in (3.99), or equivalently in (3.107). In this way, the beliefs-preferences gauge symmetry group $\hat{\mathcal{G}}$ provides us with the complete description of the degrees of freedom that Markovian market participants $\mathcal{H} = (\mathcal{B}, \mathcal{U})$ in $\mathbb{H} = \mathbb{B} \times \mathbb{U}$ or more precisely $\mathcal{H} = (\mathfrak{L}, \mathcal{U})$ in $\mathbb{H} = \mathbb{L} \times \mathbb{U}$ that populate a marketplace have in terms of their beliefs $\mathcal{B}$ in $\mathbb{B}$, or more precisely $\mathfrak{L}$ in $\mathbb{L}$ and preferences $\mathcal{U}$ in $\mathbb{U}$. That is, the set of all Markovian market participants $\mathcal{H} = (\mathcal{B}, \mathcal{U})$ in $\mathbb{H} = \mathbb{B} \times \mathbb{U}$ or more precisely $\mathcal{H} = (\mathfrak{L}, \mathcal{U})$ in $\mathbb{H} = \mathbb{L} \times \mathbb{U}$ that agree at all times t in $\mathcal{T}$ upon the values at the time t of a set of European contingent claims with inception time t and expiration time T for all T in $\mathcal{T}$ with $t \leq T$ whose payoffs form a dense set is nothing but an orbit of the group $\hat{\mathcal{G}}$.

However, now our goal is to determine under what conditions European contingent claims in a general market environment $\mathbf{V}$ can be valued *independently* of the beliefs $\mathcal{B}$ in $\mathbb{B}$, or more precisely $\mathfrak{L}$ in $\mathbb{L}$ and preferences $\mathcal{U}$ in $\mathbb{U}$ of Markovian market participants $\mathcal{H} = (\mathcal{B}, \mathcal{U})$ in the orbit of the group $\hat{\mathcal{G}}$ in $\mathbb{H} = \mathbb{B} \times \mathbb{U}$, or more precisely $\mathcal{H} = (\mathfrak{L}, \mathcal{U})$ in the orbit of the group $\hat{\mathcal{G}}$ in $\mathbb{H} = \mathbb{L} \times \mathbb{U}$. The degrees of freedom that Markovian market participants $\mathcal{H} = (\mathcal{B}, \mathcal{U})$ in the orbit of the group $\hat{\mathcal{G}}$ in $\mathbb{H} = \mathbb{B} \times \mathbb{U}$, or more precisely $\mathcal{H} = (\mathfrak{L}, \mathcal{U})$ in the orbit of the group $\hat{\mathcal{G}}$ in $\mathbb{H} = \mathbb{L} \times \mathbb{U}$ have in terms of their beliefs $\mathcal{B}$ in $\mathbb{B}$, or more precisely $\mathfrak{L}$ in $\mathbb{L}$ and preferences $\mathcal{U}$ in $\mathbb{U}$ given by the beliefs-preferences gauge symmetry group $\hat{\mathcal{G}}$ allows us to formulate this problem rigorously. Indeed, the beliefs-preferences gauge symmetry group $\hat{\mathcal{G}}$ states that the values v of European contingent claims remain unchanged if the beliefs and preferences are both transformed in the consistent manner as indicated in (3.107). In order to have the desired independence of the values of European contingent claims of the beliefs $\mathcal{B}$ in $\mathbb{B}$, or more precisely $\mathfrak{L}$ in $\mathbb{L}$ and preferences $\mathcal{U}$ in $\mathbb{U}$ of Markovian market participants $\mathcal{H} = (\mathcal{B}, \mathcal{U})$ in the orbit of the group $\hat{\mathcal{G}}$ in $\mathbb{H} = \mathbb{B} \times \mathbb{U}$, or more precisely $\mathcal{H} = (\mathfrak{L}, \mathcal{U})$ in the orbit of the group $\hat{\mathcal{G}}$ in $\mathbb{H} = \mathbb{L} \times \mathbb{U}$ we have to require that these values v remain unchanged under the following *independent* transformations of the beliefs $\mathcal{B}$ in $\mathbb{B}$, or more precisely $\mathfrak{L}$ in $\mathbb{L}$ and preferences $\mathcal{U}$ in $\mathbb{U}$:

$$\mathfrak{L}(t) \xrightarrow{\hat{g}^{(1)}_{\mathcal{B}}} \hat{\mathbf{u}}_1'^{-1}(t,t)\, \mathfrak{L}(t)\, \hat{\mathbf{u}}_1'(t,t) + \frac{\hat{\mathbf{u}}_{1t}'(t,t)}{\hat{\mathbf{u}}_1'(t,t)} \quad \text{and}$$

$$\boldsymbol{u}'(t,T) \xrightarrow{\hat{g}^{(2)}_{\mathcal{U}}} \hat{\mathbf{u}}_2'^{-1}(t,T)\boldsymbol{u}'(t,T), \tag{6.41}$$

where $\hat{\mathbf{u}}_1'(t,T)$ and $\hat{\mathbf{u}}_2'(t,T)$ are generated by $\mathbf{u}_1'(t,T)$ and $\mathbf{u}_2'(t,T)$.

Now the desired independence of the values of European contingent claims of the beliefs $\mathcal{B}$ in $\mathbb{B}$, or more precisely $\mathfrak{L}$ in $\mathbb{L}$ and preferences $\mathcal{U}$ in $\mathbb{U}$ of Markovian market participants $\mathcal{H} = (\mathcal{B}, \mathcal{U})$ in the orbit of the group $\hat{\mathcal{G}}$ in $\mathbb{H} = \mathbb{B} \times \mathbb{U}$, or more precisely $\mathcal{H} = (\mathfrak{L}, \mathcal{U})$ in the orbit of the group $\hat{\mathcal{G}}$ in $\mathbb{H} = \mathbb{L} \times \mathbb{U}$ can be restated as follows. The values v of European contingent claims in a general market environment $\mathbf{V}$ have to remain unchanged under the action of the group $G \times H$ of transformations of the Markovian market populace $\mathbb{H} = \mathbb{B} \times \mathbb{U}$, or more precisely $\mathbb{H} = \mathbb{L} \times \mathbb{U}$ defined by

$$\big(\mathfrak{L}(t), \boldsymbol{u}'(t,T)\big) \xrightarrow{g} \Big(\hat{\mathbf{u}}_1'^{-1}(t,t)\, \mathfrak{L}(t)\, \hat{\mathbf{u}}_1'(t,t) + \frac{\hat{\mathbf{u}}_{1t}'(t,t)}{\hat{\mathbf{u}}_1'(t,t)}, \boldsymbol{u}'(t,T)\Big)$$

$$\big(\mathfrak{L}(t), \boldsymbol{u}'(t,T)\big) \xrightarrow{h} \big(\mathfrak{L}(t), \hat{\mathbf{u}}_2'^{-1}(t,T)\boldsymbol{u}'(t,T)\big), \tag{6.42}$$

where g is in G and h is in H, and where $\hat{\mathbf{u}}'_1(t,T)$ and $\hat{\mathbf{u}}'_2(t,T)$ are generated by $\mathbf{u}'_1(t,T)$ and $\mathbf{u}'_2(t,T)$.

6.37. Remark. We comment that the groups G and H are in fact defined as the sets of all transformations g and h in (6.42) with the group operations of composition.

6.38. Remark. Since the groups G and H defined in the preceding relation (6.42) are abelian groups, $G \times H$ is also an abelian group.

6.39. Remark. Denote the element (g,h) in $G \times H$ defined in (6.42) by $(\hat{\mathbf{u}}'_1(t,T), \hat{\mathbf{u}}'_2(t,T))$. It is clear that the beliefs-preferences gauge symmetry group $\hat{\mathcal{G}}$ of transformations of Markovian market populace $\mathbb{H} = \mathbb{B} \times \mathbb{U}$, or more precisely $\mathbb{H} = \mathbb{L} \times \mathbb{U}$ is the diagonal subgroup of the group $G \times H$ of transformations of the Markovian market populace $\mathbb{H} = \mathbb{B} \times \mathbb{U}$, or more precisely $\mathbb{H} = \mathbb{L} \times \mathbb{U}$. That is, the group $\hat{\mathcal{G}}$ is a subgroup of the group $G \times H$ consisting of the elements of $G \times H$ of the form $(\hat{\mathbf{u}}'(t,T), \hat{\mathbf{u}}'(t,T))$. In this regard the desired independence of the values of European contingent claims of the beliefs $\mathcal{B}$ in $\mathbb{B}$, or more precisely $\mathfrak{L}$ in $\mathbb{L}$ and preferences $\mathcal{U}$ in $\mathbb{U}$ of Markovian market participants $\mathcal{H} = (\mathcal{B}, \mathcal{U})$ in the orbit of the group $\hat{\mathcal{G}}$ in $\mathbb{H} = \mathbb{B} \times \mathbb{U}$, or more precisely $\mathcal{H} = (\mathfrak{L}, \mathcal{U})$ in the orbit of the group $\hat{\mathcal{G}}$ in $\mathbb{H} = \mathbb{L} \times \mathbb{U}$ is equivalent to promoting the beliefs-preferences gauge symmetry group $\hat{\mathcal{G}}$ of transformations of Markovian market populace $\mathbb{H} = \mathbb{B} \times \mathbb{U}$, or more precisely $\mathbb{H} = \mathbb{L} \times \mathbb{U}$ viewed as the diagonal subgroup of the group $G \times H$ of transformations of the Markovian market populace $\mathbb{H} = \mathbb{B} \times \mathbb{U}$, or more precisely $\mathbb{H} = \mathbb{L} \times \mathbb{U}$ to the group $G \times H$ itself.

Now we make the following crucial observation. Suppose that the values v of European contingent claims remain unchanged under the action of the beliefs-preferences gauge symmetry group $\hat{\mathcal{G}}$ of transformations of the Markovian market populace $\mathbb{H} = \mathbb{B} \times \mathbb{U}$, or more precisely $\mathbb{H} = \mathbb{L} \times \mathbb{U}$. Then, in order for the values v of European contingent claims in a general market environment $\mathbf{V}$ to remain unchanged under the action of the group $G \times H$ of transformations of the Markovian market populace $\mathbb{H} = \mathbb{B} \times \mathbb{U}$, or more precisely $\mathbb{H} = \mathbb{L} \times \mathbb{U}$ it is enough to require that these values v remain unchanged under the actions of the groups G and H of transformations of the Markovian market populace $\mathbb{H} = \mathbb{B} \times \mathbb{U}$, or more precisely $\mathbb{H} = \mathbb{L} \times \mathbb{U}$ separately, where we have identified the groups G and H with the subgroups (G, e_H) and (e_G, H) of the group $G \times H$ with e_G and e_H being the identity elements of G and H. Indeed, denote by $G \times H/\hat{\mathcal{G}}$ the factor group of $G \times H$ relative to $\hat{\mathcal{G}}$ where $\hat{\mathcal{G}}$ is identified with the diagonal subgroup of $G \times H$ as in Remark (6.39). For any $[(\hat{\mathbf{u}}_1'(t,T), \hat{\mathbf{u}}_2'(t,T))]$ in $G \times H/\hat{\mathcal{G}}$ where $[(\hat{\mathbf{u}}_1'(t,T), \hat{\mathbf{u}}_2'(t,T))]$ stands for the coset of $(\hat{\mathbf{u}}_1'(t,T), \hat{\mathbf{u}}_2'(t,T))$ in $G \times H$ we have the following chain of equalities

$$
\begin{aligned}
&[(\hat{\mathbf{u}}_1'(t,T), \hat{\mathbf{u}}_2'(t,T))] = \\
&\quad [(\hat{\mathbf{u}}_2'^{-1}(t,T), \hat{\mathbf{u}}_2'^{-1}(t,T)) \cdot (\hat{\mathbf{u}}_1'(t,T), \hat{\mathbf{u}}_2'(t,T))] = \\
&\quad [(\hat{\mathbf{u}}_2'^{-1}(t,T)\, \hat{\mathbf{u}}_1'(t,T), \hat{\mathbf{u}}_2'^{-1}(t,T)\, \hat{\mathbf{u}}_2'(t,T))] = \\
&\quad [(\hat{\mathbf{u}}_2'^{-1}(t,T)\, \hat{\mathbf{u}}_1'(t,T), \mathbf{1}_H)],
\end{aligned}
$$

where $\mathbf{1}_H$ is the identity operator on $\Pi(\mathbb{R}^n_{++} \times \mathbb{R}^n_{++})$ so that $(\hat{\mathbf{u}}'(t,T), \mathbf{1}_H)$ is in G, or more precisely in (G, e_H).

On the other hand, for any $[(\hat{\mathbf{u}}_1'(t,T), \hat{\mathbf{u}}_2'(t,T))]$ in $G \times H/\hat{\mathcal{G}}$ where $[(\hat{\mathbf{u}}_1'(t,T), \hat{\mathbf{u}}_2'(t,T))]$ again stands for the coset of $(\hat{\mathbf{u}}_1'(t,T), \hat{\mathbf{u}}_2'(t,T))$ in $G \times H$ we have the following chain of equalities

$$
\begin{aligned}
&[(\hat{\mathbf{u}}_1'(t,T), \hat{\mathbf{u}}_2'(t,T))] = \\
&\quad [(\hat{\mathbf{u}}_1'^{-1}(t,T), \hat{\mathbf{u}}_1'^{-1}(t,T)) \cdot (\hat{\mathbf{u}}_1'(t,T), \hat{\mathbf{u}}_2'(t,T))] = \\
&\quad [(\hat{\mathbf{u}}_1'^{-1}(t,T)\, \hat{\mathbf{u}}_1'(t,T), \hat{\mathbf{u}}_1'^{-1}(t,T)\, \hat{\mathbf{u}}_2'(t,T))] = \\
&\quad [(\mathbf{1}_G, \hat{\mathbf{u}}_1'^{-1}(t,T)\, \hat{\mathbf{u}}_2'(t,T))],
\end{aligned}
$$

where $\mathbf{1}_G$ is the identity operator on $\Pi(\mathbb{R}^n_{++} \times \mathbb{R}^n_{++})$ so that $(\mathbf{1}_G, \hat{\mathbf{u}}'(t,T))$ is in H, or more precisely in (e_G, H).

Since $(\hat{\mathbf{u}}_2'^{-1}(t,T)\,\hat{\mathbf{u}}_1'(t,T), \mathbf{1}_H)$ and $(\mathbf{1}_G, \hat{\mathbf{u}}_1'^{-1}(t,T)\,\hat{\mathbf{u}}_2'(t,T))$ are arbitrary elements of G and H, or more precisely (G, e_H) and (e_G, H), we arrive at the desired result. In light of Remark (6.39) this result can also be stated as follows. In order to promote the beliefs-preferences gauge symmetry group $\hat{\mathcal{G}}$ of transformations of Markovian market populace $\mathbb{H} = \mathbb{B} \times \mathbb{U}$, or more precisely $\mathbb{H} = \mathbb{L} \times \mathbb{U}$ viewed as the diagonal subgroup of the group $G \times H$ of transformations of the Markovian market populace $\mathbb{H} = \mathbb{B} \times \mathbb{U}$, or more precisely $\mathbb{H} = \mathbb{L} \times \mathbb{U}$ to the group $G \times H$ itself so that the values v of European contingent claims in a general market environment $\mathbf{V}$ remain unchanged under the action of the group $G \times H$ of transformations of the Markovian market populace $\mathbb{H} = \mathbb{B} \times \mathbb{U}$, or more precisely $\mathbb{H} = \mathbb{L} \times \mathbb{U}$ it is enough to require that these values v remain unchanged under the action of the group G or H of transformations of the Markovian market populace $\mathbb{H} = \mathbb{B} \times \mathbb{U}$, or more precisely $\mathbb{H} = \mathbb{L} \times \mathbb{U}$ separately, where we again have identified the groups G and H with the subgroups (G, e_H) and (e_G, H) of the group $G \times H$ with e_G and e_H being the identity elements of G and H.

Taking advantage of this result with the group H, or more precisely (e_G, H) of transformations of the Markovian market populace $\mathbb{H} = \mathbb{B} \times \mathbb{U}$, or more precisely $\mathbb{H} = \mathbb{L} \times \mathbb{U}$, the requirement that the values v of European contingent claims in a general market environment $\mathbf{V}$ have to remain unchanged under the action of the group $G \times H$ of transformations of the Markovian market populace $\mathbb{H} = \mathbb{B} \times \mathbb{U}$, or more precisely $\mathbb{H} = \mathbb{L} \times \mathbb{U}$ can be restated as follows.

For a fixed Markovian market participant $\boldsymbol{\mathcal{H}} = (\boldsymbol{\mathcal{B}}, \boldsymbol{\mathcal{U}})$ in $\mathbb{H} = \mathbb{B} \times \mathbb{U}$, or more precisely $\boldsymbol{\mathcal{H}} = (\boldsymbol{\mathfrak{L}}, \boldsymbol{\mathcal{U}})$ in $\mathbb{H} = \mathbb{L} \times \mathbb{U}$ with

$$\boldsymbol{\mathfrak{L}} = \{\boldsymbol{\mathfrak{L}}(t) : \Pi \to \Pi \,|\, t \in \mathcal{T}\}$$

and

$$\boldsymbol{\mathcal{U}} = \{\boldsymbol{u}'(t,T) : \Pi(\mathbb{R}^{2n}_{++}) \to \Pi(\mathbb{R}^{2n}_{++}) \,|\, t,\, T \in \mathcal{T}, t \leq T\}$$

the value $v = v(t)$ of the European contingent claim with inception time t, expiration time T and payoff v_T determined by the Cauchy problem (3.118) has to remain unchanged under the action of the group H, or more precisely (e_G, H). However, it is clear that this is not the case, that is, that value $v = v(t)$ of the European contingent claim with inception time t, expiration time T and payoff v_T determined by the Cauchy problem (3.118) does not in general remain unchanged under the action of the group H, or more precisely (e_G, H).

6.40. Remark. Under each transformation $(\mathbf{1}_G, \hat{\mathbf{u}}'(t,T))$ from the group H, or more precisely (e_G, H) the preference $\boldsymbol{u}'(t,T)$ from $\boldsymbol{\mathcal{U}}$ in the evolution equation (3.118) is transformed to the preference $\hat{\mathbf{u}}'^{-1}(t,T)\,\boldsymbol{u}'(t,T)$ from

$$\hat{\mathbf{u}}'^{-1}\boldsymbol{\mathcal{U}} = \{\hat{\mathbf{u}}'^{-1}(t,T)\,\boldsymbol{u}'(t,T) : \Pi(\mathbb{R}^{2n}_{++}) \to \Pi(\mathbb{R}^{2n}_{++}) \,|\, t,\, T \in \mathcal{T}, t \leq T\}.$$

Therefore in order for the value $v = v(t)$ of the European contingent claim with inception time t, expiration time T and payoff v_T determined by the Cauchy problem (3.118) to remain unchanged under the action of the group H, or more precisely (e_G, H) it is enough to require that the value $v = v(t)$ of the European contingent claim with inception time t, expiration time T and payoff v_T determined by the Cauchy problem (3.118) remains unchanged for all preferences $\boldsymbol{u}'(t,T)$, that is, does not depend on the preference $\boldsymbol{u}'(t,T)$.

In order to achieve the goal of finding the values v of European contingent claims in a general market environment $\mathbf{V}$ that remain unchanged under the action of the group $G \times H$ of transformations of the Markovian market populace $\mathbb{H} = \mathbb{B} \times \mathbb{U}$, or more precisely $\mathbb{H} = \mathbb{L} \times \mathbb{U}$ we choose an alternative route.

Denote by Ω an index set which is assumed to be a measurable space, that is, to be equipped with a sigma algebra. For each t in $\mathcal{T}$ and s_t in $\mathbb{R}^n_{++}$ let $\pi(t, s_t, d\omega)$ be a signed measure on Ω. Denote by $\boldsymbol{\pi}(t, d\omega)$ the operator-valued measure on Ω defined by

$$(\boldsymbol{\pi}(t, d\omega)\, h)(s_t) = \pi(t, s_t, d\omega) h(s_t), \quad h \in \Pi.$$

6.41. Remark. It is clear that $\pi(t, d\omega) = \pi(t, \cdot, d\omega)$ is a Π-valued measure on Ω for each t in $\mathcal{T}$. In this regard the relation between the Π-valued measure $\pi(t, d\omega)$ on Ω and the operator-valued measure $\boldsymbol{\pi}(t, d\omega)$ on Ω is self-explanatory.

6.42. Definition. Let $\{\boldsymbol{\mathfrak{v}}_\omega : \omega \in \Omega\}$ be a set of traded European contingent claims with inception time t, expiration time T, payoffs $\{v_T^\omega : \omega \in \Omega\}$ and values $\{v_\omega : \omega \in \Omega\}$ with the following property. For a European contingent claim $\boldsymbol{\mathfrak{v}}$ with inception time t, expiration time T, payoff v_T and value v there exists an operator-valued measure $\boldsymbol{\pi}(t, d\omega)$ on Ω denoted by $\boldsymbol{\pi}_v(t, d\omega)$ such that

$$\overset{2}{\frac{d}{dt}}\boldsymbol{u}'(\overset{3}{t},\overset{1}{t})\,v+\boldsymbol{\mathfrak{L}}(\overset{2}{t})\,\boldsymbol{u}'(\overset{3}{t},\overset{1}{t})\,v=$$

$$\int_\Omega \boldsymbol{\pi}_v(t,d\omega)\Big(\overset{2}{\frac{d}{dt}}\boldsymbol{u}'(\overset{3}{t},\overset{1}{t})\,v_\omega+\boldsymbol{\mathfrak{L}}(\overset{2}{t})\,\boldsymbol{u}'(\overset{3}{t},\overset{1}{t})\,v_\omega\Big),\quad t<T, \tag{6.43}$$

$$v(T) = v_T$$

for any preference $\boldsymbol{u}'(t, T)$.

If in addition

$$v(t) = \int_\Omega \boldsymbol{\pi}_v(t, d\omega)\, v_\omega(t), \quad t < T, \tag{6.44}$$

we will say that the set $\{\boldsymbol{\mathfrak{v}}_\omega : \omega \in \Omega\}$ of the European contingent claims *dynamically replicates* the European contingent claim $\boldsymbol{\mathfrak{v}}$. The portfolio of the European contingent claims $\{\boldsymbol{\mathfrak{v}}_\omega : \omega \in \Omega\}$ with operator weights $\boldsymbol{\pi}_v(t, d\omega)$ we will call a *dynamically replicating portfolio.*

6.43. Remark. We comment that the evolution equation in the Cauchy problem (6.43) and identity (6.44) in the preceding

Definition (6.42) are understood as follows

$$\frac{\overset{2}{d}}{d\tau}\boldsymbol{u}'(\overset{3}{\tau},\overset{1}{\tau})\,v+\boldsymbol{\mathfrak{L}}(\overset{2}{\tau})\,\boldsymbol{u}'(\overset{3}{\tau},\overset{1}{\tau})\,v=$$

$$\int_{\Omega}\boldsymbol{\pi}_v(\tau,d\omega)\Big(\frac{\overset{2}{d}}{d\tau}\boldsymbol{u}'(\overset{3}{\tau},\overset{1}{\tau})\,v_\omega+\boldsymbol{\mathfrak{L}}(\overset{2}{\tau})\,\boldsymbol{u}'(\overset{3}{\tau},\overset{1}{\tau})\,v_\omega\Big),$$

and

$$v(\tau)=\int_{\Omega}\boldsymbol{\pi}_v(\tau,d\omega)\,v_\omega(\tau),$$

where $t\le\tau<T$.

6.44. Remark. We comment that a portfolio of the European contingent claims $\{\mathfrak{v}_\omega:\omega\in\Omega\}$ with operator weights $\boldsymbol{\pi}(t,d\omega)$ is understood as a portfolio of the European contingent claims $\{\mathfrak{v}_\omega:\omega\in\Omega\}$ with weights $\pi(t,s_t,d\omega)$ for each $t<T$ and s_t in $\mathbb{R}^n_{++}$. In this regard, a portfolio of the European contingent claims $\{\mathfrak{v}_\omega:\omega\in\Omega\}$ with operator weights $\boldsymbol{\pi}(t,d\omega)$ is, from the financial standpoint, nothing but a portfolio of the European contingent claims $\{\mathfrak{v}_\omega:\omega\in\Omega\}$ with weights that depend on time t and the state of the market as expressed by the prices of the underlying securities s_t at this time t.

6.45. Remark. We comment that, due to Remark (3.148), Definition (6.42) is not affected if a Markovian market participant $\boldsymbol{\mathcal{H}}=(\boldsymbol{\mathcal{B}},\boldsymbol{\mathcal{U}})$ in $\mathbb{H}=\mathbb{B}\times\mathbb{U}$, or more precisely $\boldsymbol{\mathcal{H}}=(\boldsymbol{\mathfrak{L}},\boldsymbol{\mathcal{U}})$ in $\mathbb{H}=\mathbb{L}\times\mathbb{U}$ is replaced by a generalized Markovian market participant $\boldsymbol{\mathfrak{H}}=(\boldsymbol{\mathfrak{B}},\boldsymbol{\mathcal{U}})$ in $\boldsymbol{\mathbb{H}}=\boldsymbol{\mathbb{B}}\times\mathbb{U}$, or more precisely $\boldsymbol{\mathfrak{H}}=(\mathsf{L},\boldsymbol{\mathcal{U}})$ in $\boldsymbol{\mathbb{H}}=\boldsymbol{\mathbb{L}}\times\mathbb{U}$.

6.46. Definition. We call a market environment $\mathbf{V}$, or simply a market *dynamically complete* if for each t and T in $\mathcal{T}$ with $t<T$ there exists a set $\{\mathfrak{v}_\omega:\omega\in\Omega\}$ of the European contingent claims with inception time t, expiration time T and the payoffs $\{\mathfrak{v}^\omega_T:\omega\in\Omega\}$ that dynamically replicates each European contingent claim with inception time t, expiration time T

and the payoff v_T in some dense set of payoffs. In this case the set $\{\mathfrak{v}_\omega : \omega \in \Omega\}$ for t and T in $\mathcal{T}$ with $t < T$ of the European contingent claims is said to *dynamically span* the market environment $\mathbf{V}$, or simply the market and we will call the set $\{\mathfrak{v}_\omega : \omega \in \Omega\}$ for t and T in $\mathcal{T}$ with $t < T$ of the European contingent claims itself *dynamically spanning.*

6.47. Remark. We comment that in the preceding Definitions (6.42) and (6.46) the generators $\mathfrak{L}(t)$ in $\mathfrak{L}$ of the belief $\boldsymbol{\mathcal{B}}$ are related to the market environment $\mathbf{V}$, or more precisely to the generators $\boldsymbol{L}(t)$ in $\boldsymbol{L}$ of the market environment $\mathbf{V}$ by means of equality (3.104).

6.48. Remark. The stochastic dimension defined in Definition (6.11) of the generators $\mathfrak{L}(t)$ in $\mathfrak{L}$ of a belief $\boldsymbol{\mathcal{B}}$ is a certain measure of randomness associated with $\mathfrak{L}(t)$.

Now we present financial justification for the terminology introduced in Definitions (6.42) and (6.46).

Since the European contingent claims $\{\mathfrak{v}_\omega : \omega \in \Omega\}$ and $\mathfrak{v}$ are traded, their values $\{v_\omega : \omega \in \Omega\}$ and v are the solutions of the Cauchy problem (3.118), that is

$$\begin{aligned} \overset{2}{\frac{d}{dt}} \boldsymbol{u}'(\overset{3}{t}, \overset{1}{t})\, v_\omega + \mathfrak{L}(\overset{2}{t})\, \boldsymbol{u}'(\overset{3}{t}, \overset{1}{t})\, v_\omega = 0, \quad t < T, \quad \omega \in \Omega \\ v_\omega(T) = v_T^\omega, \end{aligned} \tag{6.45}$$

and

$$\begin{aligned} \overset{2}{\frac{d}{dt}} \boldsymbol{u}'(\overset{3}{t}, \overset{1}{t})\, v + \mathfrak{L}(\overset{2}{t})\, \boldsymbol{u}'(\overset{3}{t}, \overset{1}{t})\, v = 0, \quad t < T \\ v(T) = v_T. \end{aligned} \tag{6.46}$$

It is clear that the values v_ω with ω in Ω and v of the European contingent claims determined by the preceding Cauchy problems (6.45) and (6.46) do not separately remain unchanged under the action of the group H, or more precisely (e_G, H). However, if for a European contingent claim $\mathfrak{v}$ there exists a set $\{\mathfrak{v}_\omega : \omega \in \Omega\}$ of European contingent claims that dynamically replicates $\mathfrak{v}$ then the value

$$v - \int_\Omega \boldsymbol{\pi}_v(t, d\omega) v_\omega$$

of the portfolio consisting of a long position on European contingent claim $\mathfrak{v}$ and a short position on the dynamically replicating portfolio of European contingent claims $\{\mathfrak{v}_\omega : \omega \in \Omega\}$ with the operator weights $\boldsymbol{\pi}_v(t, d\omega)$ with the value $\int_\Omega \boldsymbol{\pi}_v(t, d\omega) v_\omega$ is such a solution of the Cauchy problem (3.118) that it remains unchanged under the action of the group H, or more precisely (e_G, H). In order to see this it is enough to rewrite the Cauchy problem (6.43) as follows

$$\Big(\overset{2}{\frac{d}{dt}} + \boldsymbol{\mathfrak{L}}(\overset{2}{t})\Big) \left(\boldsymbol{u}'(\overset{3}{t}, \overset{1}{t})\big(v - \int_\Omega \overset{3}{\boldsymbol{\pi}}_v(t, d\omega) v_\omega\big)\right) = 0, \quad t < T,$$
$$v(T) = v_T \qquad (6.47)$$

for any preference $\boldsymbol{u}'(t, T)$

Since $\boldsymbol{\mathfrak{L}}(t)$ is in $\boldsymbol{\mathfrak{L}}$ that generates the belief $\boldsymbol{\mathcal{B}}$ of the Markovian market participant $\boldsymbol{\mathcal{H}} = (\boldsymbol{\mathcal{B}}, \boldsymbol{\mathcal{U}})$ in the Markovian market populace $\mathbb{H} = \mathbb{B} \times \mathbb{U}$, the equation (6.47) and hence the equation (6.43) means that the value

$$v - \int_\Omega \boldsymbol{\pi}_v(t, d\omega) v_\omega$$

at time t of the portfolio consisting of a long position on European contingent claim $\mathfrak{v}$ and a short position on the dynamically replicating portfolio of European contingent claims $\{\mathfrak{v}_\omega : \omega \in \Omega\}$ with the operator weights $\boldsymbol{\pi}_v(t, d\omega)$ is nothing but the expected value of the value

$$v_T - \int_\Omega \boldsymbol{\pi}_v(T, d\omega) v_T^\omega$$

of this portfolio at time T with respect to the probability measures generated by $\boldsymbol{F}(t, T)$ in $\boldsymbol{\mathcal{B}}$.

Due to the fact that $v - \int_\Omega \boldsymbol{\pi}_v(t, d\omega)v_\omega$ is such a solution of the Cauchy problem (6.47) and hence (6.43) that it remains unchanged under the action of the group H, or more precisely (e_G, H) the results of this Subsection imply that $v-\int_\Omega \boldsymbol{\pi}_v(t, d\omega)v_\omega$ remains unchanged under the action of the group $G \times H$ of transformations of the Markovian market populace $\mathbb{H} = \mathbb{B} \times \mathbb{U}$, or more precisely $\mathbb{H} = \mathbb{L} \times \mathbb{U}$ defined in (6.42). Therefore $v - \int_\Omega \boldsymbol{\pi}_v(t, d\omega)v_\omega$ is independent of the choice of the belief $\boldsymbol{\mathcal{B}}$ generated by $\mathfrak{L}$, or equivalently of $\mathfrak{L}$ in the orbit of the group G, or more precisely (G, e_H) of transformations of the Markovian market populace $\mathbb{H} = \mathbb{B} \times \mathbb{U}$, or more precisely $\mathbb{H} = \mathbb{L} \times \mathbb{U}$. From the financial standpoint this means that the value

$$v - \int_\Omega \boldsymbol{\pi}_v(t, d\omega)v_\omega$$

at time t of the portfolio consisting of a long position on European contingent claim $\mathfrak{v}$ and a short position on the dynamically replicating portfolio of European contingent claims $\{\mathfrak{v}_\omega : \omega \in \Omega\}$ with the operator weights $\boldsymbol{\pi}_v(t, d\omega)$ is nothing but the expected value of the value

$$v_T - \int_\Omega \boldsymbol{\pi}_v(T, d\omega)v_T^\omega$$

of this portfolio at time T with respect to the probability measures generated by $\boldsymbol{F}(t, T)$ in the belief $\boldsymbol{\mathcal{B}}$ generated by $\mathfrak{L}$ for any Markovian market participant $\boldsymbol{\mathcal{H}} = (\boldsymbol{\mathcal{B}}, \boldsymbol{\mathcal{U}})$ in the orbit of the beliefs-preferences gauge symmetry group $\hat{\boldsymbol{\mathcal{G}}}$ in $\mathbb{H} = \mathbb{B} \times \mathbb{U}$, or more precisely $\boldsymbol{\mathcal{H}} = (\mathfrak{L}, \boldsymbol{\mathcal{U}})$ in the orbit of the beliefs-preferences gauge symmetry group $\hat{\boldsymbol{\mathcal{G}}}$ in $\mathbb{H} = \mathbb{L} \times \mathbb{U}$. We recall that such an orbit of the beliefs-preferences gauge symmetry group $\hat{\boldsymbol{\mathcal{G}}}$ is nothing but the set of all Markovian market participants $\boldsymbol{\mathcal{H}} = (\boldsymbol{\mathcal{B}}, \boldsymbol{\mathcal{U}})$ in $\mathbb{H} = \mathbb{B} \times \mathbb{U}$, or more precisely $\boldsymbol{\mathcal{H}} = (\mathfrak{L}, \boldsymbol{\mathcal{U}})$ in $\mathbb{H} = \mathbb{L} \times \mathbb{U}$ that agree at all times t in $\mathcal{T}$ upon the values of a set of European contingent claims with inception time t, expiration time T for all T in $\mathcal{T}$ with $t \leq T$ whose payoffs form a dense set. It is clear that by the no-arbitrage argument only such Markovian market participants are actually allowed to populate a marketplace.

Finally due to relation (6.44) in Definition (6.42) the value

$$v - \int_\Omega \boldsymbol{\pi}_v(t, d\omega) v_\omega$$

at time t of the portfolio consisting of a long position on a European contingent claim $\mathfrak{v}$ and a short position on the dynamically replicating portfolio of European contingent claims $\{\mathfrak{v}_\omega : \omega \in \Omega\}$ with the operator weights $\boldsymbol{\pi}_v(t, d\omega)$ which is the expected value of the value

$$v_T - \int_\Omega \boldsymbol{\pi}_v(T, d\omega) v_T^\omega$$

of this portfolio at time T with respect to the probability measures generated by $\boldsymbol{F}(t,T)$ from the belief $\mathcal{B}$ generated by $\mathfrak{L}$ is zero for each time t in $\mathcal{T}$ with $t < T$ and the state of the market as expressed by the prices of the underlying securities s_t at this time t for any Markovian market participant $\mathcal{H} = (\mathcal{B}, \mathcal{U})$ in the orbit of the beliefs-preferences gauge symmetry group $\hat{\mathcal{G}}$ in $\mathbb{H} = \mathbb{B} \times \mathbb{U}$ or more precisely $\mathcal{H} = (\mathfrak{L}, \mathcal{U})$ in the orbit of the beliefs-preferences gauge symmetry group $\hat{\mathcal{G}}$ in $\mathbb{H} = \mathbb{L} \times \mathbb{U}$.

6.49. Remark. Due to Definition (6.42) if the set $\{\mathfrak{v}_\omega : \omega \in \Omega\}$ of European contingent claims dynamically replicates a European contingent claim $\mathfrak{v}$ then its value v determined by the Cauchy problem (6.43) is independent of the preference $\boldsymbol{u}'(t,T)$, or equivalently remains unchanged under the action of the group H or more precisely (e_G, H) and hence under the action of the group $G \times H$. Therefore in order to find the value v of the European contingent claim $\mathfrak{v}$ in a general market environment $\mathbf{V}$ independent of the beliefs and preferences of Markovian market participants $\mathcal{H} = (\mathcal{B}, \mathcal{U})$ in the orbit of the beliefs-preferences gauge symmetry group $\hat{\mathcal{G}}$ in $\mathbb{H} = \mathbb{B} \times \mathbb{U}$ or more precisely $\mathcal{H} = (\mathfrak{L}, \mathcal{U})$ in the orbit of the beliefs-preferences gauge symmetry group $\hat{\mathcal{G}}$ in $\mathbb{H} = \mathbb{L} \times \mathbb{U}$ it is enough to solve the Cauchy problem (6.43) with arbitrary chosen preference $\boldsymbol{u}'(t,T)$, for example, with preference $\boldsymbol{u}'(t,T)$ chosen as the identity operator on $\Pi(\mathbb{R}^n_{++} \times \mathbb{R}^n_{++})$.

Now, motivated by the fact that the solution v of the evolution equation in (6.43) is independent of the preference $\boldsymbol{u}'(t,T)$, we represent the evolution equation in (6.43) in such a way that the preference $\boldsymbol{u}'(t,T)$ does not enter it explicitly, that is, solely in terms of the generator $\mathfrak{L}(t)$. In order to do this we rewrite the evolution equation in (6.43) as follows

$$\Big(\overset{2}{\frac{d}{dt}} + \mathfrak{L}(\overset{2}{t})\Big)\, \boldsymbol{u}'(\overset{3}{t}, \overset{1}{t})\, \boldsymbol{v}\, \mathbf{1} = \int_\Omega \Big(\boldsymbol{\pi}_v(t, d\omega)\Big(\overset{2}{\frac{d}{dt}} + \mathfrak{L}(\overset{2}{t})\Big)\, \boldsymbol{u}'(\overset{3}{t}, \overset{1}{t})\, \boldsymbol{v}_\omega\, \mathbf{1}\Big) \tag{6.48}$$

where $\boldsymbol{v} = \boldsymbol{v}(t)$ and $\boldsymbol{v}_\omega = \boldsymbol{v}_\omega(t)$ stand for the operators on Π of multiplication by the functions $v = v(t)$ and $v_\omega = v_\omega(t)$, and where $\mathbf{1}$ is the function in Π identically equal to unity.

Denote by $\Pi(\mathbb{R}^n_{++} \times \mathcal{T})$ the vector space of all real-valued functions on the set $\mathbb{R}^n_{++} \times \mathcal{T}$. Let $\Pi_+(\mathbb{R}^n_{++} \times \mathcal{T})$ be the nonnegative cone of $\Pi(\mathbb{R}^n_{++} \times \mathcal{T})$, that is, the set of all nonnegative real-valued functions on the set $\mathbb{R}^n_{++} \times \mathcal{T}$.

We note that the vector space $\Pi(\mathbb{R}^n_{++} \times \mathcal{T})$ with the partial order generated by the nonnegative cone $\Pi_+(\mathbb{R}^n_{++} \times \mathcal{T})$ is a partially ordered vector space. Moreover, equipped with the lattice operations of supremum and infimum defined as pointwise maximum and minimum $\Pi(\mathbb{R}^n_{++} \times \mathcal{T})$ is a vector lattice.

6.50. Remark. We comment that in the preceding evolution equation (6.48) the operators $\frac{d}{dt} + \mathfrak{L}(t)$, $\boldsymbol{v} = \boldsymbol{v}(t)$, $\boldsymbol{v}_\omega = \boldsymbol{v}_\omega(t)$, $\boldsymbol{\pi}_v(t, d\omega)$ and $\boldsymbol{u}'(t,t)$ can also be interpreted as operators on $\Pi(\mathbb{R}^n_{++} \times \mathcal{T})$ with $\mathbf{1}$ being the function in $\Pi(\mathbb{R}^n_{++} \times \mathcal{T})$ identically equal to unity. In this regard we note that a family of linear operators

$$A = \{A(t) : \Pi \to \Pi \,|\, t \in \mathcal{T}\}$$

can be interpreted as a linear operator on $\Pi(\mathbb{R}^n_{++} \times \mathcal{T})$ as follows

$$(A\,h)(t) = A(t)\,h(t), \quad t \in \mathcal{T},$$

where $h = h(s,t)$ in $\Pi(\mathbb{R}^n_{++} \times \mathcal{T})$ is interpreted as $h : \mathcal{T} \to \Pi$ defined by $h(t) = h(\cdot, t)$. Whenever ambiguity is unlikely we will assume this interpretation of these operators.

Consider the operators

$$\Big(\overset{2}{\frac{d}{dt}} + \mathfrak{L}(\overset{2}{t})\Big)\, \boldsymbol{u}'(\overset{3}{t}, \overset{1}{t})\, \boldsymbol{v}$$

and

$$\Big(\overset{2}{\frac{d}{dt}} + \mathfrak{L}(\overset{2}{t})\Big)\, \boldsymbol{u}'(\overset{3}{t}, \overset{1}{t})\, \boldsymbol{v}_\omega,$$

with ω in Ω from the preceding evolution equation (6.48) separately. We comment that we interpret these operators as operators on $\Pi(\mathbb{R}^n_{++} \times \mathcal{T})$.

For the operator $\big(\overset{2}{\frac{d}{dt}} + \mathfrak{L}(\overset{2}{t})\big)\, \boldsymbol{u}'(\overset{3}{t}, \overset{1}{t})\, \boldsymbol{v}$ we have the following chain of equalities

$$\begin{aligned}
&\Big(\overset{2}{\frac{d}{dt}} + \mathfrak{L}(\overset{2}{t})\Big)\, \boldsymbol{u}'(\overset{3}{t}, \overset{1}{t})\, \boldsymbol{v} = \\
&\quad \boldsymbol{v}\, \Big(\overset{2}{\frac{d}{dt}} + \mathfrak{L}(\overset{2}{t})\Big)\, \boldsymbol{u}'(\overset{3}{t}, \overset{1}{t}) + \Big[\Big(\overset{2}{\frac{d}{dt}} + \mathfrak{L}(\overset{2}{t})\Big), \boldsymbol{v}\Big]\, \boldsymbol{u}'(\overset{3}{t}, \overset{1}{t}) = \\
&\quad \boldsymbol{v}\, \boldsymbol{u}'(t,t)\, \Big(\frac{d}{dt} + \mathfrak{L}(t)\Big) + \boldsymbol{v}\, \Big[\Big(\overset{2}{\frac{d}{dt}} + \mathfrak{L}(\overset{2}{t})\Big), \boldsymbol{u}'(\overset{3}{t}, \overset{1}{t})\Big] + \\
&\quad\quad \boldsymbol{u}'(t,t)\, \Big[\Big(\frac{d}{dt} + \mathfrak{L}(t)\Big), \boldsymbol{v}\Big] + \Big[\Big[\Big(\overset{2}{\frac{d}{dt}} + \mathfrak{L}(\overset{2}{t})\Big), \boldsymbol{v}\Big], \boldsymbol{u}'(\overset{3}{t}, \overset{1}{t})\Big] \overset{(6.49)}{=} \\
&\quad \boldsymbol{v}\, \Big(\frac{d}{dt} + \mathfrak{L}(t)\Big) + \boldsymbol{v}\, \Big[\Big(\overset{2}{\frac{d}{dt}} + \mathfrak{L}(\overset{2}{t})\Big), \boldsymbol{u}'(\overset{3}{t}, \overset{1}{t})\Big] + \\
&\quad\quad \Big[\Big(\frac{d}{dt} + \mathfrak{L}(t)\Big), \boldsymbol{v}\Big] + \Big[\Big[\Big(\overset{2}{\frac{d}{dt}} + \mathfrak{L}(\overset{2}{t})\Big), \boldsymbol{v}\Big], \boldsymbol{u}'(\overset{3}{t}, \overset{1}{t})\Big],
\end{aligned}$$

where in the last equality we have taken into account the fact that due to Theorem (3.81) for each time t in $\mathcal{T}$ and each state of the market as expressed by the prices of the underlying securities s_t' at this time t there exists a global transformation from the beliefs-preferences gauge symmetry group $\hat{\mathcal{G}}$ such that the marginal utility $\boldsymbol{u}'(t,t)$ is the operator of multiplication by the function $u'(t,t,s_t,s_t)$ with the following property

$$u'(t,t,s_t = s_t', s_t = s_t') = 1.$$

For the operator $\big(\overset{2}{\frac{d}{dt}} + \mathfrak{L}(\overset{2}{t})\big)\, \boldsymbol{u}'(\overset{3}{t},\overset{1}{t})\, \boldsymbol{v}_\omega$ with ω in Ω we have the following chain of equalities

$$\begin{aligned}
&\big(\overset{2}{\frac{d}{dt}} + \mathfrak{L}(\overset{2}{t})\big)\, \boldsymbol{u}'(\overset{3}{t},\overset{1}{t})\, \boldsymbol{v}_\omega = \\
&\boldsymbol{v}_\omega \big(\overset{2}{\frac{d}{dt}} + \mathfrak{L}(\overset{2}{t})\big)\, \boldsymbol{u}'(\overset{3}{t},\overset{1}{t}) + \big[\big(\overset{2}{\frac{d}{dt}} + \mathfrak{L}(\overset{2}{t})\big), \boldsymbol{v}_\omega\big]\, \boldsymbol{u}'(\overset{3}{t},\overset{1}{t}) = \\
&\boldsymbol{v}_\omega\, \boldsymbol{u}'(t,t)\, \big(\frac{d}{dt} + \mathfrak{L}(t)\big) + \boldsymbol{v}_\omega \big[\big(\overset{2}{\frac{d}{dt}} + \mathfrak{L}(\overset{2}{t})\big), \boldsymbol{u}'(\overset{3}{t},\overset{1}{t})\big] + \\
&\quad \boldsymbol{u}'(t,t)\, \big[\big(\frac{d}{dt} + \mathfrak{L}(t)\big), \boldsymbol{v}_\omega\big] + \big[\big[\big(\overset{2}{\frac{d}{dt}} + \mathfrak{L}(\overset{2}{t})\big), \boldsymbol{v}_\omega\big], \boldsymbol{u}'(\overset{3}{t},\overset{1}{t})\big] \overset{(6.50)}{=} \\
&\boldsymbol{v}_\omega \big(\frac{d}{dt} + \mathfrak{L}(t)\big) + \boldsymbol{v}_\omega \big[\big(\overset{2}{\frac{d}{dt}} + \mathfrak{L}(\overset{2}{t})\big), \boldsymbol{u}'(\overset{3}{t},\overset{1}{t})\big] + \\
&\quad \big[\big(\frac{d}{dt} + \mathfrak{L}(t)\big), \boldsymbol{v}_\omega\big] + \big[\big[\big(\overset{2}{\frac{d}{dt}} + \mathfrak{L}(\overset{2}{t})\big), \boldsymbol{v}_\omega\big], \boldsymbol{u}'(\overset{3}{t},\overset{1}{t})\big],
\end{aligned}$$

where again in the last equality we have taken into account the fact that due to the Theorem (3.81) for each time t in $\mathcal{T}$ and each state of the market as expressed by the prices of the underlying securities s_t' at this time t there exists a global transformation from the beliefs-preferences gauge symmetry group $\hat{\mathcal{G}}$ such that the marginal utility $\boldsymbol{u}'(t,t)$ is the operator of multiplication by the function $u'(t,t,s_t,s_t)$ with the following property

$$u'(t,t,s_t = s_t', s_t = s_t') = 1.$$

Now we need the following assumption, which is natural from the financial standpoint, about the nature of the set $\{\mathfrak{v}_\omega : \omega \in \Omega\}$ of European contingent claims that dynamically replicates a European contingent claim $\mathfrak{v}$. We suppose that for each t and T in $\mathcal{T}$ with $t \leq T$ the pure discount bond with inception time t, maturity time T and with the face value of one unit of account is traded. Let the pure discount bond be in the set $\{\mathfrak{v}_\omega : \omega \in \Omega\}$, that is, let there exist ω_B in Ω such that the European contingent claim $\mathfrak{v}_{\omega_B}$ has inception time t, expiration time T and payoff $\mathbf{1}$ where $\mathbf{1}$ is the function in Π identically equal to unity. The value v_{ω_B} of the pure discount bond $\mathfrak{v}_{\omega_B}$ is the solution of the Cauchy problem (6.45), that is:

$$\overset{2}{\frac{d}{dt}} \boldsymbol{u}'(\overset{3}{t}, \overset{1}{t})\, v_{\omega_B} + \mathfrak{L}(\overset{2}{t})\, \boldsymbol{u}'(\overset{3}{t}, \overset{1}{t})\, v_{\omega_B} = 0, \quad t < T,$$
$$v_{\omega_B}(T) = \mathbf{1}. \tag{6.51}$$

In terms of the continuously compounded interest rate $r(s_t, t)$ the value v_{ω_B} of the pure discount bond incepted at time t and maturing at time T an instant later is formally given by

$$v_{\omega_B} = e^{-\int_{\overset{1}{(t)}}^{\overset{3}{(t)}} r(s_t, \tau) d\tau}$$

so that the evolution equation in (6.51) can be rewritten as follows

$$(\overset{2}{\frac{d}{dt}} + \mathfrak{L}(\overset{2}{t}))\, \boldsymbol{u}'(\overset{3}{t}, \overset{1}{t})\, e^{-\int_{\overset{1}{(t)}}^{\overset{3}{(t)}} \boldsymbol{r}(\overset{3}{s}, \tau) d\tau}\, \mathbf{1} = 0,$$

or equivalently

$$(\overset{2}{\frac{d}{dt}} + \mathfrak{L}(\overset{2}{t}))\, \boldsymbol{u}'(\overset{3}{t}, \overset{1}{t})\, \mathbf{1} + r(s, t) = 0, \tag{6.52}$$

where $\boldsymbol{r}(s, \tau)$ is the operator of multiplication by the function $r(s, t)$, and where the indexes over the operators indicate the order in which these operators act. We comment that **1** is the function in $\Pi(\mathbb{R}^n_{++} \times \mathcal{T})$ identically equal to unity.

With the help of the evolution equation (6.52) the evolution equation (6.48) can be rewritten as follows

$$\begin{aligned}
&\Big(\overset{2}{\frac{d}{dt}} + \mathfrak{L}(\overset{2}{t})\Big)\, \boldsymbol{u}'(\overset{3}{t}, \overset{1}{t})\, \boldsymbol{v}\, \mathbf{1} = \\
&\qquad \int_{\Omega \setminus \omega_B} \Big(\boldsymbol{\pi}_v(t, d\omega) \Big(\overset{2}{\frac{d}{dt}} + \mathfrak{L}(\overset{2}{t})\Big)\, \boldsymbol{u}'(\overset{3}{t}, \overset{1}{t})\, \boldsymbol{v}_\omega\, \mathbf{1} \Big) + \\
&\qquad\qquad \boldsymbol{\pi}_v(t, B) \Big(\Big(\overset{2}{\frac{d}{dt}} + \mathfrak{L}(\overset{2}{t})\Big)\, \boldsymbol{u}'(\overset{3}{t}, \overset{1}{t})\, \mathbf{1} + r(s,t) \Big),
\end{aligned} \tag{6.53}$$

where $\boldsymbol{\pi}_v(t, B) = \boldsymbol{\pi}_v(t, \omega_B)$ is the operator weight of the pure discount bond in the dynamically replicating portfolio for the European contingent claim $\mathfrak{v}$. We comment that **1** is the function in $\Pi(\mathbb{R}^n_{++} \times \mathcal{T})$ identically equal to unity.

6.51. Remark. It is clear that $\boldsymbol{\pi}_v(t, B) = \boldsymbol{\pi}_v(t, \omega_B)$ is nothing but the operator-valued measure of ω_B in Ω.

Consider the operators

$$\Big(\overset{2}{\frac{d}{dt}} + \mathfrak{L}(\overset{2}{t})\Big)\, \boldsymbol{u}'(\overset{3}{t}, \overset{1}{t})\, \boldsymbol{v}$$

and

$$\Big(\overset{2}{\frac{d}{dt}} + \mathfrak{L}(\overset{2}{t})\Big)\, \boldsymbol{u}'(\overset{3}{t}, \overset{1}{t})\, \boldsymbol{v}_\omega$$

with ω in $\Omega \setminus \omega_B$ from the preceding equation (6.53) separately. We comment that we interpret these operators as operators on $\Pi(\mathbb{R}^n_{++} \times \mathcal{T})$.

With the help of the chain of equalities (6.49) for the operator

$(\overset{2}{\frac{d}{dt}} + \mathfrak{L}(\overset{2}{t}))\, \boldsymbol{u}'(\overset{3}{t}, \overset{1}{t})\, \boldsymbol{v}$ we have the following equality

$$\begin{aligned}(\overset{2}{\frac{d}{dt}} + \mathfrak{L}(\overset{2}{t}))\, \boldsymbol{u}'(\overset{3}{t},\overset{1}{t})\,\boldsymbol{v} &= \\ &\boldsymbol{v}\,(\overset{2}{\frac{d}{dt}} + \mathfrak{L}(\overset{2}{t}))\,\boldsymbol{u}'(\overset{3}{t},\overset{1}{t}) + \\ &\quad [(\frac{d}{dt}+\mathfrak{L}(t)),\boldsymbol{v}] + [[(\overset{2}{\frac{d}{dt}} + \mathfrak{L}(\overset{2}{t})),\boldsymbol{v}],\boldsymbol{u}'(\overset{3}{t},\overset{1}{t})],\end{aligned} \tag{6.54}$$

where again we have taken into account the fact that due to Theorem (3.81) for each time t in $\mathcal{T}$ and each state of the market as expressed by the prices of the underlying securities s'_t at this time t there exists a global transformation from the beliefs-preferences gauge symmetry group $\hat{\mathcal{G}}$ such that the marginal utility $\boldsymbol{u}'(t,t)$ is the operator of multiplication by the function $u'(t,t,s_t,s_t)$ with the following property

$$u'(t,t,s_t = s'_t, s_t = s'_t) = 1.$$

With the help of the chain of equalities (6.50) for the operator $(\overset{2}{\frac{d}{dt}} + \mathfrak{L}(\overset{2}{t}))\, \boldsymbol{u}'(\overset{3}{t}, \overset{1}{t})\, \boldsymbol{v}_\omega$ with ω in $\Omega \setminus \omega_B$ we have the following equality

$$\begin{aligned}(\overset{2}{\frac{d}{dt}} + \mathfrak{L}(\overset{2}{t}))\, \boldsymbol{u}'(\overset{3}{t},\overset{1}{t})\,\boldsymbol{v}_\omega &= \\ &\boldsymbol{v}_\omega\,(\overset{2}{\frac{d}{dt}} + \mathfrak{L}(\overset{2}{t}))\,\boldsymbol{u}'(\overset{3}{t},\overset{1}{t}) + \\ &\quad [(\frac{d}{dt}+\mathfrak{L}(t)),\boldsymbol{v}_\omega] + [[(\overset{2}{\frac{d}{dt}} + \mathfrak{L}(\overset{2}{t})),\boldsymbol{v}_\omega],\boldsymbol{u}'(\overset{3}{t},\overset{1}{t})],\end{aligned} \tag{6.55}$$

where again we have taken into account the fact that due to Theorem (3.81) for each time t in $\mathcal{T}$ and each state of the market as expressed by the prices of the underlying securities s'_t at this time t there exists a global transformation from the beliefs-preferences gauge symmetry group $\hat{\boldsymbol{\mathcal{G}}}$ such that the marginal utility $\boldsymbol{u}'(t,t)$ is the operator of multiplication by the function $u'(t,t,s_t,s_t)$ with the following property

$$u'(t,t,s_t = s'_t, s_t = s'_t) = 1.$$

With the help of the preceding equalities (6.54) and (6.55) we can rewrite the evolution equation (6.53) as follows

$$\begin{aligned}
&\Big(\boldsymbol{v}\,\big(\overset{2}{\frac{d}{dt}} + \mathfrak{L}(\overset{2}{t})\big)\,\boldsymbol{u}'(\overset{3}{t},\overset{1}{t}) + \\
&\quad [(\frac{d}{dt} + \mathfrak{L}(t)), \boldsymbol{v}] + [[(\overset{2}{\frac{d}{dt}} + \mathfrak{L}(\overset{2}{t})), \boldsymbol{v}], \boldsymbol{u}'(\overset{3}{t},\overset{1}{t})]\Big)\mathbf{1} = \\
&\int_{\Omega\setminus\omega_B}\Big(\boldsymbol{\pi}_v(t,d\omega)\Big(\boldsymbol{v}_\omega\,\big(\overset{2}{\frac{d}{dt}} + \mathfrak{L}(\overset{2}{t})\big)\,\boldsymbol{u}'(\overset{3}{t},\overset{1}{t}) + \\
&\qquad [(\frac{d}{dt} + \mathfrak{L}(t)), \boldsymbol{v}_\omega] + [[(\overset{2}{\frac{d}{dt}} + \mathfrak{L}(\overset{2}{t})), \boldsymbol{v}_\omega], \boldsymbol{u}'(\overset{3}{t},\overset{1}{t})]\Big)\mathbf{1}\Big) + \\
&\quad \boldsymbol{\pi}_v(t,B)\Big(\big(\overset{2}{\frac{d}{dt}} + \mathfrak{L}(\overset{2}{t})\big)\,\boldsymbol{u}'(\overset{3}{t},\overset{1}{t})\,\mathbf{1} + r(s,t)\Big),
\end{aligned} \tag{6.56}$$

where $\mathbf{1}$ is the function in $\Pi(\mathbb{R}^n_{++} \times T)$ identically equal to unity.

Let the operator weight $\boldsymbol{\pi}_v(t,B)$ of the pure discount bond in the dynamically replicating portfolio for the European contingent claim $\mathfrak{v}$ be chosen according to relation (6.44), that is

$$\boldsymbol{\pi}_v(t,B) = \boldsymbol{v} - \int_{\Omega\setminus\omega_B} \boldsymbol{\pi}_v(t,d\omega)\,\boldsymbol{v}_\omega. \tag{6.57}$$

With operator weight $\boldsymbol{\pi}_v(t,B)$ of the pure discount bond in the dynamically replicating portfolio for the European contingent claim $\mathfrak{v}$ chosen as in the preceding relation (6.57) we can rewrite the evolution equation (6.56) as follows

$$\begin{aligned}\Big([(\frac{d}{dt} + \mathfrak{L}(t)), \boldsymbol{v}] + [[(\overset{2}{\frac{d}{dt}} + \mathfrak{L}(\overset{2}{t})), \boldsymbol{v}], \boldsymbol{u}'(\overset{3}{t}, \overset{1}{t})]\Big)\mathbf{1} = \\ \int_{\Omega\backslash\omega_B} \Big(\boldsymbol{\pi}_v(t, d\omega)\Big([(\frac{d}{dt} + \mathfrak{L}(t)), \boldsymbol{v}_\omega] + \\ [[(\overset{2}{\frac{d}{dt}} + \mathfrak{L}(\overset{2}{t})), \boldsymbol{v}_\omega], \boldsymbol{u}'(\overset{3}{t}, \overset{1}{t})]\Big)\mathbf{1}\Big) + \\ \boldsymbol{\pi}_v(t, B)\, r(s, t),\end{aligned} \tag{6.58}$$

where $\mathbf{1}$ is the function in $\Pi(\mathbb{R}^n_{++} \times \mathcal{T})$ identically equal to unity.

Since the solution $\boldsymbol{v}$ of the preceding evolution equation (6.58) has to remain unchanged under the action of the group H or more precisely (e_G, H), that is, has to be independent of preference $\boldsymbol{u}'(t, T)$, then the terms in this equation that possess the explicit dependence of $\boldsymbol{u}'(t, T)$ must be equal separately for any $\boldsymbol{u}'(t, T)$:

$$\begin{aligned}[[(\overset{2}{\frac{d}{dt}} + \mathfrak{L}(\overset{2}{t})), \boldsymbol{v}], \boldsymbol{u}'(\overset{3}{t}, \overset{1}{t})]\,\mathbf{1} = \\ \int_{\Omega\backslash\omega_B} \Big(\boldsymbol{\pi}_v(t, d\omega)[[(\overset{2}{\frac{d}{dt}} + \mathfrak{L}(\overset{2}{t})), \boldsymbol{v}_\omega], \boldsymbol{u}'(\overset{3}{t}, \overset{1}{t})]\,\mathbf{1}\Big),\end{aligned} \tag{6.59}$$

where $\mathbf{1}$ is the function in $\Pi(\mathbb{R}^n_{++} \times \mathcal{T})$ identically equal to unity.

It is this equation (6.59) that determines the operator weights $\boldsymbol{\pi}_v(t, d\omega)$ of the European contingent claims $\{\mathfrak{v}_\omega : \omega \in \Omega\}$ in the dynamically replicating portfolio for the European contingent claim $\mathfrak{v}$. More precisely, the preceding equation (6.59) determines the operator weights $\boldsymbol{\pi}_v(t, d\omega)$ of the European contingent claims $\{\mathfrak{v}_\omega : \omega \in \Omega\backslash\omega_B\}$ in the dynamically replicating portfolio for the European contingent claim $\mathfrak{v}$ not including the pure discount bond $\mathfrak{v}_{\omega_B}$. After these operator weights are determined then the operator weight $\boldsymbol{\pi}_v(t, B)$ of the pure discount bond $\mathfrak{v}_{\omega_B}$ in the dynamically replicating portfolio for the European contingent claim $\mathfrak{v}$ can be found from relation (6.57).

6.52. Remark. More precisely, equation (6.59) for each t in $\mathcal{T}$ determines the map $\boldsymbol{\pi}_{(\cdot)}(t, d\omega)$ defined on Π.

Before we represent the evolution equation (6.58) in such a way that it does not possess explicit dependence on the preference $\boldsymbol{u}'(t,T)$ we analyze equation (6.59) for the operator weights $\boldsymbol{\pi}_v(t, d\omega)$ of the European contingent claims in the dynamically replicating portfolio for the European contingent claim $\mathfrak{v}$ in more detail.

It is clear from the financial standpoint that, since equation (6.59) determines all the operator weights $\boldsymbol{\pi}_v(t, d\omega)$ of the European contingent claims $\{\mathfrak{v}_\omega : \omega \in \Omega \setminus \omega_B\}$ in the dynamically replicating portfolio for the European contingent claim $\mathfrak{v}$ except for the operator weight $\boldsymbol{\pi}_v(t, B)$ of the pure discount bond $\mathfrak{v}_{\omega_B}$ and since the operator weight $\boldsymbol{\pi}_v(t, B)$ of the pure discount bond $\mathfrak{v}_{\omega_B}$ does not enter this equation, then the operator weights $\boldsymbol{\pi}_v(t, d\omega)$ of the European contingent claims $\{\mathfrak{v}_\omega : \omega \in \Omega \setminus \omega_B\}$ must depend only on the "random" component of the generators $\mathfrak{L}(t)$ with t in $\mathcal{T}$. More precisely, the operator weights $\boldsymbol{\pi}_v(t, d\omega)$ of the European contingent claims $\{\mathfrak{v}_\omega : \omega \in \Omega \setminus \omega_B\}$ must remain unchanged under the following group $\mathfrak{R}$ of transformations of $\mathbb{L}$:

$$\mathsf{L} \rightarrow \mathfrak{r}\,\mathsf{L}, \quad \mathfrak{r} \in \mathfrak{R},$$

with each $\mathfrak{r}$ in $\mathfrak{R}$ defined by

$$\mathsf{L}(t) \xrightarrow{\mathfrak{r}} \mathsf{L}(t) + \sum_{i=1}^{n} a_i(s,t)\frac{\partial}{\partial s_i} + b(s,t),$$

where $a_i(s,t)$ and $b(s,t)$ are admissible functions in $\Pi(\mathbb{R}^n_{++} \times \mathcal{T})$, and where $\mathsf{L}(t)$ is in L and

$$\mathsf{L}(t) + \sum_{i=1}^{n} a_i(s,t)\frac{\partial}{\partial s_i} + b(s,t)$$

is in $\mathfrak{r}\,\mathsf{L}$.

6.53. Remark. We comment that for simplicity we have used the same notations for the operators of multiplication by the functions $a_i(s,t)$ and $b(s,t)$ and for the functions $a_i(s,t)$ and $b(s,t)$ themselves.

6.54. Remark. We also comment that the family

$$\mathbf{L} = \{\mathbf{L}(t) : \Pi \to \Pi \,|\, t \in \mathcal{T}\}$$

is interpreted as an operator on $\Pi(\mathbb{R}^n_{++} \times \mathcal{T})$ in the standard way as indicated in Remark (6.50).

6.55. Remark. It is clear that $\mathfrak{R}$ is an abelian group isomorphic to the direct product, or more precisely direct sum of $n+1$ abelian groups of functions in $\Pi(\mathbb{R}^n_{++} \times \mathcal{T})$ with the group operation of addition.

6.56. Remark. We comment that we have treated the set $\mathbb{L}$ of all families $\mathbf{L}$ as a subset of the set $\mathbb{L}$ of all families $\mathfrak{L}$. In order to restrict the group $\mathfrak{R}$ to $\mathbb{L}$ it is enough to consider its subgroup of transformations $\mathfrak{r}$ of the form

$$\mathbf{L}(t) \xrightarrow{\mathfrak{r}} \mathbf{L}(t) + \sum_{i=1}^{n} a_i(s,t)\frac{\partial}{\partial s_i}.$$

It is clear that this subgroup is an abelian group isomorphic to the direct product, or more precisely direct sum of n abelian groups of functions in $\Pi(\mathbb{R}^n_{++} \times \mathcal{T})$ with the group operation of addition.

The fact that the operator weights $\boldsymbol{\pi}_v(t, d\omega)$ of the European contingent claims $\{\mathfrak{v}_\omega : \omega \in \Omega \setminus \omega_B\}$ remain unchanged under the group $\mathfrak{R}$ of transformations of $\mathbb{L}$ directly follows from the fact that each linear partial differential operator of the first order

$$\sum_{i=1}^{n} a_i(s,t)\frac{\partial}{\partial s_i} + b(s,t)$$

on $\Pi(\mathbb{R}^n_{++} \times \mathcal{T})$ is in the kernel subspace of the double commutator with operators $\boldsymbol{\alpha}(s,t)$ and $\boldsymbol{\beta}(s,t)$ on $\Pi(\mathbb{R}^n_{++} \times \mathcal{T})$ of multiplication by arbitrary admissible functions $\alpha(s,t)$ and $\beta(s,t)$ in $\Pi(\mathbb{R}^n_{++} \times \mathcal{T})$:

$$[[\sum_{i=1}^{n} a_i(s,t)\frac{\partial}{\partial s_i} + b(s,t), \boldsymbol{\alpha}(s,t)], \boldsymbol{\beta}(s,t)] = \mathbf{0},$$

where $\mathbf{0}$ is the zero operator on $\Pi(\mathbb{R}^n_{++} \times \mathcal{T})$.

6.57. Remark. The fact that the operator weights $\boldsymbol{\pi}_v(t, d\omega)$ of the European contingent claims $\{\mathfrak{v}_\omega : \omega \in \Omega \setminus \omega_B\}$ remain unchanged under the group $\mathfrak{R}$ of transformations of $\mathbb{L}$ can be restated as the fact that these operator weights can be defined on the orbits of the group $\mathfrak{R}$.

Now our goal is to express equation (6.59) for the operator weights $\boldsymbol{\pi}_v(t, d\omega)$ of the European contingent claims in the dynamically replicating portfolio for the European contingent claim $\mathfrak{v}$ solely in terms of the generator $\mathfrak{L}(t)$ without the operator of differentiation with respect to time.

Denote by $\mathbb{D}$ the set of all linear operators

$$\mathbf{D} : \Pi(\mathbb{R}^n_{++} \times \mathcal{T}) \to \Pi(\mathbb{R}^n_{++} \times \mathcal{T})$$

of the form

$$\mathbf{D} = d(s,t)\frac{d}{dt} + \mathbf{L}(t)$$

where $d(s,t)$ is in $\Pi(\mathbb{R}^n_{++} \times \mathcal{T})$, and where $\mathbf{L}(t)$ is from $\mathbf{L}$ in $\mathbb{L}$.

6.58. Remark. We comment that for simplicity we have used the same notation for the operator of multiplication by the function $d(s,t)$ and for the function $d(s,t)$ itself.

The operator weights $\boldsymbol{\pi}_v(t, d\omega)$ of the European contingent claims $\{\mathfrak{v}_\omega : \omega \in \Omega \setminus \omega_B\}$ remain unchanged under the following group $\hat{\mathfrak{R}}$ of transformations of the set $\mathbb{D}$:

$$\mathbf{D} \xrightarrow{\hat{\mathfrak{r}}} \mathbf{D} + c(s,t)\frac{d}{dt} + \sum_{i=1}^{n} a_i(s,t)\frac{\partial}{\partial s_i} + b(s,t), \quad \hat{\mathfrak{r}} \in \hat{\mathfrak{R}},$$

where $a_i(s,t)$, $b(s,t)$ and $c(s,t)$ are admissible functions in $\Pi(\mathbb{R}^n_{++} \times \mathcal{T})$.

6.59. Remark. We comment that again for simplicity we have used the same notations for the operators of multiplication by the functions $a_i(s,t)$, $b(s,t)$ and $c(s,t)$ and for the functions $a_i(s,t)$, $b(s,t)$ and $c(s,t)$ themselves.

6.60. Remark. It is clear that $\hat{\mathfrak{R}}$ is an abelian group isomorphic to the direct product of $n+2$ abelian groups of functions in $\Pi(\mathbb{R}^n_{++} \times \mathcal{T})$ with the group operation of addition.

6.61. Remark. We comment that we have treated the set $\mathbb{D}$ of all operators

$$\mathfrak{D} : \Pi(\mathbb{R}^n_{++} \times \mathcal{T}) \to \Pi(\mathbb{R}^n_{++} \times \mathcal{T})$$

of the form

$$\mathfrak{D} = d(s,t)\frac{d}{dt} + \mathfrak{L}(t)$$

as a subset of $\mathbb{D}$, where $\mathfrak{L}(t)$ is from $\mathfrak{L}$ in $\mathbb{L}$. In order to restrict the group $\mathfrak{R}$ to $\mathbb{D}$ it is enough to consider its subgroup of transformations $\mathfrak{r}$ of the form

$$\mathbf{D} \xrightarrow{\hat{\mathfrak{r}}} \mathbf{D} + c(s,t)\frac{d}{dt} + \sum_{i=1}^{n} a_i(s,t)\frac{\partial}{\partial s_i}.$$

It is clear that this subgroup is an abelian group isomorphic to the direct product, or more precisely direct sum of $n+1$ abelian groups of functions in $\Pi(\mathbb{R}^n_{++} \times \mathcal{T})$ with the group operation of addition.

The fact that the operator weights $\boldsymbol{\pi}_v(t, d\omega)$ of the European contingent claims $\{\mathfrak{v}_\omega : \omega \in \Omega \setminus \omega_B\}$ remain unchanged under the group $\hat{\mathfrak{R}}$ of transformations of $\mathbb{D}$ directly follows from the fact that each linear partial differential operator of the first order

$$c(s,t)\frac{d}{dt} + \sum_{i=1}^{n} a_i(s,t)\frac{\partial}{\partial s_i} + b(s,t)$$

on $\Pi(\mathbb{R}^n_{++} \times \mathcal{T})$ is in the kernel subspace of the double commutator with operators $\boldsymbol{\alpha}(s,t)$ and $\boldsymbol{\beta}(s,t)$ on $\Pi(\mathbb{R}^n_{++} \times \mathcal{T})$ of multiplication by arbitrary admissible real-valued functions $\alpha(s,t)$ and $\beta(s,t)$ in $\Pi(\mathbb{R}^n_{++} \times \mathcal{T})$:

$$[[c(s,t)\frac{d}{dt} + \sum_{i=1}^{n} a_i(s,t)\frac{\partial}{\partial s_i} + b(s,t), \boldsymbol{\alpha}(s,t)], \boldsymbol{\beta}(s,t)] = \mathbf{0},$$

where $\mathbf{0}$ is the zero operator on $\Pi(\mathbb{R}^n_{++} \times \mathcal{T})$.

6.62. Remark. The fact that the operator weights $\boldsymbol{\pi}_v(t, d\omega)$ of the European contingent claims $\{\mathfrak{v}_\omega : \omega \in \Omega \setminus \omega_B\}$ remain unchanged under the group $\hat{\mathfrak{R}}$ of transformations of $\mathbb{D}$ can be restated as the fact that these operator weights can be defined on the orbits of the group $\hat{\mathfrak{R}}$.

Finally, for the operator

$$\mathfrak{D} = d(s,t)\frac{d}{dt} + \mathfrak{L}(t)$$

in $\mathbb{D}$, or more precisely in $\mathbb{D}$ with $d(s,t)$ identically equal to unity and for the transformation $\hat{\mathfrak{r}}$ from the group $\hat{\mathfrak{R}}$ with $c(s,t) = -d(s,t)$ we can rewrite equation (6.59) for the operator weights $\boldsymbol{\pi}_v(t, d\omega)$ of the European contingent claims in the dynamically replicating portfolio for the European contingent claim $\mathfrak{v}$ solely in terms of the generator $\mathfrak{L}(t)$ without the operator of differentiation with respect to time:

$$[[\mathfrak{L}(\overset{2}{t}), \boldsymbol{v}], \boldsymbol{u}'(\overset{3}{t}, \overset{1}{t})]\,\mathbf{1} = \int_{\Omega\setminus\omega_B} \Big(\boldsymbol{\pi}_v(t, d\omega)[[\mathfrak{L}(\overset{2}{t}), \boldsymbol{v}_\omega], \boldsymbol{u}'(\overset{3}{t}, \overset{1}{t})]\,\mathbf{1}\Big), \tag{6.60}$$

for any preference $\boldsymbol{u}'(t,T)$. We comment that $\mathbf{1}$ is the function in Π identically equal to unity.

Now with the help of equation (6.59), or equivalently (6.60) we represent the evolution equation (6.58) in such a way that it does not possess explicit dependence on the preference $\boldsymbol{u}'(t,T)$:

$$
\begin{aligned}
&[(\frac{d}{dt} + \mathfrak{L}(t)), \boldsymbol{v}]\mathbf{1} = \\
&\quad \int_{\Omega\backslash\omega_B} \Big(\boldsymbol{\pi}_v(t,d\omega)[(\frac{d}{dt} + \mathfrak{L}(t)), \boldsymbol{v}_\omega]\mathbf{1}\Big) + \\
&\qquad (\boldsymbol{v} - \int_{\Omega\backslash\omega_B} \boldsymbol{\pi}_v(t,d\omega)\, \boldsymbol{v}_\omega) r(s,t),
\end{aligned}
\tag{6.61}
$$

where $\mathbf{1}$ is the function in $\Pi(\mathbb{R}^n_{++} \times \mathcal{T})$ identically equal to unity.

We note that relation (3.101) implies that the function $\mathbf{1}$ in $\Pi(\mathbb{R}^n_{++} \times \mathcal{T})$ identically equal to unity is in the kernel subspace of the operator $\frac{d}{dt} + \mathfrak{L}(t)$ on $\Pi(\mathbb{R}^n_{++} \times \mathcal{T})$, that is

$$
(\frac{d}{dt} + \mathfrak{L}(t))\mathbf{1} = \mathbf{0},
\tag{6.62}
$$

where $\mathbf{0}$ is the function in $\Pi(\mathbb{R}^n_{++} \times \mathcal{T})$ identically equal to zero.

Therefore the evolution equation (6.61) can be rewritten as follows

$$
\begin{aligned}
&(\frac{d}{dt} + \mathfrak{L}(t))\, v = \\
&\quad \int_{\Omega\backslash\omega_B} \Big(\boldsymbol{\pi}_v(t,d\omega)(\frac{d}{dt} + \mathfrak{L}(t))\, v_\omega\Big) + \\
&\qquad (v - \int_{\Omega\backslash\omega_B} \boldsymbol{\pi}_v(t,d\omega)\, v_\omega) r(s,t).
\end{aligned}
\tag{6.63}
$$

We rewrite the preceding evolution equation (6.63) as follows

$$
\begin{aligned}
&(\frac{\overset{1}{d}}{dt} + \mathfrak{L}(\overset{1}{t}))\, (v - \int_{\Omega\backslash\omega_B} \overset{2}{\boldsymbol{\pi}}_v(t,d\omega)\, v_\omega) = \\
&\quad (v - \int_{\Omega\backslash\omega_B} \boldsymbol{\pi}_v(t,d\omega)\, v_\omega) r(s,t).
\end{aligned}
\tag{6.64}
$$

Since $\mathfrak{L}(t)$ is in $\mathfrak{L}$ that generates the belief $\boldsymbol{\mathcal{B}}$ of a Markovian market participant $\boldsymbol{\mathcal{H}} = (\boldsymbol{\mathcal{B}}, \boldsymbol{\mathcal{U}})$ in a Markovian market populace $\mathbb{H} = \mathbb{B} \times \mathbb{U}$, the preceding equation (6.64) financially means that the instantaneous return on the portfolio consisting of a long position on European contingent claim $\mathfrak{v}$ and a short position on the dynamically replicating portfolio of European contingent claims $\{\mathfrak{v}_\omega : \omega \in \Omega \setminus \omega_B\}$ with the operator weights $\boldsymbol{\pi}_v(t, d\omega)$ not including the pure discount bond $\mathfrak{v}_{\omega_B}$ is equal to the instantaneous return on the portfolio consisting of $\boldsymbol{v} - \int_{\Omega\setminus\omega_B} \boldsymbol{\pi}_v(t, d\omega)$ units, or more precisely operator units of pure discount bond. In order to see this more clearly we can formally rewrite the evolution equation (6.64) as follows

$$\Big(\overset{2}{\frac{d}{dt}} + \boldsymbol{\mathfrak{L}}(\overset{2}{t})\Big) \Big(\Big(v - \int_{\Omega\setminus\omega_B} \overset{3}{\boldsymbol{\pi}}_v(t, d\omega)\, v_\omega\Big) - \overbrace{\Big(\boldsymbol{v} - \int_{\Omega\setminus\omega_B} \boldsymbol{\pi}_v(t, d\omega)\, \boldsymbol{v}_\omega\Big)}^{3} e^{-\int_{\overset{1}{(t)}}^{\overset{3}{(t)}} r(\overset{3}{s},\tau) d\tau} \Big). \tag{6.65}$$

Since the preceding evolution equation (6.65) is a particular case of the evolution equation (6.47) and hence of (6.43) the financial interpretation given for the evolution equation (6.47) and hence for (6.43) can be repeated verbatim for the evolution equation (6.65) and hence (6.64) and (6.63).

6.63. Remark. Let $\boldsymbol{L}(t)$ be a generator at time t of a market environment $\mathbf{V}$. Assume that all market participants, or more precisely Markovian market participants that populate the marketplace have agreed at all times t in $\mathcal{T}$ upon the values at time t of a set of European contingent claims with inception time t and expiration time T for all T in $\mathcal{T}$ with $t \leq T$ whose payoffs form a dense set. In this case it is possible to observe the generator $\boldsymbol{L}(t)$ at time t, or more precisely the image $\big(\boldsymbol{L}(t)\, h\big)(s_t)$ of any h in the dense set evaluated at the state of the market as expressed by the prices of the underlying securities s_t at the time t, directly from the market data. Indeed

$$\big(\boldsymbol{L}(t)\,h\big)(s_t) = \Big(\lim_{\Delta t \downarrow 0} \frac{\mathbf{V}(t,t+\Delta t) - \boldsymbol{I}}{\Delta t}\,h\Big)(s_t) = \Big(\lim_{\Delta t \downarrow 0} \frac{\big(\mathbf{V}(t,t+\Delta t)\,h\big)(s_t) - h(s_t)}{\Delta t}\Big),$$

where $\mathbf{V}(t,T)$ is an evolution operator in the market environment $\mathbf{V}$, and where $\boldsymbol{I}$ is the identity operator on Π. We recall that $\mathbf{V}(t,t+\Delta t)\,h$ is the value in Π at the inception time t of the European contingent claim with expiration time $t+\Delta t$ and the payoff h in Π, so that $\big(\mathbf{V}(t,t+\Delta t)\,h\big)(s_t)$ is the value in units of account at the inception time t of this European contingent claim, when the state of the market as expressed by the prices of the underlying securities is s_t at this time t.

Now let $\mathfrak{L}(t)$ be a generator at time t of the belief $\mathcal{B}$ of a Markovian market participant $\mathcal{H} = (\mathcal{B},\mathcal{U})$ that populates the marketplace. Due to relations (3.104) and (3.100) the transformation of $\mathfrak{L}(t)$ from the beliefs-preferences gauge symmetry group $\hat{\mathcal{G}}$ defined in (3.107) with $\hat{\mathbf{u}}'(t,T)$ generated by $\boldsymbol{u}'(t,T)$ in the preference $\mathcal{U}$ takes the following form

$$\begin{aligned}
\mathfrak{L}(t) \xrightarrow{\hat{g}_{\mathcal{B}}} & \hat{\mathbf{u}}'^{-1}(t,t)\,\mathfrak{L}(t)\,\hat{\mathbf{u}}'(t,t) + \frac{\hat{\mathbf{u}}'_t(t,t)}{\hat{\mathbf{u}}'(t,t)} = \\
& \boldsymbol{u}'^{-1}(t,t)\,\mathfrak{L}(t)\,\boldsymbol{u}'(t,t) + \frac{\boldsymbol{u}'_t(t,t)}{\boldsymbol{u}'(t,t)} - \mathfrak{d}(t) = \\
& \boldsymbol{u}'^{-1}(t,t)\,\mathfrak{L}(t)\,\boldsymbol{u}'(t,t) + \frac{\boldsymbol{u}'_t(t,t)}{\boldsymbol{u}'(t,t)} - \\
& \quad \Big(\boldsymbol{u}'^{-1}(t,t)\,\mathfrak{L}(t)\,\boldsymbol{u}'(t,t) + \frac{\boldsymbol{u}'_t(t,t)}{\boldsymbol{u}'(t,t)}\Big)\,\mathbf{1} = \\
& \boldsymbol{L}(t) + r(s,t),
\end{aligned} \tag{6.66}$$

where

$$r(s,t) = -\boldsymbol{L}(t)\,\mathbf{1},$$

with $\mathbf{1}$ being the function in Π identically equal to unity, is the continuously compounded interest rate, and where we have used the same notation for the operator $\boldsymbol{r}(s,t)$ on Π of multiplication by the function $r(s,t)$ in Π and for the function $r(s,t)$ itself. Therefore the operator

$$\mathfrak{L}'(t) = \boldsymbol{L}(t) + r(s,t)$$

on Π is a generator at time t of the belief $\boldsymbol{\mathcal{B}}'$ of a Markovian market participant $\boldsymbol{\mathcal{H}}' = (\boldsymbol{\mathcal{B}}', \boldsymbol{\mathcal{U}}')$ in the same orbit of the group $\hat{\boldsymbol{\mathcal{G}}}$ in $\mathbb{H} = \mathbb{B} \times \mathbb{U}$ as the Markovian market participant $\boldsymbol{\mathcal{H}} = (\boldsymbol{\mathcal{B}}, \boldsymbol{\mathcal{U}})$. Therefore in the case under consideration it is possible to observe $\mathfrak{L}'(t)$, or more precisely the image $\big(\mathfrak{L}'(t)\,h\big)(s_t)$ of any h in the dense set evaluated at the state of the market as expressed by the prices of the underlying securities s_t at the time t in $\mathcal{T}$, directly from the market data, at least for some Markovian market participant $\boldsymbol{\mathcal{H}}' = (\boldsymbol{\mathcal{B}}', \boldsymbol{\mathcal{U}}')$ that populates the marketplace, that is, is in the orbit of the group $\hat{\boldsymbol{\mathcal{G}}}$:

$$\big(\mathfrak{L}'(t)\,h\big)(s_t) = \big(\boldsymbol{L}(t)\,h\big)(s_t) + r(s_t,t)\,h(s_t).$$

We comment that to be able to observe $\mathfrak{L}'(t)$ for at least one Markovian market participant $\boldsymbol{\mathcal{H}}' = (\boldsymbol{\mathcal{B}}', \boldsymbol{\mathcal{U}}')$ that populates the marketplace is enough for the dynamic replication at the time t of European contingent claims. Finally we note that in order to determine the continuously compounded interest rate $r(s,t)$ it is enough to assume that the pure discount bond with inception time t, maturity time T and with the face value of one unit of account is traded only effectively, that is, that the function $\mathbf{1}$ in Π identically equal to unity is in the dense set. This completes the Remark.

6.64. Remark. We make the following observation, which is crucial for practical applications of the results on the dynamic replication of European contingent claims in a general market environment $\mathbf{V}$ that satisfies the intervention condition (2.4) in the case of a Markovian market populace $\mathbb{H} = \mathbb{B} \times \mathbb{U}$. Assume that all market participants, or more precisely Markovian market participants that populate the marketplace have agreed at all times t in $\mathcal{T}$ upon the values at time t of a set of European contingent claims with inception time t and expiration time T for all T in $\mathcal{T}$ with $t \leq T$ whose payoffs form a dense set. In this case due to the preceding Remark (6.63) it is possible to observe the generator $\mathfrak{L}(t)$ at time t, or more precisely the image $\big(\mathfrak{L}(t)\,h\big)(s_t)$ of any h in the dense set evaluated at the state of the market as expressed by the prices of the underlying securities s_t at the time t, directly from the market data. Then in order to determine the operator weights $\boldsymbol{\pi}_v(t, d\omega)$, or more precisely the weights $\pi_v(t, s_t, d\omega)$ of the European contingent claims $\{\mathfrak{v}_\omega : \omega \in \Omega\}$ in the dynamically replicating portfolio at time t in $\mathcal{T}$ for the European contingent claim $\mathfrak{v}$ with the help of equation (6.59), or equivalently (6.60) and relation (6.57) we need to be able to evaluate the double commutator of the operator $\mathfrak{L}(t)$ with operators $\boldsymbol{\alpha}(s,t)$ and $\boldsymbol{\beta}(s,t)$ of multiplication by arbitrary admissible real-valued functions $\alpha(s,t)$ and $\beta(s,t)$ in Π:

$$[[\mathfrak{L}(t), \boldsymbol{\alpha}(s,t)], \boldsymbol{\beta}(s,t)],$$

or more precisely the image

$$\big([[\mathfrak{L}(t), \boldsymbol{\alpha}(s,t)], \boldsymbol{\beta}(s,t)]\,h\big)(s_t) \tag{6.67}$$

of any h in the dense set evaluated at the state of the market as expressed by the prices of the underlying securities s_t at the time t. This is indeed possible since what we need in order to evaluate the image of the double commutator in (6.67) is only the image $\big(\mathfrak{L}(t)\,h\big)(s_t)$ of any h in the dense set evaluated at the state of the market as expressed by the prices of the underlying securities s_t at the time t, which is directly observable from the market data.

Now we consider the general case when the set $\{\mathfrak{v}_\omega : \omega \in \Omega\}$ of European contingent claims dynamically replicates a European contingent claim $\mathfrak{v}$ without the assumption that the pure discount bond is traded.

Instead of the European contingent claims $\{\mathfrak{v}_\omega : \omega \in \Omega\}$ and $\mathfrak{v}$ with values $\{v_\omega : \omega \in \Omega\}$ and v we consider portfolios of

$\prod_{\omega' \in \Omega \cup \omega_0 \setminus \omega} \boldsymbol{v}_{\omega'}$ units of $\mathfrak{v}_\omega$ with ω in Ω and of $\prod_{\omega \in \Omega} \boldsymbol{v}_\omega$ units of $\mathfrak{v}$ with values

$$\{(\prod_{\omega' \in \Omega \cup \omega_0 \setminus \omega} v_{\omega'})\, v_\omega : \omega \in \Omega\} \quad \text{and} \quad (\prod_{\omega \in \Omega} v_\omega)\, v$$

where $\boldsymbol{v}_\omega$ and $\boldsymbol{v}$ again stand for the operators of multiplication by the functions v_ω and v, and where the products are understood formally in the case when the set Ω is uncountable. We comment that ω_0, or more precisely $\mathfrak{v}_{\omega_0}$ denotes the European contingent claim $\mathfrak{v}$.

6.65. Remark. We comment that a portfolio of $\prod_{\omega' \in \Omega \cup \omega_0 \setminus \omega} \boldsymbol{v}_{\omega'}$ units of $\mathfrak{v}_\omega$ with ω in Ω and of $\prod_{\omega \in \Omega} \boldsymbol{v}_\omega$ units of $\mathfrak{v}$, or more precisely of $\prod_{\omega' \in \Omega \cup \omega_0 \setminus \omega} \boldsymbol{v}_{\omega'}$ operator units of $\mathfrak{v}_\omega$ with ω in Ω and of $\prod_{\omega \in \Omega} \boldsymbol{v}_\omega$ operator units of $\mathfrak{v}$ are financially understood as portfolios of $\prod_{\omega' \in \Omega \cup \omega_0 \setminus \omega} v_{\omega'}(t, s_t)$ units of $\mathfrak{v}_\omega$ with ω in Ω and of $\prod_{\omega \in \Omega} v_\omega(t, s_t)$ units of $\mathfrak{v}$ when the state of the market as expressed by the prices of the underlying securities is s_t in $\mathbb{R}^n_{++}$ at time t in $\mathcal{T}$. In other words, the portfolios of $\prod_{\omega' \in \Omega \cup \omega_0 \setminus \omega} \boldsymbol{v}_{\omega'}$ operator units of $\mathfrak{v}_\omega$ with ω in Ω and of $\prod_{\omega \in \Omega} \boldsymbol{v}_\omega$ operator units of $\mathfrak{v}$ are portfolios with amounts of units that depend on the time t and the state of the market as expressed by the prices of the underlying securities s_t at the time t.

It is clear that the values of all the portfolios of $\prod_{\omega' \in \Omega \cup \omega_0 \setminus \omega} \boldsymbol{v}_{\omega'}$ units of $\mathfrak{v}_\omega$ with ω in Ω and of $\prod_{\omega \in \Omega} \boldsymbol{v}_\omega$ units of $\mathfrak{v}$ are equal to each other, that is

$$(\prod_{\omega' \in \Omega \cup \omega_0 \setminus \omega} v_{\omega'})\, v_\omega = (\prod_{\omega \in \Omega} v_\omega)\, v, \quad \omega \in \Omega. \tag{6.68}$$

For the portfolios of $\prod_{\omega' \in \Omega \cup \omega_0 \setminus \omega} \boldsymbol{v}_{\omega'}$ units of $\mathfrak{v}_\omega$ with ω in Ω and of $\prod_{\omega \in \Omega} \boldsymbol{v}_\omega$ units of $\mathfrak{v}$ we can rewrite the evolution equation

(6.48) as follows

$$\Big(\prod_{\omega\in\Omega} \boldsymbol{v}_\omega\Big)\Big(\frac{\overset{2}{d}}{dt} + \mathfrak{L}(\overset{2}{t})\Big)\,\boldsymbol{u}'(\overset{3}{t},\overset{1}{t})\,\boldsymbol{v}\,\mathbf{1} = \int_\Omega \Big(\boldsymbol{\pi}_v(t,d\omega)\Big(\prod_{\omega'\in\Omega\cup\omega_0\setminus\omega}\boldsymbol{v}_{\omega'}\Big)\times \Big(\frac{\overset{2}{d}}{dt}+\mathfrak{L}(\overset{2}{t})\Big)\,\boldsymbol{u}'(\overset{3}{t},\overset{1}{t})\,\boldsymbol{v}_\omega\,\mathbf{1}\Big) \tag{6.69}$$

where $\boldsymbol{\pi}_v(t,d\omega)$ is the operator weight of the portfolio of $\prod_{\omega'\in\Omega\cup\omega_0\setminus\omega}\boldsymbol{v}_{\omega'}$ units of $\mathfrak{v}_\omega$ with ω in Ω in the dynamically replicating portfolio for the portfolio of $\prod_{\omega\in\Omega}\boldsymbol{v}_\omega$ units of $\mathfrak{v}$.

With the help of equalities (6.54) and (6.55) we can rewrite the preceding evolution equation (6.69) as follows

$$\begin{aligned}&\Big(\prod_{\omega\in\Omega} \boldsymbol{v}_\omega\Big)\Big(\boldsymbol{v}\Big(\frac{\overset{2}{d}}{dt} + \mathfrak{L}(\overset{2}{t})\Big)\,\boldsymbol{u}'(\overset{3}{t},\overset{1}{t}) + \\ &\quad [(\frac{d}{dt}+\mathfrak{L}(t)),\boldsymbol{v}] + [[(\frac{\overset{2}{d}}{dt}+\mathfrak{L}(\overset{2}{t})),\boldsymbol{v}],\boldsymbol{u}'(\overset{3}{t},\overset{1}{t})]\Big)\,\mathbf{1} = \\ &\int_\Omega\Big(\boldsymbol{\pi}_v(t,d\omega)\Big(\prod_{\omega'\in\Omega\cup\omega_0\setminus\omega}\boldsymbol{v}_{\omega'}\Big)\Big(\boldsymbol{v}_\omega\Big(\frac{\overset{2}{d}}{dt}+\mathfrak{L}(\overset{2}{t})\Big)\,\boldsymbol{u}'(\overset{3}{t},\overset{1}{t}) + \\ &\quad [(\frac{d}{dt}+\mathfrak{L}(t)),\boldsymbol{v}_\omega] + [[(\frac{\overset{2}{d}}{dt}+\mathfrak{L}(\overset{2}{t})),\boldsymbol{v}_\omega],\boldsymbol{u}'(\overset{3}{t},\overset{1}{t})]\Big)\,\mathbf{1}\Big),\end{aligned} \tag{6.70}$$

where $\mathbf{1}$ is the function in $\Pi(\mathbb{R}^n_{++}\times\mathcal{T})$ identically equal to unity.

Without loss of generality we choose the total operator-valued measure, or equivalently the total operator weight for the portfolios of $\prod_{\omega'\in\Omega\cup\omega_0\setminus\omega}\boldsymbol{v}_{\omega'}$ units of $\mathfrak{v}_\omega$ with ω in Ω in the dynamically replicating portfolio for the portfolio of $\prod_{\omega\in\Omega}\boldsymbol{v}_\omega$ units of $\mathfrak{v}$ equal to the identity operator $\boldsymbol{I}$ on Π, that is

$$\int_\Omega \boldsymbol{\pi}_v(t,d\omega) = \boldsymbol{I}. \tag{6.71}$$

Indeed, if this is not the case we can formally choose the operator weight $\boldsymbol{\pi}_v(t, \omega_*)$ for one of the portfolios of $\prod_{\omega' \in \Omega \cup \omega_0 \backslash \omega_*} \boldsymbol{v}_{\omega'}$ units of $\mathfrak{v}_{\omega_*}$ with ω_* in Ω in the dynamically replicating portfolio for the portfolio of $\prod_{\omega \in \Omega} \boldsymbol{v}_\omega$ units of $\mathfrak{v}$ as follows

$$\boldsymbol{\pi}_v(t, \omega_*) = \boldsymbol{I} - \int_{\Omega \backslash \omega_*} \boldsymbol{\pi}_v(t, d\omega), \quad t \in \mathcal{T}. \tag{6.72}$$

6.66. Remark. Due to equality (6.68) the choice of the operator weights $\boldsymbol{\pi}_v(t, d\omega)$ of the portfolios of $\prod_{\omega' \in \Omega \cup \omega_0 \backslash \omega} \boldsymbol{v}_{\omega'}$ units of $\mathfrak{v}_\omega$ with ω in Ω in the dynamically replicating portfolio for the portfolio of $\prod_{\omega \in \Omega} \boldsymbol{v}_\omega$ units of $\mathfrak{v}$ as given in (6.71) is consistent with equality (6.44). Indeed

$$\begin{aligned}
&\int_\Omega \Big(\boldsymbol{\pi}_v(t, d\omega)\big(\prod_{\omega' \in \Omega \cup \omega_0 \backslash \omega} \boldsymbol{v}_{\omega'}\big)\, v_\omega\Big) = \\
&\int_\Omega \Big(\boldsymbol{\pi}_v(t, d\omega)\big(\prod_{\omega \in \Omega} \boldsymbol{v}_\omega\big)\, v\Big) = \\
&\Big(\int_\Omega \boldsymbol{\pi}_v(t, d\omega)\Big)\Big(\big(\prod_{\omega \in \Omega} \boldsymbol{v}_\omega\big)\, v\Big) = \\
&\big(\prod_{\omega \in \Omega} \boldsymbol{v}_\omega\big)\, v.
\end{aligned} \tag{6.73}$$

With the choice of the operator weights $\boldsymbol{\pi}_v(t, d\omega)$ of the portfolios of $\prod_{\omega' \in \Omega \cup \omega_0 \backslash \omega} \boldsymbol{v}_{\omega'}$ units of $\mathfrak{v}_\omega$ with ω in Ω in the dynamically replicating portfolio for the portfolio of $\prod_{\omega \in \Omega} \boldsymbol{v}_\omega$ units of $\mathfrak{v}$ as given in (6.71) and with the help of equality (6.68) we rewrite the evolution equation (6.70) as follows

$$
\begin{aligned}
&\Big(\prod_{\omega\in\Omega} \boldsymbol{v}_\omega\Big)\Big(([[(\frac{d}{dt}+\mathfrak{L}(t)),\boldsymbol{v}] + [[(\overset{2}{\frac{d}{dt}}+\mathfrak{L}(\overset{2}{t})),\boldsymbol{v}],\boldsymbol{u}'(\overset{3}{t},\overset{1}{t})]\Big)\,\mathbf{1} = \\
&\qquad \int_\Omega \Big(\boldsymbol{\pi}_v(t,d\omega)\Big(\prod_{\omega'\in\Omega\cup\omega_0\setminus\omega} \boldsymbol{v}_{\omega'}\Big)\Big([[(\frac{d}{dt}+\mathfrak{L}(t)),\boldsymbol{v}_\omega] + \\
&\qquad\qquad [[(\overset{2}{\frac{d}{dt}}+\mathfrak{L}(\overset{2}{t})),\boldsymbol{v}_\omega],\boldsymbol{u}'(\overset{3}{t},\overset{1}{t})]\Big)\,\mathbf{1}\Big).
\end{aligned}
\tag{6.74}
$$

Since the solution $\boldsymbol{v}$ of the preceding evolution equation (6.74) has to remain unchanged under the action of the group H or more precisely (e_G, H), that is, has to be independent of the preference $\boldsymbol{u}'(t,T)$ then the terms in this equation that possess the explicit dependence of $\boldsymbol{u}'(t,T)$ must be equal separately for any $\boldsymbol{u}'(t,T)$:

$$
\begin{aligned}
&\Big(\prod_{\omega\in\Omega} \boldsymbol{v}_\omega\Big)\Big([[(\overset{2}{\frac{d}{dt}}+\mathfrak{L}(\overset{2}{t})),\boldsymbol{v}],\boldsymbol{u}'(\overset{3}{t},\overset{1}{t})]\Big)\,\mathbf{1} = \\
&\qquad \int_\Omega \Big(\boldsymbol{\pi}_v(t,d\omega)\Big(\prod_{\omega'\in\Omega\cup\omega_0\setminus\omega} \boldsymbol{v}_{\omega'}\Big) \times \\
&\qquad\qquad [[(\overset{2}{\frac{d}{dt}}+\mathfrak{L}(\overset{2}{t})),\boldsymbol{v}_\omega],\boldsymbol{u}'(\overset{3}{t},\overset{1}{t})]\Big)\,\mathbf{1}\Big),
\end{aligned}
\tag{6.75}
$$

where $\mathbf{1}$ is the function in $\Pi(\mathbb{R}^n_{++}\times\mathcal{T})$ identically equal to unity.

It is this equation (6.75) that determines the operator weights $\boldsymbol{\pi}_v(t,d\omega)$ of the portfolios of $\prod_{\omega'\in\Omega\cup\omega_0\setminus\omega} \boldsymbol{v}_{\omega'}$ units of $\mathfrak{v}_\omega$ with ω in Ω in the dynamically replicating portfolio for the portfolio of $\prod_{\omega\in\Omega} \boldsymbol{v}_\omega$ units of $\mathfrak{v}$.

6.67. Remark. More precisely, equation (6.75) for each t in $\mathcal{T}$ determines the map $\boldsymbol{\pi}_{(\cdot)}(t,d\omega)$ defined on Π.

Before we represent the evolution equation (6.74) in such a way that it does not possess explicit dependence on the preference $\boldsymbol{u}'(t,T)$, we analyze equation (6.75) for the operator weights $\boldsymbol{\pi}_v(t,d\omega)$ in more detail.

It is clear that the operator weights $\boldsymbol{\pi}_v(t,d\omega)$ of the portfolios of $\prod_{\omega'\in\Omega\cup\omega_0\backslash\omega} \boldsymbol{v}_{\omega'}$ units of $\mathfrak{v}_\omega$ with ω in Ω in the dynamically replicating portfolio for the portfolio of $\prod_{\omega\in\Omega} \boldsymbol{v}_\omega$ units of $\mathfrak{v}$ remain unchanged under the group $\mathfrak{R}$ of transformations of $\mathbb{L}$.

6.68. Remark. As we have commented in Remark (6.56) we have treated $\mathbb{L}$ as a subset of $\mathbb{L}$.

6.69. Remark. The fact that the operator weights $\boldsymbol{\pi}_v(t,d\omega)$ of the portfolios of $\prod_{\omega'\in\Omega\cup\omega_0\backslash\omega} \boldsymbol{v}_{\omega'}$ units of $\mathfrak{v}_\omega$ with ω in Ω in the dynamically replicating portfolio for the portfolio of $\prod_{\omega\in\Omega} \boldsymbol{v}_\omega$ units of $\mathfrak{v}$ remain unchanged under the group $\mathfrak{R}$ of transformations of $\mathbb{L}$ can be restated as the fact that these operator weights can be defined on the orbits of the group $\mathfrak{R}$.

Now our goal is to express equation (6.75) for the operator weights $\boldsymbol{\pi}_v(t,d\omega)$ of the portfolios of $\prod_{\omega'\in\Omega\cup\omega_0\backslash\omega} \boldsymbol{v}_{\omega'}$ units of $\mathfrak{v}_\omega$ with ω in Ω in the dynamically replicating portfolio for the portfolio of $\prod_{\omega\in\Omega} \boldsymbol{v}_\omega$ units of $\mathfrak{v}$ solely in terms of the generator $\mathfrak{L}(t)$ without the operator of differentiation with respect to time.

It is clear that the operator weights $\boldsymbol{\pi}_v(t,d\omega)$ of the portfolios of $\prod_{\omega'\in\Omega\cup\omega_0\backslash\omega} \boldsymbol{v}_{\omega'}$ units of $\mathfrak{v}_\omega$ with ω in Ω in the dynamically replicating portfolio for the portfolio of $\prod_{\omega\in\Omega} \boldsymbol{v}_\omega$ units of $\mathfrak{v}$ remain unchanged under the group $\hat{\mathfrak{R}}$ of transformations of $\mathbb{D}$.

6.70. Remark. As we have commented in Remark (6.61) we have treated $\mathbb{D}$ as a subset of $\mathbb{D}$.

6.71. Remark. The fact that the operator weights $\boldsymbol{\pi}_v(t,d\omega)$ of the portfolios of $\prod_{\omega'\in\Omega\cup\omega_0\backslash\omega} \boldsymbol{v}_{\omega'}$ units of $\mathfrak{v}_\omega$ with ω in Ω in the dynamically replicating portfolio for the portfolio of $\prod_{\omega\in\Omega} \boldsymbol{v}_\omega$ units of $\mathfrak{v}$ remain unchanged under the group $\hat{\mathfrak{R}}$ of transformations of $\mathbb{D}$ can be restated as the fact that these operator weights can be defined on the orbits of the group $\hat{\mathfrak{R}}$.

Finally, for the operator

$$\mathfrak{D} = d(s,t)\frac{d}{dt} + \mathfrak{L}(t)$$

in $\mathbb{D}$, or more precisely in $\mathbb{D}$ with $d(s,t)$ identically equal to unity and for the transformation $\hat{\mathfrak{r}}$ from the group $\hat{\mathfrak{R}}$ with $c(s,t) = -d(s,t)$ we can rewrite equation (6.75) for the operator weights $\boldsymbol{\pi}_v(t, d\omega)$ of the portfolios of $\prod_{\omega' \in \Omega \cup \omega_0 \backslash \omega} \boldsymbol{v}_{\omega'}$ units of $\mathfrak{v}_\omega$ with ω in Ω in the dynamically replicating portfolio for the portfolio of $\prod_{\omega \in \Omega} \boldsymbol{v}_\omega$ units of $\mathfrak{v}$ solely in terms of the generator $\mathfrak{L}(t)$ without the operator of differentiation with respect to time:

$$\begin{aligned}(\prod_{\omega\in\Omega} \boldsymbol{v}_\omega)\left([[(\mathfrak{L}(\overset{2}{t})), \boldsymbol{v}], \boldsymbol{u}'(\overset{3}{t}, \overset{1}{t})]\right) \mathbf{1} = \\ \int_\Omega \Big(\boldsymbol{\pi}_v(t, d\omega)(\prod_{\omega'\in\Omega\cup\omega_0\backslash\omega} \boldsymbol{v}_{\omega'}) \times \\ [[(\mathfrak{L}(\overset{2}{t})), \boldsymbol{v}_\omega], \boldsymbol{u}'(\overset{3}{t}, \overset{1}{t})]\big)\, \mathbf{1}\Big),\end{aligned} \tag{6.76}$$

for any preference $\boldsymbol{u}'(t,T)$. We comment that $\mathbf{1}$ is the function in Π identically equal to unity.

Now with the help of equation (6.75), or equivalently (6.76) we represent the evolution equation (6.74) in such a way that it does not possess explicit dependence on the preference $\boldsymbol{u}'(t,T)$:

$$\begin{aligned}(\prod_{\omega\in\Omega} \boldsymbol{v}_\omega)\, [(\frac{d}{dt} + \mathfrak{L}(t)), \boldsymbol{v}]\, \mathbf{1} = \\ \int_\Omega \Big(\boldsymbol{\pi}_v(t, d\omega)(\prod_{\omega'\in\Omega\cup\omega_0\backslash\omega} \boldsymbol{v}_{\omega'})[(\frac{d}{dt} + \mathfrak{L}(t)), \boldsymbol{v}_\omega]\, \mathbf{1}\Big).\end{aligned} \tag{6.77}$$

Due to relation (6.62) the evolution equation (6.77) can be rewritten as follows

$$\begin{aligned}(\prod_{\omega\in\Omega} \boldsymbol{v}_\omega)\, (\frac{d}{dt} + \mathfrak{L}(t))\, v = \\ \int_\Omega \Big(\boldsymbol{\pi}_v(t, d\omega)(\prod_{\omega'\in\Omega\cup\omega_0\backslash\omega} \boldsymbol{v}_{\omega'})(\frac{d}{dt} + \mathfrak{L}(t))\, v_\omega\Big).\end{aligned} \tag{6.78}$$

Since $\mathfrak{L}(t)$ is in $\mathfrak{L}$ that generates the belief $\mathcal{B}$ of a Markovian market participant $\mathcal{H} = (\mathcal{B}, \mathcal{U})$ in a Markovian market populace $\mathbb{H} = \mathbb{B} \times \mathbb{U}$, the preceding equation (6.78) financially means that the instantaneous return on the portfolio consisting of the portfolio of $\prod_{\omega \in \Omega} \boldsymbol{v}_\omega$ units of the European contingent claim $\mathfrak{v}$ is equal to the instantaneous return on the portfolio consisting of the portfolios of $\prod_{\omega' \in \Omega \cup \omega_0 \setminus \omega} \boldsymbol{v}_{\omega'}$ units of the European contingent claims $\mathfrak{v}_\omega$ with ω in Ω with the operator weights $\boldsymbol{\pi}_v(t, d\omega)$. In order to see this more clearly we can rewrite the evolution equation (6.78) as follows

$$\Big(\overset{1}{\frac{d}{dt}} + \mathfrak{L}(\overset{1}{t})\Big)\Big(\big(\prod_{\omega \in \Omega} \overset{2}{\boldsymbol{v}}_\omega\big) v - \int_\Omega \Big(\overset{2}{\boldsymbol{\pi}}_v(t, d\omega)\big(\prod_{\omega' \in \Omega \cup \omega_0 \setminus \omega} \overset{2}{\boldsymbol{v}}_{\omega'}\big)\, v_\omega\Big)\Big) = 0. \tag{6.79}$$

Since the preceding evolution equation (6.79) is a particular case of the evolution equation (6.47) and hence of (6.43) the financial interpretation given for the evolution equation (6.47) and hence for (6.43) can be repeated verbatim for the evolution equation (6.79) and hence (6.78).

6.72. Remark. Let the map $\hat{\pi}(t, d\omega) : \Pi \to \Pi$ for each ω in Ω and t in $\mathcal{T}$ be formally defined by

$$\hat{\pi}(t, d\omega)\, v = \pi_v(t, d\omega),$$

where $\pi_v(t, d\omega)$ is the Π-valued measure on Ω associated as in Remark (6.41) with the operator-valued measure, or equivalently operator weights $\boldsymbol{\pi}_v(t, d\omega)$ of the European contingent claims $\{\mathfrak{v}_\omega : \omega \in \Omega\}$ in the dynamically replicating portfolio for the European contingent claim $\mathfrak{v}$ with the value $v = v(t)$.

It is clear that by the no-arbitrage argument the map $\hat{\pi}(t, d\omega)$ is linear for each ω in Ω and t in $\mathcal{T}$. We will refer to each linear operator $\hat{\pi}(t, d\omega)$ as a *portfolio operator*. It is also clear that in general the linear operators $\hat{\pi}(t, d\omega)$ on Π and linear operators on Π of multiplication by arbitrary admissible functions in Π do not commute. It is this noncommutativity of the linear operators $\hat{\pi}(t, d\omega)$ on Π and linear operators on Π of multiplication by arbitrary admissible functions in Π that is, in the essence, financially responsible for the randomness of the prices of the underlying securities, that is, for the first quantization in finance. This issue will be presented in detail in forthcoming articles.

7 Application of the Beliefs-Preferences Gauge Symmetry Group to the Dynamic Replication of European Contingent Claims for a Markovian Market Populace with the Beliefs Determined by Diffusion Processes

We illustrate the dynamic replication of European contingent claims based on the beliefs-preferences gauge symmetry group $\hat{\mathcal{G}}$ for the Markovian market populace $\mathbb{H} = \mathbb{B} \times \mathbb{U}$, or more precisely $\mathbb{H} = \mathbb{L} \times \mathbb{U}$ presented in Subsection (6.2) of Section (6) in the particular case when each belief $\boldsymbol{\mathcal{B}}$ in the market populace belief $\mathbb{B}$ is determined by a diffusion process.

7.1 The Case of a Single Underlying Security

First we consider the dynamic replication of European contingent claims based on the beliefs-preferences gauge symmetry group $\hat{\mathcal{G}}$ for the Markovian market populace $\mathbb{H} = \mathbb{B} \times \mathbb{U}$, or more precisely $\mathbb{H} = \mathbb{L} \times \mathbb{U}$ in the particular case of a single underlying security and when each belief $\boldsymbol{\mathcal{B}}$ in the market populace belief $\mathbb{B}$ is generated by the family

$$\mathfrak{L} = \{\mathfrak{L}(t) : \Pi \to \Pi \,|\, t \in \mathcal{T}\},$$

in $\mathbb{L}$ where each generator $\mathfrak{L}(t)$ at time t is of the form (5.1).

Now we need the following assumption, which is natural from the financial standpoint, about the nature of the set $\{\mathfrak{v}_\omega : \omega \in \Omega\}$ of European contingent claims that dynamically replicates a given European contingent claim $\mathfrak{v}$.

We suppose that in addition to the pure discount bond $\mathfrak{v}_{\omega_B}$ with inception time t, maturity time T and with the face value of one unit of account with t and T in $\mathcal{T}$ and $t \leq T$, the underlying security itself is traded at each time t in $\mathcal{T}$. Then for each t and

T in $\mathcal{T}$ with $t \leq T$ and for each European contingent claim $\boldsymbol{\mathfrak{v}}$ with inception time t, expiration time T and payoff v_T we assume that the set $\{\boldsymbol{\mathfrak{v}}_\omega : \omega \in \Omega\}$ of European contingent claims that dynamically replicates $\boldsymbol{\mathfrak{v}}$ consists of the pure discount bond $\boldsymbol{\mathfrak{v}}_{\omega_B}$ and the underlying security $\boldsymbol{\mathfrak{v}}_{\omega_S}$ itself. That is, we assume that the set Ω consists of two elements ω_B and ω_S and is equipped with the standard sigma algebra. We comment that we view the underlying security $\boldsymbol{\mathfrak{v}}_{\omega_S}$ as the European contingent claim with inception time t, expiration time T and payoff $v_T^{\omega_S}$ such that $v_T^{\omega_S}(s_T) = s_T$ with t and T in $\mathcal{T}$ and $t \leq T$.

7.1. Remark. Later in this Subsection we will show that the assumption we have made about the nature of the set of European contingent claims that dynamically replicates a given European contingent claim is correct. More precisely, we will show that in the case under consideration, for each t and T in $\mathcal{T}$ with $t \leq T$ and for each European contingent claim $\boldsymbol{\mathfrak{v}}$ with inception time t, expiration time T and payoff v_T, the set $\{\boldsymbol{\mathfrak{v}}_\omega : \omega \in \Omega\}$ of European contingent claims that dynamically replicates $\boldsymbol{\mathfrak{v}}$ can, in fact, be taken to consist of the pure discount bond $\boldsymbol{\mathfrak{v}}_{\omega_B}$ and the underlying security $\boldsymbol{\mathfrak{v}}_{\omega_S}$ itself.

The value v_{ω_S} of the underlying security $\boldsymbol{\mathfrak{v}}_{\omega_S}$ is the solution of the Cauchy problem (6.45) that is

$$\begin{aligned} \frac{\overset{2}{d}}{dt}\boldsymbol{u}'(\overset{3}{t},\overset{1}{t})\, v_{\omega_S} + \boldsymbol{\mathfrak{L}}(\overset{2}{t})\, \boldsymbol{u}'(\overset{3}{t},\overset{1}{t})\, v_{\omega_S} &= 0, \quad t < T, \\ v_{\omega_S}(T) &= v_T^{\omega_S}. \end{aligned} \tag{7.1}$$

At the same time the value v_{ω_S} of the underlying security $\boldsymbol{\mathfrak{v}}_{\omega_S}$ as a European contingent claim incepted at time t and expiring at time T an instant later is formally given by

$$v_{\omega_S} = e^{-\int_{\overset{1}{(t)}}^{\overset{3}{(t)}} d(\overset{3}{s}_t,\tau)d\tau} \, s_t$$

so that the evolution equation in (7.1) can be rewritten as follows

$$\Big(\overset{2}{\frac{d}{dt}} + \mathfrak{L}(\overset{2}{t})\Big)\, \boldsymbol{u}'(\overset{3}{t},\overset{1}{t})\, e^{-\int_{\overset{1}{(t)}}^{\overset{3}{(t)}} \boldsymbol{d}(\overset{3}{s},\tau)d\tau}\, \overset{1}{s}\,\mathbf{1} = 0,$$

or equivalently

$$\Big(\overset{2}{\frac{d}{dt}} + \mathfrak{L}(\overset{2}{t})\Big)\, \boldsymbol{u}'(\overset{3}{t},\overset{1}{t})\, \overset{1}{s}\,\mathbf{1} + d(s,t)\, s = 0, \tag{7.2}$$

where $\boldsymbol{d}(s,t)$ is the operator of multiplication by the function $d(s,t)$ and $\mathbf{1}$ is the function in $\Pi(\mathbb{R}^n_{++} \times \mathcal{T})$ identically equal to unity, and where the indexes over the operators indicate the order in which these operators act.

7.2. Remark. We comment that $\overset{1}{s}$ is the operator on Π of multiplication by the argument s, that is, by the function $h(s) = s$ in Π. We also comment that $\overset{1}{s}$ can be interpreted as an operator on $\Pi(\mathbb{R}^n_{++} \times \mathcal{T})$ in the standard way as indicated in Remark (6.50).

7.3. Remark. In terms of the underlying security being stock, $d(s_t, t)$ is the continuously compounded dividend yield.

7.4. Remark. It is clear that the evolution equation (7.2) remains true in the general case of the generator $\mathfrak{L}(t)$ in $\mathfrak{L}$ from $\mathbb{L}$ not necessarily of the form (5.1).

In order to obtain the explicit form of equation (6.59) for the operator weight $\boldsymbol{\pi}_v(t,S) = \boldsymbol{\pi}_v(t,\omega_S)$ of the underlying security $\mathfrak{v}_{\omega_S}$ in the dynamically replicating portfolio for the European contingent claim $\mathfrak{v}$ with the value v in the case under consideration we need to evaluate the following double commutators

$$\Big[\Big[\Big(\overset{2}{\frac{d}{dt}} + \mathfrak{L}(\overset{2}{t})\Big), \boldsymbol{v}\Big], \boldsymbol{u}'(\overset{3}{t},\overset{1}{t})\Big] \quad \text{and} \quad \Big[\Big[\Big(\overset{2}{\frac{d}{dt}} + \mathfrak{L}(\overset{2}{t})\Big), \boldsymbol{v}_{\omega_S}\Big], \boldsymbol{u}'(\overset{3}{t},\overset{1}{t})\Big],$$

where $\boldsymbol{v} = \boldsymbol{v}(t)$ and $\boldsymbol{v}_{\omega_S} = \boldsymbol{v}_{\omega_S}(t)$ are the operators of multiplication by the functions $v = v(t)$ and $v_{\omega_S} = v_{\omega_S}(t)$.

In order to do this we first we evaluate the following commutators

$$[(\overset{2}{\frac{d}{dt}} + \mathfrak{L}(\overset{2}{t})), \boldsymbol{v}] \quad \text{and} \quad [(\overset{2}{\frac{d}{dt}} + \mathfrak{L}(\overset{2}{t})), \boldsymbol{v}_{\omega_S}].$$

For the commutator $[(\overset{2}{\frac{d}{dt}} + \mathfrak{L}(\overset{2}{t})), \boldsymbol{v}]$ we have the following expression

$$\begin{aligned}
&[(\frac{d}{dt} + \mathfrak{L}(t)), \boldsymbol{v}] = \\
&\quad [\Big(\frac{d}{dt} + \big(\frac{1}{2}\sigma^2(s,t)\frac{\partial^2}{\partial s^2} + \mu(s,t)\frac{\partial}{\partial s}\big)\Big), \boldsymbol{v}] = \\
&\quad \sigma^2(s,t)\, \boldsymbol{v}_s \frac{\partial}{\partial s} + \big(\boldsymbol{v}_t + \frac{1}{2}\sigma^2(s,t)\, \boldsymbol{v}_{ss} + \mu(s,t)\, \boldsymbol{v}_s\big),
\end{aligned} \tag{7.3}$$

where $\boldsymbol{v}_t = \boldsymbol{v}_t(t)$, $\boldsymbol{v}_{ss} = \boldsymbol{v}_{ss}(t)$ and $\boldsymbol{v}_s = \boldsymbol{v}_s(t)$ stand for the operators of multiplication by the functions $v_t = \frac{\partial}{\partial t} v$, $v_{ss} = \frac{\partial^2}{\partial s^2} v$ and $v_s = \frac{\partial}{\partial s} v$.

For the commutator $[(\overset{2}{\frac{d}{dt}} + \mathfrak{L}(\overset{2}{t})), \boldsymbol{v}_{\omega_S}]$ we have the following expression

$$\begin{aligned}
&[(\overset{2}{\frac{d}{dt}} + \mathfrak{L}(\overset{2}{t})), \boldsymbol{v}_{\omega_S}] = \\
&\quad [\overbrace{\Big(\frac{d}{dt} + \big(\frac{1}{2}\sigma^2(s,t)\frac{\partial^2}{\partial s^2} + \mu(s,t)\frac{\partial}{\partial s}\big)\Big)}^{2}, \boldsymbol{v}_{\omega_S}] = \\
&\quad [\overbrace{\Big(\frac{d}{dt} + \big(\frac{1}{2}\sigma^2(s,t)\frac{\partial^2}{\partial s^2} + \mu(s,t)\frac{\partial}{\partial s}\big)\Big)}^{2}, e^{-\int_{\overset{1}{(t)}}^{\overset{3}{(t)}} d(\overset{3}{s},\tau)d\tau}\, \overset{1}{s}] = \\
&\quad \sigma^2(s,t)\, \frac{\partial}{\partial s} + \big(d(s,t)\, s + \mu(s,t)\big),
\end{aligned} \tag{7.4}$$

where we have used the same notation for the operator $\boldsymbol{d}(s,t)$ of multiplication by the function $d(s,t)$ and for the function $d(s,t)$ itself.

Now we are ready to evaluate the double commutators

$$[[(\overset{2}{\frac{d}{dt}} + \mathfrak{L}(\overset{2}{t})), \boldsymbol{v}], \boldsymbol{u}'(\overset{3}{t}, \overset{1}{t})] \quad \text{and} \quad [[(\overset{2}{\frac{d}{dt}} + \mathfrak{L}(\overset{2}{t})), \boldsymbol{v}_{\omega S}], \boldsymbol{u}'(\overset{3}{t}, \overset{1}{t})].$$

For the double commutator $[[(\overset{2}{\tfrac{d}{dt}} + \mathfrak{L}(\overset{2}{t})), \boldsymbol{v}], \boldsymbol{u}'(\overset{3}{t}, \overset{1}{t})]$ with the help of expression (7.3) we have the following expression

$$[[(\overset{2}{\frac{d}{dt}} + \mathfrak{L}(\overset{2}{t})), \boldsymbol{v}], \boldsymbol{u}'(\overset{3}{t}, \overset{1}{t})] =$$

$$[[\overbrace{\Big(\frac{d}{dt} + \big(\frac{1}{2}\sigma^2(s,t)\frac{\partial^2}{\partial s^2} + \mu(s,t)\frac{\partial}{\partial s}\big)\Big)}^{2}, \boldsymbol{v}], \boldsymbol{u}'(\overset{3}{t}, \overset{1}{t})] = \tag{7.5}$$
$$= \sigma^2(s,t)\boldsymbol{v}_{\boldsymbol{s}}\, \boldsymbol{u}'_{\boldsymbol{s}}(t,t)$$

where $\boldsymbol{u}'_{\boldsymbol{s}}(t,t)$ is the operator on Π of multiplication by the function $u'_s(t,t,s_t,s_t)$ with $u'_s(t,t,s_t,s_t) = \frac{\partial}{\partial s}u'(t,t,s_t,s)|_{s=s_t}$.

For the double commutator $[[(\overset{2}{\tfrac{d}{dt}} + \mathfrak{L}(\overset{2}{t})), \boldsymbol{v}_{\omega S}], \boldsymbol{u}'(\overset{3}{t}, \overset{1}{t})]$ with the help of expression (7.4) we have the following expression

$$[[(\overset{2}{\frac{d}{dt}} + \mathfrak{L}(\overset{2}{t})), \boldsymbol{v}_{\omega S}], \boldsymbol{u}'(\overset{3}{t}, \overset{1}{t})] =$$

$$[[\overbrace{\Big(\frac{d}{dt} + \big(\frac{1}{2}\sigma^2(s,t)\frac{\partial^2}{\partial s^2} + \mu(s,t)\frac{\partial}{\partial s}\big)\Big)}^{2}, \boldsymbol{v}_{\omega S}], \boldsymbol{u}'(\overset{3}{t}, \overset{1}{t})] = \tag{7.6}$$
$$= \sigma^2(s,t)\boldsymbol{u}'_{\boldsymbol{s}}(t,t).$$

Now the equation (6.59) for the operator weight $\boldsymbol{\pi}_v(t,S)$ of the underlying security $\mathfrak{v}_{\omega S}$ in the dynamically replicating portfolio for the European contingent claim $\mathfrak{v}$ in the case under consideration takes the following form

$$\sigma^2(s,t)\boldsymbol{v}_{\boldsymbol{s}}\, \boldsymbol{u}'_{\boldsymbol{s}}(t,t)\,\mathbf{1} = \boldsymbol{\pi}_v(t,S)\,\sigma^2(s,t)\boldsymbol{u}'_{\boldsymbol{s}}(t,t)\,\mathbf{1}, \tag{7.7}$$

where $\mathbf{1}$ is the function in $\Pi(\mathbb{R}^n_{++} \times \mathcal{T})$ identically equal to unity.

Since the preceding equation (7.7) has to hold for all preferences $\boldsymbol{u}'(t,t)$ we conclude that $\boldsymbol{\pi}_v(t,S)$ is equal to $\boldsymbol{v_s} = \boldsymbol{v_s}(t)$:

$$\boldsymbol{\pi}_v(t,S) = \boldsymbol{v_s}(t), \quad t \in \mathcal{T}. \tag{7.8}$$

7.5. Remark. We comment that the uniqueness of the solution in (7.8) of the equation (7.7) for the operator weight $\boldsymbol{\pi}_v(t,S)$ of the underlying security $\mathfrak{v}_{\omega_S}$ in the dynamically replicating portfolio for the European contingent claim $\mathfrak{v}$ in the case under consideration directly follows from the fact that $\sigma^2(s,t) > 0$ is not equal to zero for all s in $\mathbb{R}_{++}$ and t in $\mathcal{T}$.

7.6. Remark. It is clear that the same equation (7.7) for the operator weight $\boldsymbol{\pi}_v(t,S)$ of the underlying security $\mathfrak{v}_{\omega_S}$ in the dynamically replicating portfolio for the European contingent claim $\mathfrak{v}$ can also be obtained from equation (6.60).

7.7. Remark. It is clear that $\boldsymbol{\pi}_v(t,S) = \boldsymbol{\pi}_v(t,\omega_S)$ is nothing but the operator-valued measure of ω_S in Ω.

Now the expression (6.57) for the operator weight $\boldsymbol{\pi}_v(t,B)$ of the pure discount bond $\mathfrak{v}_{\omega_B}$ in the dynamically replicating portfolio for the European contingent claim $\mathfrak{v}$ with the value $v = v(t)$ in the case under consideration takes the following form

$$\begin{aligned} \boldsymbol{\pi}_v(t,B) =& \boldsymbol{v}(t) - \boldsymbol{\pi}_v(t,S)\, \boldsymbol{v}_{\omega_S}(t) = \\ & \boldsymbol{v}(t) - s\, \boldsymbol{v_s}(t), \quad t \in \mathcal{T} \end{aligned} \tag{7.9}$$

where we have used the same notation for the operator of multiplication by the argument s and for argument s itself, and where we have taken into account the fact that the operators $\boldsymbol{v_s} = \boldsymbol{v_s}(t)$ and s commute.

7.8. Remark. According to Remark (6.72) define for ω_B and ω_S in $\Omega = \{\omega_B, \omega_S\}$ and for each t in $\mathcal{T}$ the linear operators

$$\hat{\pi}(t,B) = \hat{\pi}(t,\omega_B) : \Pi \to \Pi$$

and

$$\hat{\pi}(t,S) = \hat{\pi}(t,\omega_S) : \Pi \to \Pi$$

by

$$\hat{\pi}(t,B)\,v = \pi_v(t,B)$$

and

$$\hat{\pi}(t,S)\,v = \pi_v(t,S),$$

where $\pi_v(t,B) = \pi_v(t,\omega_B)$ and $\pi_v(t,S) = \pi_v(t,\omega_S)$ are the Π-valued measures of ω_B and ω_S in Ω associated as in Remark (6.41) with the operator-valued measures, or equivalently operator weights $\boldsymbol{\pi}_v(t,B) = \boldsymbol{\pi}_v(t,\omega_B)$ and $\boldsymbol{\pi}_v(t,S) = \boldsymbol{\pi}_v(t,\omega_S)$ of the European contingent claims $\mathfrak{v}_{\omega_B}$ and $\mathfrak{v}_{\omega_S}$ in the dynamically replicating portfolio for the European contingent claim $\mathfrak{v}$ with the value $v = v(t)$. In the case under consideration $\boldsymbol{\pi}_v(t,B)$ and $\boldsymbol{\pi}_v(t,S)$ are the linear operators on Π of multiplication by the functions $\pi_v(t,B)$ and $\pi_v(t,S)$ in Π.

It is clear that due to relations (7.9) and (7.8) the linear operators $\hat{\pi}(t,B)$ and $\hat{\pi}(t,S)$ on Π are explicitly given by

$$\hat{\pi}(t,B) = \boldsymbol{I} - s\,\frac{\partial}{\partial s}$$

and

$$\hat{\pi}(t,S) = \frac{\partial}{\partial s},$$

where $\boldsymbol{I}$ is the identity operator on Π. It is also clear that the linear operators $\hat{\pi}(t,B)$ and $\hat{\pi}(t,S)$ on Π and linear operators on Π of multiplication by functions in Π do not commute in general. Indeed

$$[\hat{\pi}(t,B), h] = -s\,h_s$$

and

$$[\hat{\pi}(t,S), h] = h_s$$

where we have used the same notations for the operators on Π of multiplication by the functions $h = h(s)$ and $h_s = \frac{\partial}{\partial s}h(s)$ in Π and for the functions $h = h(s)$ and $h_s = \frac{\partial}{\partial s}h(s)$ in Π themselves, and where the function h in Π is assumed to be sufficiently smooth in an appropriate sense. In this regard we note that the linear operators $\hat{\pi}(t, B)$, $\hat{\pi}(t, S)$, s and $\boldsymbol{I}$ on Π generate a Lie algebra with the nonzero structure constants determined by

$$[\hat{\pi}(t, B), \hat{\pi}(t, S)] = \hat{\pi}(t, S),$$

$$[\hat{\pi}(t, B), s] = -s$$

and

$$[\hat{\pi}(t, S), s] = \boldsymbol{I},$$

where we have used the same notation for the operator on Π of multiplication by the argument s and for the argument s itself. Finally we note that it is this noncommutativity of the linear operator $\hat{\pi}(t, S)$ on Π and hence $\hat{\pi}(t, B)$ on Π and linear operators on Π of multiplication by arbitrary admissible functions in Π that is, in the essence, financially responsible for the randomness of the prices of the underlying securities, that is, for the first quantization in finance in the case under consideration. This issue will be presented in detail in forthcoming articles.

With the operator weights $\boldsymbol{\pi}_v(t, B)$ and $\boldsymbol{\pi}_v(t, S)$ of the pure discount bond $\mathfrak{v}_{\omega_B}$ and the underlying security $\mathfrak{v}_{\omega_S}$ in the dynamically replicating portfolio for the European contingent claim $\mathfrak{v}$ defined as in relations (7.9) and (7.8), the evolution equation (6.61) in the case under consideration, with the help of relations (7.3) and (7.4), takes the following form

$$\begin{aligned}\left(\sigma^2(s,t)\,\boldsymbol{v}_s\,\frac{\partial}{\partial s} + \left(\boldsymbol{v}_t + \frac{1}{2}\sigma^2(s,t)\,\boldsymbol{v}_{ss} + \mu(s,t)\,\boldsymbol{v}_s\right)\right)\mathbf{1} = \\ \boldsymbol{v}_s\left(\sigma^2(s,t)\,\frac{\partial}{\partial s} + \left(d(s,t)\,s + \mu(s,t)\right)\right)\mathbf{1} + \\ (\boldsymbol{v} - s\,\boldsymbol{v}_s)r(s,t),\end{aligned} \tag{7.10}$$

where $\mathbf{1}$ is the function in $\Pi(\mathbb{R}^n_{++} \times \mathcal{T})$ identically equal to unity.

Now the evolution equation (6.63) in the case under consideration takes the following form

$$\begin{aligned} \Big(\frac{d}{dt} + \big(\frac{1}{2}\sigma^2(s,t)\frac{\partial^2}{\partial s^2} + \mu(s,t)\frac{\partial}{\partial s}\big)\Big)\, v = \\ \boldsymbol{v_s}\left(d(s,t)\, s + \mu(s,t)\right)\Big) + \\ (\boldsymbol{v} - s\,\boldsymbol{v_s})r(s,t). \end{aligned} \tag{7.11}$$

Finally with the help of simple algebra the preceding evolution equation (7.11) can be rewritten as follows

$$\begin{aligned} \frac{d}{dt}\, v + \frac{1}{2}\sigma^2(s,t)\, \frac{\partial^2}{\partial s^2}\, v + \\ \big(r(s,t) - d(s,t)\big)\, s\, \frac{\partial}{\partial s}\, v - r(s,t)\, v = 0, \end{aligned} \tag{7.12}$$

or equivalently

$$\begin{aligned} \frac{d}{dt}\, v + \frac{1}{2}\hat{\sigma}^2(s,t)\, s^2\, \frac{\partial^2}{\partial s^2}\, v + \\ \big(r(s,t) - d(s,t)\big)\, s\, \frac{\partial}{\partial s}\, v - r(s,t)\, v = 0, \end{aligned} \tag{7.13}$$

where $\hat{\sigma}(s,t)\, s = \sigma(s,t)$.

We make the following observation, which is crucial from the financial standpoint. The preceding evolution equation (7.13) is nothing but the Black and Scholes equation (5.50).

7.9. Remark. We comment that the time derivative $\frac{d}{dt}$ in the evolution equation (7.12), or equivalently (7.13) can be interpreted as the partial time derivative $\frac{\partial}{\partial t}$.

7.10. Remark. It was solely for the purpose of illustration that we started the derivation of the evolution equation (7.12), or equivalently (7.13) with the evolution equation (7.10) and not with the evolution equation (7.11).

7.11. Remark. To the best of our knowledge the presented derivation of the Black and Scholes equation (5.50) in seed form was encountered by Garman in his pioneering work [22].

7.12. Remark. As we have seen in Section (5) the behavior of the generator $\mathfrak{L}(t)$ of the form (5.1) under the transformations $\hat{g}$ defined in (3.99) in the form (3.107) from the beliefs-preferences gauge symmetry group $\hat{\mathcal{G}}$ for a Markovian market populace $\mathbb{H} = \mathbb{B} \times \mathbb{U}$, or more precisely $\mathbb{H} = \mathbb{L} \times \mathbb{U}$ can be characterized solely in terms of the drift $\mu(s,t)$ as given by (5.12). Moreover, due to Section (6) the value v of the European contingent claim $\mathfrak{v}$ determined by the evolution equation (6.63) rewritten as (7.11), or equivalently as (7.12) or (7.13) in the case under consideration remains unchanged under the action of the group $G \times H$ defined in (6.42), that is, v is independent of the beliefs and preferences of Markovian market participants $\mathcal{H} = (\mathcal{B}, \mathcal{U})$ in the orbit of the beliefs-preferences gauge symmetry group $\hat{\mathcal{G}}$ in $\mathbb{H} = \mathbb{B} \times \mathbb{U}$, or more precisely $\mathcal{H} = (\mathfrak{L}, \mathcal{U})$ in the orbit of the beliefs-preferences gauge symmetry group $\hat{\mathcal{G}}$ in $\mathbb{H} = \mathbb{L} \times \mathbb{U}$. That is why the value v of the European contingent claim $\mathfrak{v}$ determined by the evolution equation (7.11) rewritten as (7.12) or (7.13), or equivalently by the Black and Scholes equation (5.50), does not depend on the drift $\mu(s,t)$ which, in turn, characterizes the belief $\mathcal{B}$ of a Markovian market participant $\mathcal{H} = (\mathcal{B}, \mathcal{U})$ in the orbit of the beliefs-preferences gauge symmetry group $\hat{\mathcal{G}}$ in $\mathbb{H} = \mathbb{B} \times \mathbb{U}$, or more precisely $\mathcal{H} = (\mathfrak{L}, \mathcal{U})$ in the orbit of the beliefs-preferences gauge symmetry group $\hat{\mathcal{G}}$ in $\mathbb{H} = \mathbb{L} \times \mathbb{U}$ under consideration.

7.2 The Case of a Multiple Underlying Security

Now we consider the dynamic replication of European contingent claims based on the beliefs-preferences gauge symmetry group $\hat{\mathcal{G}}$ for the Markovian market populace $\mathbb{H} = \mathbb{B} \times \mathbb{U}$, or more precisely $\mathbb{H} = \mathbb{L} \times \mathbb{U}$ in the general case of n underlying securities and when each belief $\mathcal{B}$ in the market populace belief

$\mathbb{B}$ is generated by the family

$$\mathfrak{L} = \{\mathfrak{L}(t) : \Pi \to \Pi \,|\, t \in \mathcal{T}\},$$

in $\mathbb{L}$ with each generator $\mathfrak{L}(t)$ at time t is of the form (5.54).

We need the following assumption, which is natural from the financial standpoint, about the nature of the set $\{\mathfrak{v}_\omega : \omega \in \Omega\}$ of European contingent claims that dynamically replicates a given European contingent claim $\mathfrak{v}$.

We suppose that in addition to the pure discount bond $\mathfrak{v}_{\omega_B}$ with inception time t, maturity time T and with the face value of one unit of account with t and T in $\mathcal{T}$ and $t \leq T$, the underlying securities themselves are traded at each time t in $\mathcal{T}$. Then, for each t and T in $\mathcal{T}$ with $t \leq T$ and for each European contingent claim $\mathfrak{v}$ with inception time t, expiration time T and payoff v_T we assume that the set $\{\mathfrak{v}_\omega : \omega \in \Omega\}$ of European contingent claims that dynamically replicates $\mathfrak{v}$ consists of the pure discount bond $\mathfrak{v}_{\omega_B}$ and the underlying securities $\mathfrak{v}_{\omega_{S_k}}$ with $k = 1, \ldots, n$ themselves. That is, we assume that the set Ω consists of $n+1$ elements ω_B and ω_{S_k} with $k = 1, \ldots, n$ and is equipped with the standard sigma algebra. We comment that we view each underlying security $\mathfrak{v}_{\omega_{S_k}}$ as the European contingent claim with inception time t, expiration time T and payoff $v_T^{\omega_{S_k}}$ such that $v_T^{\omega_{S_k}}(s_T) = s_T^k$ with t and T in $\mathcal{T}$ and $t \leq T$.

7.13. Remark. Later in this Subsection we will show that the assumption we have made about the nature of the set of European contingent claims that dynamically replicates a given European contingent claim is correct. More precisely, we will show that in the case under consideration, for each t and T in $\mathcal{T}$ with $t \leq T$ and for each European contingent claim $\mathfrak{v}$ with inception time t, expiration time T and payoff v_T, the set $\{\mathfrak{v}_\omega : \omega \in \Omega\}$ of European contingent claims that dynamically replicates $\mathfrak{v}$ can, in fact, be taken to consist of the pure discount bond $\mathfrak{v}_{\omega_B}$ and the underlying securities $\mathfrak{v}_{\omega_{S_k}}$ with $k = 1, \ldots, n$ themselves.

The value $v_{\omega_{S_k}}$ of the underlying security $\mathfrak{v}_{\omega_{S_k}}$ with $k =$

$1,\ldots,n$ is the solution of the Cauchy problem (6.45), that is:

$$\frac{\overset{2}{d}}{dt}\boldsymbol{u}'(\overset{3}{t},\overset{1}{t})\, v_{\omega s_k} + \boldsymbol{\mathfrak{L}}(\overset{2}{t})\, \boldsymbol{u}'(\overset{3}{t},\overset{1}{t})\, v_{\omega s_k} = 0, \quad t < T,$$
$$v_{\omega s_k}(T) = v_T^{\omega s_k}. \tag{7.14}$$

At the same time the value $v_{\omega s_k}$ of the underlying security $\mathfrak{v}_{\omega s_k}$ with $k = 1,\ldots,n$ as a European contingent claim incepted at time t and expiring at time T an instant later is formally given by

$$v_{\omega s_k} = e^{-\int_{\overset{1}{(t)}}^{\overset{3}{(t)}} d_k(\overset{3}{s}_t,\tau)d\tau}\, s_t^k$$

so that the evolution equation in (7.14) can be rewritten as follows

$$\Big(\frac{\overset{2}{d}}{dt} + \boldsymbol{\mathfrak{L}}(\overset{2}{t})\Big)\, \boldsymbol{u}'(\overset{3}{t},\overset{1}{t})\, e^{-\int_{\overset{1}{(t)}}^{\overset{3}{(t)}} d_k(\overset{3}{s},\tau)d\tau}\, \overset{1}{s}_k \mathbf{1} = 0,$$

or equivalently

$$\Big(\frac{\overset{2}{d}}{dt} + \boldsymbol{\mathfrak{L}}(\overset{2}{t})\Big)\, \boldsymbol{u}'(\overset{3}{t},\overset{1}{t})\, s_k \mathbf{1} + d_k(s,t)\, s_k = 0, \tag{7.15}$$

where each $\boldsymbol{d}_k(s,t)$ is the operator of multiplication by the function $d_k(s,t)$, $\mathbf{1}$ is the function in $\Pi(\mathbb{R}^n_{++} \times \mathcal{T})$ identically equal to unity, and where the indexes over the operators indicate the order in which these operators act.

7.14. Remark. We comment that each $\overset{1}{s}_k$ is the operator on Π of multiplication by the argument s_k, that is, by the function $h(s) = s_k$ in Π. We also comment that each $\overset{1}{s}_k$ can be interpreted as an operator on $\Pi(\mathbb{R}^n_{++} \times \mathcal{T})$ in the standard way as indicated in Remark (6.50).

7.15. Remark. In terms of the underlying securities being stocks, $d_k(s_t,t)$ with $k = 1,\ldots,n$ is the continuously compounded dividend yield of the k-th stock.

7.16. Remark. It is clear that the evolution equation (7.15) remains true in the general case of the generator $\mathfrak{L}(t)$ in $\mathfrak{L}$ from $\mathbb{L}$ not necessarily of the form (5.54).

In order to obtain the explicit form of the equation (6.59) for the operator weights $\boldsymbol{\pi}_v(t, S_k) = \boldsymbol{\pi}_v(t, \omega_{S_k})$ of the underlying security $\mathfrak{v}_{\omega_{S_k}}$ with $k = 1, \ldots, n$ in the dynamically replicating portfolio for the European contingent claim $\mathfrak{v}$ with value v in the case under consideration we need to evaluate the following double commutators

$$[[(\overset{2}{\frac{d}{dt}} + \mathfrak{L}(\overset{2}{t})), \boldsymbol{v}], \boldsymbol{u}'(\overset{3}{t}, \overset{1}{t})] \quad \text{and} \quad [[(\overset{2}{\frac{d}{dt}} + \mathfrak{L}(\overset{2}{t})), \boldsymbol{v}_{\omega_{S_k}}], \boldsymbol{u}'(\overset{3}{t}, \overset{1}{t})],$$

where $\boldsymbol{v} = \boldsymbol{v}(t)$ and $\boldsymbol{v}_{\omega_{S_k}} = \boldsymbol{v}_{\omega_{S_k}}(t)$ with $k = 1, \ldots, n$ are the operators of multiplication by the functions v and $v_{\omega_{S_k}}$.

In order to do this we first we evaluate the following commutators

$$[(\overset{2}{\frac{d}{dt}} + \mathfrak{L}(\overset{2}{t})), \boldsymbol{v}] \quad \text{and} \quad [(\overset{2}{\frac{d}{dt}} + \mathfrak{L}(\overset{2}{t})), \boldsymbol{v}_{\omega_{S_k}}].$$

For the commutator $[(\overset{2}{\frac{d}{dt}} + \mathfrak{L}(\overset{2}{t})), \boldsymbol{v}]$ we have the following expression

$$\begin{aligned}
&[(\frac{d}{dt} + \mathfrak{L}(t)), \boldsymbol{v}] = \\
&[\Big(\frac{d}{dt} + \big(\frac{1}{2}\sum_{i,j=1}^{n} \sigma_{ij}^2(s,t)\frac{\partial^2}{\partial s_i \partial s_j} + \sum_{i=1}^{n} \mu_i(s,t)\frac{\partial}{\partial s_i}\big)\Big), \boldsymbol{v}] = \\
&\sum_{i=1}^{n}\big(\sum_{j=1}^{n} \sigma_{ij}^2(s,t)\, \boldsymbol{v}_{s_j}\big)\, \frac{\partial}{\partial s_i} + \qquad (7.16) \\
&\qquad (\boldsymbol{v}_t + \frac{1}{2}\sum_{i,j=1}^{n} \sigma_{ij}^2(s,t)\, \boldsymbol{v}_{s_i s_j} + \sum_{i=1}^{n} \mu_i(s,t)\, \boldsymbol{v}_{s_i}),
\end{aligned}$$

where $\boldsymbol{v}_t = \boldsymbol{v}_t(t)$, $\boldsymbol{v}_{s_i s_j} = \boldsymbol{v}_{s_i s_j}(t)$ and $\boldsymbol{v}_{s_i} = \boldsymbol{v}_{s_i}(t)$ stand for the operators of multiplication by the functions $v_t = \frac{\partial}{\partial t} v$, $v_{s_i s_j} = \frac{\partial^2}{\partial s_i \partial s_j} v$ and $v_{s_i} = \frac{\partial}{\partial s_i} v$.

For the commutator $[(\overset{2}{\frac{d}{dt}} + \mathfrak{L}(\overset{2}{t})), \boldsymbol{v}_{\omega s_k}]$ we have the following expression

$$
\begin{aligned}
&[(\overset{2}{\frac{d}{dt}} + \mathfrak{L}(\overset{2}{t})), \boldsymbol{v}_{\omega s_k}] = \\
&[\overbrace{\Big(\frac{d}{dt} + \big(\frac{1}{2}\sum_{i,j=1}^{n} \sigma_{ij}^2(s,t) \frac{\partial^2}{\partial s_i \partial s_j} + \sum_{i=1}^{n} \mu_i(s,t)\frac{\partial}{\partial s_i}\big)\Big)}^{2}, \boldsymbol{v}_{\omega s_k}] = \\
&[\overbrace{\Big(\frac{d}{dt} + \big(\frac{1}{2}\sum_{i,j=1}^{n} \sigma_{ij}^2(s,t) \frac{\partial^2}{\partial s_i \partial s_j} + \sum_{i=1}^{n} \mu_i(s,t)\frac{\partial}{\partial s_i}\big)\Big)}^{2}, \\
&\qquad\qquad e^{-\int_{\overset{1}{t}}^{\overset{3}{t}} d_k(\overset{3}{s},\tau)d\tau} \, \overset{1}{s_k}] = \\
&\sum_{i=1}^{n} \sigma_{ik}^2(s,t) \frac{\partial}{\partial s_i} + \big(d_k(s,t)\, s_k + \mu_k(s,t)\big),
\end{aligned}
\tag{7.17}
$$

where we have used the same notation for the operator $\boldsymbol{d}_k(s,t)$ of multiplication by the function $d_k(s,t)$ and for the function $d_k(s,t)$ itself.

Now we are ready to evaluate the double commutators

$$
[[(\overset{2}{\frac{d}{dt}} + \mathfrak{L}(\overset{2}{t})), \boldsymbol{v}], \boldsymbol{u}'(\overset{3}{t}, \overset{1}{t})] \quad \text{and} \quad [[(\overset{2}{\frac{d}{dt}} + \mathfrak{L}(\overset{2}{t})), \boldsymbol{v}_{\omega s_k}], \boldsymbol{u}'(\overset{3}{t}, \overset{1}{t})].
$$

For the double commutator $[[(\overset{2}{\frac{d}{dt}} + \mathfrak{L}(\overset{2}{t})), \boldsymbol{v}], \boldsymbol{u}'(\overset{3}{t}, \overset{1}{t})]$ with the help of expression (7.16) we have the following expression

$$[[(\overset{2}{\frac{d}{dt}} + \mathfrak{L}(\overset{2}{t})), \boldsymbol{v}], \boldsymbol{u}'(\overset{3}{t}, \overset{1}{t})] =$$

$$[[\overbrace{\Big(\frac{d}{dt} + \big(\frac{1}{2}\sum_{i,j=1}^{n} \sigma_{ij}^2(s,t)\frac{\partial^2}{\partial s_i \partial s_j} + \sum_{i=1}^{n} \mu_i(s,t)\frac{\partial}{\partial s_i}\big)\Big)}^{2}, \boldsymbol{v}], \tag{7.18}$$

$$\boldsymbol{u}'(\overset{3}{t}, \overset{1}{t})] =$$

$$\sum_{i,j=1}^{n} \sigma_{ij}^2(s,t)\boldsymbol{v}_{s_i}\, \boldsymbol{u}'_{s_j}(t,t)$$

where $\boldsymbol{u}'_{s_i}(t,t)$ is the operator on Π of multiplication by the function $u'_{s_i}(t,t,s_t,s_t)$ with $u'_{s_i}(t,t,s_t,s_t) = \frac{\partial}{\partial s_i}u'(t,t,s_t,s)|_{s=s_t}$.

For the double commutator $[[(\overset{2}{\frac{d}{dt}} + \mathfrak{L}(\overset{2}{t})), \boldsymbol{v}_{\omega S_k}], \boldsymbol{u}'(\overset{3}{t}, \overset{1}{t})]$ with the help of expression (7.17) we have the following expression

$$[[(\overset{2}{\frac{d}{dt}} + \mathfrak{L}(\overset{2}{t})), \boldsymbol{v}_{\omega S_k}], \boldsymbol{u}'(\overset{3}{t}, \overset{1}{t})] =$$

$$[[\overbrace{\Big(\frac{d}{dt} + \big(\frac{1}{2}\sum_{i,j=1}^{n} \sigma_{ij}^2(s,t)\frac{\partial^2}{\partial s_i \partial s_j} + \sum_{i=1}^{n} \mu_i(s,t)\frac{\partial}{\partial s_i}\big)\Big)}^{2}, \boldsymbol{v}_{\omega S_k}], \tag{7.19}$$

$$\boldsymbol{u}'(\overset{3}{t}, \overset{1}{t})] =$$

$$\sum_{j=1}^{n} \sigma_{kj}^2(s,t)\boldsymbol{u}'_{s_j}(t,t).$$

7.17. Remark. It is clear that in the derivation of expressions (7.18) and (7.19) we have made use of the symmetricity of the matrix $\sigma^2(s,t)$ with entries $\sigma_{ij}^2(s,t)$.

Now the equation (6.59) for the operator weights $\boldsymbol{\pi}_v(t, S_k)$ of the underlying securities $\mathfrak{v}_{\omega S_k}$ with $k = 1, \ldots, n$ in the dynamically replicating portfolio for the European contingent claim $\mathfrak{v}$

in the case under consideration takes the following form

$$\sum_{i,j=1}^{n} \sigma_{ij}^2(s,t)\boldsymbol{v}_{s_i}\,\boldsymbol{u}'_{s_j}(t,t)\,\mathbf{1} = \sum_{k=1}^{n} \boldsymbol{\pi}_v(t,S_k) \sum_{j=1}^{n} \sigma_{kj}^2(s,t)\boldsymbol{u}'_{s_j}(t,t)\,\mathbf{1}, \tag{7.20}$$

where $\mathbf{1}$ is the function in $\Pi(\mathbb{R}^n_{++} \times \mathcal{T})$ identically equal to unity.

Since the preceding equation (7.20) has to hold for all preferences $\boldsymbol{u}'(t,t)$ we conclude that $\boldsymbol{\pi}_v(t,S_k)$ is equal to $\boldsymbol{v}_{s_k} = \boldsymbol{v}_{s_k}(t)$:

$$\boldsymbol{\pi}_v(t,S_k) = \boldsymbol{v}_{s_k}(t), \quad t \in \mathcal{T}. \tag{7.21}$$

7.18. Remark. We comment that the uniqueness of the solution in (7.21) of the equation (7.20) for the operator weights $\boldsymbol{\pi}_v(t,S_k)$ of the underlying securities $\mathfrak{v}_{\omega_{S_k}}$ with $k = 1,\ldots,n$ in the dynamically replicating portfolio for the European contingent claim $\mathfrak{v}$ in the case under consideration directly follows from the fact that the positively defined matrix $\sigma^2(s,t)$ is not degenerate for all s in $\mathbb{R}^n_{++}$ and t in $\mathcal{T}$.

7.19. Remark. It is clear that the same equation (7.20) for the operator weight $\boldsymbol{\pi}_v(t,S_k)$ of the underlying security $\mathfrak{v}_{\omega_{S_k}}$ with $k = 1,\ldots,n$ in the dynamically replicating portfolio for the European contingent claim $\mathfrak{v}$ can also be obtained from equation (6.60).

7.20. Remark. It is clear that $\boldsymbol{\pi}_v(t,S_k) = \boldsymbol{\pi}_v(t,\omega_{S_k})$ is nothing but the operator-valued measure of ω_{S_k} in Ω with $k = 1,\ldots,n$.

Now the expression (6.57) for the operator weight $\boldsymbol{\pi}_v(t,B)$ of the pure discount bond $\mathfrak{v}_{\omega_B}$ in the dynamically replicating portfolio for the European contingent claim $\mathfrak{v}$ with the value $v = v(t)$ in the case under consideration takes the following form

$$\begin{aligned}\boldsymbol{\pi}_v(t,B) =& \boldsymbol{v}(t) - \sum_{k=1}^{n} \boldsymbol{\pi}_v(t,S_k)\,\boldsymbol{v}_{\omega_{S_k}}(t) = \\ & \boldsymbol{v}(t) - \sum_{k=1}^{n} s_k\,\boldsymbol{v}_{s_k}(t), \quad t \in \mathcal{T},\end{aligned} \tag{7.22}$$

where we have used the same notation for the operator of multiplication by the argument s_k and for the argument s_k itself, and where we have taken into account the fact that the operators $\boldsymbol{v}_{s_k} = \boldsymbol{v}_{s_k}(t)$ and s_k commute.

7.21. Remark. According to Remark (6.72), define for ω_B and ω_{S_k} with $k = 1, \ldots, n$ in

$$\Omega = \{\omega_B, \omega_{S_1}, \ldots, \omega_{S_n}\}$$

and for each t in $\mathcal{T}$ the linear operators

$$\hat{\pi}(t, B) = \hat{\pi}(t, \omega_B) : \Pi \to \Pi$$

and

$$\hat{\pi}(t, S_k) = \hat{\pi}(t, \omega_{S_k}) : \Pi \to \Pi$$

by

$$\hat{\pi}(t, B)\, v = \pi_v(t, B)$$

and

$$\hat{\pi}(t, S_k)\, v = \pi_v(t, S_k),$$

where $\pi_v(t, B) = \pi_v(t, \omega_B)$ and $\pi_v(t, S_k) = \pi_v(t, \omega_{S_k})$ are the Π-valued measures of ω_B and ω_{S_k} in Ω associated as in Remark (6.41) with the operator-valued measures, or equivalently operator weights $\boldsymbol{\pi}_v(t, B) = \boldsymbol{\pi}_v(t, \omega_B)$ and $\boldsymbol{\pi}_v(t, S_k) = \boldsymbol{\pi}_v(t, \omega_{S_k})$ of the European contingent claims $\mathfrak{v}_{\omega_B}$ and $\mathfrak{v}_{\omega_{S_k}}$ in the dynamically replicating portfolio for the European contingent claim $\mathfrak{v}$ with the value $v = v(t)$. In the case under consideration $\boldsymbol{\pi}_v(t, B)$ and $\boldsymbol{\pi}_v(t, S_k)$ are the linear operators on Π of multiplication by the functions $\pi_v(t, B)$ and $\pi_v(t, S_k)$ in Π.

It is clear that due to relations (7.22) and (7.21) the linear operators $\hat{\pi}(t, B)$ and $\hat{\pi}(t, S_k)$ on Π are explicitly given by

$$\hat{\pi}(t, B) = \boldsymbol{I} - \sum_{k=1}^{n} s_k \frac{\partial}{\partial s_k}$$

and

$$\hat{\pi}(t, S_k) = \frac{\partial}{\partial s_k},$$

where $\boldsymbol{I}$ is the identity operator on Π. It is also clear that the linear operators $\hat{\pi}(t, B)$ and $\hat{\pi}(t, S_k)$ on Π and linear operators on Π of multiplication by functions in Π do not commute in general. Indeed

$$[\hat{\pi}(t, B), h] = -\sum_{k=1}^{n} s_k\, h_{s_k}$$

and

$$[\hat{\pi}(t, S_k), h] = h_{s_k}$$

where we have used the same notations for the operators on Π of multiplication by the functions $h = h(s)$ and $h_{s_k} = \frac{\partial}{\partial s_k} h(s)$ in Π and for the functions $h = h(s)$ and $h_{s_k} = \frac{\partial}{\partial s_k} h(s)$ in Π themselves, and where the function h in Π is assumed to be sufficiently smooth in an appropriate sense. In this regard we note that the linear operators $\hat{\pi}(t, B)$, $\hat{\pi}(t, S_k)$, s_k and $\boldsymbol{I}$ on Π with $k = 1, \ldots, n$ generate a Lie algebra with the nonzero structure constants determined by

$$[\hat{\pi}(t, B), \hat{\pi}(t, S_k)] = \hat{\pi}(t, S_k),$$

$$[\hat{\pi}(t, B), s_k] = -s_k$$

and

$$[\hat{\pi}(t, S_k), s_k] = \boldsymbol{I},$$

where we have used the same notation for the operator on Π of multiplication by the argument s_k and for the argument s_k itself. Finally, we note that it is this noncommutativity of the linear operators $\hat{\pi}(t, S_k)$ on Π with $k = 1, \ldots, n$ and hence $\hat{\pi}(t, B)$ on Π and linear operators on Π of multiplication by arbitrary admissible functions in Π that is, in the essence, financially responsible for the randomness of the prices of the underlying securities, that is, for the first quantization in finance in the case under consideration. This issue will be presented in detail in forthcoming articles.

With the operator weights $\boldsymbol{\pi}_v(t, B)$ and $\boldsymbol{\pi}_v(t, S_k)$ of the pure discount bond $\mathfrak{v}_{\omega_B}$ and the underlying securities $\mathfrak{v}_{\omega_{S_k}}$ with $k = 1, \ldots, n$ in the dynamically replicating portfolio for the European contingent claim $\mathfrak{v}$ defined as in relations (7.22) and (7.21) the evolution equation (6.61) in the case under consideration, with the help of relations (7.16) and (7.17), takes the following form

$$\begin{aligned}
&\Big(\sum_{i=1}^{n}\big(\sum_{j=1}^{n}\sigma_{ij}^2(s,t)\,\boldsymbol{v}_{s_j}\big)\,\frac{\partial}{\partial s_i}+\\
&\qquad\Big(\boldsymbol{v}_t+\frac{1}{2}\sum_{i,j=1}^{n}\sigma_{ij}^2(s,t)\,\boldsymbol{v}_{s_i s_j}+\sum_{i=1}^{n}\mu_i(s,t)\,\boldsymbol{v}_{s_i}\big)\Big)\mathbf{1}=\\
&\sum_{k=1}^{n}\boldsymbol{v}_{s_k}\Big(\sum_{i=1}^{n}\sigma_{ik}^2(s,t)\,\frac{\partial}{\partial s_i}+\big(d_k(s,t)\,s_k+\mu_k(s,t)\big)\Big)\mathbf{1}+\\
&\qquad\big(\boldsymbol{v}-\sum_{k=1}^{n}s_k\,\boldsymbol{v}_{s_k}\big)r(s,t),
\end{aligned}\tag{7.23}$$

where $\mathbf{1}$ is the function in $\Pi(\mathbb{R}^n_{++}\times\mathcal{T})$ identically equal to unity.

Now the evolution equation (6.63) in the case under consideration takes the following form

$$\begin{aligned}
&\Big(\frac{d}{dt}+\big(\frac{1}{2}\sum_{i,j=1}^{n}\sigma_{ij}^2(s,t)\frac{\partial^2}{\partial s_i\partial s_j}+\sum_{i=1}^{n}\mu_i(s,t)\frac{\partial}{\partial s_i}\big)\Big)\,v=\\
&\qquad\sum_{k=1}^{n}\boldsymbol{v}_{s_k}\,\big(d_k(s,t)\,s_k+\mu_k(s,t)\big)\Big)+\\
&\qquad\qquad\big(\boldsymbol{v}-\sum_{k=1}^{n}s_k\,\boldsymbol{v}_{s_k}\big)r(s,t).
\end{aligned}\tag{7.24}$$

Finally with the help of simple algebra the preceding evolution equation (7.24) can be rewritten as follows

$$\frac{d}{dt}\,v + \frac{1}{2}\sum_{i,j=1}^{n} \sigma_{ij}^2(s,t)\,\frac{\partial^2}{\partial s_i \partial s_j}\,v + \sum_{i=1}^{n}\big(r(s,t) - d_i(s,t)\big)\,s_i\,\frac{\partial}{\partial s_i}\,v - r(s,t)\,v = 0, \tag{7.25}$$

or equivalently

$$\frac{d}{dt}\,v + \frac{1}{2}\sum_{i,j=1}^{n} \hat{\sigma}_{ij}^2(s,t)\,s_i s_j\,\frac{\partial^2}{\partial s_i \partial s_j}\,v + \sum_{i=1}^{n}\big(r(s,t) - d_i(s,t)\big)\,s_i\,\frac{\partial}{\partial s_i}\,v - r(s,t)\,v = 0, \tag{7.26}$$

where the matrix $\hat{\sigma}^2(s,t)$ with entries $\hat{\sigma}_{ij}^2(s,t)$ is defined in relation (4.22).

We make the following observation, which is crucial from the financial standpoint. The preceding evolution equation (7.26) is nothing but the Black and Scholes equation (5.100).

7.22. Remark. We comment that the time derivative $\frac{d}{dt}$ in the evolution equation (7.25), or equivalently (7.26) can be interpreted as the partial time derivative $\frac{\partial}{\partial t}$.

7.23. Remark. It was solely for the purpose of illustration that we started the derivation of the evolution equation (7.25), or equivalently (7.26) with the evolution equation (7.23) and not with the evolution equation (7.24).

7.24. Remark. As we have seen in Section (5) the behavior of the generator $\mathfrak{L}(t)$ of the form (5.54) under the transformations $\hat{g}$ defined in (3.99) in the form (3.107) from the beliefs-preferences gauge symmetry group $\hat{\mathcal{G}}$ for a Markovian market populace $\mathbb{H} = \mathbb{B} \times \mathbb{U}$, or more precisely $\mathbb{H} = \mathbb{L} \times \mathbb{U}$ can be characterized solely in terms of the drift

$$\mu(s,t) = (\mu_1(s,t), \mu_2(s,t), \ldots, \mu_n(s,t))$$

as given by (5.65). Moreover, due to Section (6) the value v of the European contingent claim $\mathfrak{v}$ determined by the evolution equation (6.63) rewritten as (7.24), or equivalently as (7.25) or (7.26) in the case under consideration remains unchanged under the action of the group $G \times H$ defined in (6.42), that is, v is independent of the beliefs and preferences of Markovian market participants $\mathcal{H} = (\mathcal{B}, \mathcal{U})$ in the orbit of the beliefs-preferences gauge symmetry group $\hat{\mathcal{G}}$ in $\mathbb{H} = \mathbb{B} \times \mathbb{U}$, or more precisely $\mathcal{H} = (\mathfrak{L}, \mathcal{U})$ in the orbit of the beliefs-preferences gauge symmetry group $\hat{\mathcal{G}}$ in $\mathbb{H} = \mathbb{L} \times \mathbb{U}$. That is why the value v of the European contingent claim $\mathfrak{v}$ determined by the evolution equation (7.24) rewritten as (7.25) or (7.26), or equivalently by the Black and Scholes equation (5.100), does not depend on the drift $\mu(s,t)$ which, in turn, characterizes the belief $\mathcal{B}$ of a Markovian market participant $\mathcal{H} = (\mathcal{B}, \mathcal{U})$ in the orbit of the beliefs-preferences gauge symmetry group $\hat{\mathcal{G}}$ in $\mathbb{H} = \mathbb{B} \times \mathbb{U}$, or more precisely $\mathcal{H} = (\mathfrak{L}, \mathcal{U})$ in the orbit of the beliefs-preferences gauge symmetry group $\hat{\mathcal{G}}$ in $\mathbb{H} = \mathbb{L} \times \mathbb{U}$ under consideration.

8 Method of Quasidifferential Operators for an Approximate Dynamic Replication of European Contingent Claims Based on the Beliefs-Preferences Gauge Symmetry Group

In the preceding Sections (6) and (7) we have obtained the equations for operator weights of European contingent claims in the dynamically replicating portfolio for a given European contingent claim and solved these equations explicitly in the particular case of the Markovian market populace with the market populace beliefs determined by diffusion processes. In this Section we devise a method for explicit approximate solution of these equations in the general case of a Markovian market populace with the market populace belief, or more precisely, with the beliefs in the market populace belief generated by the families of arbitrary generators. This method is based on treating these generators as quasidifferential operators introduced by the author in [26], [27], [28], [29], [31], [30], [37], [35] and [36]. As a result the operator weights of European contingent claims in the dynamically replicating portfolio for a given European contingent claim and the dynamically replicating portfolio itself can be found explicitly with any desired level of precision.

8.1 The Concept of a Quasidifferential Operator

Let $\mathfrak{B}_1$ and $\mathfrak{B}_1$ be Banach spaces of complex-valued functions defined on a domain $\Omega \subset \mathbb{R}^n$ and let $Q : \mathfrak{B}_1 \to \mathfrak{B}_1$ be a linear operator whose domain of definition D_Q contains a subset D that is everywhere dense in $\mathfrak{B}_1$.

For each M in $\mathbb{Z}_+$, the set of nonnegative integers, let $Q_M : \mathfrak{B}_1 \to \mathfrak{B}_1$ be a (linear partial) differential operator of order M

of the form

$$Q_M = \sum_{|m|\leq M} q_m(M,\hat{\xi})\left(-i\frac{\partial}{\partial\xi}\right)^m,$$

where $\xi = (\xi_1, \xi_2, \ldots, \xi_n) \in \Omega$, $\hat{\xi} = (\hat{\xi}_1, \hat{\xi}_2, \ldots, \hat{\xi}_n)$ is the vector operator such that each entry $\hat{\xi}_i$ is the operator of multiplication by ξ_i, $q_m(M,\hat{\xi})$ are the operator coefficients with complex-valued symbols $q_m(M,\xi)$, $m = (m_1, m_2, \ldots, m_n)$ in $\mathbb{Z}_+^n$ is a multi-index with $|m| = \sum_{i=1}^n m_i$, and

$$-i\frac{\partial}{\partial\xi} = \left(-i\frac{\partial}{\partial\xi_1}, -i\frac{\partial}{\partial\xi_2}, \ldots, -i\frac{\partial}{\partial\xi_n}\right)$$

is the vector operator so that

$$\left(-i\frac{\partial}{\partial\xi}\right)^m = \left(-i\frac{\partial}{\partial\xi_1}\right)^{m_1}\left(-i\frac{\partial}{\partial\xi_2}\right)^{m_2}\cdots\left(-i\frac{\partial}{\partial\xi_n}\right)^{m_n}.$$

Denote by D_{Q_M} the domain of definition of Q_M and suppose that $D \subset D_{Q_M}$ for all M in $\mathbb{Z}_+$.

Recall that for arbitrary Banach spaces B_1 and B_2 a sequence of linear operators $A_M : B_1 \to B_2$ *converges strongly* to a linear operator $A : B_1 \to B_2$ on $D' \subset B_1$ if:

(i) $D' \subset D_A$ where D_A is the domain of definition of A,

(ii) $D' \subset D_{A_M}$ for all M in $\mathbb{Z}_+$ where D_{A_M} is the domain of definition of A_M, and

(iii) for each x in D' the sequence $A_M x$ converges to Ax in B_2.

On the set of sequences $\{Q_M\}$ we introduce an equivalence relation. Two sequences are equivalent if they converge strongly on D to the same operator Q.

8.1. Definition. The operator Q is called a *quasidifferential operator* (QDO) with *support* D if there exists a sequence of differential operators Q_M converging strongly to Q on D. The equivalence class containing the sequence Q_M is called the *defining sequence* and will be denoted by the same symbol Q_M.

8.2. Definition. We call a quasidifferential operator Q an *analytic quasidifferential operator* if its defining sequence contains a sequence Q_M such that $q_m(M, \hat{\xi})$ with $|m| \leq M$ and M in $\mathbb{Z}_+$ are independent of M.

8.3. Remark. It is clear that an analytic quasidifferential operator Q with support D is a function of the vector operators $\hat{\xi}$ and $-i\frac{\partial}{\partial\xi}$ defined by

$$Q = \sum_{m \in \mathbb{Z}_+^n} q_m(\hat{\xi})\left(-i\frac{\partial}{\partial\xi}\right)^m.$$

8.4. Definition. We call a quasidifferential operator Q a *quasidifferential operator with infinitely smooth coefficients* if its defining sequence contains a sequence Q_M such that each symbol $q_m(M, \xi)$ of $q_m(M, \hat{\xi})$ with $|m| \leq M$ and M in $\mathbb{Z}_+$ is an infinitely differentiable function of ξ in Ω.

8.5. Definition. We call a quasidifferential operator Q an *elliptically defined quasidifferential operator* if its defining sequence contains a sequence Q_M such that each Q_M is an elliptic differential operator.

Now we need the concept of a pseudodifferential operator (see, for example, [54] page 12).

Denote by $C^\infty(\Omega)$ the space of infinitely differentiable complex-valued functions on Ω and by $C_K^\infty(\Omega)$ the space of infinitely differentiable complex-valued functions on Ω with compact support.

Denote by $\hat{u}$ the Fourier image of u in $C_K^\infty(\Omega)$ given by the Fourier transform

$$\hat{u}(\eta) = (2\pi)^{-n} \int_{\mathbb{R}^n} e^{-i\xi\eta} u(\xi) d\xi,$$

with the inverse Fourier transform

$$u(\xi) = \int_{\mathbb{R}^n} e^{i\xi\eta} \hat{u}(\eta) d\eta.$$

8.6. Definition. Let $a = a(\xi, p)$ be an infinitely differentiable function on $\Omega \times \mathbb{R}^n$ such that to every compact subset $\mathcal{K}$ of Ω and to every pair α and β in $\mathbb{Z}^n_+$ there exists a constant $C_{\alpha,\beta}(\mathcal{K}) > 0$ such that

$$|\frac{\partial}{\partial \xi}^{\alpha} \frac{\partial}{\partial p}^{\beta} a(\xi, p)| \leq C_{\alpha,\beta}(\mathcal{K})(1 + |p|)^{q-|\beta|}, \quad \xi \in \mathcal{K},\, p \in \mathbb{R}^n. \tag{8.1}$$

The operator $A : C^\infty_K(\Omega) \to C^\infty(\Omega)$ of the form

$$(A\,u)(\xi) = \int_{\mathbb{R}^n} e^{i\xi p} a(\xi, p)\hat{u}(p)dp \tag{8.2}$$

is called a *standard pseudodifferential operator*, or simply a *pseudodifferential operator* (PDO) of *order* $\leq q$, or simply of order q with the *symbol* $a = a(\xi, p)$.

8.7. Remark. We note that the restrictions imposed on the symbol $a = a(\xi, p)$ of a pseudodifferential operator A can be relaxed leading to more general classes of pseudodifferential operators (see, for example, [54] page 12).

In view of expression (8.2) we can also represent a pseudodifferential operator A with symbol $a = a(\xi, p)$ formally as the following function of the vector operators $\hat{\xi}$ and $-i\frac{\partial}{\partial \xi}$:

$$A = a(\hat{\xi}, -i\frac{\partial}{\partial \xi}), \tag{8.3}$$

where the vector operator $-i\frac{\partial}{\partial \xi}$ acts first and the vector operator $\hat{\xi}$ acts second.

We note that for a pseudodifferential operator A the symbol $a = a(\xi, p)$ can be formally represented as follows (see, for example, [52] page 19)

$$a(\xi, p) = e^{-i\xi\, p}\, A\, e^{i\xi\, p} \tag{8.4}$$

or equivalently

$$a(\xi, p) = e^{-i\hat{\xi} p} A e^{i\hat{\xi} p} \mathbf{1} \tag{8.5}$$

where $\mathbf{1}$ is the function on $\mathbb{R}^n$ identically equal to unity.

In this regard we can formally view an arbitrary admissible linear operator A on an appropriate space of complex-valued functions on Ω as a pseudodifferential operator with the symbol $a = a(\xi, p)$ given by (8.4), or equivalently by (8.5).

Now with the help of the expression (8.5) we establish a certain formal expression for the symbol $a = a(\xi, p)$ of a pseudodifferential operator A that we will need later in this article.

Assume for now that $p = (p_1, p_2, \ldots, p_n)$ is in $\mathbb{R}^n_+$. Then for each $p_k \geq 0$, with k in $\{1, 2, \ldots, n\}$ arbitrary but fixed, the operator $e^{-i\hat{\xi} p} A e^{i\hat{\xi} p}$ is the formal solution of the following Cauchy problem

$$\begin{aligned} &\frac{\partial}{\partial p_k} e^{-i\hat{\xi} p} A e^{i\hat{\xi} p} = -i[\hat{\xi}_k, e^{-i\hat{\xi} p} A e^{i\hat{\xi} p}] \\ &e^{-i\hat{\xi} p} A e^{i\hat{\xi} p}\big|_{p_k=0} = e^{-i\hat{\xi} p|_{p_k=0}} A e^{i\hat{\xi} p|_{p_k=0}} \end{aligned} \tag{8.6}$$

where $p|_{p_k=0}$ in $\mathbb{R}^n_+$ is defined by

$$p|_{p_k=0} = (p_1, \ldots, p_{k-1}, 0, p_{k+1}, \ldots, p_n),$$

and where we have taken into account the fact that the operators $\hat{\xi}_i$ with $i = 1, 2, \ldots, n$ commute with each other.

The solution $e^{-i\hat{\xi} p} A e^{i\hat{\xi} p}$ of the preceding Cauchy problem (8.6) is formally given by

$$e^{-i\hat{\xi} p} A e^{i\hat{\xi} p} = e^{-ip_k \, \mathbf{ad}_{\hat{\xi}_k}} \left(e^{-i\hat{\xi} p|_{p_k=0}} A e^{i\hat{\xi} p|_{p_k=0}} \right), \quad p_k \geq 0, \tag{8.7}$$

where $\mathbf{ad}_B C$ stands for the commutator $[B, C]$, and where $e^{-ip_k \, \mathbf{ad}_{\hat{\xi}_k}}$ is formally defined as the following power series

$$e^{-ip_k \, \mathbf{ad}_{\hat{\xi}_k}} = \sum_{m=0}^{\infty} \frac{\left(-ip_k \, \mathbf{ad}_{\hat{\xi}_k}\right)^m}{m!}, \quad p_k \geq 0. \tag{8.8}$$

It is clear that due to relation (8.8) we can formally extend the solution of the Cauchy problem (8.6) formally given by (8.7) to the case when p_k is in $\mathbb{R}$:

$$e^{-i\hat{\xi}p}\,A\,e^{i\hat{\xi}p} = e^{-ip_k\mathbf{ad}_{\hat{\xi}_k}}\left(e^{-i\hat{\xi}p|_{p_k=0}}\,A\,e^{i\hat{\xi}p|_{p_k=0}}\right), \quad p_k \in \mathbb{R}, \tag{8.9}$$

where $e^{-ip_k\,\mathbf{ad}_{\hat{\xi}_k}}$ is formally defined as the following power series

$$e^{-ip_k\,\mathbf{ad}_{\hat{\xi}_k}} = \sum_{m=0}^{\infty}\frac{\left(-ip_k\,\mathbf{ad}_{\hat{\xi}_k}\right)^m}{m!}, \quad p_k \in \mathbb{R}. \tag{8.10}$$

In a similar way we have that

$$e^{-i\hat{\xi}p}\,A\,e^{i\hat{\xi}p} = e^{-ip\,\mathbf{ad}_{\hat{\xi}}}\,A, \quad p \in \mathbb{R}^n \tag{8.11}$$

where $\mathbf{ad}_{\hat{\xi}} = (\mathbf{ad}_{\hat{\xi}_1}, \mathbf{ad}_{\hat{\xi}_2}, \ldots, \mathbf{ad}_{\hat{\xi}_n})$ is the vector operator so that

$$-ip\,\mathbf{ad}_{\hat{\xi}} = -i\Big(\sum_{k=1}^{n} p_k\,\mathbf{ad}_{\hat{\xi}_k}\Big), \quad p \in \mathbb{R}^n$$

and where we have taken into account the fact that $\mathbf{ad}_{\hat{\xi}_i}$ with $i = 1, 2, \ldots, n$ commute with each other.

8.8. Remark. We comment that in order to obtain expression (8.11) we have implicitly used the following identity

$$\prod_{k=1}^{n} e^{-ip_k\,\mathbf{ad}_{\hat{\xi}_k}} = e^{-i(\sum_{k=1}^{n} p_k\,\mathbf{ad}_{\hat{\xi}_k})}$$

which is based on the fact that $\mathbf{ad}_{\hat{\xi}_i}$ with $i = 1, 2, \ldots, n$ commute with each other. The fact that $\mathbf{ad}_{\hat{\xi}_i}$ with $i = 1, 2, \ldots, n$ commute with each other, in turn, directly follows from the fact that the operators $\hat{\xi}_i$ with $i = 1, 2, \ldots, n$ commute with each other. Indeed, let x, y and z be arbitrary elements in a Lie algebra of linear operators with the Lie product being the commutator $[,]$.

Let y and z commute, that is, let $[y, z] = 0$ with 0 being the zero element in the Lie algebra. Then the Jacobi identity

$$[x, [y, z]] + [y, [z, x]] + [z, [x, y]] = 0$$

implies that

$$[y, [z, x]] = [z, [y, x]].$$

Finally, the preceding equality can be rewritten as follows

$$\mathbf{ad}_y \circ \mathbf{ad}_z\, x = \mathbf{ad}_z \circ \mathbf{ad}_y\, x,$$

or equivalently as

$$\mathbf{ad}_y \circ \mathbf{ad}_z = \mathbf{ad}_z \circ \mathbf{ad}_y.$$

This completes the Remark.

It is clear that $e^{-ip\,\mathbf{ad}_{\hat{\xi}}}$ can be formally defined as the following power series

$$e^{-ip\,\mathbf{ad}_{\hat{\xi}}} = \sum_{m=0}^{\infty} \frac{\left(-ip\,\mathbf{ad}_{\hat{\xi}}\right)^m}{m!}, \quad p \in \mathbb{R}^n, \tag{8.12}$$

or equivalently by

$$e^{-ip\,\mathbf{ad}_{\hat{\xi}}} = \sum_{m \in \mathbb{Z}_+^n} \frac{(-ip)^m\,\mathbf{ad}_{\hat{\xi}}^m}{m!}, \quad p \in \mathbb{R}^n, \tag{8.13}$$

where

$$m! = m_1!\, m_2! \ldots m_n!,$$

and where

$$(-ip)^m = (-ip_1)^{m_1} (-ip_2)^{m_2} \ldots (-ip_n)^{m_n}$$

and

$$\mathbf{ad}_{\hat{\xi}}^m = \mathbf{ad}_{\hat{\xi}_1}^{m_1}\, \mathbf{ad}_{\hat{\xi}_2}^{m_2} \ldots \mathbf{ad}_{\hat{\xi}_n}^{m_n},$$

for each $m = (m_1, m_2, \ldots, m_n)$ in $\mathbb{Z}_+^n$.

8.9. Remark. We comment that expression (8.13) directly follows from the following chain of equalities

$$e^{-ip\,\mathbf{ad}_{\hat\xi}} = e^{-i(\sum_{k=1}^{n} p_k\,\mathbf{ad}_{\hat\xi_k})} =$$

$$\prod_{k=1}^{n} e^{-ip_k\,\mathbf{ad}_{\hat\xi_k}} =$$

$$\prod_{k=1}^{n}\Big(\sum_{m=0}^{\infty}\frac{\big(-ip_k\,\mathbf{ad}_{\hat\xi_k}\big)^m}{m!}\Big) =$$

$$\sum_{m_1=0}^{\infty}\cdots\sum_{m_n=0}^{\infty}\Big(\frac{\big((-ip_1)^{m_1}\,\mathbf{ad}_{\hat\xi_1}^{m_1}\big)\dots\big((-ip_n)^{m_n}\,\mathbf{ad}_{\hat\xi_n}^{m_n}\big)}{m_1!\dots m_n!}\Big) =$$

$$\sum_{m_1=0}^{\infty}\cdots\sum_{m_n=0}^{\infty}\Big(\frac{\big((-ip_1)^{m_1}\dots(-ip_n)^{m_n}\big)\big(\mathbf{ad}_{\hat\xi_1}^{m_1}\dots\mathbf{ad}_{\hat\xi_n}^{m_n}\big)}{m_1!\dots m_n!}\Big) =$$

$$\sum_{m\in\mathbb{Z}_+^n}\frac{(-ip)^m\,\mathbf{ad}_{\hat\xi}^m}{m!}.$$

With the help of relations (8.11) and (8.13) we can rewrite expression (8.5) as follows

$$a(\xi,p) = \sum_{m\in\mathbb{Z}_+^n}\Big(\frac{(-ip)^m}{m!}\,(\mathbf{ad}_{\hat\xi}^m A)\mathbf{1}\Big), \quad p\in\mathbb{R}^n. \tag{8.14}$$

With the help of the preceding relation (8.14) we can rewrite expression (8.3) as follows

$$A = \sum_{m\in\mathbb{Z}_+^n}\Big(\frac{1}{m!}\,((-i\,\mathbf{ad}_{\hat\xi})^m A)\mathbf{1}\Big)\big(-i\frac{\partial}{\partial\xi}\big)^m, \tag{8.15}$$

or equivalently as

$$A = \sum_{m\in\mathbb{Z}_+^n} A_m(\hat\xi)\,\big(-i\frac{\partial}{\partial\xi}\big)^m, \tag{8.16}$$

where

$$A_m(\hat{\xi}) = \frac{1}{m!}\,((-i\,\mathbf{ad}_{\hat{\xi}})^m\,A)\,\mathbf{1}, \quad m \in \mathbb{Z}_+^n. \tag{8.17}$$

Therefore an arbitrary admissible linear operator A on an appropriate space of complex-valued functions on Ω viewed formally as a pseudodifferential operator with the symbol $a = a(\xi, p)$ given by (8.4), or equivalently by (8.5) can, in turn, be viewed formally as a quasidifferential operator, or more precisely as an analytic quasidifferential operator with the defining sequence given by

$$A_M = \sum_{|m|\leq M} \Big(\frac{1}{m!}\,(-i\,\mathbf{ad}_{\hat{\xi}}^m\,A)\,\mathbf{1}\Big)\,(-i\frac{\partial}{\partial \xi})^m, \tag{8.18}$$

or equivalently as

$$A = \sum_{|m|\leq M} A_m(\hat{\xi})\,(-i\frac{\partial}{\partial \xi})^m \tag{8.19}$$

and the support contained in $C^\infty(\Omega)$.

8.10. Remark. It is clear that the symbol $a_M(\xi, p)$ of the differential operator A_M is given by

$$a_M(\xi, p) = \sum_{|m|\leq M} \Big(\frac{(-ip)^m}{m!}\,(\mathbf{ad}_{\hat{\xi}}^m\,A)\,\mathbf{1}\Big), \quad p \in \mathbb{R}^n. \tag{8.20}$$

It is also clear that due to relation (8.3)

$$A_M = a_M(\hat{\xi}, -i\frac{\partial}{\partial \xi}). \tag{8.21}$$

In the case when the operator A on an appropriate space of complex-valued functions on Ω is real, that is, in the case when A can be restricted to the subspace of the real-valued functions on Ω, each differential operator A_M defined by (8.18) is also real. In order to see this it is enough to rewrite expressions (8.15) and (8.18) as follows

$$A = \sum_{m \in \mathbb{Z}_+^n} \left(\frac{1}{m!} \left((-\mathbf{ad}_{\hat{\xi}})^m A \right) \mathbf{1} \right) \frac{\partial}{\partial \xi}^m, \tag{8.22}$$

and

$$A_M = \sum_{|m| \leq M} \left(\frac{1}{m!} \left((-\mathbf{ad}_{\hat{\xi}})^m A \right) \mathbf{1} \right) \frac{\partial}{\partial \xi}^m, \tag{8.23}$$

and to note that since the vector operator $\hat{\xi}$ is real each operator $(-\mathbf{ad}_{\hat{\xi}})^m A$ is also real.

Expressions (8.22) and (8.23) can also be rewritten as follows

$$A = \sum_{m \in \mathbb{Z}_+^n} \mathcal{A}_m(\hat{\xi}) \frac{\partial}{\partial \xi}^m, \tag{8.24}$$

and

$$A_M = \sum_{|m| \leq M} \mathcal{A}_m(\hat{\xi}) \frac{\partial}{\partial \xi}^m, \tag{8.25}$$

where the operator coefficients $\mathcal{A}_m(\hat{\xi})$ are defined by

$$\mathcal{A}_m(\hat{\xi}) = \frac{1}{m!} \left((-\mathbf{ad}_{\hat{\xi}})^m A \right) \mathbf{1}, \quad m \in \mathbb{Z}_+^n. \tag{8.26}$$

8.11. Definition. Let A be a pseudodifferential operator with the symbol $a(\xi, ip)$. We call the function

$$\mathfrak{a}(\xi, p) = a(\xi, -i\,p) \tag{8.27}$$

the *real symbol* of the pseudodifferential operator A, where $a(\xi, -i\,p)$ is formally given by

$$a(\xi, -i\,p) = \sum_{m \in \mathbb{Z}_+^n} \left(\frac{p^m}{m!} \left((-\mathbf{ad}_{\hat{\xi}})^m A \right) \mathbf{1} \right), \quad p \in \mathbb{R}^n. \tag{8.28}$$

8.12. Remark. It is clear that due to relation (8.24) a pseudodifferential operator A with the real symbol $\mathfrak{a}(\xi, p)$ can be formally represented as a function of the operators $\hat{\xi}$ and $\frac{\partial}{\partial \xi}$:

$$A = \mathfrak{a}(\hat{\xi}, \frac{\partial}{\partial \xi}), \tag{8.29}$$

where the operator $\frac{\partial}{\partial \xi}$ acts first and the operator $\hat{\xi}$ acts second.

8.13. Remark. It is clear that the real symbol $\mathfrak{a}_M(\xi, p)$ of the differential operator A_M is given by

$$\mathfrak{a}_M(\xi, p) = \sum_{|m| \leq M} \Big(\frac{p^m}{m!} \left((-\mathbf{ad}_{\hat{\xi}})^m A\right)\mathbf{1}\Big), \quad p \in \mathbb{R}^n. \tag{8.30}$$

It is also clear that due to relation (8.21)

$$A_M = \mathfrak{a}_M(\hat{\xi}, \frac{\partial}{\partial \xi}). \tag{8.31}$$

Finally, as an illustration, we present, following [30], examples of quasidifferential operators in the Sobolev scale on the unit circle.

We recall [2] that the Sobolev space $H_t = H_t(S)$ of complex-valued functions on the unit circle S is the completion of the space $C^\infty(S)$ of infinitely differentiable complex-valued functions on S with respect to the norm

$$\| v \|_t = \Big(\sum_{p=-\infty}^{\infty} (1 + p^2)^t \, |C_p(v)|^2 \Big)^{1/2},$$

where $C_p(v)$ are the Fourier coefficients of the function v with respect to the system $\{e^{ip\xi},\ p \in \mathbb{Z}\}$ with $\mathbb{Z}$ being the set of integer numbers. The spaces H_t with t in $\mathbb{R}$ form a Banach scale.

8.14. Remark. Hereafter we identify a complex-valued function on S with the corresponding 2π-periodic complex-valued function on $\mathbb{R}$.

Denote by D_p the set of all trigonometric polynomials on S. It is well known that D_p is everywhere dense in each H_t (see, for example, [2]).

Example. For a fixed $\eta \in [0, 2\pi]$ let $\boldsymbol{T} : H_t \to H_t$ be the translation operator defined by:

$$(\boldsymbol{T}\,v)\,(\xi) = v\,(\xi + \eta).$$

We show that $\boldsymbol{T}$ is a quasidifferential operator with support D_p and the defining sequence given by:

$$\boldsymbol{T}_M = \sum_{m=0}^{M} \frac{(i\eta)^m}{m!}\,(-i\,\frac{d}{d\xi})^m.$$

In order to see this, notice that $D_p \subset D_{\boldsymbol{T}}$ and $D_p \subset D_{\boldsymbol{T}_M}$ for each M in $\mathbb{Z}_+$ where $D_{\boldsymbol{T}}$ and $D_{\boldsymbol{T}_M}$ are the domains of definition of $\boldsymbol{T}$ and $\boldsymbol{T}_M$. Now, letting v be an arbitrary trigonometric polynomial from D_p, notice that $\boldsymbol{T}_M\,v$, as the partial sum of the Taylor series for the function v which is analytic, converges to $\boldsymbol{T}\,v$ in H_t for each t in $\mathbb{R}$.

Recall [2] that A is called an *operator of order* r ($\operatorname{ord} A = r$) in the Sobolev scale on S if, for each t in $\mathbb{R}$, A is a bounded operator acting from H_{t+r} to H_t and is an unbounded operator acting from $H_{t+r-\epsilon}$ to H_t for any $\epsilon > 0$. If A is a bounded operator from H_{t+r} to H_t for each t and r in $\mathbb{R}$ then A is called an *operator of order* $-\infty$ ($\operatorname{ord} A = -\infty$) in the Sobolev scale on S.

In what follows in this Subsection, whenever we refer to the order of an operator we mean the order in the Sobolev scale on S.

Now we need the following definition of a classic pseudodifferential operator in the Sobolev scale on S (see, for example, [2]).

8.15. Definition. An operator A is called a *classic pseudodif-*

ferential operator of *order* r if it is of the form

$$(A\,v)\,(\xi) = \sum_{p=-\infty}^{\infty} e^{ip\xi}\,\alpha(\xi,\,p)\,C_p(v) + (T\,v)(\xi),$$

where T is an operator of order $-\infty$, and where $\alpha(\xi,\,\eta)$ is in $C^\infty(S \times \mathbb{R})$, the space of infinitely differentiable complex-valued functions on $S \times \mathbb{R}$, and has an expansion

$$\alpha(\xi,\,\eta) \sim \sum_{j=0}^{\infty} \alpha_{r-j}\,(\xi,\,\eta)$$

with:

$$\alpha_{r-j}\,(\xi,\,\eta) = |\eta|^{r-j}\,a_{r-j}\left(\xi,\,\mathrm{sign}(\eta)\right),$$

for $\eta \neq 0$, which is asymptotic in the following sense: for any l, m and k in $\mathbb{Z}_+$ there exists a positive constant $C_{l,m,k}$ such that:

$$|\frac{d}{d\xi}^{l}\frac{d}{d\eta}^{m}\left(\alpha(\xi,\eta) - \sum_{j=0}^{k} \alpha_{r-j}\,(\xi,\,\eta)\right)| \leq C_{l,m,k}\,|\eta|^{r-m-k-1}, \tag{8.32}$$

where $|\eta| \geq 1$.

It was shown in [2], [3] and [4] that any classic pseudodifferential operator A of order r can be represented as follows:

$$(A\,v)\,(\xi) = \sum_{p=-\infty}^{\infty} e^{ip\xi}\,a(\xi,\,p)\,C_p(v),$$

where the function a is in $C^\infty\,(S)$ for each p in $\mathbb{Z}$ and has an expansion:

$$a(\xi,\,p) \sim \sum_{j=0}^{\infty} a_{r-j}\,(\xi,\,p)$$

with:

$$a_{r-j}\,(\xi,\,p) = |p|^{r-j}\,a_{r-j}\left(\xi,\,\mathrm{sign}(p)\right),$$

for $p \neq 0$, which is asymptotic in the following sense: for any l and k in $\mathbb{Z}_+$ there exists a positive constant $C_{l,k}$ such that:

$$|\frac{d}{d\xi}^{l}\Big(a(\xi,\, p) - \sum_{j=0}^{k} a_{r-j}\,(\xi,\, p)\Big)| \leq C_{l,k}\, |p|^{r-k-1}, \quad |p| \geq 1. \tag{8.33}$$

The function $a = a(\xi,\, p)$ is called the *symbol*, and $a_r = a_r(\xi,\, p)$ the *principal symbol* of a classic pseudodifferential operator A. A classic pseudodifferential operator A is called *elliptic* if $a_r(\xi, p) \neq 0$ for all ξ in S and $p \neq 0$.

Denote by F the space of complex-valued functions on $S \times [0, 2\pi]$ that define an infinitely smooth map from S to $L_2\Big([0, 2\pi]\Big)$, the Hilbert space of square integrable complex-valued functions on $[0, 2\pi]$. We comment that functions $h = h(\xi, \eta)$ from F are infinitely smooth in the variable ξ in S in the sense of the norm $L_2\Big([0, 2\pi]\Big)$ with η in $[0, 2\pi]$. We define a topology on F by the system of seminorms:

$$p_M\,(h) = \sup\,\{\, \|\frac{\partial}{\partial\xi}^{m}\, h\|_{L_2\,([0,2\pi])} : \xi \in S, \quad m = 0, \ldots, M\},$$

which turns it into a Frechet space [49].

8.16. Definition. A classic pseudodifferential operator A with symbol a is called a *Fourier* pseudodifferential operator [30] if there exists a function h in F such that:

$$a(\xi,\, p) = \int_0^{2\pi} h(\xi,\, \eta)\, e^{-ip\eta}\, d\eta, \quad p \in \mathbb{Z}. \tag{8.34}$$

In that case the function h will be called a *Fourier symbol* of the classic pseudodifferential operator A.

Now, following [30], we are ready to present the following Theorem on the correspondence between classic pseudodifferential operators and quasidifferential operators in the Sobolev scale on the unit circle.

8.17. Theorem. Let A be a classic pseudodifferential operator of ord $A = r < -\frac{1}{2}$. Let $K_A(\xi, \eta)$ and a be the kernel and the symbol of A respectively. Then:

(i) A is a Fourier PDO with Fourier symbol:

$$h(\xi, \eta) = \frac{1}{2\pi} \sum_{p=-\infty}^{\infty} a(\xi, p)\, e^{ip\eta},$$

where the convergence of the series is understood in the sense of the topology on F;

(ii) The Fourier symbol h and the kernel $K_A(\xi, \eta)$ of A are related by:

$$h(\xi, \eta) = K_A(\xi, \xi - \eta);$$

(iii) For each p in Z, the symbol a admits the following power series expansion:

$$a(\xi, p) = \sum_{m=0}^{\infty} a_m(\xi)\, p^m,$$

where the convergence is understood in the sense of the topology of $C^\infty(S)$, and where:

$$a_m(\xi) = \frac{(-i)^m}{m!} \int_0^{2\pi} h(\xi, \eta)\, \eta^m \, d\eta;$$

(iv) The pseudodifferential operator $A : H_{t+r} \mapsto H_t$, for each t in $\mathbb{R}$, is an analytic quasidifferential operator with support D_p and the defining sequence given by:

$$A_M = \sum_{m=0}^{M} a_m(\hat{\xi})\, (-i \frac{d}{d\xi})^m.$$

Proof. We prove (i). It is enough to show that h is in F and satisfies equality (8.34). Using the asymptotic expansion (8.33) and the absolute convergence of the numerical series $\sum_{p=-\infty}^{\infty} \beta_p$ with $\beta_p = O(|p|^{-\alpha})$ as $|p| \to \infty$ and $\alpha > 1$, we conclude that $p_M(h) < \infty$ for each M in $\mathbb{Z}_+$ and hence h is in F. Expression (8.34) for each fixed ξ in S is, in this case, the ordinary Fourier transform in $L_2\Big([0,\, 2\pi]\Big)$.

Now we prove (ii). The symbol a of a classic pseudodifferential operator A on S can be represented [3] as:

$$a(\xi, p) = e^{-ip\xi}\, A\, e^{ip\xi},$$

or, in terms of the kernel, as

$$a(\xi, p) = e^{-ip\xi} \int_0^{2\pi} K_A(\xi, \eta)\, e^{ip\eta}\, d\eta.$$

Inserting the first exponential into the integral, making the change of variables $\xi - \eta \to \eta$, and taking into account expression (8.34), we arrive at the desired relation.

Now we prove (iv). First we note that $D_p \subset D_A$ and $D_p \subset D_{A_M}$ for each M in $\mathbb{Z}_+$. By the definition of D_p, in order to prove (iv) it is enough to show that $A_M\, e^{ip\xi}$ converges to $A\, e^{ip\xi}$ as $M \to \infty$ in H_t for each p in $\mathbb{Z}$ and t in $\mathbb{R}$. By the definition of the Fourier pseudodifferential operator we have

$$(A - A_M)\, e^{ip\xi} =$$

$$\Big(\int_0^{2\pi} h(\xi, \eta)\, e^{-ip\eta}\, d\eta - \sum_{m=0}^{M} \frac{(-ip)^m}{m!} \int_0^{2\pi} h(\xi, \eta)\, \eta^m\, d\eta\Big)\, e^{ip\xi} =$$

$$\Big(\int_0^{2\pi} h(\xi,\, \eta)\, \big(\sum_{m=M+1}^{\infty} \frac{(-ip\eta)^m}{m!} \big)\, d\eta\Big)\, e^{ip\xi}.$$

It is well known that kernel $h = h(\xi, \eta)$ in F defines a bounded linear operator from $L_2([0, 2\pi])$ to H_t for each t in $\mathbb{R}$ (see, for example, [2]). Denote by $\mathfrak{N}_{t,p}$ the product of the norm of the above operator with the norm of the operator of multiplication by the function $e^{ip\xi}$, which is a bounded operator on H_t for each t in $\mathbb{R}$. Then, using the estimate for the remainder of the Taylor series of the function $e^{-ip\eta}$, we arrive at the following inequality:

$$\|(A - A_M)\, e^{ip\xi}\|_t \leq \mathfrak{N}_{t,p}\, e^{2\pi(M+1)p}\, \frac{(2\pi)^{M+1}}{(M+1)!}. \tag{8.35}$$

To finish the proof of (iv) it is enough to note that the right hand side of this inequality converges to zero as $M \to \infty$ for each p in $\mathbb{Z}$ and t in $\mathbb{R}$.

Finally, we prove (iii). By the preceding inequality (8.35), for each p in $\mathbb{Z}$ the sequence of functions:

$$A_M\, e^{ip\xi} = \Big(\sum_{m=0}^{M} a_m\,(\xi)\, p^m\Big)\, e^{ip\xi}$$

converges as $M \to \infty$ to the function:

$$A\, e^{ip\xi} = a(\xi,\, p)\, e^{ip\xi}$$

in H_t for each t in $\mathbb{R}$, and hence (see, for example, [2]) converges in $C^\infty(S)$. To finish the proof it is enough to multiply each term in the above sequence and also the function $a(\xi,\, p)\, e^{ip\xi}$ by the function $e^{-ip\xi}$, which is in $C^\infty(S)$ for each p in $\mathbb{Z}$. □

Following [30], we illustrate the preceding Theorem with the following Example.

Example. Let $\mathfrak{I} : H_t \to H_{t+1}$ with t in $\mathbb{R}$ be the operator of integration defined as the classic pseudodifferential operator of order -1 with the symbol

$$I(p) = \begin{cases} -i\pi & \text{if } p = 0, \\ \frac{1}{p} & \text{if } p \neq 0. \end{cases}$$

Due to the preceding Theorem the operator $\mathfrak{I} : H_t \to H_{t+1}$ with t in $\mathbb{R}$ is a Fourier pseudodifferential operator with the Fourier symbol $-\frac{i}{2\pi}\eta$. Moreover, $\mathfrak{I} : H_t \to H_{t+1}$ with t in $\mathbb{R}$ is an analytic quasidifferential operator with the support D_p and the defining sequence given by

$$\mathfrak{I}_M = \sum_{m=0}^{M} \frac{(-i2\pi)^{m+1}(m+1)}{(m+2)!}(-i\frac{d}{d\xi})^m.$$

8.2 Lie Module of Quasidifferential Operators

Now our goal is to introduce a concept of a Lie module and to show that the set of all analytic quasidifferential operators with infinitely smooth coefficients on an appropriate space of complex-valued functions is in fact a Lie module.

In order to do this we need further preparation. We start with the following definition of a ring (see, for example, [25] page 115).

8.18. Definition. A *ring* is a triple $(R, +, \cdot)$ where R is a nonempty set, and where $+$ and $\cdot$ are binary operations on R such that:

(i) $(R, +)$ is an abelian group,

(ii) $(R, \cdot)$ is a semigroup, that is, the binary operation $\cdot$ on R is associative, and

(iii) $a \cdot (b + c) = a \cdot b + a \cdot c$ and $(b + c) \cdot a = b \cdot a + c \cdot a$ for all a, b and c in R.

8.19. Definition. A ring $(R, +, \cdot)$ is said to be *commutative* if the binary operation $\cdot$ is commutative.

8.20. Definition. A ring $(R, +, \cdot)$ is said to be a *ring with identity* if R contains e_R such that $e_R \cdot a = a \cdot e_R = a$ for all a in R.

Whenever ambiguity is unlikely we will denote a ring $(R, +, \cdot)$ simply by R.

Now we present the following definition of a module (see, for example, [25] page 169).

8.21. Definition. Let $(R, +, \cdot)$ be a ring. A (left) *module* over a ring $(R, +, \cdot)$ or *R-module* is a quadruple $(A, R, \oplus, \odot)$ where $(A, \oplus)$ is an abelian group, and $\odot : R \times A \to A$ is such that for all r and s in R and a and b in A:

(i) $r \odot (a \oplus b) = r \odot a \oplus r \odot b$,

(ii) $(r + s) \odot a = r \odot a \oplus s \odot a$, and

(iii) $r \odot (s \odot a) = (r \cdot s) \odot a$.

8.22. Definition. A module $(A, R, \oplus, \odot)$ is said to be a *unitary module* if $(R, +, \cdot)$ is a ring with identity e_R and $e_R \odot a = a$ for all a in A

Whenever ambiguity is unlikely we will denote a module $(A, R, \oplus, \odot)$ over a ring R simply as A.

8.23. Remark. Similarly, one can define a right module over a ring $(R, +, \cdot)$ (see, for example, [25] page 169).

8.24. Definition. Let $(A, R, \oplus, \odot)$ and $(B, R, \oplus', \odot')$ be modules over a ring $(R, +, \cdot)$. A map $f : A \to B$ is called:

(i) a *module homomorphism* or *linear* if

$$f(r \odot a \oplus s \odot b) = r \odot' f(a) \oplus' s \odot' f(b)$$

for all r and s in R and a and b in A,

(ii) *additive* if

$$f(a \oplus b) = f(a) \oplus' f(b)$$

for all a and b in A,

(iii) *homogeneous of degree one* or simply *homogeneous* if

$$f(r \odot a) = r \odot' f(a)$$

for all r in R and a in A.

Now we present the following definition of a submodule (see, for example, [25] page 171).

8.25. Definition. Let $(A, R, \oplus, \odot)$ be a module over a ring R and let B be a subset of A. If $(B, R, \oplus|_B, \odot|_B)$ is a module over the ring R then it is called a *submodule* of $(A, R, \oplus, \odot)$, where $\oplus|_B$ and $\odot|_B$ are the restrictions of $\oplus$ and $\odot$ to $B \times B$ and $R \times B$.

Whenever ambiguity is unlikely we will denote a submodule $(B, R, \oplus|_B, \odot|_B)$ of a module $(A, R, \oplus, \odot)$ simply as $(B, R, \oplus, \odot)$.

8.26. Definition. Let $(A, R, \oplus, \odot)$ be a module over a ring R and let X be a subset of A. The intersection $(C, R, \oplus, \odot)$ of all submodules $(B, R, \oplus, \odot)$ of $(A, R, \oplus, \odot)$ such that X is a subset of B is called a submodule *generated* or *spanned* by X. In this case we say that X *spans* $(C, R, \oplus, \odot)$. If X is a finite set and X generates a module $(B, R, \oplus, \odot)$ then $(B, R, \oplus, \odot)$ is said to be *finitely generated* (see, for example, [25] page 171).

8.27. Definition. Let $(A, R, \oplus, \odot)$ be a module over a ring R and let X be a subset of A. X is said to be *linearly independent* provided that for distinct $x_1, x_2, \ldots, x_n$ in X and for $r_1, r_2, \ldots, r_n$ in R

$$r_1 \odot x_1 \oplus r_2 \odot x_2 \oplus \cdots \oplus r_n \odot x_n = 0_A$$

implies that each $r_i = 0_R$ where 0_A and 0_R are the identities in the abelian groups $(A, \oplus)$ and $(R, +)$. A set X that is not linearly independent is said to be *linearly dependent* (see, for example, [25] page 181).

Now we present the following fact on modules (see, for example, [25] page 181).

8.28. Fact. If a module $(A, R, \oplus, \odot)$ over a ring $(R, +, \cdot)$ is unitary then X spans $(A, R, \oplus, \odot)$ if and only if for each a in A there exist $x_1, x_2, \ldots, x_n$ in X and $r_1, r_2, \ldots, r_n$ in R such that

$$a = r_1 \odot x_1 \oplus r_2 \odot x_2 \oplus \cdots \oplus r_n \odot x_n.$$

8.29. Definition. A linearly independent subset X of a unitary module $(A, R, \oplus, \odot)$ over a ring $(R, +, \cdot)$ that spans $(A, R, \oplus, \odot)$ is called a *basis* of $(A, R, \oplus, \odot)$. We call the cardinality of X the *dimension* of $(A, R, \oplus, \odot)$. If for any natural number n there exists a linearly independent subset X of $(A, R, \oplus, \odot)$ of cardinality n then we will say that $(A, R, \oplus, \odot)$ is infinite dimensional (see, for example, [25] page 181).

Now we are ready to introduce the concept of a Lie module.

8.30. Definition. We call a (left) *Lie module* a pair $(L, [,])$ where $(L, R, \oplus, \odot)$ is a (left) module over a ring $(R, +, \cdot)$ and $[,]$ is a binary operation on L such that:

(i) the map $a \mapsto [a, b]$ is additive for each b in L,

(ii) $[a, b] = -[b, a]$ for all a and b in L, and

(iii) the *Jacobi identity*

$$[a, [b, c]] \oplus [b, [c, a]] \oplus [c, [a, b]] = 0_L$$

holds for all a, b and c in L, where 0_L is the identity element of the abelian group $(L, \oplus)$.

We call the binary operation $[,]$ in a Lie module $(L, [,])$ a *Lie product.*

Whenever ambiguity is unlikely we will denote a Lie module $(L, [,])$ simply as L.

8.31. Remark. The relation of the concept of a Lie module and the concept of a Lie algebra is similar to that of a module and a vector space.

8.32. Definition. We call $(L', [,]_{L'})$ a *Lie submodule* of a Lie module $(L, [,])$ if:

(i) $(L', R, \oplus, \odot)$ is a submodule of a module $(L, R, \oplus, \odot)$, and

(ii) $(L', [,]_{L'})$ is a Lie module, where $[,]_{L'}$ is the restriction of $[,]$ to $L' \times L'$.

Whenever ambiguity is unlikely we will denote a Lie submodule $(L', [,]_{L'})$ of a Lie module $(L, [,])$ simply as $(L', [,])$.

8.33. Definition. We call a Lie module $(L, [,])$ a *unitary Lie module* if the module L is unitary.

We will identify the basis and the dimension of a unitary Lie module $(L, [,])$ with that of the unitary module L.

8.34. Definition. Let $X = (x_1, x_2, \dots x_n)$ be a basis of an n-dimensional unitary Lie module $(L, [,])$, where $(L, R, \oplus, \odot)$ is a unitary module over a ring $(R, +, \cdot)$. We define the *structure constants* $c_{ij}^k = c_{ij}^k(r_i, r_j)$ in $(R, +, \cdot)$ of the Lie module $(L, [,])$ by

$$[r_i \odot x_i, r_j \odot x_j] = \sum_{k=1,\dots,n}^{\oplus} c_{ij}^k \odot x_k.$$

8.35. Remark. In the case of an infinite dimensional unitary Lie module $(L, [,])$ with a basis $X = (x_1, x_2, \dots)$ the definition of structure constants $c_{ij}^k = c_{ij}^k(r_i, r_j)$ is completely analogous.

Consider the ring $\mathfrak{M}(\Omega)$ of the linear operators on $C^\infty(\Omega)$ of multiplication by functions in $C^\infty(\Omega)$ with the operations $+$ and $\cdot$ defined as the addition and product of linear operators.

It is clear that $\mathfrak{M}(\Omega)$ is a commutative ring with identity which is the operator of multiplication by the function $\mathbf{1}$ in $C^\infty(\Omega)$ identically equal to unity.

Consider the (left) module $\mathfrak{A}(\Omega)$ of all formal analytic quasidifferential operators with infinitely smooth coefficients

$$Q = \sum_{m \in \mathbb{Z}_+^n} q_m(\hat{\xi})\left(-i\frac{\partial}{\partial \xi}\right)^m, \quad q_m(\xi) \in C^\infty(\Omega)$$

over the ring $\mathfrak{M}(\Omega)$ with the operations $\oplus$ and $\odot$ defined as the addition and product of linear operators.

It is clear that $\mathfrak{A}(\Omega)$ is a unitary module. It is also clear that the unitary module $\mathfrak{A}(\Omega)$ is infinite dimensional with the basis $\{(-i\frac{\partial}{\partial\xi})^m : m \in \mathbb{Z}_+^n\}$.

Equipped with the binary operation $[,]$ defined as the commutator $[,]$ of linear operators, the unitary module $\mathfrak{A}(\Omega)$ is turned into a unitary Lie module which we denote as $\mathfrak{D}(\Omega)$.

Our immediate goal is to find the structure constants of the unitary Lie module $\mathfrak{D}(\Omega)$. In order to do this, for each m and l in $\mathbb{Z}_+^n$ we need the following chain of equalities

$$
\begin{aligned}
&[q_m(\hat{\xi})(-i\frac{\partial}{\partial\xi})^m, q_l(\hat{\xi})(-i\frac{\partial}{\partial\xi})^l] = \\
&q_m(\hat{\xi})(-i\frac{\partial}{\partial\xi})^m q_l(\hat{\xi})(-i\frac{\partial}{\partial\xi})^l - q_l(\hat{\xi})(-i\frac{\partial}{\partial\xi})^l q_m(\hat{\xi})(-i\frac{\partial}{\partial\xi})^m = \\
&q_m(\hat{\xi})\Big(\sum_{k\le m}\binom{m}{k}\Big((-i\frac{\partial}{\partial\xi})^k q_l(\hat{\xi})\Big)(-i\frac{\partial}{\partial\xi})^{m-k}\Big)(-i\frac{\partial}{\partial\xi})^l - \\
&\quad q_l(\hat{\xi})\Big(\sum_{k\le l}\binom{l}{k}\Big((-i\frac{\partial}{\partial\xi})^k q_m(\hat{\xi})\Big)(-i\frac{\partial}{\partial\xi})^{l-k}\Big)(-i\frac{\partial}{\partial\xi})^m = \\
&q_m(\hat{\xi})\sum_{k\le m}\binom{m}{k}\Big((-i\frac{\partial}{\partial\xi})^k q_l(\hat{\xi})\Big)(-i\frac{\partial}{\partial\xi})^{m+l-k} - \qquad (8.36)\\
&\quad q_l(\hat{\xi})\sum_{k\le l}\binom{l}{k}\Big((-i\frac{\partial}{\partial\xi})^k q_m(\hat{\xi})\Big)(-i\frac{\partial}{\partial\xi})^{m+l-k} = \\
&q_m(\hat{\xi})\sum_{k\le m+l} I_{k\le m}\binom{m}{k}\Big((-i\frac{\partial}{\partial\xi})^k q_l(\hat{\xi})\Big)(-i\frac{\partial}{\partial\xi})^{m+l-k} - \\
&\quad q_l(\hat{\xi})\sum_{k\le m+l} I_{k\le l}\binom{l}{k}\Big((-i\frac{\partial}{\partial\xi})^k q_m(\hat{\xi})\Big)(-i\frac{\partial}{\partial\xi})^{m+l-k} =
\end{aligned}
$$

$$\sum_{k\leq m+l}\left(I_{k\leq m}\binom{m}{k}q_m(\hat{\xi})\left((-i\frac{\partial}{\partial\xi})^k q_l(\hat{\xi})\right)-\right.$$

$$\left.I_{k\leq l}\binom{l}{k}q_l(\hat{\xi})\left((-i\frac{\partial}{\partial\xi})^k q_m(\hat{\xi})\right)\right)(-i\frac{\partial}{\partial\xi})^{m+l-k}=$$

$$\sum_{p\leq m+l}\left(I_{m+l-p\leq m}\binom{m}{m+l-p}q_m(\hat{\xi})\left((-i\frac{\partial}{\partial\xi})^{m+l-p}q_l(\hat{\xi})\right)-\right.$$

$$\left.I_{m+l-p\leq l}\binom{l}{m+l-p}q_l(\hat{\xi})\left((-i\frac{\partial}{\partial\xi})^{m+l-p}q_m(\hat{\xi})\right)\right)(-i\frac{\partial}{\partial\xi})^p=$$

$$\sum_{p\in\mathbb{Z}^n_+}I_{p\leq m+l}\left(I_{l\leq p}\binom{m}{m+l-p}q_m(\hat{\xi})\left((-i\frac{\partial}{\partial\xi})^{(m+l-p)^+}q_l(\hat{\xi})\right)-\right.$$

$$\left.I_{m\leq p}\binom{l}{m+l-p}q_l(\hat{\xi})\left((-i\frac{\partial}{\partial\xi})^{(m+l-p)^+}q_m(\hat{\xi})\right)\right)(-i\frac{\partial}{\partial\xi})^p,$$

where

$$m^+=(m_1^+,m_2^+,\ldots,m_n^+)$$

is in $\mathbb{Z}^n_+$ for each

$$m=(m_1,m_2,\ldots,m_n)$$

in $\mathbb{Z}^n$ with each $m_i^+=\max\{m_i,0\}$, and where $I_{l\leq m}$ is the indicator function of the set $\{l\in\mathbb{Z}^n_+ : l\leq m\}$ with m in $\mathbb{Z}^n_+$.

8.36. Remark. We comment that $l\leq m$ is understood as $m-l\in\mathbb{Z}^n_+$.

8.37. Remark. We also comment that in the preceding chain of equalities (8.36) have used the following identity (see, for example, [1] page 2)

$$(-i\frac{\partial}{\partial\xi})^m q(\hat{\xi})=\sum_{l\leq m}\binom{m}{l}\left((-i\frac{\partial}{\partial\xi})^l q(\hat{\xi})\right)(-i\frac{\partial}{\partial\xi})^{m-l}$$

with

$$\binom{m}{l}=\begin{cases}\frac{m!}{l!(m-l)!} & \text{if } l\leq m,\\ 0 & \text{if } l\not\leq m.\end{cases}$$

Therefore for the structure constants of the unitary Lie module $\mathfrak{D}(\Omega)$ we have the following expression

$$
\begin{aligned}
c_{ml}^{p} &= c_{ml}^{p}(q_m, q_l) = \\
&I_{p\leq m+l}\left(I_{l\leq p}\binom{m}{m+l-p} q_m(\hat{\xi})\left((-i\frac{\partial}{\partial\xi})^{(m+l-p)^+} q_l(\hat{\xi})\right) - \right. \\
&\left. I_{m\leq p}\binom{l}{m+l-p} q_l(\hat{\xi})\left((-i\frac{\partial}{\partial\xi})^{(m+l-p)^+} q_m(\hat{\xi})\right)\right).
\end{aligned}
\tag{8.37}
$$

Of particular interest to us are the structure constants $c_{ml}^{p} = c_{ml}^{p}(q_m, q_l)$ with $l = 0$ given according to (8.37) by

$$
\begin{aligned}
c_{m0}^{p} &= c_{m0}^{p}(q_m, q_0) = \\
&I_{p\leq m+0}\left(I_{0\leq p}\binom{m}{m+0-p} q_m(\hat{\xi})\left((-i\frac{\partial}{\partial\xi})^{(m+0-p)^+} q_0(\hat{\xi})\right) - \right. \\
&\qquad \left. I_{m\leq p}\binom{0}{m+0-p} q_0(\hat{\xi})\left((-i\frac{\partial}{\partial\xi})^{(m+0-p)^+} q_m(\hat{\xi})\right)\right) = \\
&I_{p\leq m}\left(\binom{m}{m-p} q_m(\hat{\xi})\left((-i\frac{\partial}{\partial\xi})^{(m-p)^+} q_0(\hat{\xi})\right) - \right. \\
&\qquad \left. I_{m\leq p}\binom{0}{m-p} q_0(\hat{\xi})\left((-i\frac{\partial}{\partial\xi})^{(m-p)^+} q_m(\hat{\xi})\right)\right) = \\
&I_{p<m}\binom{m}{m-p} q_m(\hat{\xi})\left((-i\frac{\partial}{\partial\xi})^{(m-p)^+} q_0(\hat{\xi})\right) = \\
&I_{p<m}\binom{m}{p} q_m(\hat{\xi})\left((-i\frac{\partial}{\partial\xi})^{(m-p)^+} q_0(\hat{\xi})\right),
\end{aligned}
\tag{8.38}
$$

where $l < m$ means that $l \leq m$ and $l \neq m$, and where we have used the following identity

$$
\binom{m}{m-p} = \binom{m}{p}, \quad p \leq m.
$$

Now consider the submodule $\mathfrak{A}_M(\Omega)$ of the module $\mathfrak{A}(\Omega)$ consisting of all differential operators with infinitely smooth coefficients

$$
Q_M = \sum_{|m|\leq M} q_m(\hat{\xi})(-i\frac{\partial}{\partial\xi})^m, \quad q_m(\xi) \in C^\infty(\Omega)
$$

of order not higher then M.

It is clear that the submodule $\mathfrak{A}_M(\Omega)$ is a unitary module. It is also clear that the unitary module $\mathfrak{A}_M(\Omega)$ has dimension $N(n,M) = \binom{M+n}{n}$ with the basis $\{(-i\frac{\partial}{\partial\xi})^m : |m| \le M\}$.

8.38. Remark. We comment that the dimension $N(n,M)$ of the unitary module $\mathfrak{A}_M(\Omega)$ is equal to the number of solutions to $m_1 + m_2 + \cdots + m_n \le M$ in nonnegative integers which is equal to $\binom{M+n}{n}$ (see, for example, [53] page 15).

The restriction of the map $\mathbf{ad}_{q(\hat{\xi})} : \mathfrak{A}(\Omega) \to \mathfrak{A}(\Omega)$ with $q(\hat{\xi})$ in $\mathfrak{M}(\Omega)$ defined by

$$\mathbf{ad}_{q(\hat{\xi})}\, Q = [q(\hat{\xi}), Q]$$

to $\mathfrak{A}_M(\Omega)$ has the image in $\mathfrak{A}_{M-1}(\Omega)$, that is, $\mathbf{ad}_{q(\hat{\xi})} : \mathfrak{A}_M(\Omega) \to \mathfrak{A}_{M-1}(\Omega)$. Indeed, with the help of expression (8.38) we have the following chain of equalities

$$\begin{aligned}
&\mathbf{ad}_{q(\hat{\xi})}\, Q_M = \\
&\quad [q(\hat{\xi}), \sum_{|m|\le M} q_m(\hat{\xi})(-i\frac{\partial}{\partial\xi})^m] = \\
&\quad \sum_{|m|\le M} [q(\hat{\xi}), q_m(\hat{\xi})(-i\frac{\partial}{\partial\xi})^m] = \\
&\quad -\sum_{|m|\le M}\sum_{p\in\mathbb{Z}_+^n} \left(I_{p<m} \binom{m}{p} q_m(\hat{\xi}) \times \right. \\
&\qquad \left. \left((-i\frac{\partial}{\partial\xi})^{(m-p)^+} q(\hat{\xi})\right)\right)(-i\frac{\partial}{\partial\xi})^p = \\
&\quad -\sum_{p\in\mathbb{Z}_+^n}\sum_{|m|\le M} \left(I_{p<m} \binom{m}{p} q_m(\hat{\xi}) \times \right. \\
&\qquad \left. \left((-i\frac{\partial}{\partial\xi})^{(m-p)^+} q(\hat{\xi})\right)\right)(-i\frac{\partial}{\partial\xi})^p =
\end{aligned} \tag{8.39}$$

$$- \sum_{|p| \le M-1} \Big(\sum_{|m| \le M} I_{p<m} \binom{m}{p} q_m(\hat{\xi}) \times \\ \Big(\big(-i\frac{\partial}{\partial \xi}\big)^{(m-p)^+} q(\hat{\xi}) \Big) \Big) \big(-i\frac{\partial}{\partial \xi}\big)^p.$$

8.39. Remark. We comment that for $M = 0$ the module $\mathfrak{A}_{M-1}(\Omega)$ is understood as the trivial module, that is, as the module with the single element $0_{\mathfrak{A}}$, where $0_{\mathfrak{A}}$ is the identity in the abelian group $(\mathfrak{A}, \oplus)$, namely the zero operator.

Therefore for each $q^{(1)}(\hat{\xi}), q^{(2)}(\hat{\xi}), \ldots, q^{(N)}(\hat{\xi})$ in $\mathfrak{M}(\Omega)$ the composition of the maps

$$\mathbf{ad}_{q^{(N)}(\hat{\xi})} \circ \cdots \circ \mathbf{ad}_{q^{(2)}(\hat{\xi})} \circ \mathbf{ad}_{q^{(1)}(\hat{\xi})}$$

maps $\mathfrak{A}_M(\Omega)$ to $\mathfrak{A}_{M-N}(\Omega)$ for $N \le M$ and to $0_{\mathfrak{A}}$ for $N > M$, where $0_{\mathfrak{A}}$ is the identity in the abelian group $(\mathfrak{A}, \oplus)$, that is, the zero operator.

Now our immediate goal is to find the explicit expression for the map

$$\mathbf{ad}_{q^{(2)}(\hat{\xi})} \circ \mathbf{ad}_{q^{(1)}(\hat{\xi})} : \mathfrak{A}_M(\Omega) \to \mathfrak{A}_{M-2}(\Omega),$$

where $q^{(1)}(\hat{\xi})$ and $q^{(2)}(\hat{\xi})$ are in $\mathfrak{M}(\Omega)$. With the help of expression (8.39) we obtain the following chain of equalities

$$\mathbf{ad}_{q^{(2)}(\hat{\xi})} \circ \mathbf{ad}_{q^{(1)}(\hat{\xi})} Q_M = \\ \mathbf{ad}_{q^{(2)}(\hat{\xi})} \circ \mathbf{ad}_{q^{(1)}(\hat{\xi})} \big(\sum_{|m| \le M} q_m(\hat{\xi}) (-i\frac{\partial}{\partial \xi})^m \big) = \\ - \mathbf{ad}_{q^{(2)}(\hat{\xi})} \sum_{|p| \le M-1} \Big(\sum_{|m| \le M} I_{p<m} \binom{m}{p} q_m(\hat{\xi}) \times \\ \Big(\big(-i\frac{\partial}{\partial \xi}\big)^{(m-p)^+} q^{(1)}(\hat{\xi}) \Big) \Big) \big(-i\frac{\partial}{\partial \xi}\big)^p = \tag{8.40}$$

$$\sum_{|l|\leq M-2}\left(\sum_{|p|\leq M-1} I_{l<p}\binom{p}{l}\times\right.$$
$$\left(\sum_{|m|\leq M} I_{p<m}\binom{m}{p} q_m(\hat{\xi})\left((-i\frac{\partial}{\partial\xi})^{(m-p)^+} q^{(1)}(\hat{\xi})\right)\right)\times$$
$$\left.\left((-i\frac{\partial}{\partial\xi})^{(p-l)^+} q^{(2)}(\hat{\xi})\right)\right)(-i\frac{\partial}{\partial\xi})^l.$$

Now we are ready to find the explicit expression for

$$\mathbf{ad}_{q^{(2)}(\hat{\xi})}\circ\mathbf{ad}_{q^{(1)}(\hat{\xi})} Q_M\mathbf{1},\quad M\geq 2,$$

where $q^{(1)}(\hat{\xi})$ and $q^{(2)}(\hat{\xi})$ are in $\mathfrak{M}(\Omega)$. With the help of the preceding expression (8.40) we obtain the following chain of equalities

$$\mathbf{ad}_{q^{(2)}(\hat{\xi})}\circ\mathbf{ad}_{q^{(1)}(\hat{\xi})} Q_M\mathbf{1}=$$
$$\sum_{|l|\leq M-2}\left(\sum_{|p|\leq M-1} I_{l<p}\binom{p}{l}\times\right.$$
$$\left(\sum_{|m|\leq M} I_{p<m}\binom{m}{p} q_m(\hat{\xi})\left((-i\frac{\partial}{\partial\xi})^{(m-p)^+} q^{(1)}(\hat{\xi})\right)\right)\times$$
$$\left.\left((-i\frac{\partial}{\partial\xi})^{(p-l)^+} q^{(2)}(\hat{\xi})\right)\right)(-i\frac{\partial}{\partial\xi})^l\mathbf{1}=$$
$$\sum_{|p|\leq M-1} I_{0<p}\binom{p}{0}\times \tag{8.41}$$
$$\left(\sum_{|m|\leq M} I_{p<m}\binom{m}{p} q_m(\hat{\xi})\left((-i\frac{\partial}{\partial\xi})^{(m-p)^+} q^{(1)}(\hat{\xi})\right)\right)\times$$
$$\left((-i\frac{\partial}{\partial\xi})^{(p-0)^+} q^{(2)}(\hat{\xi})\right)\mathbf{1}=$$

$$\sum_{|p|\le M-1} I_{0<p} \times$$
$$\Big(\sum_{|m|\le M} I_{p<m}\binom{m}{p}\, q_m(\xi)\,\Big(\big(-i\frac{\partial}{\partial\xi}\big)^{(m-p)^+} q^{(1)}(\xi)\Big)\Big)\times$$
$$\Big(\big(-i\frac{\partial}{\partial\xi}\big)^{p} q^{(2)}(\xi)\Big).$$

Now we find the explicit expression for the map $\mathbf{ad}_{q(\hat{\xi})}$: $\mathfrak{A}(\Omega) \to \mathfrak{A}(\Omega)$ with $q(\hat{\xi})$ in $\mathfrak{M}(\Omega)$. With the help of expression (8.38) we obtain the following chain of equalities

$$\begin{aligned}
&\mathbf{ad}_{q(\hat{\xi})}\, Q = \\
&\quad [q(\hat{\xi}), \sum_{m\in\mathbb{Z}^n_+} q_m(\hat{\xi})\big(-i\frac{\partial}{\partial\xi}\big)^m] = \\
&\quad \sum_{m\in\mathbb{Z}^n_+} [q(\hat{\xi}), q_m(\hat{\xi})\big(-i\frac{\partial}{\partial\xi}\big)^m] = \\
&\quad -\sum_{m\in\mathbb{Z}^n_+}\sum_{p\in\mathbb{Z}^n_+}\Big(I_{p<m}\binom{m}{p}\, q_m(\hat{\xi})\times \\
&\qquad\quad \Big(\big(-i\frac{\partial}{\partial\xi}\big)^{(m-p)^+} q(\hat{\xi})\Big)\Big)\big(-i\frac{\partial}{\partial\xi}\big)^p = \\
&\quad -\sum_{p\in\mathbb{Z}^n_+}\sum_{m\in\mathbb{Z}^n_+}\Big(I_{p<m}\binom{m}{p}\, q_m(\hat{\xi})\times \\
&\qquad\quad \Big(\big(-i\frac{\partial}{\partial\xi}\big)^{(m-p)^+} q(\hat{\xi})\Big)\Big)\big(-i\frac{\partial}{\partial\xi}\big)^p = \\
&\quad -\sum_{p\in\mathbb{Z}^n_+}\Big(\sum_{m\in\mathbb{Z}^n_+} I_{p<m}\binom{m}{p}\, q_m(\hat{\xi})\times \\
&\qquad\quad \Big(\big(-i\frac{\partial}{\partial\xi}\big)^{(m-p)^+} q(\hat{\xi})\Big)\Big)\big(-i\frac{\partial}{\partial\xi}\big)^p.
\end{aligned} \tag{8.42}$$

Now we find the explicit expression for the map

$$\mathbf{ad}_{q^{(2)}(\hat{\xi})} \circ \mathbf{ad}_{q^{(1)}(\hat{\xi})} : \mathfrak{A}(\Omega) \to \mathfrak{A}(\Omega)$$

with $q^{(1)}(\hat{\xi})$ and $q^{(2)}(\hat{\xi})$ in $\mathfrak{M}(\Omega)$. With the help of the preceding expression (8.42) we obtain the following chain of equalities

$$\begin{aligned}
&\mathbf{ad}_{q^{(2)}(\hat{\xi})} \circ \mathbf{ad}_{q^{(1)}(\hat{\xi})} Q = \\
&-\mathbf{ad}_{q^{(2)}(\hat{\xi})} \sum_{p\in\mathbb{Z}_+^n} \left(\sum_{m\in\mathbb{Z}_+^n} I_{p<m} \binom{m}{p} q_m(\hat{\xi}) \times \right. \\
&\qquad \left. \left(\left(-i\frac{\partial}{\partial\xi}\right)^{(m-p)^+} q^{(1)}(\hat{\xi}) \right) \right) \left(-i\frac{\partial}{\partial\xi}\right)^p = \\
&\sum_{l\in\mathbb{Z}_+^n} \left(\sum_{p\in\mathbb{Z}_+^n} I_{l<p} \binom{p}{l} \times \right. \\
&\qquad \left(\sum_{m\in\mathbb{Z}_+^n} I_{p<m} \binom{m}{p} q_m(\hat{\xi}) \left(\left(-i\frac{\partial}{\partial\xi}\right)^{(m-p)^+} q^{(1)}(\hat{\xi}) \right) \right) \times \\
&\qquad \left. \left(\left(-i\frac{\partial}{\partial\xi}\right)^{(p-l)^+} q^{(2)}(\hat{\xi}) \right) \right) \left(-i\frac{\partial}{\partial\xi}\right)^l.
\end{aligned} \tag{8.43}$$

Now we are ready to find the explicit expression for

$$\mathbf{ad}_{q^{(2)}(\hat{\xi})} \circ \mathbf{ad}_{q^{(1)}(\hat{\xi})} Q\, \mathbf{1}$$

with Q in $\mathfrak{A}(\Omega)$ and $q^{(1)}(\hat{\xi})$ and $q^{(2)}(\hat{\xi})$ in $\mathfrak{M}(\Omega)$. With the help of the preceding expression (8.43) we obtain the following chain of equalities

$$\begin{aligned}
&\mathbf{ad}_{q^{(2)}(\hat{\xi})} \circ \mathbf{ad}_{q^{(1)}(\hat{\xi})} Q\, \mathbf{1} = \\
&\sum_{l\in\mathbb{Z}_+^n} \left(\sum_{p\in\mathbb{Z}_+^n} I_{l<p} \binom{p}{l} \times \right. \\
&\qquad \left(\sum_{m\in\mathbb{Z}_+^n} I_{p<m} \binom{m}{p} q_m(\hat{\xi}) \left(\left(-i\frac{\partial}{\partial\xi}\right)^{(m-p)^+} q^{(1)}(\hat{\xi}) \right) \right) \times \\
&\qquad \left. \left(\left(-i\frac{\partial}{\partial\xi}\right)^{(p-l)^+} q^{(2)}(\hat{\xi}) \right) \right) \left(-i\frac{\partial}{\partial\xi}\right)^l \mathbf{1} =
\end{aligned} \tag{8.44}$$

$$\sum_{p\in\mathbb{Z}_+^n} I_{0<p}\binom{p}{0}\times$$

$$\left(\sum_{m\in\mathbb{Z}_+^n} I_{p<m}\binom{m}{p}\, q_m(\hat{\xi})\left(\left(-i\frac{\partial}{\partial\xi}\right)^{(m-p)^+} q^{(1)}(\hat{\xi})\right)\right)\times$$

$$\left(\left(-i\frac{\partial}{\partial\xi}\right)^{(p-0)^+} q^{(2)}(\hat{\xi})\right)\mathbf{1} =$$

$$\sum_{p\in\mathbb{Z}_+^n} I_{0<p}\times$$

$$\left(\sum_{m\in\mathbb{Z}_+^n} I_{p<m}\binom{m}{p}\, q_m(\xi)\left(\left(-i\frac{\partial}{\partial\xi}\right)^{(m-p)^+} q^{(1)}(\xi)\right)\right)\times$$

$$\left(\left(-i\frac{\partial}{\partial\xi}\right)^{p} q^{(2)}(\xi)\right).$$

Denote by $R^\infty(\Omega)$ the subspace of the space $C^\infty(\Omega)$ consisting of all infinitely differentiable real-valued functions on Ω.

Consider the subring $\mathfrak{M}(\Omega)$ of the ring $\boldsymbol{\mathfrak{M}}(\Omega)$ consisting of operators on $R^\infty(\Omega)$ of multiplication by functions in $R^\infty(\Omega)$.

It is clear that $\mathfrak{M}(\Omega)$ is a commutative ring with the identity which is the operator of multiplication by the function $\mathbf{1}$ in $R^\infty(\Omega)$ identically equal to unity.

Consider the submodule $\mathfrak{A}(\Omega)$ of the module $\boldsymbol{\mathfrak{A}}(\Omega)$ consisting of all real formal analytic quasidifferential operators with infinitely smooth coefficients

$$\mathfrak{Q} = \sum_{m\in\mathbb{Z}_+^n} \mathfrak{q}_m(\hat{\xi})\frac{\partial}{\partial\xi}^m, \quad \mathfrak{q}_m(\xi)\in R^\infty(\Omega)$$

over the ring $\mathfrak{M}(\Omega)$.

It is clear that $\mathfrak{A}(\Omega)$ is a unitary module. It is also clear that the unitary module $\mathfrak{A}(\Omega)$ is infinite dimensional with the basis $\{\frac{\partial}{\partial\xi}^m : m\in\mathbb{Z}_+^n\}$.

Equipped with the binary operation $[,]$ defined as the commutator $[,]$ of linear operators the unitary module $\mathfrak{A}(\Omega)$ is turned into a unitary Lie module which we denote as $\mathfrak{D}(\Omega)$.

8.40. Remark. It is clear that $\mathfrak{D}(\Omega)$ is the Lie submodule of the Lie module $\mathfrak{D}(\Omega)$.

Our immediate goal is to find the structure constants of the unitary Lie module $\mathfrak{D}(\Omega)$. In order to do this, for each m and l in $\mathbb{Z}_+^n$ we need the following chain of equalities

$$\begin{aligned}
&[\mathfrak{q}_m(\hat{\xi})\frac{\partial}{\partial\xi}^m, \mathfrak{q}_l(\hat{\xi})\frac{\partial}{\partial\xi}^l] = \\
&\mathfrak{q}_m(\hat{\xi})\frac{\partial}{\partial\xi}^m \mathfrak{q}_l(\hat{\xi})\frac{\partial}{\partial\xi}^l - \mathfrak{q}_l(\hat{\xi})\frac{\partial}{\partial\xi}^l \mathfrak{q}_m(\hat{\xi})\frac{\partial}{\partial\xi}^m = \\
&\mathfrak{q}_m(\hat{\xi})\Big(\sum_{k\le m}\binom{m}{k}\Big(\frac{\partial}{\partial\xi}^k \mathfrak{q}_l(\hat{\xi})\Big)\frac{\partial}{\partial\xi}^{m-k}\Big)\frac{\partial}{\partial\xi}^l - \\
&\quad\mathfrak{q}_l(\hat{\xi})\Big(\sum_{k\le l}\binom{l}{k}\Big(\frac{\partial}{\partial\xi}^k \mathfrak{q}_m(\hat{\xi})\Big)\frac{\partial}{\partial\xi}^{l-k}\Big)\frac{\partial}{\partial\xi}^m = \\
&\mathfrak{q}_m(\hat{\xi})\sum_{k\le m}\binom{m}{k}\Big(\frac{\partial}{\partial\xi}^k \mathfrak{q}_l(\hat{\xi})\Big)\frac{\partial}{\partial\xi}^{m+l-k} - \\
&\quad\mathfrak{q}_l(\hat{\xi})\sum_{k\le l}\binom{l}{k}\Big(\frac{\partial}{\partial\xi}^k \mathfrak{q}_m(\hat{\xi})\Big)\frac{\partial}{\partial\xi}^{m+l-k} = \qquad (8.45)\\
&\mathfrak{q}_m(\hat{\xi})\sum_{k\le m+l} I_{k\le m}\binom{m}{k}\Big(\frac{\partial}{\partial\xi}^k \mathfrak{q}_l(\hat{\xi})\Big)\frac{\partial}{\partial\xi}^{m+l-k} - \\
&\quad\mathfrak{q}_l(\hat{\xi})\sum_{k\le m+l} I_{k\le l}\binom{l}{k}\Big(\frac{\partial}{\partial\xi}^k \mathfrak{q}_m(\hat{\xi})\Big)\frac{\partial}{\partial\xi}^{m+l-k} = \\
&\sum_{k\le m+l}\Big(I_{k\le m}\binom{m}{k}\mathfrak{q}_m(\hat{\xi})\Big(\frac{\partial}{\partial\xi}^k \mathfrak{q}_l(\hat{\xi})\Big) - \\
&\quad I_{k\le l}\binom{l}{k}\mathfrak{q}_l(\hat{\xi})\Big(\frac{\partial}{\partial\xi}^k \mathfrak{q}_m(\hat{\xi})\Big)\Big)\frac{\partial}{\partial\xi}^{m+l-k} =
\end{aligned}$$

$$\sum_{p\leq m+l}\left(I_{m+l-p\leq m}\binom{m}{m+l-p}\mathfrak{q}_m(\hat{\xi})\left(\frac{\partial}{\partial\xi}^{m+l-p}\mathfrak{q}_l(\hat{\xi})\right)-\right.$$
$$\left.I_{m+l-p\leq l}\binom{l}{m+l-p}\mathfrak{q}_l(\hat{\xi})\left(\frac{\partial}{\partial\xi}^{m+l-p}\mathfrak{q}_m(\hat{\xi})\right)\right)\frac{\partial}{\partial\xi}^{p}=$$
$$\sum_{p\in\mathbb{Z}_+^n}I_{p\leq m+l}\left(I_{l\leq p}\binom{m}{m+l-p}\mathfrak{q}_m(\hat{\xi})\left(\frac{\partial}{\partial\xi}^{(m+l-p)^+}\mathfrak{q}_l(\hat{\xi})\right)-\right.$$
$$\left.I_{m\leq p}\binom{l}{m+l-p}\mathfrak{q}_l(\hat{\xi})\left(\frac{\partial}{\partial\xi}^{(m+l-p)^+}\mathfrak{q}_m(\hat{\xi})\right)\right)\frac{\partial}{\partial\xi}^{p}.$$

8.41. Remark. We also comment that in the preceding chain of equalities (8.36) have used the following identity (see, for example, [1] page 2)

$$\frac{\partial}{\partial\xi}^{m}\mathfrak{q}(\hat{\xi})=\sum_{l\leq m}\binom{m}{l}\left(\frac{\partial}{\partial\xi}^{l}\mathfrak{q}(\hat{\xi})\right)\frac{\partial}{\partial\xi}^{m-l}. \qquad (8.46)$$

Therefore for the structure constants of the unitary Lie module $\mathfrak{D}(\Omega)$ we have the following expression

$$c^p_{ml}=c^p_{ml}(\mathfrak{q}_m,\mathfrak{q}_l)=$$
$$I_{p\leq m+l}\left(I_{l\leq p}\binom{m}{m+l-p}\mathfrak{q}_m(\hat{\xi})\left(\frac{\partial}{\partial\xi}^{(m+l-p)^+}\mathfrak{q}_l(\hat{\xi})\right)-\right.$$
$$\left.I_{m\leq p}\binom{l}{m+l-p}\mathfrak{q}_l(\hat{\xi})\left(\frac{\partial}{\partial\xi}^{(m+l-p)^+}\mathfrak{q}_m(\hat{\xi})\right)\right). \qquad (8.47)$$

Of particular interest to us are the structure constants $c^p_{ml}=$

$c^p_{ml}(\mathfrak{q}_m, \mathfrak{q}_l)$ with $l = 0$ given according to (8.47) by

$$\begin{aligned}
c^p_{m0} &= c^p_{m0}(\mathfrak{q}_m, \mathfrak{q}_0) = \\
&I_{p\leq m+0}\left(I_{0\leq p}\binom{m}{m+0-p}\mathfrak{q}_m(\hat{\xi})\left(\frac{\partial}{\partial\xi}^{(m+0-p)^+}\mathfrak{q}_0(\hat{\xi})\right) - \right. \\
&\qquad \left. I_{m\leq p}\binom{0}{m+0-p}\mathfrak{q}_0(\hat{\xi})\left(\frac{\partial}{\partial\xi}^{(m+0-p)^+}\mathfrak{q}_m(\hat{\xi})\right)\right) = \\
&I_{p\leq m}\left(\binom{m}{m-p}\mathfrak{q}_m(\hat{\xi})\left(\frac{\partial}{\partial\xi}^{(m-p)^+}\mathfrak{q}_0(\hat{\xi})\right) - \right. \\
&\qquad \left. I_{m\leq p}\binom{0}{m-p}\mathfrak{q}_0(\hat{\xi})\left(\frac{\partial}{\partial\xi}^{(m-p)^+}\mathfrak{q}_m(\hat{\xi})\right)\right) = \\
&I_{p<m}\binom{m}{m-p}\mathfrak{q}_m(\hat{\xi})\left(\frac{\partial}{\partial\xi}^{(m-p)^+}\mathfrak{q}_0(\hat{\xi})\right) = \\
&I_{p<m}\binom{m}{p}\mathfrak{q}_m(\hat{\xi})\left(\frac{\partial}{\partial\xi}^{(m-p)^+}\mathfrak{q}_0(\hat{\xi})\right).
\end{aligned} \tag{8.48}$$

Now consider a submodule $\mathfrak{A}_M(\Omega)$ of the module $\mathfrak{A}(\Omega)$ consisting of all real differential operators with infinitely smooth coefficients

$$\mathfrak{Q}_M = \sum_{|m|\leq M} \mathfrak{q}_m(\hat{\xi})\frac{\partial}{\partial\xi}^m, \quad \mathfrak{q}_m(\xi) \in R^\infty(\Omega)$$

of order not higher then M.

It is clear that the submodule $\mathfrak{A}_M(\Omega)$ is a unitary module. It is also clear that the unitary module $\mathfrak{A}_M(\Omega)$ has dimension $N(n, M) = \binom{M+n}{n}$ with the basis $\{\frac{\partial}{\partial\xi}^m : |m| \leq M\}$.

8.42. Remark. We comment that the dimension $N(n, M)$ of the unitary module $\mathfrak{A}_M(\Omega)$ is equal to the number of solutions to $m_1 + m_2 + \cdots + m_n \leq M$ in nonnegative integers which is equal to $\binom{M+n}{n}$ (see, for example, [53] page 15).

The restriction of the map $\mathbf{ad}_{\mathfrak{q}(\hat{\xi})} : \mathfrak{A}(\Omega) \to \mathfrak{A}(\Omega)$ with $\mathfrak{q}(\hat{\xi})$ in $\mathfrak{M}(\Omega)$ defined by

$$\mathbf{ad}_{\mathfrak{q}(\hat{\xi})}\mathfrak{Q} = [\mathfrak{q}(\hat{\xi}), \mathfrak{Q}]$$

to $\mathfrak{A}_M(\Omega)$ has the image in $\mathfrak{A}_{M-1}(\Omega)$, that is, $\mathbf{ad}_{\mathfrak{q}(\hat{\xi})} : \mathfrak{A}_M(\Omega) \to \mathfrak{A}_{M-1}(\Omega)$. Indeed, with the help of expression (8.48) we have the following chain of equalities

$$\begin{aligned}
&\mathbf{ad}_{\mathfrak{q}(\hat{\xi})}\,\mathfrak{Q}_M = \\
&\quad [\mathfrak{q}(\hat{\xi}), \sum_{|m|\le M} \mathfrak{q}_m(\hat{\xi}) \frac{\partial}{\partial \xi}^m] = \\
&\quad \sum_{|m|\le M} [\mathfrak{q}(\hat{\xi}), \mathfrak{q}_m(\hat{\xi}) \frac{\partial}{\partial \xi}^m] = \\
&\quad -\sum_{|m|\le M} \sum_{p\in\mathbb{Z}^n_+} \left(I_{p<m} \binom{m}{p} \mathfrak{q}_m(\hat{\xi}) \times \right. \\
&\quad \left. \left(\frac{\partial}{\partial \xi}^{(m-p)^+} \mathfrak{q}(\hat{\xi}) \right) \right) \frac{\partial}{\partial \xi}^p = \\
&\quad -\sum_{p\in\mathbb{Z}^n_+} \sum_{|m|\le M} \left(I_{p<m} \binom{m}{p} \mathfrak{q}_m(\hat{\xi}) \times \right. \\
&\quad \left. \left(\frac{\partial}{\partial \xi}^{(m-p)^+} \mathfrak{q}(\hat{\xi}) \right) \right) \frac{\partial}{\partial \xi}^p = \\
&\quad -\sum_{|p|\le M-1} \left(\sum_{|m|\le M} I_{p<m} \binom{m}{p} \mathfrak{q}_m(\hat{\xi}) \times \right. \\
&\quad \left. \left(\frac{\partial}{\partial \xi}^{(m-p)^+} \mathfrak{q}(\hat{\xi}) \right) \right) \frac{\partial}{\partial \xi}^p .
\end{aligned} \tag{8.49}$$

8.43. Remark. We comment that for $M = 0$ the module $\mathfrak{A}_{M-1}(\Omega)$ is understood as the trivial module, that is, as the module with the single element $0_{\mathfrak{A}}$, where $0_{\mathfrak{A}}$ is the identity in the abelian group $(\mathfrak{A}, \oplus)$, namely the zero operator.

Therefore for each $\mathfrak{q}^{(1)}(\hat{\xi}), \mathfrak{q}^{(2)}(\hat{\xi}), \ldots, \mathfrak{q}^{(N)}(\hat{\xi})$ in $\mathfrak{M}(\Omega)$ the composition of the maps

$$\mathbf{ad}_{\mathfrak{q}^{(N)}(\hat{\xi})} \circ \cdots \circ \mathbf{ad}_{\mathfrak{q}^{(2)}(\hat{\xi})} \circ \mathbf{ad}_{\mathfrak{q}^{(1)}(\hat{\xi})}$$

maps $\mathfrak{A}_M(\Omega)$ to $\mathfrak{A}_{M-N}(\Omega)$ for $N \le M$ and to $0_{\mathfrak{A}}$ for $N > M$.

Now our immediate goal is to find the explicit expression for the map

$$\mathbf{ad}_{\mathfrak{q}^{(2)}(\hat{\xi})} \circ \mathbf{ad}_{\mathfrak{q}^{(1)}(\hat{\xi})} : \mathfrak{A}_M(\Omega) \to \mathfrak{A}_{M-2}(\Omega),$$

where $\mathfrak{q}^{(1)}(\hat{\xi})$ and $\mathfrak{q}^{(2)}(\hat{\xi})$ are in $\mathfrak{M}(\Omega)$. With the help of expression (8.49) we obtain the following chain of equalities

$$\begin{aligned}
&\mathbf{ad}_{\mathfrak{q}^{(2)}(\hat{\xi})} \circ \mathbf{ad}_{\mathfrak{q}^{(1)}(\hat{\xi})} \mathfrak{Q}_M = \\
&\mathbf{ad}_{\mathfrak{q}^{(2)}(\hat{\xi})} \circ \mathbf{ad}_{\mathfrak{q}^{(1)}(\hat{\xi})} \Big(\sum_{|m|\le M} \mathfrak{q}_m(\hat{\xi}) \frac{\partial}{\partial \xi}^{m} \Big) = \\
&- \mathbf{ad}_{\mathfrak{q}^{(2)}(\hat{\xi})} \sum_{|p|\le M-1} \Bigg(\sum_{|m|\le M} I_{p<m} \binom{m}{p} \mathfrak{q}_m(\hat{\xi}) \times \\
&\qquad \Big(\frac{\partial}{\partial \xi}^{(m-p)^+} \mathfrak{q}^{(1)}(\hat{\xi}) \Big) \Bigg) \frac{\partial}{\partial \xi}^{p} = \\
&\sum_{|l|\le M-2} \Bigg(\sum_{|p|\le M-1} I_{l<p} \binom{p}{l} \times \\
&\qquad \Bigg(\sum_{|m|\le M} I_{p<m} \binom{m}{p} \mathfrak{q}_m(\hat{\xi}) \Big(\frac{\partial}{\partial \xi}^{(m-p)^+} \mathfrak{q}^{(1)}(\hat{\xi}) \Big) \Bigg) \times \\
&\qquad \Big(\frac{\partial}{\partial \xi}^{(p-l)^+} \mathfrak{q}^{(2)}(\hat{\xi}) \Big) \Bigg) \frac{\partial}{\partial \xi}^{l}.
\end{aligned} \tag{8.50}$$

Now we are ready to find the explicit expression for

$$\mathbf{ad}_{\mathfrak{q}^{(2)}(\hat{\xi})} \circ \mathbf{ad}_{\mathfrak{q}^{(1)}(\hat{\xi})} \mathfrak{Q}_M \mathbf{1}, \quad M \ge 2,$$

where $\mathfrak{q}^{(1)}(\hat{\xi})$ and $\mathfrak{q}^{(2)}(\hat{\xi})$ are in $\mathfrak{M}(\Omega)$. With the help of the preceding expression (8.50) we obtain the following chain of equalities

$$\mathbf{ad}_{\mathfrak{q}^{(2)}(\hat{\xi})} \circ \mathbf{ad}_{\mathfrak{q}^{(1)}(\hat{\xi})} \mathfrak{Q}_M \mathbf{1} =$$

$$\sum_{|l| \le M-2} \left(\sum_{|p| \le M-1} I_{l<p} \binom{p}{l} \times \right.$$

$$\left(\sum_{|m| \le M} I_{p<m} \binom{m}{p} \mathfrak{q}_m(\hat{\xi}) \left(\frac{\partial}{\partial \xi}^{(m-p)^+} \mathfrak{q}^{(1)}(\hat{\xi}) \right) \right) \times$$

$$\left. \left(\frac{\partial}{\partial \xi}^{(p-l)^+} \mathfrak{q}^{(2)}(\hat{\xi}) \right) \right) \frac{\partial}{\partial \xi}^{l} \mathbf{1} =$$

$$\sum_{|p| \le M-1} I_{0<p} \binom{p}{0} \times$$

$$\left(\sum_{|m| \le M} I_{p<m} \binom{m}{p} \mathfrak{q}_m(\hat{\xi}) \left(\frac{\partial}{\partial \xi}^{(m-p)^+} \mathfrak{q}^{(1)}(\hat{\xi}) \right) \right) \times \tag{8.51}$$

$$\left(\frac{\partial}{\partial \xi}^{(p-0)^+} \mathfrak{q}^{(2)}(\hat{\xi}) \right) \mathbf{1} =$$

$$\sum_{|p| \le M-1} I_{0<p} \times$$

$$\left(\sum_{|m| \le M} I_{p<m} \binom{m}{p} \mathfrak{q}_m(\xi) \left(\frac{\partial}{\partial \xi}^{(m-p)^+} \mathfrak{q}^{(1)}(\xi) \right) \right) \times$$

$$\left(\frac{\partial}{\partial \xi}^{p} \mathfrak{q}^{(2)}(\xi) \right).$$

Now we find the explicit expression for the map $\mathbf{ad}_{\mathfrak{q}(\hat{\xi})} : \mathfrak{A}(\Omega) \to \mathfrak{A}(\Omega)$ with $\mathfrak{q}(\hat{\xi})$ in $\mathfrak{M}(\Omega)$. With the help of expression (8.48) we obtain the following chain of equalities

$$\mathbf{ad}_{\mathfrak{q}(\hat{\xi})} \mathfrak{Q} =$$

$$[\mathfrak{q}(\hat{\xi}), \sum_{m \in \mathbb{Z}_+^n} \mathfrak{q}_m(\hat{\xi}) \frac{\partial}{\partial \xi}^{m}] = \tag{8.52}$$

$$\sum_{m\in\mathbb{Z}_+^n} [\mathfrak{q}(\hat{\xi}), \mathfrak{q}_m(\hat{\xi})\frac{\partial}{\partial\xi}^m] =$$

$$-\sum_{m\in\mathbb{Z}_+^n}\sum_{p\in\mathbb{Z}_+^n}\left(I_{p<m}\binom{m}{p}\mathfrak{q}_m(\hat{\xi})\times\right.$$
$$\left.\left(\frac{\partial}{\partial\xi}^{(m-p)^+}\mathfrak{q}(\hat{\xi})\right)\right)\frac{\partial}{\partial\xi}^p =$$
$$-\sum_{p\in\mathbb{Z}_+^n}\sum_{m\in\mathbb{Z}_+^n}\left(I_{p<m}\binom{m}{p}\mathfrak{q}_m(\hat{\xi})\times\right.$$
$$\left.\left(\frac{\partial}{\partial\xi}^{(m-p)^+}\mathfrak{q}(\hat{\xi})\right)\right)\frac{\partial}{\partial\xi}^p =$$
$$-\sum_{p\in\mathbb{Z}_+^n}\left(\sum_{m\in\mathbb{Z}_+^n}I_{p<m}\binom{m}{p}\mathfrak{q}_m(\hat{\xi})\times\right.$$
$$\left.\left(\frac{\partial}{\partial\xi}^{(m-p)^+}\mathfrak{q}(\hat{\xi})\right)\right)\frac{\partial}{\partial\xi}^p.$$

Now we find the explicit expression for the map

$$\mathbf{ad}_{\mathfrak{q}^{(2)}(\hat{\xi})}\circ\mathbf{ad}_{\mathfrak{q}^{(1)}(\hat{\xi})}:\mathfrak{A}(\Omega)\to\mathfrak{A}(\Omega)$$

with $\mathfrak{q}^{(1)}(\hat{\xi})$ and $\mathfrak{q}^{(2)}(\hat{\xi})$ in $\mathfrak{M}(\Omega)$. With the help of the preceding expression (8.52) we obtain the following chain of equalities

$$\mathbf{ad}_{\mathfrak{q}^{(2)}(\hat{\xi})}\circ\mathbf{ad}_{\mathfrak{q}^{(1)}(\hat{\xi})}\mathfrak{Q} =$$
$$-\,\mathbf{ad}_{\mathfrak{q}^{(2)}(\hat{\xi})}\sum_{p\in\mathbb{Z}_+^n}\left(\sum_{m\in\mathbb{Z}_+^n}I_{p<m}\binom{m}{p}\mathfrak{q}_m(\hat{\xi})\times\right.$$
$$\left.\left(\frac{\partial}{\partial\xi}^{(m-p)^+}\mathfrak{q}^{(1)}(\hat{\xi})\right)\right)\frac{\partial}{\partial\xi}^p = \tag{8.53}$$

$$\sum_{l\in\mathbb{Z}^n_+}\Bigg(\sum_{p\in\mathbb{Z}^n_+} I_{l<p}\binom{p}{l}\times$$

$$\bigg(\sum_{m\in\mathbb{Z}^n_+} I_{p<m}\binom{m}{p}\,\mathfrak{q}_m(\hat{\xi})\Big(\frac{\partial}{\partial\xi}^{(m-p)^+}\mathfrak{q}^{(1)}(\hat{\xi})\Big)\bigg)\times$$

$$\Big(\frac{\partial}{\partial\xi}^{(p-l)^+}\mathfrak{q}^{(2)}(\hat{\xi})\Big)\Bigg)\frac{\partial}{\partial\xi}^{l}.$$

Now we are ready to find the explicit expression for

$$\mathbf{ad}_{\mathfrak{q}^{(2)}(\hat{\xi})}\circ\mathbf{ad}_{\mathfrak{q}^{(1)}(\hat{\xi})}\,\mathfrak{Q}\,\mathbf{1}$$

with $\mathfrak{Q}$ in $\mathfrak{A}(\Omega)$ and $\mathfrak{q}^{(1)}(\hat{\xi})$ and $\mathfrak{q}^{(2)}(\hat{\xi})$ in $\mathfrak{M}(\Omega)$. With the help of the preceding expression (8.53) we obtain the following chain of equalities

$$\begin{aligned}
&\mathbf{ad}_{\mathfrak{q}^{(2)}(\hat{\xi})}\circ\mathbf{ad}_{\mathfrak{q}^{(1)}(\hat{\xi})}\,\mathfrak{Q}\,\mathbf{1}=\\
&\quad\sum_{l\in\mathbb{Z}^n_+}\Bigg(\sum_{p\in\mathbb{Z}^n_+} I_{l<p}\binom{p}{l}\times\\
&\qquad\bigg(\sum_{m\in\mathbb{Z}^n_+} I_{p<m}\binom{m}{p}\,\mathfrak{q}_m(\hat{\xi})\Big(\frac{\partial}{\partial\xi}^{(m-p)^+}\mathfrak{q}^{(1)}(\hat{\xi})\Big)\bigg)\times\\
&\qquad\Big(\frac{\partial}{\partial\xi}^{(p-l)^+}\mathfrak{q}^{(2)}(\hat{\xi})\Big)\Bigg)\frac{\partial}{\partial\xi}^{l}\,\mathbf{1}=\\
&\quad\sum_{p\in\mathbb{Z}^n_+} I_{0<p}\binom{p}{0}\times\\
&\qquad\bigg(\sum_{m\in\mathbb{Z}^n_+} I_{p<m}\binom{m}{p}\,\mathfrak{q}_m(\hat{\xi})\Big(\frac{\partial}{\partial\xi}^{(m-p)^+}\mathfrak{q}^{(1)}(\hat{\xi})\Big)\bigg)\times\\
&\qquad\Big(\frac{\partial}{\partial\xi}^{(p-0)^+}\mathfrak{q}^{(2)}(\hat{\xi})\Big)\,\mathbf{1}=
\end{aligned}\tag{8.54}$$

$$\sum_{p \in \mathbb{Z}_+^n} I_{0<p} \times$$
$$\left(\sum_{m \in \mathbb{Z}_+^n} I_{p<m} \binom{m}{p} \mathfrak{q}_m(\xi) \left(\frac{\partial}{\partial \xi}^{(m-p)^+} \mathfrak{q}^{(1)}(\xi) \right) \right) \times$$
$$\left(\frac{\partial}{\partial \xi}^{p} \mathfrak{q}^{(2)}(\xi) \right).$$

8.3 Beliefs-Preferences Gauge Symmetry Group for a Markovian Generalized Market Populace with Generalized Beliefs Generated by Quasidifferential Operators

Consider a Markovian generalized market populace $\mathbb{H} = \mathbb{B} \times \mathbb{U}$, or more precisely $\mathbb{H} = \mathbb{L} \times \mathbb{U}$. We formally represent each generator $\mathsf{L}(t)$ in L from $\mathbb{L}$ as a real pseudodifferential operator on an appropriate space of real-valued functions on Ω equal to $\mathbb{R}^n_{++}$, that is, on an appropriate subspace of Π. According to relations (8.27) and (8.28) the real symbol $\mathsf{L}(t, s, p)$ of $\mathsf{L}(t)$ is given by

$$\mathsf{L}(t, s, p) = \sum_{m \in \mathbb{Z}_+^n} \left(\frac{p^m}{m!} \left((-\mathbf{ad}_{\hat{s}})^m \, \mathsf{L}(t) \right) \mathbf{1} \right), \tag{8.55}$$

where s is in $\mathbb{R}^n_{++}$ and p is in $\mathbb{R}^n$. Now according to relation (8.29) each generator $\mathsf{L}(t)$ can be formally represented as a function of the vector operators

$$\hat{s} = (\hat{s}_1, \hat{s}_2, \ldots, \hat{s}_n)$$

and

$$\frac{\partial}{\partial s} = \left(\frac{\partial}{\partial s_1}, \frac{\partial}{\partial s_2}, \ldots, \frac{\partial}{\partial s_n}\right)$$

as follows

$$\mathsf{L}(t) = \mathsf{L}(t, \hat{s}, \frac{\partial}{\partial s}), \quad t \in \mathcal{T}, \tag{8.56}$$

where each $\hat{s}_i$ is the operator of multiplication by s_i.

Moreover, according to relations (8.24), (8.25) and (8.26) each generator $\mathsf{L}(t)$ can also be formally represented as an analytic quasidifferential operator

$$\mathsf{L}(t) = \sum_{m \in \mathbb{Z}^n_+} \mathsf{L}_m(t, \hat{s}) \frac{\partial}{\partial s}^m, \tag{8.57}$$

with the defining sequence given by

$$\mathsf{L}_M(t) = \sum_{|m| \leq M} \mathsf{L}_m(t, \hat{s}) \frac{\partial}{\partial s}^m, \tag{8.58}$$

where the operator coefficients $\mathsf{L}_m(t, \hat{s})$ are defined by

$$\mathsf{L}_m(t, \hat{s}) = \frac{1}{m!} \left((-\mathbf{ad}_{\hat{s}})^m \, \mathsf{L}(t) \right) \mathbf{1}, \quad m \in \mathbb{Z}^n_+. \tag{8.59}$$

Since a market environment $\mathbf{V}$ generated by

$$\boldsymbol{L} = \{\boldsymbol{L}(t) : \Pi \to \Pi \,|\, t \in \mathcal{T}\},$$

is a particular case of a generalized belief for a generalized market participant with the preference consisting of the identity operators, that is, for a representative generalized market participant we can formally represent each generator $\boldsymbol{L}(t)$ as a real pseudodifferential operator on an appropriate space of real-valued functions on Ω equal to $\mathbb{R}^n_{++}$, that is, on an appropriate subspace of Π. According to relation (8.55) the real symbol $\boldsymbol{L}(t, s, p)$ of $\boldsymbol{L}(t)$ is given by

$$\boldsymbol{L}(t, s, p) = \sum_{m \in \mathbb{Z}^n_+} \Big(\frac{p^m}{m!} \left((-\mathbf{ad}_{\hat{s}})^m \, \boldsymbol{L}(t) \right) \mathbf{1} \Big). \tag{8.60}$$

According to relation (8.56) each generator $\boldsymbol{L}(t)$ can be formally represented as a function of the vector operators $\hat{s}$ and $\frac{\partial}{\partial s}$ as follows

$$\boldsymbol{L}(t) = \boldsymbol{L}(t, \hat{s}, \frac{\partial}{\partial s}), \quad t \in \mathcal{T}. \tag{8.61}$$

Moreover, according to relations (8.57), (8.58) and (8.59) each generator $\boldsymbol{L}(t)$ can also be formally represented as a real analytic quasidifferential operator

$$\boldsymbol{L}(t) = \sum_{m \in \mathbb{Z}^n_+} \boldsymbol{L}_m(t, \hat{s}) \frac{\partial}{\partial s}^m, \tag{8.62}$$

with the defining sequence given by

$$\boldsymbol{L}_M(t) = \sum_{|m| \le M} \boldsymbol{L}_m(t, \hat{s}) \frac{\partial}{\partial s}^m, \tag{8.63}$$

where the operator coefficients $\boldsymbol{L}_m(t, \hat{s})$ are defined by

$$\boldsymbol{L}_m(t, \hat{s}) = \frac{1}{m!} \left((-\mathbf{ad}_{\hat{s}})^m \boldsymbol{L}(t)\right)\mathbf{1}, \quad m \in \mathbb{Z}^n_+. \tag{8.64}$$

8.44. Remark. We note that since

$$\boldsymbol{L}(t)\, \mathbf{1} = -r(s, t)$$

the operator coefficient $\boldsymbol{L}_m(t, \hat{s})$ with $m = 0$ in $\mathbb{Z}^n_+$ is nothing but the operator of multiplication by the function $-r(s, t)$, where $r(s, t)$ is the continuously compounded interest rate.

The transformations $\hat{\mathfrak{g}} = (\hat{\mathfrak{g}}_{\mathsf{L}}, \hat{\mathfrak{g}}_{\mathcal{U}})$ in the beliefs-preferences gauge symmetry group $\hat{\mathfrak{G}}$ defined in relations (3.72) and (3.73) take the following form

$$\mathsf{L}(t, \hat{s}, \frac{\partial}{\partial s}) \xrightarrow{\hat{\mathfrak{g}}_{\mathsf{L}}} \mathsf{L}\left(t, \hat{s}, \frac{\partial}{\partial s} + \frac{\mathbf{u}'_s(t,t)}{\mathbf{u}'(t,t)}\right) + \frac{\mathbf{u}'_t(t,t)}{\mathbf{u}'(t,t)} \quad \text{and}$$

$$\boldsymbol{u}'(t, T) \xrightarrow{\hat{\mathfrak{g}}_{\mathcal{U}}} \mathbf{u}'^{-1}(t, T)\boldsymbol{u}'(t, T), \tag{8.65}$$

where $\mathbf{u}'_s(t,t)$ is defined in the comments to relation (4.18), and where the operator $\mathsf{L}\big(t,\hat{s},\frac{\partial}{\partial s}+\frac{\mathbf{u}'_s(t,t)}{\mathbf{u}'(t,t)}\big)$ is understood as the formal power series

$$\mathsf{L}\big(t,\hat{s},\frac{\partial}{\partial s}+\frac{\mathbf{u}'_s(t,t)}{\mathbf{u}'(t,t)}\big)=\sum_{m\in\mathbb{Z}^n_+}\boldsymbol{L}_m(t,\hat{s})\,\big(\frac{\partial}{\partial s}+\frac{\mathbf{u}'_s(t,t)}{\mathbf{u}'(t,t)}\big)^m. \tag{8.66}$$

8.45. Remark. It is clear that the operator $\mathsf{L}\big(t,\hat{s},\frac{\partial}{\partial s}+\frac{\mathbf{u}'_s(t,t)}{\mathbf{u}'(t,t)}\big)$ given by the preceding expression (8.66) can also be formally interpreted as a pseudodifferential operator and as an analytic quasidifferential operator.

8.46. Remark. It is clear that in the case when the generator $\mathsf{L}(t)$ is formally represented as a real analytic quasidifferential operator

$$\mathsf{L}(t)=\sum_{m\in\mathbb{Z}^n_+}\mathsf{L}_m(t,\hat{s})\,\frac{\partial}{\partial s}^m,$$

the transformations $\hat{\mathfrak{g}}=(\hat{\mathfrak{g}}_{\mathsf{L}},\hat{\mathfrak{g}}_{\mathcal{U}})$ in the beliefs-preferences gauge symmetry group $\hat{\mathfrak{G}}$ given explicitly in (8.65) can be represented solely in terms of the operator coefficients $\mathsf{L}_m(t,\hat{s})$. This representation is analogous to the representation of the transformations in (3.84) of the Hamiltonian $\boldsymbol{H}(t)$ of the form (3.81) as the transformations in (3.82) from the gauge symmetry group $\boldsymbol{U}(1)$ of the vector potential $A(x,t)$ and the scalar potential $U(x,t)$.

8.47. Remark. In this way relation (3.74) takes the following form

$$\boldsymbol{L}(t,\hat{s},\frac{\partial}{\partial s})=\mathsf{L}\big(t,\hat{s},\frac{\partial}{\partial s}+\frac{\boldsymbol{u}'_s(t,t)}{\boldsymbol{u}'(t,t)}\big)+\frac{\boldsymbol{u}'_t(t,t)}{\boldsymbol{u}'(t,t)}. \tag{8.67}$$

In terms of the operator $\boldsymbol{\Lambda}(t,T)$ defined in relation (5.68) the transformations $\hat{\mathfrak{g}}=(\hat{\mathfrak{g}}_{\mathsf{L}},\hat{\mathfrak{g}}_{\mathcal{U}})$ in the beliefs-preferences gauge symmetry group $\hat{\mathfrak{G}}$ in the relation (8.65) take the following form

$$\mathsf{L}(t,\hat{s},\frac{\partial}{\partial s})\xrightarrow{\hat{\mathfrak{g}}_{\mathsf{L}}}\mathsf{L}\big(t,\hat{s},\frac{\partial}{\partial s}+\boldsymbol{\Lambda}_s(t,t)\big)+\boldsymbol{\Lambda}_t(t,t)\quad\text{and}$$
$$\boldsymbol{u}'(t,T)\xrightarrow{\hat{\mathfrak{g}}_{\mathcal{U}}}\mathbf{u}'^{-1}(t,T)\boldsymbol{u}'(t,T), \tag{8.68}$$

where $\boldsymbol{\Lambda}_s(t,t)$ is defined in relation (5.69), $\boldsymbol{\Lambda}_t(t,t)$ stands for the partial derivative of $\boldsymbol{\Lambda}(t,t)$ with respect to the second time variable, and where the operator $\mathsf{L}\big(t,\hat{s},\frac{\partial}{\partial s}+\boldsymbol{\Lambda}_s(t,t)\big)$ is understood as the formal power series

$$\mathsf{L}\big(t,\hat{s},\frac{\partial}{\partial s}+\boldsymbol{\Lambda}_s(t,t)\big)=\sum_{m\in\mathbb{Z}_+^n} \boldsymbol{L}_m(t,\hat{s})\,\big(\frac{\partial}{\partial s}+\boldsymbol{\Lambda}_s(t,t)\big)^m. \tag{8.69}$$

8.48. Remark. It is clear that the operator $\mathsf{L}\big(t,\hat{s},\frac{\partial}{\partial s}+\boldsymbol{\Lambda}_s(t,t)\big)$ given by the preceding expression (8.69) can also be formally interpreted as a pseudodifferential operator and as an analytic quasidifferential operator.

8.49. Remark. In terms of the operator $\boldsymbol{\Lambda}(t,T)$ relation (8.67) takes the following form

$$\boldsymbol{L}(t,\hat{s},\frac{\partial}{\partial s})=\mathsf{L}\big(t,\hat{s},\frac{\partial}{\partial s}+\boldsymbol{\Lambda}_s(t,t)\big)+\boldsymbol{\Lambda}_t(t,t), \tag{8.70}$$

where the operator $\boldsymbol{\Lambda}(t,T)$ is defined in relation (3.16).

Now we are ready to present financial interpretation of the price-time $\mathbb{P}$ in terms of a connection on the account bundle $\mathfrak{A}$ promised in Remark (3.66).

Consider a Markovian generalized market populace $\mathbb{H}=\mathbb{B}\times\mathbb{U}$, or more precisely $\mathbb{H}=\mathbb{L}\times\mathbb{U}$ with local generalized market populace preference $\mathbb{U}$. In this case according to relation (3.75) the transformations $\hat{\mathfrak{g}}=(\hat{\mathfrak{g}}_{\mathsf{L}},\hat{\mathfrak{g}}_{\mathcal{U}})$ in the beliefs-preferences gauge symmetry group $\hat{\mathfrak{G}}$ in relation (8.65) take the following form

$$\mathsf{L}(t,\hat{s},\frac{\partial}{\partial s})\xrightarrow{\hat{\mathfrak{g}}_{\mathsf{L}}}\mathsf{L}\big(t,\hat{s},\frac{\partial}{\partial s}+\frac{\mathbf{u}'_s(t)}{\mathbf{u}'(t)}\big)+\frac{\mathbf{u}'_t(t)}{\mathbf{u}'(t)}\quad\text{and}$$
$$\boldsymbol{u}'(t)\xrightarrow{\hat{\mathfrak{g}}_{\mathcal{U}}}\mathbf{u}'^{-1}(t)\boldsymbol{u}'(t). \tag{8.71}$$

Similarly, in terms of the operator $\boldsymbol{\Lambda}(t)$ the transformations $\hat{\mathfrak{g}}=(\hat{\mathfrak{g}}_{\mathsf{L}},\hat{\mathfrak{g}}_{\mathcal{U}})$ in the beliefs-preferences gauge symmetry group $\hat{\mathfrak{G}}$ in relation (8.68) take the following form

$$\mathsf{L}(t, \hat{s}, \frac{\partial}{\partial s}) \xrightarrow{\hat{\mathfrak{g}}_{\mathsf{L}}} \mathsf{L}\big(t, \hat{s}, \frac{\partial}{\partial s} + \boldsymbol{\Lambda}_{s}(t)\big) + \boldsymbol{\Lambda}_{t}(t) \quad \text{and}$$

$$\boldsymbol{u}'(t) \xrightarrow{\hat{\mathfrak{g}}_{\mathcal{U}}} \mathbf{u}'^{-1}(t)\boldsymbol{u}'(t). \tag{8.72}$$

8.50. Remark. It is clear that according to relation (5.68) the operator $\boldsymbol{\Lambda}(t)$ in (8.72) is defined by

$$\mathbf{u}'(t) = e^{\boldsymbol{\Lambda}(t)}.$$

Similar to relation (3.51), define now the gauge symmetry with the gauge group $\mathfrak{G}(\mathbb{R}_{++})$ for the account bundle $\mathfrak{A}$ as follows. Define the action of the gauge group on the fiber $\mathbb{R}$ over (s, τ) in $\mathbb{P}$ as multiplication by $\mathrm{u}'(\tau, s_\tau) > 0$ in $\mathfrak{G}(\mathbb{R}_{++})$ so that the value $v(\tau, s_\tau)$ in the fiber $\mathbb{R}$ over (s, τ) in $\mathbb{P}$ of a European contingent claim with inception time t and expiration time T with $t \leq \tau \leq T$ is transformed into $\mathrm{u}'^{-1}(\tau, s_\tau)\, v(\tau, s_\tau)$. In this way the transformations $\hat{\mathfrak{g}} = (\hat{\mathfrak{g}}_{\mathsf{L}}, \hat{\mathfrak{g}}_{\mathcal{U}})$ in the beliefs-preferences gauge symmetry group $\hat{\mathfrak{G}}$ in relation (8.71) with the help of relation (8.67) take the following form

$$\boldsymbol{L}(t, \hat{s}, \frac{\partial}{\partial s}) \xrightarrow{\hat{\mathfrak{g}}_{\mathsf{L}}} \boldsymbol{L}\big(t, \hat{s}, \frac{\partial}{\partial s} + \frac{\mathbf{u}'_{s}(t)}{\mathbf{u}'(t)}\big) + \frac{\mathbf{u}'_{t}(t)}{\mathbf{u}'(t)} \quad \text{and}$$

$$v(t) \xrightarrow{\hat{\mathfrak{g}}_{\mathcal{U}}} \mathbf{u}'^{-1}(t)v(t). \tag{8.73}$$

Similarly, in terms of the operator $\boldsymbol{\Lambda}(t)$ the transformations $\hat{\mathfrak{g}} = (\hat{\mathfrak{g}}_{\mathsf{L}}, \hat{\mathfrak{g}}_{\mathcal{U}})$ in the beliefs-preferences gauge symmetry group $\hat{\mathfrak{G}}$ in relation (8.72) with the help of relation (8.70) take the following form

$$\boldsymbol{L}(t, \hat{s}, \frac{\partial}{\partial s}) \xrightarrow{\hat{\mathfrak{g}}_{\mathsf{L}}} \boldsymbol{L}\big(t, \hat{s}, \frac{\partial}{\partial s} + \boldsymbol{\Lambda}_{s}(t)\big) + \boldsymbol{\Lambda}_{t}(t) \quad \text{and}$$

$$v(t) \xrightarrow{\hat{\mathfrak{g}}_{\mathcal{U}}} \mathbf{u}'^{-1}(t)v(t). \tag{8.74}$$

Now we take the following decisive step. We interpret the Cauchy problem in (2.6) as the Cauchy problem

$$\begin{aligned} \nabla_t\, v + \boldsymbol{L}(t, \hat{s}, \nabla_s)\, v &= 0, \\ v(T) &= v_T \end{aligned} \tag{8.75}$$

in the particular gauge associated with the representative generalized market participant, where ∇_t and ∇_s are defined by

$$\begin{aligned} \nabla_t &= \frac{\partial}{\partial t} + \frac{\mathbf{u}'_t(t)}{\mathbf{u}'(t)} \\ \nabla_s &= \frac{\partial}{\partial s} + \frac{\mathbf{u}'_s(t)}{\mathbf{u}'(t)}, \end{aligned} \tag{8.76}$$

or equivalently

$$\begin{aligned} \nabla_t &= \frac{\partial}{\partial t} + \mathbf{\Lambda}_t(t) \\ \nabla_s &= \frac{\partial}{\partial s} + \mathbf{\Lambda}_s(t). \end{aligned} \tag{8.77}$$

8.51. Remark. It is clear that the value v of the European contingent claim determined by the preceding Cauchy problem (8.75) in the gauge associated with the representative generalized market participant remains unchanged under the action of the beliefs-preferences gauge symmetry group $\hat{\mathfrak{G}}$ in the form of (8.73) or equivalently (8.74).

We make the following crucial observation. The family

$$\{\frac{\mathbf{u}'_t(t)}{\mathbf{u}'(t)}, \frac{\mathbf{u}'_s(t)}{\mathbf{u}'(t)}\} = \{\mathbf{\Lambda}_t(t), \mathbf{\Lambda}_s(t)\},$$

or more precisely

$$\{\frac{\mathrm{u}'_t(t,s)}{\mathrm{u}'(t,s)}, \frac{\mathrm{u}'_s(t,s)}{\mathrm{u}'(t,s)}\} = \{\Lambda_t(t,s), \Lambda_s(t,s)\}$$

is nothing but a differential-geometric connection on the account bundle $\mathfrak{A}$ with the gauge group $\mathfrak{G}(\mathbb{R}_{++})$, and ∇_t and ∇_s are nothing but the covariant derivatives (see, for example, [15] pages 393 and 623). In this regard we will call the evolution equation in (8.75) the *evolution equation for European contingent claims in the covariant form.*

8.52. Remark. It is clear that the differential-geometric connection

$$\{\frac{\mathbf{u}'_t(t)}{\mathbf{u}'(t)}, \frac{\mathbf{u}'_s(t)}{\mathbf{u}'(t)}\} = \{\mathbf{\Lambda}_t(t), \mathbf{\Lambda}_s(t)\},$$

or more precisely

$$\{\frac{\mathrm{u}'_t(t,s)}{\mathrm{u}'(t,s)}, \frac{\mathrm{u}'_s(t,s)}{\mathrm{u}'(t,s)}\} = \{\Lambda_t(t,s), \Lambda_s(t,s)\}$$

on the account bundle $\mathfrak{A}$ is trivial (see, for example, [15] pages 394 and 626). In this way, in the case of a Markovian generalized market populace $\mathbb{H} = \mathbb{B} \times \mathbb{U}$, or more precisely $\mathbb{H} = \mathbb{L} \times \mathbb{U}$ with local generalized market populace preference $\mathbb{U}$ under consideration, the price-time $\mathbb{P}$ is a flat space.

8.53. Remark. We make the crucial observation that even though we did not introduce any metric on the base space of the account bundle $\mathfrak{A}$, that is, on the price-time $\mathbb{P}$ defined as $\mathbb{R}^n_{++} \times \mathcal{T}$, it is the fact that we have introduced a connection on $\mathbb{P}$ that allows for the financially meaningful unification of the set $\mathbb{R}^n_{++}$ of all possible states of the market as expressed by the prices of the underlying securities and the trading time set $\mathcal{T}$ into a single object, the price-time $\mathbb{P}$.

8.54. Definition. We call the vector bundle A with the fiber $\mathbb{R}$ and the base space $\mathbb{R}^n_{++} \times \mathbb{R}^n_{++} \times \Delta_{\mathcal{T}}$ with

$$\Delta_{\mathcal{T}} = \{t, T \in \mathcal{T} : t \leq T\}$$

a *contingent account bundle.*

8.55. Remark. We comment that each element (s_t, s_T, t, T) in the base space $\mathbb{R}^n_{++} \times \mathbb{R}^n_{++} \times \Delta_{\mathcal{T}}$ financially represents a pair of the states of the market at times t and T in $\mathcal{T}$ with $t \leq T$ as expressed by the prices s_t and s_T in $\mathbb{R}^n_{++}$ of the underlying securities at these times t and T. In this regard the base space $\mathbb{R}^n_{++} \times \mathbb{R}^n_{++} \times \Delta_{\mathcal{T}}$ itself is, financially, the set of all possible pairs of states of the market as expressed by the prices of the underlying securities s_t and s_T at all pairs of times t and T in $\mathcal{T}$ with $t \leq T$. Each element from the fiber $\mathbb{R}$ over (s_t, s_T, t, T) in $\mathbb{R}^n_{++} \times \mathbb{R}^n_{++} \times \Delta_{\mathcal{T}}$ represents an amount of the units of account to be received or paid at time T in $\mathcal{T}$ if the state of the market as expressed by the prices of the underlying securities is s_T at this time T, given that the state of the market as expressed by the prices of the underlying securities is s_t at time t in $\mathcal{T}$ with $t \leq T$. In this regard, the fiber $\mathbb{R}$ over (s_t, s_T, t, T) in $\mathbb{R}^n_{++} \times \mathbb{R}^n_{++} \times \Delta_{\mathcal{T}}$ represents all possible amounts of the units of account to be received or paid at time T in $\mathcal{T}$ if the state of the market as expressed by the prices of the underlying securities is s_T at this time T, given that the state of the market as expressed by the prices of the underlying securities is s_t at time t in $\mathcal{T}$ with $t \leq T$.

Now we consider the general case of a Markovian generalized market populace $\mathbb{H} = \mathbb{B} \times \mathbb{U}$ or more precisely $\mathbb{H} = \mathbb{L} \times \mathbb{U}$ without the assumption that the Markovian generalized market populace preference $\mathbb{U}$ is local.

Define the gauge symmetry with the gauge group $\mathfrak{G}(\mathbb{R}_{++})$ for the contingent account bundle $\mathbf{A}$ as follows. Define the action of the gauge group on the fiber $\mathbb{R}$ over (s_t, s_τ, t, τ) in $\mathbb{R}^n_{++} \times \mathbb{R}^n_{++} \times \Delta_{\mathcal{T}}$ as multiplication by $\mathfrak{u}'(t, \tau, s_t, s_\tau) > 0$ in $\mathfrak{G}(\mathbb{R}_{++})$ so that the value $v(\tau, s_\tau)$ in the fiber $\mathbb{R}$ over (s_t, s_τ, t, τ) in $\mathbb{R}^n_{++} \times \mathbb{R}^n_{++} \times \Delta_{\mathcal{T}}$ of a European contingent claim with inception time t and expiration time T with $t \leq \tau \leq T$ is transformed into $\mathfrak{u}'^{-1}(t, \tau, s_t, s_\tau)\, v(\tau, s_\tau)$. In this way the transformations $\hat{\mathfrak{g}} = (\hat{\mathfrak{g}}_{\mathsf{L}}, \hat{\mathfrak{g}}_{\mathcal{U}})$ in the beliefs-preferences gauge symmetry group $\hat{\mathfrak{G}}$ in relation (8.65) with the help of relation (8.67) take the following form

$$\boldsymbol{L}(t, \hat{s}, \frac{\partial}{\partial s}) \xrightarrow{\hat{\mathfrak{g}}_{\mathsf{L}}} \boldsymbol{L}\Big(t, \hat{s}, \frac{\partial}{\partial s} + \frac{\mathfrak{u}'_s(t,t)}{\mathfrak{u}'(t,t)}\Big) + \frac{\mathfrak{u}'_t(t,t)}{\mathfrak{u}'(t,t)} \quad \text{and}$$

$$v(t) \xrightarrow{\hat{\mathfrak{g}}_{\mathcal{U}}} \mathfrak{u}'^{-1}(\overset{3}{t}, \overset{1}{t})v(t). \tag{8.78}$$

Similarly, in terms of the operator $\boldsymbol{\Lambda}(t,t)$ the transformations $\hat{\mathfrak{g}} = (\hat{\mathfrak{g}}_{\mathsf{L}}, \hat{\mathfrak{g}}_{\mathcal{U}})$ in the beliefs-preferences gauge symmetry group

$\hat{\mathfrak{G}}$ in relation (8.68) with the help of relation (8.70) take the following form

$$\boldsymbol{L}(t,\hat{s},\frac{\partial}{\partial s}) \xrightarrow{\hat{\mathfrak{g}}_{\mathsf{L}}} \boldsymbol{L}\big(t,\hat{s},\frac{\partial}{\partial s}+\boldsymbol{\Lambda}_{s}(t,t)\big)+\boldsymbol{\Lambda}_{t}(t,t) \quad \text{and}$$
$$v(t) \xrightarrow{\hat{\mathfrak{g}}_{\mathcal{U}}} \mathbf{u}'^{-1}(\overset{3}{t},\overset{1}{t})v(t). \tag{8.79}$$

Now we take the following decisive step. We interpret the Cauchy problem in (2.6) as the Cauchy problem

$$\begin{aligned} \nabla_t v+\boldsymbol{L}(t,\hat{s},\nabla_s)\,v&=0,\\ v(T)&=v_T \end{aligned} \tag{8.80}$$

in the particular gauge associated with the representative generalized market participant, where ∇_t and ∇_s are defined by

$$\begin{aligned} \nabla_t&=\frac{\partial}{\partial t}+\frac{\mathbf{u}'_t(t,t)}{\mathbf{u}'(t,t)}\\ \nabla_s&=\frac{\partial}{\partial s}+\frac{\mathbf{u}'_s(t,t)}{\mathbf{u}'(t,t)}, \end{aligned} \tag{8.81}$$

or equivalently

$$\begin{aligned} \nabla_t&=\frac{\partial}{\partial t}+\boldsymbol{\Lambda}_t(t,t)\\ \nabla_s&=\frac{\partial}{\partial s}+\boldsymbol{\Lambda}_s(t,t). \end{aligned} \tag{8.82}$$

8.56. Remark. It is clear that the value v of the European contingent claim determined by the preceding Cauchy problem (8.80) in the gauge associated with a representative generalized market participant remains unchanged under the action of the beliefs-preferences gauge symmetry group $\hat{\mathfrak{G}}$ in the form of (8.78) or equivalently (8.79).

We make the following crucial observation. The family

$$\{\frac{\mathbf{u}'_t(t,t)}{\mathbf{u}'(t,t)},\,\frac{\mathbf{u}'_s(t,t)}{\mathbf{u}'(t,t)}\}=\{\boldsymbol{\Lambda}_t(t,t),\,\boldsymbol{\Lambda}_s(t,t)\}$$

or more precisely

$$\{\frac{\mathrm{u}'_t(t,t,s_t,s_t)}{\mathrm{u}'(t,t,s_t,s_t)}, \frac{\mathrm{u}'_s(t,t,s_t,s_t)}{\mathrm{u}'(t,t,s_t,s_t)}\} = \{\Lambda_t(t,t,s_t,s_t), \Lambda_s(t,t,s_t,s_t)\}$$

can be interpreted as the restriction to

$$\mathbb{R}^n_{++} \times \mathbb{R}^n_{++} \times \{(t,T) \in \Delta_{\mathcal{T}} : t = T\}$$

of a certain differential-geometric connection on the contingent account bundle **A** with the gauge group $\mathfrak{G}(\mathbb{R}_{++})$. The restriction to

$$\mathbb{R}^n_{++} \times \mathbb{R}^n_{++} \times \{(t,T) \in \Delta_{\mathcal{T}} : t = T\}$$

of the covariant derivatives in the appropriate directions are given by ∇_t and ∇_s. In this regard we will call the evolution equation in (8.80) the *evolution equation for European contingent claims in the covariant form.* This connection on **A** will be studied in more detail in forthcoming articles.

8.57. Remark. The results of this Subsection can be restated verbatim for the case of the dynamic beliefs-preferences gauge symmetry group for a generalized market populace presented in Subsection (3.4) of Section (3).

8.58. Remark. Assume the setting in Remark (6.28), that is, let $\boldsymbol{L}(t)$ be the derivative of $-\mathbf{V}(t,T)$ with respect to t evaluated at t equal to T understood in an appropriate sense, where $\mathbf{V}(t,T)$ is an evolution operator in a market environment $\mathbf{V}$. It is clear that $\boldsymbol{L}(t)$ is also equal to the derivative of $\mathbf{V}(t,T)$ with respect to T evaluated at T equal to t understood in an appropriate sense. Assume that all market participants that populate the marketplace at the time t in $\mathcal{T}$ have agreed upon the values at the time t of a set of European contingent claims with inception time t and the expiration time T for all T in some $\mathcal{N}_t(\mathcal{T})$ with $t \leq T$ whose payoffs form a dense set. In this case due to Remark (6.28) it is possible to observe the derivative $\boldsymbol{L}(t)$, or more precisely the image $\big(\boldsymbol{L}(t)\,h\big)(s_t)$ of any h in the dense set evaluated at the state of the market as expressed by the prices of the underlying securities s_t at the time t, directly from the market data. Moreover, it is possible to observe the defining sequence given by $\boldsymbol{L}_M(t)$ in (8.63) of the derivative $\boldsymbol{L}(t)$ viewed as an analytic quasidifferential operator, or more precisely the image $\big(\boldsymbol{L}_M(t)\,h\big)(s_t)$ of any h in the dense set evaluated at the state of the market as expressed by the prices of the underlying securities s_t at the time t, directly from the market data. Indeed, in order to observe the operator $\boldsymbol{L}_M(t)$, or more precisely the image $\big(\boldsymbol{L}_M(t)\,h\big)(s_t)$ we need to observe the operator coefficients $\boldsymbol{L}_m(t,\hat{s})$ with $|m| \leq M$, or more precisely the image $\big(\boldsymbol{L}_m(t,\hat{s})\,h\big)(s_t)$ of any h in the dense set evaluated at the state of the market as expressed by the prices of the underlying securities s_t at the time t, directly from the market data. In order to observe the image $\big(\boldsymbol{L}_m(t,\hat{s})\,h\big)(s_t)$ it is enough to observe $\boldsymbol{L}_m(t,s_t)$ since

$$\big(\boldsymbol{L}_m(t,\hat{s})\,h\big)(s_t) = \boldsymbol{L}_m(t,s_t)\,h(s_t).$$

Due to relation (8.64), in order to observe $\boldsymbol{L}_m(t,s_t)$ we have to be able to evaluate the commutators $\big((-\mathbf{ad}_{\hat{s}})^m\,\boldsymbol{L}(t)\big)$, or more precisely the value $\Big(\big((-\mathbf{ad}_{\hat{s}})^m\,\boldsymbol{L}(t)\big)\mathbf{1}\Big)(s_t)$ of the function $\big((-\mathbf{ad}_{\hat{s}})^m\,\boldsymbol{L}(t)\big)\mathbf{1}$ at the state of the market as expressed by the prices of the underlying securities s_t at the time t directly from the market data. This is indeed possible since what we need in order to evaluate $\Big(\big((-\mathbf{ad}_{\hat{s}})^m\,\boldsymbol{L}(t)\big)\mathbf{1}\Big)(s_t)$ is only the image $\big(\boldsymbol{L}(t)\,h\big)(s_t)$ of any h in the dense set evaluated at the state of the market as expressed by the prices of the underlying securities s_t at the time t, which is directly observable from the market data.

8.59. Remark. Similar to the preceding Remark (8.58), assuming the setting in Remark (6.63) it is possible to observe the defining sequence given by $\boldsymbol{L}_M(t)$ in (8.63) of the generator $\boldsymbol{L}(t)$ at the time t, viewed as an analytic quasidifferential operator, of a market environment $\mathbf{V}$, or more precisely the image

$\big(\boldsymbol{L}_M(t)\,h\big)(s_t)$ of any h in the dense set evaluated at the state of the market as expressed by the prices of the underlying securities s_t at the time t, directly from the market data.

8.60. Remark. Consider a Markovian generalized market populace $\mathbb{H} = \mathbb{B} \times \mathbb{U}$, or more precisely $\mathbb{H} = \mathbb{L} \times \mathbb{U}$. Suppose that the family

$$\mathsf{L} = \{\mathsf{L}(t) : B \to B \,|\, t \in \mathcal{T}\}$$

in $\mathbb{L}$ is such that each generator $\mathsf{L}(t)$ is a quasidifferential operator with a support D and the defining sequence $\mathsf{L}_M(t)$, where B is a suitable Banach space of real-valued functions on the set $\mathbb{R}^n_{++}$. Moreover, suppose that L generates a Markovian generalized belief

$$\mathfrak{B} = \{\boldsymbol{D}(t,T) : B \to B \,|\, t, T \in \mathcal{T}, t \leq T\}$$

in $\mathbb{B}$ such that $\boldsymbol{D}(t,T)$ is strongly continuous in t and T. Then it is natural to expect that for each t and T in $\mathcal{T}$ with $t \leq T$ and for each v_T in D the solution $v_M = v_M(t)$, possibly generalized, of the Cauchy problem

$$\begin{gathered} \frac{d}{dt} v_M + \mathsf{L}_M(t)\, v_M = 0, \quad t < T \\ v_M(T) = v_T \end{gathered} \tag{8.83}$$

converges in B to the solution $v = v(t)$ of the Cauchy problem (3.6) as M goes to infinity, at least for even M and elliptically defined quasidifferential operators $\mathsf{L}(t)$ (see, for example, [11], [48], [23], [21], [17] and [56]).

Denote by $\boldsymbol{D}_M(t,T)$ the evolution operator for the evolution equation in (8.83) formally given by

$$\boldsymbol{D}_M(t,T) = e^{\int_t^T \mathsf{L}_M(\tau) d\tau},$$

where each $\mathsf{L}_M(\tau)$ acts in the order opposite to that of τ. Since $v_M(t) = \boldsymbol{D}_M(t,T)\, v_T$, the convergence of the sequence $v_M = v_M(t)$ to $v = v(t)$ for each t and T in $\mathcal{T}$ with $t \leq T$ as M goes to infinity can be restated as the strong convergence of $\boldsymbol{D}_M(t,T)$ to $\boldsymbol{D}(t,T)$ on D for each t and T in $\mathcal{T}$ with $t \leq T$ as M goes to infinity. In this regard, even though the operators $\mathsf{L}_M(t)$ with $M > 2$ are not dispersive in general and hence $\boldsymbol{D}_M(t,T)$ with $M > 2$ does not in general preserve the nonnegative cone in B induced by that of Π, so that $\boldsymbol{D}_M(t,T)$ with $M > 2$ does not in general determine measures on $\mathbb{R}^n_{++}$, it is natural to expect that $\boldsymbol{D}_M(t,T)$ preserves such a nonnegative cone and that $\boldsymbol{D}_M(t,T)$ determines such measures with any level of accuracy as M goes to infinity. We comment that we have loosely interpreted the Banach space B as a subspace of Π.

8.4 Beliefs-Preferences Gauge Symmetry Group for a Markovian Market Populace with Beliefs Generated by Quasidifferential Operators

Consider a Markovian market populace $\mathbb{H} = \mathbb{B} \times \mathbb{U}$, or more precisely $\mathbb{H} = \mathbb{L} \times \mathbb{U}$. We formally represent each generator $\mathfrak{L}(t)$ in $\mathfrak{L}$ from $\mathbb{L}$ as a real pseudodifferential operator on an appropriate space of real-valued functions on Ω equal to $\mathbb{R}^n_{++}$, that is, on an appropriate subspace of Π. According to relations (8.27) and (8.28) the real symbol $\mathfrak{L}(t,s,p)$ of $\mathfrak{L}(t)$ is given by

$$\mathfrak{L}(t,s,p) = \sum_{m \in \mathbb{Z}^n_{++}} \left(\frac{p^m}{m!} \left((-\mathbf{ad}_{\hat{\xi}})^m \, \mathfrak{L}(t) \right) \mathbf{1} \right), \tag{8.84}$$

where s is in $\mathbb{R}^n_{++}$ and p is in $\mathbb{R}^n$, and where $\mathbb{Z}^n_{++}$ stands for $\mathbb{Z}^n_+ \setminus 0$.

8.61. Remark. We comment that due to relation (3.101) the term

$$\left(\frac{p^m}{m!} \left((-\mathbf{ad}_{\hat{\xi}})^m \, \mathfrak{L}(t) \right) \mathbf{1} \right)$$

with $m = 0$ in $\mathbb{Z}^n_+$ in the preceding relation (8.84) is equal to zero.

Now according to relation (8.29) each generator $\mathfrak{L}(t)$ can be formally represented as a function of the vector operators

$$\hat{s} = (\hat{s}_1, \hat{s}_2, \ldots, \hat{s}_n)$$

and

$$\frac{\partial}{\partial s} = (\frac{\partial}{\partial s_1}, \frac{\partial}{\partial s_2}, \ldots, \frac{\partial}{\partial s_n})$$

as follows

$$\mathfrak{L}(t) = \mathfrak{L}(t, \hat{s}, \frac{\partial}{\partial s}), \quad t \in \mathcal{T}, \tag{8.85}$$

where each $\hat{s}_i$ is the operator of multiplication by s_i.

Moreover, according to relations (8.24), (8.25) and (8.26) each generator $\mathfrak{L}(t)$ can also be formally represented as an analytic quasidifferential operator

$$\mathfrak{L}(t) = \sum_{m \in \mathbb{Z}^n_{++}} \mathfrak{L}_m(t, \hat{s}) \frac{\partial}{\partial s}^m, \tag{8.86}$$

with the defining sequence given by

$$\mathfrak{L}_M(t) = \sum_{0<|m|\leq M} \mathfrak{L}_m(t, \hat{s}) \frac{\partial}{\partial s}^m, \tag{8.87}$$

where the operator coefficients $\mathfrak{L}_m(t, \hat{s})$ are defined by

$$\mathfrak{L}_m(t, \hat{s}) = \frac{1}{m!} ((-\mathbf{ad}_{\hat{s}})^m \mathfrak{L}(t))\mathbf{1}, \quad m \in \mathbb{Z}^n_{++}. \tag{8.88}$$

8.62. Remark. We comment that due to relation (3.101) the operator coefficient $\mathfrak{L}_m(t, \hat{s})$ with $m = 0$ in $\mathbb{Z}^n_+$ in the preceding relations (8.86), (8.87) and (8.88) is equal to the zero operator.

8.63. Remark. We comment that formal representation of the generator of the belief $\mathfrak{L}(t)$ in (8.86) as an analytic quasidifferential operator, that is, as the expansion of $\mathfrak{L}(t)$ in a formal power series over the vector operator $\frac{\partial}{\partial s}$ corresponds to the expansion of the probability measures generated by $\mathfrak{L}(t)$ over the mixed moments of the increasing orders so that each term

$$\mathfrak{L}_m(t, \hat{s}) = \frac{1}{m!}\left((-\mathbf{ad}_{\hat{s}})^m\, \mathfrak{L}(t)\right)\mathbf{1},$$

corresponds to the mixed moment of the order m in $\mathbb{Z}_+^n$. (For the definition of a mixed moment of the order m in $\mathbb{Z}_+^n$ see, for example, [51] page 289.)

The transformations $\hat{g} = (\hat{g}_{\mathfrak{L}}, \hat{g}_{\mathcal{U}})$ in the beliefs-preferences gauge symmetry group $\hat{\mathcal{G}}$ defined in relations (3.98) and (3.99), or equivalently (3.107) take the following form

$$\mathfrak{L}(t, \hat{s}, \frac{\partial}{\partial s}) \xrightarrow{\hat{g}_{\mathfrak{L}}} \mathfrak{L}\big(t, \hat{s}, \frac{\partial}{\partial s} + \frac{\hat{\mathbf{u}}'_s(t,t)}{\hat{\mathbf{u}}'(t,t)}\big) + \frac{\hat{\mathbf{u}}'_t(t,t)}{\hat{\mathbf{u}}'(t,t)} \quad \text{and}$$
$$u'(t,T) \xrightarrow{\hat{g}_{\mathcal{U}}} \hat{\mathbf{u}}'^{-1}(t,T)u'(t,T), \tag{8.89}$$

where $\hat{\mathbf{u}}'_s(t,t)$ is defined in the comments to relation (5.64), and where the operator $\mathfrak{L}\big(t, \hat{s}, \frac{\partial}{\partial s} + \frac{\hat{\mathbf{u}}'_s(t,t)}{\hat{\mathbf{u}}'(t,t)}\big)$ is understood as the formal power series

$$\mathfrak{L}\big(t, \hat{s}, \frac{\partial}{\partial s} + \frac{\hat{\mathbf{u}}'_s(t,t)}{\hat{\mathbf{u}}'(t,t)}\big) = \sum_{m \in \mathbb{Z}_{++}^n} \mathfrak{L}_m(t, \hat{s}) \left(\frac{\partial}{\partial s} + \frac{\hat{\mathbf{u}}'_s(t,t)}{\hat{\mathbf{u}}'(t,t)}\right)^m. \tag{8.90}$$

8.64. Remark. It is clear that the operator $\mathfrak{L}\big(t, \hat{s}, \frac{\partial}{\partial s} + \frac{\hat{\mathbf{u}}'_s(t,t)}{\hat{\mathbf{u}}'(t,t)}\big)$ given by the preceding expression (8.90) can also be formally interpreted as a pseudodifferential operator and as an analytic quasidifferential operator.

8.65. Remark. It is clear that in the case when the generator $\mathfrak{L}(t)$ is formally represented as a real analytic quasidifferential operator

$$\mathfrak{L}(t) = \sum_{m \in \mathbb{Z}_{++}} \mathfrak{L}_m(t, \hat{s}) \frac{\partial}{\partial s}^m,$$

the transformations $\hat{\boldsymbol{g}} = (\hat{\boldsymbol{g}}_{\mathfrak{L}}, \hat{\boldsymbol{g}}_{\mathcal{U}})$ in the beliefs-preferences gauge symmetry group $\hat{\boldsymbol{\mathcal{G}}}$ given explicitly in (8.89) can be represented solely in terms of the operator coefficients $\boldsymbol{\mathfrak{L}}_m(t, \hat{s})$. This representation is analogous to the representation of the transformations in (3.84) of the Hamiltonian $\boldsymbol{H}(t)$ of the form (3.81) as the transformations in (3.82) from the gauge symmetry group $\boldsymbol{U}(1)$ of the vector potential $A(x,t)$ and the scalar potential $U(x,t)$.

Define the operator $\hat{\boldsymbol{\Lambda}}(t,T)$ according to (3.16) as

$$\hat{\mathbf{u}}'(t,T) = e^{\hat{\boldsymbol{\Lambda}}(t,T)}. \tag{8.91}$$

8.66. Remark. It is clear that the $\hat{\boldsymbol{\Lambda}}(t,T)$ is the operator on $\Pi(\mathbb{R}^n_{++} \times \mathbb{R}^n_{++})$ of multiplication by the function $\hat{\Lambda}(t,T,s_t,s_T)$ in $\Pi(\mathbb{R}^n_{++} \times \mathbb{R}^n_{++})$ defined according to (3.17) as

$$\hat{\mathrm{u}}'(t,T,s_t,s_T) = e^{\hat{\Lambda}(t,T,s_t,s_T)}. \tag{8.92}$$

8.67. Remark. It is clear that due to relation (3.105) we have that

$$\hat{\boldsymbol{\Lambda}}(\overset{t}{t},\overset{T}{T}) = \boldsymbol{\Lambda}(\overset{t}{t},\overset{T}{T}) - \int_t^T \boldsymbol{\mathfrak{d}}(\overset{\tau}{\tau})d\tau, \tag{8.93}$$

where the indexes over the operators indicate the order inverse to the order in which these operators act, and where the operator $\boldsymbol{\Lambda}(t,T)$ is defined in relation (5.68).

8.68. Remark. It is clear that due to relation (3.106) we have that

$$\hat{\Lambda}(t,T,s_t,s_T) = \Lambda(t,T,s_t,s_T) - \int_t^T \mathfrak{d}(\tau, s_t)d\tau, \tag{8.94}$$

where the function $\Lambda(t,T,s_t,s_T)$ in $\Pi(\mathbb{R}^n_{++} \times \mathbb{R}^n_{++})$ is defined in relation (5.70).

8.69. Remark. It is clear, due to relation (5.72) or equivalently (8.93), that

$$\hat{\mathbf{\Lambda}}(t,t) = \mathbf{\Lambda}(t,t). \tag{8.95}$$

8.70. Remark. It is clear that due to relation (8.94) we have

$$\hat{\Lambda}(t,t,s_t,s_t') = \Lambda(t,t,s_t,s_t'). \tag{8.96}$$

8.71. Remark. It is clear that due to relation (8.93) we have

$$\hat{\mathbf{\Lambda}}_t(t,t) = \mathbf{\Lambda}_t(t,t) - \mathfrak{d}(t), \tag{8.97}$$

where $\hat{\mathbf{\Lambda}}_t(t,t)$ and $\mathbf{\Lambda}_t(t,t)$ stand for the partial derivative of $\hat{\mathbf{\Lambda}}(t,t)$ and $\mathbf{\Lambda}(t,t)$ with respect to the second time variable.

8.72. Remark. It is clear that due to relations (8.93) and (8.94) we have

$$\hat{\mathbf{\Lambda}}_{\mathbf{s}}(t,t) = \mathbf{\Lambda}_{\mathbf{s}}(t,t), \tag{8.98}$$

where $\mathbf{\Lambda}_{\mathbf{s}}(t,t)$ is defined in relation (5.69), and where

$$\hat{\mathbf{\Lambda}}_{\mathbf{s}}(t,t) = (\hat{\mathbf{\Lambda}}_{\mathbf{s_1}}(t,t), \hat{\mathbf{\Lambda}}_{\mathbf{s_2}}(t,t), \dots, \hat{\mathbf{\Lambda}}_{\mathbf{s_n}}(t,t))$$

with each $\hat{\mathbf{\Lambda}}_{\mathbf{s_i}}(t,t)$ being the operator on Π of multiplication by the function

$$\hat{\Lambda}_{s_i}(t,t,s_t,s_t) = \frac{\partial}{\partial s_i}\hat{\Lambda}(t,t,s_t,s)|_{s=s_t}.$$

8.73. Remark. It is clear that due to relation (8.94) we have

$$\hat{\Lambda}_s(t,t,s_t,s_t) = \Lambda_s(t,t,s_t,s_t), \tag{8.99}$$

where

$$\Lambda_s(t,t,s_t,s_t) = (\Lambda_{s_1}(t,t,s_t,s_t), \Lambda_{s_2}(t,t,s_t,s_t), \dots, \Lambda_{s_n}(t,t,s_t,s_t))$$

with

$$\Lambda_{s_i}(t,t,s_t,s_t) = \frac{\partial}{\partial s_i}\Lambda(t,t,s_t,s)|_{s=s_t},$$

and where

$$\hat{\Lambda}_s(t,t,s_t,s_t) = (\hat{\Lambda}_{s_1}(t,t,s_t,s_t), \hat{\Lambda}_{s_2}(t,t,s_t,s_t), \dots, \hat{\Lambda}_{s_n}(t,t,s_t,s_t)).$$

Now relation (5.75) financially justifies the following Definitions.

8.74. Definition. We call the vector operator $\boldsymbol{\Lambda}_s(t,t)$ the *generalized relative price of risk operator.* Similarly we call the vector function $\Lambda_s(t,t,s_t,s_t)$ the *generalized relative price of risk.*

8.75. Definition. We call the operator $\hat{\boldsymbol{\Lambda}}(t,T)$ the *generalized relative price of risk potential operator.* Similarly we call the function $\hat{\Lambda}(t,T,s_t,s_T)$ the *generalized relative price of risk potential.*

In terms of the operator $\hat{\boldsymbol{\Lambda}}(t,T)$ the transformations $\hat{\boldsymbol{g}} = (\hat{\boldsymbol{g}}_{\mathfrak{L}}, \hat{\mathfrak{g}}_{\mathcal{U}})$ in the beliefs-preferences gauge symmetry group $\hat{\boldsymbol{\mathcal{G}}}$ in relation (8.89) take the following form

$$\begin{aligned}
&\boldsymbol{\mathfrak{L}}(t,\hat{s},\frac{\partial}{\partial s}) \xrightarrow{\hat{g}_{\mathfrak{L}}} \boldsymbol{\mathfrak{L}}\big(t,\hat{s},\frac{\partial}{\partial s}+\hat{\boldsymbol{\Lambda}}_s(t,t)\big)+\hat{\boldsymbol{\Lambda}}_t(t,t) \quad \text{and}\\
&\boldsymbol{u}'(t,T) \xrightarrow{\hat{g}_{\mathcal{U}}} \hat{\mathbf{u}}'^{-1}(t,T)\boldsymbol{u}'(t,T),
\end{aligned} \tag{8.100}$$

where the operator $\boldsymbol{\mathfrak{L}}\big(t,\hat{s},\frac{\partial}{\partial s}+\hat{\boldsymbol{\Lambda}}_s(t,t)\big)$ is understood as the formal power series

$$\boldsymbol{\mathfrak{L}}\big(t,\hat{s},\frac{\partial}{\partial s}+\hat{\boldsymbol{\Lambda}}_s(t,t)\big) = \sum_{m\in\mathbb{Z}^n_{++}} \boldsymbol{\mathfrak{L}}_m(t,\hat{s})\,\big(\frac{\partial}{\partial s}+\hat{\boldsymbol{\Lambda}}_s(t,t)\big)^m. \tag{8.101}$$

8.76. Remark. It is clear that the operator $\boldsymbol{\mathfrak{L}}\big(t,\hat{s},\frac{\partial}{\partial s}+\hat{\boldsymbol{\Lambda}}_s(t,t)\big)$ given by the preceding expression (8.101) can also be formally interpreted as a pseudodifferential operator and as an analytic quasidifferential operator.

8.77. Remark. It is clear that relation (3.104) takes the following form

$$\boldsymbol{L}(t,\hat{s},\frac{\partial}{\partial s}) = \boldsymbol{\mathfrak{L}}\big(t,\hat{s},\frac{\partial}{\partial s}+\frac{\boldsymbol{u}'_s(t,t)}{\boldsymbol{u}'(t,t)}\big)+\frac{\boldsymbol{u}'_t(t,t)}{\boldsymbol{u}'(t,t)}, \tag{8.102}$$

or equivalently

$$\boldsymbol{L}(t, \hat{s}, \frac{\partial}{\partial s}) = \mathfrak{L}\big(t, \hat{s}, \frac{\partial}{\partial s} + \boldsymbol{\Lambda}_s(t,t)\big) + \boldsymbol{\Lambda}_t(t,t), \tag{8.103}$$

where the operator $\boldsymbol{\Lambda}(t, T)$ is defined in relation (3.16). In this regard it is clear, due to relation (8.67) or equivalently (8.70), that $\mathfrak{L}(t)$ is formally represented as a pseudodifferential operator or as an analytic quasidifferential operator if and only if either $\mathsf{L}(t)$ or $\boldsymbol{L}(t)$ is formally represented as a pseudodifferential operator or as an analytic quasidifferential operator.

Define now the gauge symmetry with the gauge group $\mathfrak{G}(\mathbb{R}_{++})$ for the contingent account bundle $\mathbf{A}$ as follows. The action of the gauge group on the fiber $\mathbb{R}$ over (s_t, s_τ, t, τ) in $\mathbb{R}^n_{++} \times \mathbb{R}^n_{++} \times \Delta_T$ is defined as multiplication by $\hat{\mathfrak{u}}'(t, \tau, s_t, s_\tau) > 0$ in $\mathfrak{G}(\mathbb{R}_{++})$ so that the value $v(\tau, s_\tau)$ in the fiber $\mathbb{R}$ over (s_t, s_τ, t, τ) in $\mathbb{R}^n_{++} \times \mathbb{R}^n_{++} \times \Delta_T$ of the solution of the Cauchy problem (3.3) with $t \leq \tau \leq T$ is transformed into $\hat{\mathfrak{u}}'^{-1}(t, \tau, s_t, s_\tau)\, v(\tau, s_\tau)$. In this way the transformations $\hat{g} = (\hat{g}_{\mathfrak{L}}, \hat{g}_{\mathcal{U}})$ in the beliefs-preferences gauge symmetry group $\hat{\mathcal{G}}$ in relation (8.89) take the following form

$$\mathfrak{L}(t, \hat{s}, \frac{\partial}{\partial s}) \xrightarrow{\hat{g}_{\mathfrak{L}}} \mathfrak{L}\big(t, \hat{s}, \frac{\partial}{\partial s} + \frac{\hat{\mathfrak{u}}'_s(t,t)}{\hat{\mathfrak{u}}'(t,t)}\big) + \frac{\hat{\mathfrak{u}}'_t(t,t)}{\hat{\mathfrak{u}}'(t)} \quad \text{and}$$
$$v(t) \xrightarrow{\hat{g}_{\mathcal{U}}} \hat{\mathfrak{u}}'^{-1}(\overset{3}{t}, \overset{1}{t})v(t). \tag{8.104}$$

Similarly, in terms of the operator $\hat{\boldsymbol{\Lambda}}(t, t)$ the transformations $\hat{g} = (\hat{g}_{\mathfrak{L}}, \hat{g}_{\mathcal{U}})$ in the beliefs-preferences gauge symmetry group $\hat{\mathcal{G}}$ in relation (8.100) take the following form

$$\mathfrak{L}(t, \hat{s}, \frac{\partial}{\partial s}) \xrightarrow{\hat{g}_{\mathfrak{L}}} \mathfrak{L}\big(t, \hat{s}, \frac{\partial}{\partial s} + \hat{\boldsymbol{\Lambda}}_s(t,t)\big) + \hat{\boldsymbol{\Lambda}}_t(t,t) \quad \text{and}$$
$$v(t) \xrightarrow{\hat{g}_{\mathcal{U}}} \hat{\mathfrak{u}}'^{-1}(\overset{3}{t}, \overset{1}{t})v(t). \tag{8.105}$$

Now we take the following decisive step. We interpret the Cauchy problem in (3.3) as the Cauchy problem

$$\begin{aligned} \nabla_t v + \mathfrak{L}(t, \hat{s}, \nabla_s)\, v = 0, \\ v(T) = v_T \end{aligned} \tag{8.106}$$

in the appropriate gauge, where ∇_t and ∇_s are defined by

$$\begin{aligned} \nabla_t &= \frac{\partial}{\partial t} + \frac{\hat{\mathbf{u}}'_t(t,t)}{\hat{\mathbf{u}}'(t,t)} \\ \nabla_s &= \frac{\partial}{\partial s} + \frac{\hat{\mathbf{u}}'_s(t,t)}{\hat{\mathbf{u}}'(t,t)}, \end{aligned} \tag{8.107}$$

or equivalently

$$\begin{aligned} \nabla_t &= \frac{\partial}{\partial t} + \hat{\mathbf{\Lambda}}_t(t,t) \\ \nabla_s &= \frac{\partial}{\partial s} + \hat{\mathbf{\Lambda}}_s(t,t). \end{aligned} \tag{8.108}$$

8.78. Remark. It is clear that the solution v of the Cauchy problem (8.106) remains unchanged under the action of the beliefs-preferences gauge symmetry group $\hat{\mathcal{G}}$ in the form of (8.104) or equivalently (8.105).

We make the following crucial observation. The family

$$\{\frac{\hat{\mathbf{u}}'_t(t,t)}{\hat{\mathbf{u}}'(t,t)}, \frac{\hat{\mathbf{u}}'_s(t,t)}{\hat{\mathbf{u}}'(t,t)}\} = \{\hat{\mathbf{\Lambda}}_t(t,t), \hat{\mathbf{\Lambda}}_s(t,t)\}$$

or more precisely

$$\{\frac{\hat{\mathrm{u}}'_t(t,t,s_t,s_t)}{\hat{\mathrm{u}}'(t,t,s_t,s_t)}, \frac{\hat{\mathrm{u}}'_s(t,t,s_t,s_t)}{\hat{\mathrm{u}}'(t,t,s_t,s_t)}\} = \{\hat{\Lambda}_t(t,t,s_t,s_t), \hat{\Lambda}_s(t,t,s_t,s_t)\}$$

can be interpreted as the restriction to

$$\mathbb{R}^n_{++} \times \mathbb{R}^n_{++} \times \{(t,T) \in \Delta_T : t = T\}$$

of a certain differential-geometrical connection on the contingent account bundle **A** with the gauge group $\mathfrak{G}(\mathbb{R}_{++})$. The restriction to

$$\mathbb{R}^n_{++} \times \mathbb{R}^n_{++} \times \{(t,T) \in \Delta_{\mathcal{T}} : t = T\}$$

of the covariant derivatives in the appropriate directions are given by ∇_t and ∇_s. In this regard we will call the evolution equation in (8.106) the *evolution equation for the belief in the covariant form.* This connection on **A** will be studied in more detail in forthcoming articles.

8.79. Remark. The results of this Subsection can be restated verbatim for the case of the dynamic beliefs-preferences gauge symmetry group for a market populace presented in Subsection (3.5) of Section (3).

8.80. Remark. Assume the setting in Remark (6.28), that is, let $\boldsymbol{L}(t)$ be the derivative of $-\mathbf{V}(t,T)$ with respect to t evaluated at t equal to T understood in an appropriate sense, where $\mathbf{V}(t,T)$ is an evolution operator in a market environment $\mathbf{V}$. It is clear that $\boldsymbol{L}(t)$ is also equal to the derivative of $\mathbf{V}(t,T)$ with respect to T evaluated at T equal to t understood in an appropriate sense. Assume that all market participants that populate the marketplace at the time t in $\mathcal{T}$ have agreed upon the values at the time t of a set of European contingent claims with inception time t and the expiration time T for all T in some $\mathcal{N}_t(\mathcal{T})$ with $t \leq T$ whose payoffs form a dense set. In this case due to Remark (6.28) it is possible to observe the derivative $\boldsymbol{L}(t)$, or more precisely the image $\big(\boldsymbol{L}(t)\,h\big)(s_t)$ of any h in the dense set evaluated at the state of the market as expressed by the prices of the underlying securities s_t at the time t, directly from the market data. Moreover, in the case under consideration it is possible to observe the derivative $\mathfrak{L}(t)$ of $-\boldsymbol{F}(t,T)$ with respect to t evaluated at t equal to T understood in an appropriate sense with $\boldsymbol{F}(t,T)$ in the belief $\mathcal{B}$ of a market participant $\mathcal{H} = (\mathcal{B},\mathcal{U})$ that populates the marketplace at the time t in $\mathcal{T}$, directly from the market data. More precisely, in the case under consideration it is possible to observe the image $\big(\mathfrak{L}(t)\,h\big)(s_t)$ of any h in the dense set evaluated at the state of the market as expressed by the prices of the underlying securities s_t at the time t, directly from the market data:

$$\big(\mathfrak{L}(t)\,h\big)(s_t) = \big(\boldsymbol{L}(t)\,h\big)(s_t) + r(s_t, t)\,h(s_t)$$

where $r(s_t, t)$ is the continuously compounded interest rate, and where we have used the same notation for the operator $\boldsymbol{r}(s, t)$ on Π of multiplication by the function $r(s, t)$ in Π and for the function $r(s, t)$ itself. Furthermore, it is possible to observe the defining sequence given by $\mathfrak{L}_M(t)$ in (8.87) of the derivative $\mathfrak{L}(t)$ viewed as an analytic quasidifferential operator, or more precisely the image $\big(\mathfrak{L}_M(t)\,h\big)(s_t)$ of any h in a dense set evaluated at the state of the market as expressed by the prices of the underlying securities s_t at the time t, directly from the market data. Indeed, in order to observe the operator $\mathfrak{L}_M(t)$, or more precisely the image $\big(\mathfrak{L}_M(t)\,h\big)(s_t)$ we need to observe the operator coefficients $\mathfrak{L}_m(t, \hat{s})$ with $|m| \le M$, or more precisely the image $\big(\mathfrak{L}_m(t, \hat{s})\,h\big)(s_t)$ of any h in the dense set evaluated at the state of the market as expressed by the prices of the underlying securities s_t at the time t, directly from the market data. In order to observe the image $\big(\mathfrak{L}_m(t, \hat{s})\,h\big)(s_t)$ it is enough to observe $\mathfrak{L}_m(t, s_t)$ since

$$\big(\mathfrak{L}_m(t, \hat{s})\,h\big)(s_t) = \mathfrak{L}_m(t, s_t)\,h(s_t).$$

Due to relation (8.88) in order to observe $\mathfrak{L}_m(t, s_t)$ we have to be able to evaluate the commutators $\big((-\mathbf{ad}_{\hat{\mathfrak{s}}})^m\,\mathfrak{L}(t)\big)$, or more precisely the value $\Big(\big((-\mathbf{ad}_{\hat{\mathfrak{s}}})^m\,\mathfrak{L}(t)\big)\mathbf{1}\Big)(s_t)$ of the function $\big((-\mathbf{ad}_{\hat{\mathfrak{s}}})^m\,\mathfrak{L}(t)\big)\mathbf{1}$ at the state of the market as expressed by the prices of the underlying securities s_t at the time t, directly from the market data. This is indeed possible since what we need in order to evaluate $\Big(\big((-\mathbf{ad}_{\hat{\mathfrak{s}}})^m\,\mathfrak{L}(t)\big)\mathbf{1}\Big)(s_t)$ is only the image $\Big(\mathfrak{L}(t)\,h\Big)(s_t)$ of any h in the dense set evaluated at the state of the market as expressed by the prices of the underlying securities s_t at the time t, which is directly observable from the market data.

8.81. Remark. Similar to the preceding Remark (8.80), assuming the setting in Remark (6.63) it is possible to observe the defining sequence given by $\mathfrak{L}_M(t)$ in (8.87) of the generator $\mathfrak{L}(t)$ at time t, viewed as an analytic quasidifferential operator, of the belief $\mathcal{B}$ of a Markovian market participant $\mathcal{H} = (\mathcal{B}, \mathcal{U})$ that populates the marketplace at the time t in $\mathcal{T}$, directly from the market data. More precisely it is possible to observe the image $\big(\mathfrak{L}_M(t)\, h\big)(s_t)$ of any h in the dense set evaluated at the state of the market as expressed by the prices of the underlying securities s_t at the time t, directly from the market data.

8.82. Remark. Consider a Markovian market populace $\mathbb{H} = \mathbb{B} \times \mathbb{U}$, or more precisely $\mathbb{H} = \mathbb{L} \times \mathbb{U}$. Suppose that the family

$$\mathfrak{L} = \{\mathfrak{L}(t) : B \to B \,|\, t \in \mathcal{T}\}$$

in $\mathbb{L}$ is such that each generator $\mathfrak{L}(t)$ is a quasidifferential operator with a support D and the defining sequence $\mathfrak{L}_M(t)$, where B is a suitable Banach space of real-valued functions on the set $\mathbb{R}^n_{++}$. Moreover, suppose that $\mathfrak{L}$ generates a Markovian belief

$$\mathcal{B} = \{\boldsymbol{F}(t,T) : B \to B \,|\, t, T \in \mathcal{T}, t \leq T\}$$

in $\mathbb{B}$ such that $\boldsymbol{F}(t,T)$ is strongly continuous in t and T. Then it is natural to expect that for each t and T in $\mathcal{T}$ with $t \leq T$ and for each v_T in D the solution $v_M = v_M(t)$, possibly generalized, of the Cauchy problem

$$\begin{gathered} \frac{d}{dt} v_M + \mathfrak{L}_M(t)\, v_M = 0, \quad t < T \\ v_M(T) = v_T \end{gathered} \tag{8.109}$$

converges in B to the solution $v = v(t)$ of the Cauchy problem (3.3) as M goes to infinity, at least for even M and elliptically defined quasidifferential operators $\mathfrak{L}(t)$ (see, for example, [11], [48], [23], [21], [17] and [56]).

Denote by $\boldsymbol{F}_M(t,T)$ the evolution operator for the evolution equation in (8.109) formally given by

$$\boldsymbol{F}_M(t,T) = e^{\int_t^T \mathfrak{L}_M(\tau)d\tau},$$

where each $\mathfrak{L}_M(\tau)$ acts in the order opposite to that of τ. Since $v_M(t) = \boldsymbol{F}_M(t,T)\, v_T$, the convergence of the sequence $v_M = v_M(t)$ to $v = v(t)$ for each t and T in $\mathcal{T}$ with $t \leq T$ as M goes to infinity can be restated as the strong convergence of $\boldsymbol{F}_M(t,T)$ to $\boldsymbol{F}(t,T)$ on D for each t and T in $\mathcal{T}$ with $t \leq T$ as M goes to infinity. In this regard even though the operator $\mathfrak{L}_M(t)$ with $M > 2$ is not dispersive in general and hence $\boldsymbol{F}_M(t,T)$ with $M > 2$ does not in general preserve the nonnegative cone in B induced by that of Π, so that $\boldsymbol{F}_M(t,T)$ with $M > 2$ does not in general determine measures, much less probability measures on $\mathbb{R}^n_{++}$, it is natural to expect that $\boldsymbol{F}_M(t,T)$ preserves such a nonnegative cone and that $\boldsymbol{F}_M(t,T)$ determines such probability measures with any level of accuracy as M goes to infinity. We comment that we have loosely interpreted the Banach space B as a subspace of Π.

8.5 Method of Quasidifferential Operators for an Approximate Dynamic Replication of European Contingent Claims in the Case of a Single Underlying Security

Consider a Markovian market populace $\mathbb{H} = \mathbb{B} \times \mathbb{U}$, or more precisely $\mathbb{H} = \mathbb{L} \times \mathbb{U}$ in the case of a single underlying security.

Suppose that the set of European contingent claims $\{\mathfrak{v}_{S_i} : i = 0, \ldots, N\}$ with inception time t, expiration time T and the payoffs $v_T^{S_i}$ such that $v_T^{S_i}(s_T) = s_T^i$ is traded for each t and T in $\mathcal{T}$ with $t \leq T$.

8.83. Remark. We comment that throughout this Subsection s_t^i stands for the s_t in $\mathbb{R}_{++}$ to the power i in $\mathbb{Z}_+$.

8.84. Remark. It is clear that the European contingent claim $\boldsymbol{\mathfrak{v}}_{S_i}$ with $i = 0$ is nothing but the pure discount bond $\boldsymbol{\mathfrak{v}}_{\omega_B}$ with inception time t, maturity time T and the face value of one unit of account. It is also clear that the European contingent claim $\boldsymbol{\mathfrak{v}}_{S_i}$ with $i = 1$ is nothing but the underlying security $\boldsymbol{\mathfrak{v}}_{\omega_S}$ itself.

Since the European contingent claims $\boldsymbol{\mathfrak{v}}_{S_i}$ with $i = 0, \ldots N$ are traded their values $v_{S_i} = v_{S_i}(t)$ are the solutions of the Cauchy problem (6.45), that is

$$\frac{\overset{2}{d}}{dt}\boldsymbol{u}'(\overset{3}{t},\overset{1}{t})\, v_{S_i} + \mathfrak{L}(\overset{2}{t})\,\boldsymbol{u}'(\overset{3}{t},\overset{1}{t})\, v_{S_i} = 0, \quad t < T, \quad i = 0, \ldots, N,$$
$$v_{S_i}(T) = v_T^{S_i}. \tag{8.110}$$

At the same time the values $v_{S_i} = v_{S_i}(t)$ of the European contingent claims $\boldsymbol{\mathfrak{v}}_{S_i}$ with $i = 0, \ldots N$ incepted at time t and expiring at time T an instant later can be formally represented as follows

$$v_{S_i} = e^{-\int_{\overset{1}{(t)}}^{\overset{3}{(t)}} \mathfrak{d}_i(\overset{3}{s}_t,\tau)d\tau}\, s_t^i, \quad i = 0, \ldots, N, \tag{8.111}$$

so that the evolution equation in (8.110) can be rewritten as follows

$$\Big(\frac{\overset{2}{d}}{dt} + \mathfrak{L}(\overset{2}{t})\Big)\,\boldsymbol{u}'(\overset{3}{t},\overset{1}{t})\, e^{-\int_{\overset{1}{(t)}}^{\overset{3}{(t)}} \mathfrak{d}_i(\overset{3}{s},\tau)d\tau}\, \overset{1}{s^i}\,\mathbf{1} = 0, \quad t < T, \quad i = 0, \ldots, N,$$

or equivalently

$$\Big(\frac{\overset{2}{d}}{dt} + \mathfrak{L}(\overset{2}{t})\Big)\,\boldsymbol{u}'(\overset{3}{t},\overset{1}{t})\, \overset{1}{s^i}\,\mathbf{1} + \mathfrak{d}_i(s,t)\, s^i = 0, \quad t < T, \quad i = 0, \ldots, N, \tag{8.112}$$

where $\mathfrak{d}_i(s,t)$ is the operator of multiplication by the function $\mathfrak{d}_i(s,t)$ and where the indexes over the operators indicate the order in which these operators act. We comment that here $\mathbf{1}$ is the function in $\Pi(\mathbb{R}_{++} \times \mathcal{T})$ identically equal to unity.

8.85. Remark. We comment that $\overset{1}{s^i}$ is the i-th power of the operator $\overset{1}{s}$ on Π of multiplication by the argument s, that is, by the function $h(s) = s$ in Π. We also comment that $\overset{1}{s^i}$ can be interpreted as the operator on $\Pi(\mathbb{R}_{++} \times \mathcal{T})$ in the standard way as indicated in Remark (6.50).

8.86. Remark. We comment that the functions $\mathfrak{d}_i(s_t,t)$ with $i = 0, \ldots N$, or more precisely their values $\mathfrak{d}_i(s_t,t)$ at the state of the market as expressed by the price s_t of the underlying security at time t, are observable directly from the market data. Indeed

$$\mathfrak{d}_i(s_t,t)\, s_t^i = \frac{d}{dt}\mathbf{V}(t,T)|_{t=T}\, s_T^i, \tag{8.113}$$

or equivalently

$$\mathfrak{d}_i(s_t,t)\, s_t^i = -\frac{d}{dT}\mathbf{V}(t,T)|_{T=t}\, s_T^i, \tag{8.114}$$

where $\mathbf{V}(t,T)\, s_T^i$ is the value $v_{S_i} = v_{S_i}(t)$ at inception time t of the European contingent claims $\mathfrak{v}_{S_i}$ with expiration time T and the payoff $v_T^{S_i}(s_T) = s_T^i$, and where the derivatives with respect to time are understood in an appropriate sense. We also note that the preceding relation (8.113), or equivalently (8.114) can be rewritten in terms of the generators $\boldsymbol{L}(t)$ of the market environment $\mathbf{V}$ with the evolution operators $\mathbf{V}(t,T)$ as follows

$$\mathfrak{d}_i(s_t,t)\, s_t^i = -\boldsymbol{L}(t)\, s_t^i. \tag{8.115}$$

In this regard the fact that the functions $\mathfrak{d}_i(s_t,t)$ with $i = 0, \ldots N$ are observable directly from the market data also follows from the fact that, according to Remarks (6.28) and (6.63), the generators $\boldsymbol{L}(t)$ are directly observable from the market data.

8.87. Remark. It is clear that $\mathfrak{d}_i(s_t, t)$ with $i = 0$ and $i = 1$ are nothing but the continuously compounded interest rate $r(s_t, t)$ and the continuously compounded dividend yield $d(s_t, t)$ in terms of the underlying security being stock.

8.88. Remark. We comment that it is in the sense of relation (8.113), or equivalently (8.114) that we interpret the formal expressions in (8.111) for the values $v_{S_i} = v_{S_i}(t)$ of the European contingent claims $\mathfrak{v}_{S_i}$ with $i = 0, \ldots N$ incepted at time t and expiring at time T an instant later. In more detail, the formal expressions in (8.111) imitate the following two crucial properties of the values $v_{S_i} = v_{S_i}(t)$ of the European contingent claims $\mathfrak{v}_{S_i}$ with $i = 0, \ldots N$ incepted at time t and expiring at time T an instant later. The first property is that the time derivative $\frac{\overset{2}{d}}{dt}$ of the values $v_{S_i} = v_{S_i}(t)$ of the European contingent claims $\mathfrak{v}_{S_i}$ with $i = 0, \ldots N$ incepted at time t and expiring at time T an instant later given by

$$\frac{\overset{2}{d}}{dt} e^{-\int_{\overset{1}{(t)}}^{\overset{3}{(t)}} \mathfrak{d}_i(\overset{3}{s}_t,\tau)d\tau} s_t^i = \mathfrak{d}_i(s_t, t)\, s_t^i, \quad i = 0, \ldots, N,$$

coincides with the time derivative with respect to t evaluated at t equal to T understood in an appropriate sense of the value $v_{S_i} = v_{S_i}(t)$ equal to $\mathbf{V}(t, T)\, s_T^i$ at inception time t of the European contingent claims $\mathfrak{v}_{S_i}$ with expiration time T and the payoffs $v_T^{S_i}(s_T) = s_T^i$ given by relation (8.113). The second property is that the action of the generator $\mathfrak{L}(\overset{2}{t})$ on the values $v_{S_i} = v_{S_i}(t)$ of the European contingent claims $\mathfrak{v}_{S_i}$ with $i = 0, \ldots N$ incepted at time t and expiring at time T an instant later given by

$$\mathfrak{L}(\overset{2}{t})\, e^{-\int_{\overset{1}{(t)}}^{\overset{3}{(t)}} \mathfrak{d}_i(\overset{3}{s}_t,\tau)d\tau} s_t^i = \mathfrak{L}(t)\, s_t^i, \quad i = 0, \ldots, N,$$

coincides with the action of the generator $\mathfrak{L}(\overset{2}{t})$ on the values $v_{S_i} = v_{S_i}(t)$ equal to $\mathbf{V}(t, T)\, s_T^i$ at the inception time t of the

European contingent claims $\mathfrak{v}_{S_i}$ with expiration time T and the payoffs $v_T^{S_i}(s_T) = s_T^i$ when $t = T$. Finally, we note that the formal expressions in (8.111) for the values $v_{S_i} = v_{S_i}(t)$ of the European contingent claims $\mathfrak{v}_{S_i}$ with $i = 0, \dots N$ incepted at time t and expiring at time T an instant later can also be rewritten as follows

$$v_{S_i} = \mathbf{V}(\overset{1}{t}, \overset{3}{t})\, s_t^i, \quad i = 0, \dots, N.$$

This completes the Remark.

Now we consider the portfolios $\{\mathfrak{p}_i : i = 0, \dots, N\}$ such that each $\mathfrak{p}_i$ is a portfolio of the European contingent claims $\mathfrak{v}_{S_j}$, $j = 0, \dots, i$ with operator weights $\binom{i}{j}(-1)^{i-j}\, s_t^{i-j}$.

8.89. Remark. We comment that each portfolio $\mathfrak{p}_i$, $i = 0, \dots, N$, of the European contingent claims $\mathfrak{v}_{S_j}$, $j = 0, \dots, i$, with operator weights $\binom{i}{j}(-1)^{i-j}\, s_t^{i-j}$ is, from the financial standpoint, nothing but the portfolio of the European contingent claims $\mathfrak{v}_{S^j}$, $j = 0, \dots, i$ with weights $\binom{i}{j}(-1)^{i-j}\, s_t^{i-j}$ that depend on the state of the market as expressed by the price of the underlying security s_t at their inception time t. In this regard the portfolio $\mathfrak{p}_i$ with $i = 0$ is nothing but the pure discount bond with inception time t, maturity time T and the face value of one unit of account.

8.90. Remark. It is clear that the values $p_T^{(i)} = p_T^{(i)}(s_T)$ in Π of the portfolios $\mathfrak{p}_i$, $i = 0, \dots, N$, at expiration time T are given by

$$p_T^{(i)} = \sum_{j=1}^{i} \binom{i}{j} (-1)^{i-j}\, s_t^{i-j}\, s_T^j = (s_T - s_t)^i, \quad i = 0, \dots, N. \tag{8.116}$$

In this regard each portfolio $\mathfrak{p}_i$, $i = 0, \dots, N$, itself is, from the financial standpoint, nothing but the European contingent claim with the inception time t, expiration time T and the payoff $p_T^{(i)}$

in Π for each state of the market as expressed by the price of the underlying security s_t in $\mathbb{R}_{++}$ at the inception time t. We note that since each payoff $p_T^{(i)} = p_T^{(i)}(s_T)$ in Π is contingent upon the state of the market as expressed by the price of the underlying security s_t in $\mathbb{R}_{++}$ at the inception time t then the payoff $p_T^{(i)} = p_T^{(i)}(s_T)$ as a Π-valued function of s_t in $\mathbb{R}_{++}$ can be interpreted as a member of $\Pi(\mathbb{R}_{++} \times \mathbb{R}_{++})$.

8.91. Remark. Since each of the European contingent claims $\mathfrak{v}_{S_i}$, $i = 0, \ldots, N$, with inception time t, expiration time T and the payoff $v_T^{S_i}$ is traded for each t and T in $\mathcal{T}$ with $t \leq T$ then, by the no-arbitrage argument, each portfolio $\mathfrak{p}_i$, $i = 0, \ldots, N$, or equivalently each European contingent claim $\mathfrak{p}_i$, $i = 0, \ldots, N$, with inception time t, expiration time T and the payoff $p_T^{(i)}$ is effectively traded for each t and T in $\mathcal{T}$ with $t \leq T$.

Since the portfolios, or equivalently, the European contingent claims $\mathfrak{p}_i$, $i = 0, \ldots, N$ are traded, or more precisely, effectively traded, their values $p_i = p_i(t)$ are, by the no-arbitrage argument, the solutions of the Cauchy problem (6.45), that is:

$$\frac{\overset{2}{d}}{dt}\boldsymbol{u}'(\overset{3}{t},\overset{1}{t})\,p_i + \mathfrak{L}(\overset{2}{t})\,\boldsymbol{u}'(\overset{3}{t},\overset{1}{t})\,p_i = 0, \quad t < T, \quad i = 0, \ldots, N,$$
$$p_i(T) = p_T^{(i)}, \tag{8.117}$$

Due to relation (8.111) we can formally represent the values $p_i = p_i(t)$ of portfolios, or equivalently, of the European contingent claims $\mathfrak{p}_i$, $i = 0, \ldots, N$, incepted at time t and expiring at time T an instant later as follows

$$p_i = \sum_{j=0}^{i} \binom{i}{j} (-1)^{i-j}\, \overset{3}{s_t^{i-j}}\, e^{-\int_{\overset{1}{(t)}}^{\overset{3}{(t)}} \mathfrak{d}_j(\overset{3}{s}_t,\tau)d\tau}\, s_t^j, \quad i = 0, \ldots, N, \tag{8.118}$$

so that the evolution equation in (8.117) can be rewritten as follows

$$\Big(\frac{\overset{2}{d}}{dt} + \mathfrak{L}(\overset{2}{t})\Big)\, \boldsymbol{u}'(\overset{3}{t},\overset{1}{t})\, \Big(\sum_{j=0}^{i} \binom{i}{j} (-1)^{i-j}\, \overset{3}{s^{i-j}}\, e^{-\int_{\overset{1}{(t)}}^{\overset{3}{(t)}} \mathfrak{d}_j(\overset{3}{s},\tau)d\tau}\, \overset{1}{s^j}\Big)\, \mathbf{1} = 0,$$

or equivalently

$$\Big(\overset{2}{\frac{d}{dt}} + \mathfrak{L}(\overset{2}{t})\Big)\, \boldsymbol{u}'(\overset{3}{t},\overset{1}{t})\,(\overset{1}{s} - \overset{3}{s})^i\, \mathbf{1} + \Big(\sum_{j=0}^{i} \binom{i}{j} (-1)^{i-j}\, \mathfrak{v}_j(s,t)\Big)\, s^i = 0, \tag{8.119}$$

where $t < T$ and $i = 0, \ldots, N$.

8.92. Remark. We comment that the values $v_{S_i} = v_{S_i}(t)$ at the inception time t of the European contingent claims $\mathfrak{v}_{S_i}$, $i = 0, \ldots, N$, with expiration time T and the payoffs $v_T^{S_i}$ can be expressed in terms of the evolution operator $\mathbf{V}(t,T)$ from the market environment $\mathbf{V}$ as follows

$$v_{S_i}(t) = \mathbf{V}(t,T)\, v_T^{S_i}, \quad i = 0, \ldots, N,$$

where $v_T^{S_i}(s_T) = s_T^i$. Similarly, the values $p_i = p_i(t)$ at the inception time t of the portfolios, or equivalently, of the European contingent claims $\mathfrak{p}_i$, $i = 0, \ldots, N$, with the expiration time T and the payoffs $p_T^{(i)}$ can be expressed in terms of the evolution operator $\mathbf{V}(t,T)$ from the market environment $\mathbf{V}$ as follows

$$p_i(t) = \mathbf{V}(t,T)\, p_T^{(i)}, \quad i = 0, \ldots, N,$$

where $p_T^{(i)}(s_T) = (s_T - s_t)^i$. More precisely, the values $p_i = p_i(t)$ at the inception time t of the portfolios, or equivalently, of the European contingent claims $\mathfrak{p}_i$, $i = 0, \ldots, N$, with the expiration time T and the payoffs $p_T^{(i)}$ can be expressed in terms of the evolution operator $\mathbf{V}(t,T)$ from the market environment $\mathbf{V}$ as follows

$$p_i(t, s_t) = \big(\mathbf{V}(t,T)\,(\cdot - s_t)^i\big)(s_t), \quad i = 0, \ldots, N,$$

or equivalently as

$$p_i(t) = \overset{2}{\mathbf{V}}(t,T)\,(\overset{1}{s} - \overset{3}{s})^i \mathbf{1}, \quad i = 0, \ldots, N,$$

where $\mathbf{1}$ is the function in Π identically equal to unity.

Since $\mathbf{V}(t,T)$ is an absolutely positive operator and since each $v_T^{S_i} = v_T^{S_i}(s_T) > 0$ for each s_T in $\mathbb{R}_{++}$ we have that each $v_{S_i}(t, s_t) > 0$ for each s_t in $\mathbb{R}_{++}$. Therefore, each function $\mathfrak{d}_i(t, s_t)$ defined in (8.111), or equivalently in (8.113), (8.114) or (8.115) is not singular in the sense that, roughly speaking, $\mathfrak{d}_i(t, s_t) \neq \infty$ for each t in $\mathcal{T}$ and s_t in $\mathbb{R}_{++}$. At the same time since each $p_T^{(i)} = p_T^{(i)}(s_T) \geq 0$ for each s_T in $\mathbb{R}_{++}$ and $p_T^{(i)}(s_T)|_{s_T=s_t} = 0$, that is, since each $p_T^{(i)}$ is only in Π_{++}, the fact that $\mathbf{V}(t,T)$ is an absolutely positive operator implies only that each $p_i(t, s_t) \geq 0$ and $p_i(t, s_t) \not\equiv 0$, that is, that each $p_i(t)$ is in Π_{++}. Therefore, if we would formally represent the values $p_i = p_i(t)$ of the portfolios, or equivalently, of the European contingent claims $\mathfrak{p}_i$, $i = 0, \ldots, N$, incepted at time t and expiring at time T an instant later as follows

$$p_i = e^{-\int_{\overset{1}{(t)}}^{\overset{3}{(t)}} \boldsymbol{\mathfrak{d}'}_i(\overset{3}{s}_t, \tau) d\tau} (s_t - \overset{3}{s}_t)^i, \quad i = 0, \ldots, N,$$

where each $\boldsymbol{\mathfrak{d}'}_i(t, s)$ is the operator of multiplication by the function $\mathfrak{d}'_i(t, s)$, then $\mathfrak{d}'_i(t, s_t)$ might be singular in the sense that, roughly speaking, $\mathfrak{d}'_i(t, s_t) = \infty$ for some s_t in $\mathbb{R}_{++}$. Indeed

$$\mathfrak{d}'_i(s'_t, t)\,(s'_t - s_t)^i = \frac{d}{dt}\mathbf{V}(t,T)|_{t=T}\,(\cdot - s_t)^i, \tag{8.120}$$

or equivalently

$$\mathfrak{d}'_i(s'_t, t)\,(s'_t - s_t)^i = -\frac{d}{dT}\mathbf{V}(t,T)|_{T=t}\,(\cdot - s_t)^i, \tag{8.121}$$

where s_t in $\mathbb{R}_{++}$ is treated as a parameter, and where the derivatives with respect to time are understood in an appropriate sense. We also note that the preceding relation (8.120), or equivalently (8.121) can be rewritten in terms of the generators $\boldsymbol{L}(t)$ of the market environment $\mathbf{V}$ with the evolution operators $\mathbf{V}(t,T)$ as follows

$$\mathfrak{d}'_i(s'_t, t)\,(s'_t - s_t)^i = -\boldsymbol{L}(t)\,(\cdot - s_t)^i, \tag{8.122}$$

where s_t in $\mathbb{R}_{++}$ is again treated as a parameter. It is the possible singularity of $\mathfrak{d}'_i(t, s_t)$ that is one of the main reasons why we have considered $\mathfrak{v}_{S_i}$, $i = 0, \ldots, N$, as the traded European contingent claims and $\mathfrak{p}_i$, $i = 0, \ldots, N$, only as the portfolios of $\mathfrak{v}_{S_i}$, $i = 0, \ldots, N$, and not vice versa. This completes the Remark.

Now we assume that the set of the portfolios, or equivalently, of the European contingent claims $\{\mathfrak{p}_i : i = 0, \ldots, N\}$ approximately, in the sense to be specified below, dynamically replicates each European contingent claim $\mathfrak{v}$ with inception time t, expiration time T and payoff v_T.

Due to the fact that the portfolios, or equivalently European contingent claims $\mathfrak{p}_i$, $i = 0, \ldots, N$ are effectively traded and since the portfolio, or equivalently European contingent claim $\mathfrak{p}_i$ with $i = 0$ is nothing but the pure discount bond, for the operator weights $\boldsymbol{\pi}_v(t, P_i)$ of the portfolios, or equivalently European contingent claims $\mathfrak{p}_i$, $i = 1, \ldots, N$ in the dynamically replicating portfolio for the European contingent claim $\mathfrak{v}$ with the value $v = v(t)$, with the help of equation (6.59) or equivalently (6.60), we obtain the following equation

$$[[(\overset{2}{\frac{d}{dt}} + \mathfrak{L}(\overset{2}{t})), \boldsymbol{v}], \boldsymbol{u}'(\overset{3}{t}, \overset{1}{t})]\, \mathbf{1} = \sum_{i=1}^{N} \Big(\boldsymbol{\pi}_v(t, P_i) [[(\overset{2}{\frac{d}{dt}} + \mathfrak{L}(\overset{2}{t})), \boldsymbol{p}_i], \boldsymbol{u}'(\overset{3}{t}, \overset{1}{t})]\, \mathbf{1} \Big), \tag{8.123}$$

or equivalently

$$[[\mathfrak{L}(\overset{2}{t}), \boldsymbol{v}], \boldsymbol{u}'(\overset{3}{t}, \overset{1}{t})]\, \mathbf{1} = \sum_{i=1}^{N} \Big(\boldsymbol{\pi}_v(t, P_i) [[\mathfrak{L}(\overset{2}{t}), \boldsymbol{p}_i], \boldsymbol{u}'(\overset{3}{t}, \overset{1}{t})]\, \mathbf{1} \Big), \tag{8.124}$$

where $\boldsymbol{v} = \boldsymbol{v}(t)$ and $\boldsymbol{p}_i = \boldsymbol{p}_i(t)$ are the operators on Π of multiplication by the functions $v = v(t)$ and $p_i = p_i(t)$.

Now we formally represent each generator $\mathfrak{L}(t)$ in $\mathfrak{L}$ from $\mathbb{L}$ as a real quasidifferential operator on an appropriate space of real-valued functions on Ω equal to $\mathbb{R}_{++}$, that is, on an appropriate subspace of Π. Let the defining sequence of $\mathfrak{L}(t)$ be given by

$$\mathfrak{L}_M(t) = \sum_{m=1}^{M} \mathfrak{L}_m(M, t, \hat{s}) \, \frac{\partial}{\partial s}^{\,m} . \tag{8.125}$$

8.93. Remark. We comment that due to relation (3.101) the terms $\mathfrak{L}_m(M, t, \hat{s})$ with $m = 0$ in the preceding relation (8.125) can be put equal to zero for each $M \geq 0$.

8.94. Remark. We comment that due to relation (8.86) each generator $\mathfrak{L}(t)$ in $\mathfrak{L}$ from $\mathbb{L}$ can be formally represented as an analytic quasidifferential operator with the defining sequence given in relations (8.87) and (8.88).

Approximating the generator $\mathfrak{L}(t)$ by $\mathfrak{L}_M(t)$ defined in the expression (8.125), the equations (8.123) and (8.124) can be approximated by the following equations

$$\begin{aligned} &[[(\overset{2}{\frac{d}{dt}} + \mathfrak{L}_M(\overset{2}{t})), \boldsymbol{v}], \boldsymbol{u}'(\overset{3}{t}, \overset{1}{t})]\, \mathbf{1} = \\ &\qquad \sum_{i=1}^{N} \Big(\boldsymbol{\pi}_v(t, P_i) [[(\overset{2}{\frac{d}{dt}} + \mathfrak{L}_M(\overset{2}{t})), \boldsymbol{p}_i], \boldsymbol{u}'(\overset{3}{t}, \overset{1}{t})]\, \mathbf{1} \Big), \end{aligned} \tag{8.126}$$

or equivalently

$$\begin{aligned} &[[\mathfrak{L}_M(\overset{2}{t}), \boldsymbol{v}], \boldsymbol{u}'(\overset{3}{t}, \overset{1}{t})]\, \mathbf{1} = \\ &\qquad \sum_{i=1}^{N} \Big(\boldsymbol{\pi}_v(t, P_i) [[\mathfrak{L}_M(\overset{2}{t}), \boldsymbol{p}_i], \boldsymbol{u}'(\overset{3}{t}, \overset{1}{t})]\, \mathbf{1} \Big). \end{aligned} \tag{8.127}$$

With the help of identity (8.51) we rewrite the preceding

equation (8.126), or equivalently (8.127) as follows

$$\begin{aligned}
&\sum_{l=1}^{M-1}\Big(\sum_{m=l+1}^{M}\binom{m}{l}\,\mathfrak{L}_m(M,t,s)\times \\
&\qquad\Big(\frac{\partial}{\partial s}^{(m-l)^+} v(s,t)\Big)\Big)\Big(\frac{\partial}{\partial s}^{l} u(t,t,\overset{1}{\underset{2}{s}},s)\Big) = \\
&\sum_{i=1}^{N}\boldsymbol{\pi}_v(t,P_i)\Big(\sum_{l=1}^{M-1}\Big(\sum_{m=l+1}^{M}\binom{m}{l}\,\mathfrak{L}_m(M,t,s)\times \\
&\qquad\Big(\frac{\partial}{\partial s}^{(m-l)^+} p_i(s,t)\Big)\Big)\Big(\frac{\partial}{\partial s}^{l} u(t,t,\overset{1}{\underset{2}{s}},s)\Big)\Big).
\end{aligned} \tag{8.128}$$

Since the preceding equation (8.128) has to hold for all preferences $u(t,T,s_t,s_T)$, we obtain the following system of $M-1$ equations

$$\begin{aligned}
&\sum_{m=l+1}^{M}\binom{m}{l}\,\mathfrak{L}_m(M,t,s)\,\Big(\frac{\partial}{\partial s}^{(m-l)^+} v\Big) = \\
&\sum_{i=1}^{N}\boldsymbol{\pi}_v(t,P_i)\Big(\sum_{m=l+1}^{M}\binom{m}{l}\times \\
&\qquad\mathfrak{L}_m(M,t,s)\,\Big(\frac{\partial}{\partial s}^{(m-l)^+} p_i\Big)\Big),
\end{aligned} \tag{8.129}$$

for $l = 1,\ldots,M-1$.

Our goal is to solve the preceding system (8.129) of $M-1$ equations explicitly. In order to do this we need the following obvious identity

$$
\begin{aligned}
\frac{\partial}{\partial s}^{k} p_i = & \frac{\overset{2}{\partial}}{\partial s}^{k} \Big(\sum_{j=1}^{i} \binom{i}{j} (-1)^{i-j}\, \overset{3}{s}^{i-j}\, e^{-\int_{\overset{1}{(t)}}^{\overset{3}{(t)}} \mathfrak{d}_j(\overset{3}{s},\tau)d\tau}\, s^j\Big) = \\
& \frac{\overset{2}{\partial}}{\partial s}^{k} \Big(\sum_{j=1}^{i} \binom{i}{j} (-1)^{i-j}\, \overset{3}{s}^{i-j}\, s^j\Big) = \\
& \frac{\overset{2}{\partial}}{\partial s}^{k} (s - \overset{3}{s})^i = \\
& k!\, \delta(k-i),
\end{aligned}
\tag{8.130}
$$

where $\delta(k)$ is the Kronecker symbol.

With the help of the preceding identity (8.130) we can rewrite the system (8.129) as follows

$$
\begin{aligned}
& \sum_{m=l+1}^{M} \binom{m}{l} \mathfrak{L}_m(M,t,s) \Big(\frac{\partial}{\partial s}^{(m-l)^+} v\Big) = \\
& \sum_{m=l+1}^{M} \binom{m}{l} \mathfrak{L}_m(M,t,s) \big(\boldsymbol{\pi}_v(t, P_{m-l})\,(m-l)!\big),
\end{aligned}
\tag{8.131}
$$

for $l = 1, \ldots, M-1$.

8.95. Remark. We comment that in the preceding system (8.131) we have used the same notation for the function in Π, or more precisely in $\Pi(\mathbb{R}_{++} \times \mathcal{T})$ identically equal to $(m-l)!$ and for the integer $(m-l)!$ itself.

Finally, if we choose N equal to $M-1$ then we obtain that the solution to the system (8.131) and therefore to the original equation (8.126) or equivalently (8.127) is given by

$$
\boldsymbol{\pi}_v(t, P_i) = \frac{1}{i!}\, \boldsymbol{v}^{(i)}(t), \quad i = 1, \ldots, N,
\tag{8.132}
$$

where $\boldsymbol{v}^{(i)}(t)$ stands for the operator of multiplication by the function $\frac{\partial}{\partial s}^{i} v(t)$. In more detail

$$\big(\boldsymbol{\pi}_v(t, P_i)\, h\big)(s_t) = \pi_v(t, s_t, P_i)\, h(s_t), \quad h \in \Pi, \tag{8.133}$$

where

$$\pi_v(t, s_t, P_i) = \frac{1}{i!} \frac{\partial}{\partial s_t}^{i} v(s_t, t). \tag{8.134}$$

8.96. Remark. It is clear that we have obtained the solution (8.132) of equation (8.126) or equivalently (8.127) under the assumption that the value $v = v(t)$ of the European contingent claim $\mathfrak{v}$ is in an appropriate sense $N = M-1$ times differentiable with respect to the price of the underlying security.

8.97. Remark. Assume that according to relation (8.86) each generator $\mathfrak{L}(t)$ in $\mathfrak{L}$ from $\mathbb{L}$ is formally represented as an analytic quasidifferential operator with the defining sequence given in relations (8.87) and (8.88). Then with the help of relation (8.54) it is easy to see that the expression (8.132) determines the exact formal solution to the original equation (8.123) or equivalently (8.124) where $N = \infty$.

For the operator weight $\boldsymbol{\pi}_v(t, P_0)$ of the pure discount bond $\mathfrak{p}_0$ with the help of relation (6.57) we obtain the following expression

$$\boldsymbol{\pi}_v(t, P_0) = \boldsymbol{v}(t) - \sum_{i=1}^{N} \frac{1}{i!} \boldsymbol{v}^{(i)}(t)\, \boldsymbol{p}_i(t) =$$

$$\boldsymbol{v}(t) - \sum_{i=1}^{N} \frac{1}{i!} \boldsymbol{v}^{(i)}(t) \Big(\sum_{j=0}^{i} \binom{i}{j} (-1)^{i-j} \overset{3}{s}{}^{i-j} e^{-\int_{\overset{1}{(t)}}^{\overset{3}{(t)}} \mathfrak{d}_j(\overset{3}{s},\tau)d\tau} \overset{1}{s}{}^{j}\Big) = \tag{8.135}$$

$$\boldsymbol{v}(t) - \sum_{i=1}^{N} \frac{1}{i!} \boldsymbol{v}^{(i)}(t) \Big(\sum_{j=0}^{i} \binom{i}{j} (-1)^{i-j} \overset{3}{s}{}^{i-j} \overset{1}{s}{}^{j}\Big) =$$

$$\boldsymbol{v}(t) - \sum_{i=1}^{N} \frac{1}{i!} \boldsymbol{v}^{(i)}(t) \, (\overset{1}{s} - \overset{3}{s})^i =$$

$$\boldsymbol{v}(t)$$

where $N = M - 1$.

8.98. Remark. We comment that the reason we have used notation $\boldsymbol{\pi}_v(t, P_0)$ for the operator weight of the pure discount bond instead of $\mathfrak{v}_{\omega_B}$ as used in Section (6) is that, contrary to the set $\{\mathfrak{v}_\omega : \omega \in \Omega\}$ that dynamically replicates a European contingent claim $\mathfrak{v}$, the set of portfolios or equivalently of European contingent claims $\{\mathfrak{p}_i : i = 0, \dots, N\}$ dynamically replicates the European contingent claim $\mathfrak{v}$ only approximately.

8.99. Remark. According to Remarks (6.72) and (8.97), define for each ω_i in $\Omega = \{\omega_i : i \in \mathbb{Z}_+\}$ and for each t in $\mathcal{T}$ the linear operators

$$\hat{\pi}(t, P_i) = \hat{\pi}(t, \omega_i) : \Pi \to \Pi$$

by

$$\hat{\pi}(t, P_i) \, v = \pi_v(t, P_i),$$

where $\pi_v(t, P_i) = \pi_v(t, \omega_i)$ are the Π-valued measures of ω_i in Ω associated as in Remark (6.41) with the operator-valued measures, or equivalently operator weights $\boldsymbol{\pi}_v(t, P_i) = \boldsymbol{\pi}_v(t, \omega_i)$ of the portfolios, or more precisely European contingent claims $\{\mathfrak{p}_i : i \in \mathbb{Z}_+\}$ in the dynamically replicating portfolio for the European contingent claim $\mathfrak{v}$ with the value $v = v(t)$. In the case under consideration $\boldsymbol{\pi}_v(t, P_i)$, $i \in \mathbb{Z}_+$, are the linear operators on Π of multiplication by the functions $\pi_v(t, P_i) = \pi_v(t, \cdot, P_i)$ in Π.

It is clear that due to relations (8.135) and (8.132) the linear operators $\hat{\pi}(t, P_i)$, $i \in \mathbb{Z}_+$, on Π are explicitly given by

$$\hat{\pi}(t, P_i) = \frac{1}{i!} \frac{\partial}{\partial s}^{i}.$$

It is also clear that the linear operators $\hat{\pi}(t, P_i)$, $i \in \mathbb{Z}_+$, on Π and linear operators on Π of multiplication by functions in Π do not commute in general. Indeed, with the help of relation (8.46) we obtain

$$[\hat{\pi}(t, P_i), h(\hat{s})] = \frac{1}{i!} \sum_{l=0}^{m-1} l! \binom{m}{l} \left(\frac{\partial}{\partial s}^{m-l} h(\hat{s}) \right) \hat{\pi}(t, P_l),$$

where $h(\hat{s})$ is the operator on Π of multiplication by the function $h = h(s)$ in Π, and where the function h in Π is assumed to be sufficiently smooth in an appropriate sense.

In this regard we note that the linear operators $\hat{\pi}(t, P_i)$, $i \in \mathbb{Z}_+$, on Π form a basis of the Lie module $\mathfrak{D}(\mathbb{R}_{++})$ with the structure constants determined according to relation (8.47). Finally, we note that it is this noncommutativity of the linear operators $\hat{\pi}(t, P_i)$ on Π and linear operators on Π of multiplication by arbitrary admissible functions in Π that is, in the essence, financially responsible for the randomness of the prices of the underlying securities, that is, for the first quantization in finance in the case under consideration. This issue will be presented in detail in forthcoming articles.

8.100. Remark. Let

$$\mathfrak{Q}_M = \sum_{m=0}^{M} \mathfrak{q}_m(\hat{\xi}) \frac{\partial}{\partial \xi}^m, \quad \mathfrak{q}_m(\xi) \in R^\infty(\Omega)$$

be a linear differential operator of order M on $R^\infty(\Omega)$. It is clear that the stochastic dimension of $\mathfrak{Q}_M$ does not exceed M, and in fact is equal to M.

8.101. Remark. Let

$$\mathfrak{Q} = \sum_{m=0}^{\infty} \mathfrak{q}_m(\hat{\xi}) \frac{\partial}{\partial \xi}^m, \quad \mathfrak{q}_m(\xi) \in R^\infty(\Omega)$$

be a real analytic quasidifferential operator. It is clear that the stochastic dimensionality of $\mathfrak{Q}$ does not exceed the cardinality of an infinite countable set, and in fact is equal to this cardinality.

8.102. Remark. Let

$$Q_M = \sum_{m=0}^{M} q_m(M, \hat{\xi})\big(-i\frac{\partial}{\partial \xi}\big)^m, \quad q_m(M, \xi) \in C^\infty(\Omega)$$

be a linear differential operator of order M on $C^\infty(\Omega)$. It is clear that the stochastic dimension of Q_M does not exceed M, and in fact is equal to M.

8.103. Remark. Let

$$Q = \sum_{m=0}^{\infty} q_m(M, \hat{\xi})\big(-i\frac{\partial}{\partial \xi}\big)^m, \quad q_m(M, \xi) \in C^\infty(\Omega)$$

be an analytic quasidifferential operator. It is clear that the stochastic dimensionality of Q does not exceed the cardinality of an infinite countable set, and in fact is equal to this cardinality.

8.104. Remark. In light of Remarks (6.48), (8.100) and (8.101) the formal representation of a generator $\mathfrak{L}(t)$ in $\mathfrak{L}$ from $\mathbb{L}$ in relation (8.86) as an analytic quasidifferential operator with the defining sequence $\mathfrak{L}_M(t)$ given in relations (8.87) and (8.88), that is, the expansion of $\mathfrak{L}(t)$ in a formal power series over the operator $\frac{\partial}{\partial s}$ corresponds to the expansion of the generator $\mathfrak{L}(t)$ over increasing measures of randomness.

Now with the help of the evolution equation (6.64), for the approximate value $v_M = v_M(t)$ of the European contingent claim $\mathfrak{v}$ we obtain the following evolution equation

$$\Big(\overset{1}{\frac{d}{dt}} + \mathfrak{L}_M(\overset{1}{t})\Big)\,\Big(v_M(t) - \sum_{i=1}^{M-1} \overset{2}{\boldsymbol{\pi}}_{v_M}(t, P_i)p_i(t)\Big) = \boldsymbol{v}_M(t)\,r(s,t), \tag{8.136}$$

or equivalently

$$
\begin{aligned}
&\Big(\frac{d}{dt} + \mathfrak{L}_M(t)\Big)\, v_M(t) - \\
&\quad \Big(\frac{\overset{2}{d}}{dt} + \mathfrak{L}_M(\overset{2}{t})\Big)\Big(\sum_{i=1}^{M-1} \frac{1}{i!} \overset{4}{\boldsymbol{v}}{}_M^{(i)}(t) \times \\
&\qquad \Big(\sum_{j=0}^{i} \binom{i}{j} (-1)^{i-j}\, \overset{3}{s}{}^{i-j}\, e^{-\int_{\overset{1}{(t)}}^{\overset{3}{(t)}} \mathfrak{d}_j(\overset{3}{s},\tau)d\tau}\, s^j\Big)\Big) = \\
&\qquad\quad \boldsymbol{v}_M(t)\, r(s,t),
\end{aligned}
\tag{8.137}
$$

or equivalently

$$
\begin{aligned}
&\Big(\frac{d}{dt} + \mathfrak{L}_M(t)\Big)\, v_M(t) - \\
&\quad \sum_{i=1}^{M-1} \frac{1}{i!} \boldsymbol{v}_M^{(i)} \Big(\sum_{j=0}^{i} \binom{i}{j} (-1)^{i-j}\, \mathfrak{d}_j(s,t)\Big) s^i - \\
&\quad \mathfrak{L}_M(\overset{1}{t}) \sum_{i=1}^{M-1} \frac{1}{i!} \overset{3}{\boldsymbol{v}}{}_M^{(i)}(t)(s - \overset{2}{s})^i = \\
&\qquad \boldsymbol{v}_M(t)\, r(s,t),
\end{aligned}
\tag{8.138}
$$

or equivalently

$$
\begin{aligned}
&\Big(\frac{d}{dt} + \sum_{m=1}^{M} \mathfrak{L}_m(M,t,\hat{s}) \frac{\partial}{\partial s}^{m}\Big)\, v_M(t) - \\
&\quad \sum_{i=1}^{M-1} \Big(\frac{s^i}{i!} \Big(\sum_{j=0}^{i} \binom{i}{j} (-1)^{i-j}\, \mathfrak{d}_j(s,t)\Big)\Big) \frac{\partial}{\partial s}^{i} v_M(t) - \\
&\quad \Big(\sum_{m=1}^{M} \mathfrak{L}_m(M,t,\overset{2}{\hat{s}}) \frac{\overset{1}{\partial}}{\partial s}^{m}\Big) \sum_{i=1}^{M-1} \frac{1}{i!} \overset{4}{\boldsymbol{v}}{}_M^{(i)}(t)(s - \overset{3}{s})^i = \\
&\qquad \boldsymbol{v}_M(t)\, r(s,t),
\end{aligned}
\tag{8.139}
$$

or equivalently

$$\begin{aligned}&\Big(\frac{d}{dt}+\sum_{m=1}^{M}\mathfrak{L}_m(M,t,\hat{s})\frac{\partial}{\partial s}^{m}\Big)\,v_M(t)-\\&\quad\sum_{i=1}^{M-1}\Big(\frac{s^i}{i!}\Big(\sum_{j=0}^{i}\binom{i}{j}(-1)^{i-j}\,\mathfrak{v}_j(s,t)\Big)\Big)\frac{\partial}{\partial s}^{i}v_M(t)-\\&\quad\sum_{m=1}^{M-1}\mathfrak{L}_m(M,t,\hat{s})\frac{\partial}{\partial s}^{m}v_M(t)=\\&\qquad\quad \mathfrak{v}_M(t)\,r(s,t),\end{aligned}\tag{8.140}$$

or finally as

$$\begin{aligned}&\frac{d}{dt}v_M+\mathfrak{L}_M(M,t,\hat{s})\frac{\partial}{\partial s}^{M}v_M-\\&\quad\sum_{i=1}^{M-1}\Big(\frac{s^i}{i!}\Big(\sum_{j=0}^{i}\binom{i}{j}(-1)^{i-j}\,\mathfrak{v}_j(s,t)\Big)\Big)\frac{\partial}{\partial s}^{i}v_M-\\&\quad r(s,t)v_M=0.\end{aligned}\tag{8.141}$$

8.105. Remark. It is clear that in order to determine the approximate value $v_M = v_M(t)$ of the European contingent claim $\mathfrak{v}$ with inception time t, expiration time T and payoff v_T the preceding evolution equation (8.141) must be equipped with the initial, or more precisely, final condition $v_M(T) = v_T$.

8.106. Remark. We comment that the time derivative $\frac{d}{dt}$ in the evolution equation (8.141) can be interpreted as the partial time derivative $\frac{\partial}{\partial t}$.

8.107. Remark. It is clear that if the generators $\mathfrak{L}(t)$ are of the form (5.1) then for $M = 2$ the evolution equation (8.141) is nothing but the Black and Scholes equation (5.50). In this regard for the generators $\mathfrak{L}(\mathrm{t})$ of a general form, the Black and Scholes equation (5.50) can be considered as the evolution equation (8.141) for the approximate value $v_M = v_M(t)$ of the European contingent claim $\mathfrak{v}$ with $M = 2$.

If in the evolution equation (8.141) M goes to infinity then under the assumption that the term

$$\mathfrak{L}_M(M,t,\hat{s})\frac{\partial}{\partial s}^{M} v_M(t)$$

tends in an appropriate sense to the zero function in $\Pi(\mathbb{R}_{++}\times\mathcal{T})$ we obtain the following evolution equation for the value $v = v(t)$ of the European contingent claim $\mathfrak{v}$

$$\frac{d}{dt}v - \sum_{i=1}^{\infty}\Big(\frac{s^i}{i!}\big(\sum_{j=0}^{i}\binom{i}{j}(-1)^{i-j}\,\mathfrak{d}_j(s,t)\big)\Big)\frac{\partial}{\partial s}^{i} v - r(s,t)v = 0. \tag{8.142}$$

8.108. Remark. We comment that in the preceding evolution equation (8.142) we have also assumed that the approximate value $v_M = v_M(t)$ of the European contingent claim $\mathfrak{v}$ tends, in an appropriate sense, to the value $v = v(t)$ of the European contingent claim $\mathfrak{v}$ as M goes to infinity.

8.109. Remark. We note that a generator $\boldsymbol{L}(t)$ in $\boldsymbol{L}$ of a market environment $\mathbf{V}$ with the help of the evolution equation (8.142) can be represented as the following analytic quasidifferential operator

$$\boldsymbol{L}(t) = -\sum_{i=1}^{\infty}\Big(\frac{s^i}{i!}\big(\sum_{j=0}^{i}\binom{i}{j}(-1)^{i-j}\,\mathfrak{d}_j(s,t)\big)\Big)\frac{\partial}{\partial s}^{i} - \boldsymbol{r}(s,t),$$

or equivalently

$$\boldsymbol{L}(t) = -\sum_{i=0}^{\infty}\Big(\frac{s^i}{i!}\big(\sum_{j=0}^{i}\binom{i}{j}(-1)^{i-j}\,\mathfrak{d}_j(s,t)\big)\Big)\frac{\partial}{\partial s}^{i}.$$

We make the following crucial observation. The evolution equation (8.142) does not depend on the generator $\mathfrak{L}(t)$ at all. The reason for this is as follows. Consider a market in which each European contingent claim $\mathfrak{v}$ with inception time t and expiration time T has payoff $v_T = v_T(s_T)$ in Π such that it is an analytic function of s_T at s_t. It is clear that the set of portfolios, or more precisely European contingent claims $\{\mathfrak{p}_i : i \in \mathbb{Z}_+\}$ spans such a market. Indeed

$$v_T(s_T) = \sum_{i=0}^{\infty}\Big(\frac{1}{i!}\big(\frac{\partial}{\partial s_T}^{i} v_T\big)(s_t)\Big)\, p_T^{(i)}(s_T) = \sum_{i=0}^{\infty}\Big(\frac{1}{i!}\big(\frac{\partial}{\partial s_T}^{i} v_T\big)(s_t)\Big)\,(s_T - s_t)^i. \tag{8.143}$$

Then the instantaneous return on the European contingent claim $\mathfrak{v}$ with the value $v = v(t)$ has to be equal to that of the portfolios of $\{\mathfrak{p}_i : i \in \mathbb{Z}_+\}$ with operator weights $\boldsymbol{\pi}_v(t, P_i)$ given in relations (8.132) and (8.135):

$$\begin{aligned}
\frac{d}{dt}v(t, s_t) = {} & \\
& \overset{2}{\frac{d}{dt}} \mathbf{V}(\overset{1}{t}, \overset{3}{t})\Big(\sum_{i=0}^{\infty}\Big(\frac{1}{i!}\big(\frac{\partial}{\partial s_t}^{i} v(\overset{3}{t}, s_t)\big)\Big)(\cdot - s_t)^i\Big) = \\
& \overset{2}{\frac{d}{dt}} \sum_{i=0}^{\infty}\Big(\frac{1}{i!}\big(\frac{\partial}{\partial s_t}^{i} v(\overset{3}{t}, s_t)\big)\Big)\Big(\mathbf{V}(\overset{1}{t}, \overset{3}{t})(\cdot - s_t)^i\Big) = \\
& \overset{2}{\frac{d}{dt}} \sum_{i=0}^{\infty}\Big(\frac{1}{i!}\big(\frac{\partial}{\partial s_t}^{i} v(\overset{3}{t}, s_t)\big)\Big) \times \\
& \qquad \Big(\sum_{j=0}^{i}\binom{i}{j}(-1)^{i-j}\,\overset{3}{s}{}_t^{\,i-j}\, e^{-\int_{\overset{1}{(t)}}^{\overset{3}{(t)}} \mathfrak{v}_j(\overset{3}{s}_t,\tau)d\tau}\, s_t^j\Big) = \\
& \sum_{i=0}^{\infty}\Big(\frac{1}{i!}\big(\frac{\partial}{\partial s_t}^{i} v(t, s_t)\big)\Big)\Big(\sum_{j=0}^{i}\binom{i}{j}(-1)^{i-j}\,\mathfrak{v}_j(s_t, t)\Big)s_t^i,
\end{aligned} \tag{8.144}$$

which coincides with the evolution equation (8.142).

8.110. Remark. We comment that in the preceding chain of equalities (8.144) we have again used the following expression for the instantaneous return on the portfolio, or more precisely European contingent claim $\mathfrak{p}_i$ with $i \in \mathbb{Z}_+$:

$$\begin{aligned}
&\frac{d}{dt} p_i(t, s_t) = \\
&\quad \frac{\overset{2}{d}}{dt} \mathbf{V}(\overset{1}{t}, \overset{3}{t})(\cdot - s_t)^i = \\
&\quad \frac{\overset{2}{d}}{dt} \Big(\sum_{j=0}^{i} \binom{i}{j} (-1)^{i-j} \overset{3}{s}_t^{\,i-j} e^{-\int_{\overset{1}{(t)}}^{\overset{3}{(t)}} \mathfrak{d}_j(\overset{3}{s}_t, \tau) d\tau} s_t^j\Big) = \qquad (8.145) \\
&\quad \Big(\sum_{j=0}^{i} \binom{i}{j} (-1)^{i-j} \mathfrak{d}_j(s_t, t)\Big) s_t^i .
\end{aligned}$$

8.111. Remark. The discussion preceding the chain of equalities (8.144) provides the financial indication of when the term

$$\mathfrak{L}_M(M, t, \hat{s}) \frac{\partial}{\partial s}^M v_M(t)$$

in the evolution equation (8.141) tends in an appropriate sense to the zero function in $\Pi(\mathbb{R}_{++} \times \mathcal{T})$ as M goes to infinity. It is natural to expect this to happen when the value $v = v(t)$ of the European contingent claim $\mathfrak{v}$, in addition to being a sufficiently regular function of time, is an analytic function of the price of the underlying security.

Now our goal is to examine the error due to the approximation of the generators $\mathfrak{L}(t)$ by $\mathfrak{L}_M(t)$ and the value $v = v(t)$ of the European contingent claim $\mathfrak{v}$ by $v_M = v_M(t)$ in equation (8.123), or equivalently (8.124).

Define the linear operator $\Delta\mathfrak{L}_M(t)$ on Π by

$$\mathfrak{L}(t) = \mathfrak{L}_M(t) + \Delta\mathfrak{L}_M(t). \qquad (8.146)$$

With the help of the preceding expression (8.146) we can

rewrite equations (8.123) and (8.124) as follows

$$[[(\overset{2}{\frac{d}{dt}} + \boldsymbol{\mathfrak{L}}_M(\overset{2}{t}) + \Delta\boldsymbol{\mathfrak{L}}_M(\overset{2}{t})), \boldsymbol{v}_M], \boldsymbol{u}'(\overset{3}{t}, \overset{1}{t})]\, \mathbf{1} = \sum_{i=1}^{M-1} \Big(\boldsymbol{\pi}_{v_M}(t, P_i)[[(\overset{2}{\frac{d}{dt}} + \boldsymbol{\mathfrak{L}}_M(\overset{2}{t}) + \Delta\boldsymbol{\mathfrak{L}}_M(\overset{2}{t})), \boldsymbol{p}_i], \boldsymbol{u}'(\overset{3}{t}, \overset{1}{t})]\, \mathbf{1}\Big), \tag{8.147}$$

or equivalently

$$[[(\boldsymbol{\mathfrak{L}}_M(\overset{2}{t}) + \Delta\boldsymbol{\mathfrak{L}}_M(\overset{2}{t})), \boldsymbol{v}_M], \boldsymbol{u}'(\overset{3}{t}, \overset{1}{t})]\, \mathbf{1} = \sum_{i=1}^{M-1} \Big(\boldsymbol{\pi}_{v_M}(t, P_i)[[(\boldsymbol{\mathfrak{L}}_M(\overset{2}{t}) + \Delta\boldsymbol{\mathfrak{L}}_M(\overset{2}{t})), \boldsymbol{p}_i], \boldsymbol{u}'(\overset{3}{t}, \overset{1}{t})]\, \mathbf{1}\Big), \tag{8.148}$$

where $\boldsymbol{v}_M = \boldsymbol{v}_M(t)$ is the operator of multiplication by the function $v_M = v_M(t)$.

Using the linearity of the commutator $[,]$ we can rewrite the preceding equations (8.147) and (8.148) as follows

$$[[(\overset{2}{\frac{d}{dt}} + \boldsymbol{\mathfrak{L}}_M(\overset{2}{t})), \boldsymbol{v}_M], \boldsymbol{u}'(\overset{3}{t}, \overset{1}{t})]\, \mathbf{1} + [[\Delta\boldsymbol{\mathfrak{L}}_M(\overset{2}{t})), \boldsymbol{v}_M], \boldsymbol{u}'(\overset{3}{t}, \overset{1}{t})]\, \mathbf{1} = \sum_{i=1}^{M-1} \Big(\boldsymbol{\pi}_{v_M}(t, P_i)[[(\overset{2}{\frac{d}{dt}} + \boldsymbol{\mathfrak{L}}_M(\overset{2}{t})), \boldsymbol{p}_i], \boldsymbol{u}'(\overset{3}{t}, \overset{1}{t})]\, \mathbf{1}\Big) + \sum_{i=1}^{M-1} \Big(\boldsymbol{\pi}_{v_M}(t, P_i)[[\Delta\boldsymbol{\mathfrak{L}}_M(\overset{2}{t}), \boldsymbol{p}_i], \boldsymbol{u}'(\overset{3}{t}, \overset{1}{t})]\, \mathbf{1}\Big), \tag{8.149}$$

or equivalently

$$
\begin{aligned}
&[[\mathfrak{L}_M(\overset{2}{t}), \boldsymbol{v}_M], \boldsymbol{u}'(\overset{3}{t}, \overset{1}{t})]\,\mathbf{1} + \\
&\qquad [[\Delta\mathfrak{L}_M(\overset{2}{t}), \boldsymbol{v}_M], \boldsymbol{u}'(\overset{3}{t}, \overset{1}{t})]\,\mathbf{1} = \\
&\sum_{i=1}^{M-1} \Big(\boldsymbol{\pi}_{v_M}(t, P_i)[[\mathfrak{L}_M(\overset{2}{t}), \boldsymbol{p}_i], \boldsymbol{u}'(\overset{3}{t}, \overset{1}{t})]\,\mathbf{1} \Big) + \\
&\qquad \sum_{i=1}^{M-1} \Big(\boldsymbol{\pi}_{v_M}(t, P_i)[[\Delta\mathfrak{L}_M(\overset{2}{t}), \boldsymbol{p}_i], \boldsymbol{u}'(\overset{3}{t}, \overset{1}{t})]\,\mathbf{1} \Big).
\end{aligned} \tag{8.150}
$$

Due to the fact that the operator weights $\boldsymbol{\pi}_{v_M}(t, P_i)$ defined in (8.132) are the solutions of the equation (8.126) or equivalently (8.127) with $N = M - 1$ we conclude that the preceding equations (8.149) and (8.150) and hence (8.123) and (8.124) are satisfied up to the following defect

$$
\begin{aligned}
&[[\Delta\mathfrak{L}_M(\overset{2}{t}), \boldsymbol{v}_M], \boldsymbol{u}'(\overset{3}{t}, \overset{1}{t})]\,\mathbf{1} - \\
&\quad \sum_{i=1}^{M-1} \Big(\boldsymbol{\pi}_{v_M}(t, P_i)[[\Delta\mathfrak{L}_M(\overset{2}{t}), \boldsymbol{p}_i], \boldsymbol{u}'(\overset{3}{t}, \overset{1}{t})]\,\mathbf{1} \Big).
\end{aligned} \tag{8.151}
$$

Finally, our goal is to examine the error due to the approximation of the generators $\mathfrak{L}(t)$ by $\mathfrak{L}_M(t)$ and the value $v = v(t)$ of the European contingent claim $\mathfrak{v}$ by $v_M = v_M(t)$ in the evolution equation (6.58), which in the case under consideration can be rewritten as follows

$$
\begin{aligned}
&\Big([(\frac{d}{dt} + \mathfrak{L}(t)), \boldsymbol{v}] + [[(\frac{\overset{2}{d}}{dt} + \mathfrak{L}(\overset{2}{t})), \boldsymbol{v}], \boldsymbol{u}'(\overset{3}{t}, \overset{1}{t})] \Big)\,\mathbf{1} = \\
&\sum_{i=1}^{M-1} \Big(\boldsymbol{\pi}_v(t, P_i) \Big([(\frac{d}{dt} + \mathfrak{L}(t)), \boldsymbol{p}_i] + \\
&\qquad [[(\frac{\overset{2}{d}}{dt} + \mathfrak{L}(\overset{2}{t})), \boldsymbol{p}_i], \boldsymbol{u}'(\overset{3}{t}, \overset{1}{t})] \Big)\,\mathbf{1} \Big) + \\
&\quad \boldsymbol{\pi}_v(t, P_0)\, r(s, t),
\end{aligned} \tag{8.152}
$$

where $\mathbf{1}$ is the function in $\Pi(\mathbb{R}_{++} \times \mathcal{T})$ identically equal to unity.

8.112. Remark. In the preceding evolution equation (8.152) we have used the fact that $\mathfrak{d}_i(s_t, t)$ with $i = 0$ is nothing but the continuously compounded interest rate $r(s_t, t)$.

With the help of relation (6.62) we can rewrite the preceding evolution equation (8.152) in the case under consideration as follows

$$\begin{aligned}
&\Big(\frac{d}{dt} + \mathfrak{L}(t)\Big)\, v + [[(\overset{2}{\frac{d}{dt}} + \mathfrak{L}(\overset{2}{t})), \boldsymbol{v}], \boldsymbol{u}'(\overset{3}{t}, \overset{1}{t})]\mathbf{1} = \\
&\quad \sum_{i=1}^{M-1} \Big(\boldsymbol{\pi}_v(t, P_i)\Big(\big(\frac{d}{dt} + \mathfrak{L}(t)\big)\, p_i + \\
&\qquad\qquad [[(\overset{2}{\frac{d}{dt}} + \mathfrak{L}(\overset{2}{t})), \boldsymbol{p}_i], \boldsymbol{u}'(\overset{3}{t}, \overset{1}{t})]\,\mathbf{1}\Big)\Big) + \\
&\qquad \boldsymbol{\pi}_v(t, P_0)\, r(s, t),
\end{aligned} \tag{8.153}$$

With the help of expression (8.146) from the preceding evolution equation (8.153) we obtain

$$\begin{aligned}
&\Big(\frac{d}{dt} + \mathfrak{L}_M(t) + \Delta\mathfrak{L}_M(t)\Big)\, v_M + \\
&\qquad [[(\overset{2}{\frac{d}{dt}} + \mathfrak{L}_M(\overset{2}{t}) + \Delta\mathfrak{L}_M(\overset{2}{t})), \boldsymbol{v}_M], \boldsymbol{u}'(\overset{3}{t}, \overset{1}{t})]\mathbf{1} = \\
&\sum_{i=1}^{M-1} \Big(\boldsymbol{\pi}_{v_M}(t, P_i)\Big(\big(\frac{d}{dt} + \mathfrak{L}_M(t) + \Delta\mathfrak{L}_M(t)\big)\, p_i + \\
&\qquad [[(\overset{2}{\frac{d}{dt}} + \mathfrak{L}_M(\overset{2}{t}) + \Delta\mathfrak{L}_M(\overset{2}{t})), \boldsymbol{p}_i], \boldsymbol{u}'(\overset{3}{t}, \overset{1}{t})]\,\mathbf{1}\Big)\Big) + \\
&\quad \boldsymbol{\pi}_{v_M}(t, P_0)\, r(s, t).
\end{aligned} \tag{8.154}$$

Using the linearity of the commutator $[,]$ we can rewrite the preceding equation (8.154) as follows

$$
\begin{aligned}
&\Big(\big(\frac{d}{dt} + \mathfrak{L}_M(t)\big)\, v_M + \Delta\mathfrak{L}_M(t)\, v_M + \\
&\qquad [[(\overset{2}{\frac{d}{dt}} + \mathfrak{L}_M(\overset{2}{t})), \boldsymbol{v}_M], \boldsymbol{u}'(\overset{3}{t}, \overset{1}{t})]\mathbf{1} + \\
&\qquad [[\Delta\mathfrak{L}_M(\overset{2}{t}), \boldsymbol{v}_M], \boldsymbol{u}'(\overset{3}{t}, \overset{1}{t})]\mathbf{1} = \\
&\sum_{i=1}^{M-1} \Big(\boldsymbol{\pi}_{v_M}(t, P_i) \Big(\big(\frac{d}{dt} + \mathfrak{L}_M(t)\big)\, p_i + \\
&\qquad\qquad [[(\overset{2}{\frac{d}{dt}} + \mathfrak{L}_M(\overset{2}{t})), \boldsymbol{p}_i], \boldsymbol{u}'(\overset{3}{t}, \overset{1}{t})]\Big)\mathbf{1}\Big) + \\
&\qquad \sum_{i=1}^{M-1} \Big(\boldsymbol{\pi}_{v_M}(t, P_i) \Big(\Delta\mathfrak{L}_M(t)\, p_i + \\
&\qquad\qquad [[\Delta\mathfrak{L}_M(\overset{2}{t}), \boldsymbol{p}_i], \boldsymbol{u}'(\overset{3}{t}, \overset{1}{t})]\, \mathbf{1}\Big)\Big) + \\
&\qquad \boldsymbol{\pi}_{v_M}(t, P_0)\, r(s,t).
\end{aligned}
\tag{8.155}
$$

Due to the fact that $v_M = v_M(t)$ is the solution of the evolution equation (8.141) and hence (8.136) and due to the fact that the operator weights $\boldsymbol{\pi}_{v_M}(t, P_i)$ defined in (8.132) are the solutions of the equation (8.126) or equivalently (8.127) with $N = M - 1$, we conclude that the preceding evolution equation (8.155) and hence (8.152) are satisfied up to the following defect

$$
\begin{aligned}
&\Delta\mathfrak{L}_M(t)\, v_M + [[\Delta\mathfrak{L}_M(\overset{2}{t}), \boldsymbol{v}_M], \boldsymbol{u}'(\overset{3}{t}, \overset{1}{t})]\mathbf{1} - \\
&\qquad \sum_{i=1}^{M-1} \Big(\boldsymbol{\pi}_{v_M}(t, P_i) \Big(\Delta\mathfrak{L}_M(t)\, p_i + \\
&\qquad\qquad [[\Delta\mathfrak{L}_M(\overset{2}{t}), \boldsymbol{p}_i], \boldsymbol{u}'(\overset{3}{t}, \overset{1}{t})]\, \mathbf{1}\Big)\Big).
\end{aligned}
\tag{8.156}
$$

In the case when the generator $\mathfrak{L}(t)$ is formally represented as an analytic quasidifferential operator the preceding expression for the defect (8.156) can be rewritten as follows

$$\Delta\mathfrak{L}_M(t)\, v_M + [[\Delta\mathfrak{L}_M(\overset{2}{t}), \boldsymbol{v}_M], \boldsymbol{u}'(\overset{3}{t}, \overset{1}{t})]\mathbf{1} - \sum_{i=1}^{M-1}\left(\boldsymbol{\pi}_{v_M}(t,P_i)[[\Delta\mathfrak{L}_M(\overset{2}{t}), \boldsymbol{p}_i], \boldsymbol{u}'(\overset{3}{t},\overset{1}{t})]\,\mathbf{1}\right). \qquad (8.157)$$

Indeed, each term $\Delta\mathfrak{L}_M(t)\,p_i$ in expression (8.156) is equal to the zero function in $\Pi(\mathbb{R}_{++}\times\mathcal{T})$ due to the following chain of equalities

$$\Delta\mathfrak{L}_M(t)\,p_i = \Delta\mathfrak{L}_M(\overset{2}{t})\left(\sum_{j=0}^{i}\binom{i}{j}(-1)^{i-j}\overset{3}{s}^{\,i-j}\, e^{-\int_{\overset{1}{(t)}}^{\overset{3}{(t)}}\mathfrak{d}_j(\overset{3}{s},\tau)d\tau}\, s^j\right) = \Delta\mathfrak{L}_M(\overset{2}{t})(s-\overset{3}{s})^i = \sum_{m=M+1}^{\infty}\mathfrak{L}_m(t,\overset{2}{\hat{s}})\frac{\overset{1}{\partial}}{\partial s}^{m}(s-\overset{3}{s})^i$$

where each power m of the operator of differentiation $\frac{\overset{1}{\partial}}{\partial s}$ is strictly greater than the power i of $(s-\overset{3}{s})$.

8.113. Remark. The results of this Subsection can be restated verbatim for the case of the dynamic beliefs-preferences gauge symmetry group for a market populace presented in Subsection (6.1) of Section (6).

8.6 Method of Quasidifferential Operators for Approximate Dynamic Replication of European Contingent Claims in the Case of a Multiple Underlying Security

Consider a Markovian market populace $\mathbb{H}=\mathbb{B}\times\mathbb{U}$, or more precisely $\mathbb{H}=\mathbb{L}\times\mathbb{U}$ in the general case of n underlying securities.

Suppose that the set of European contingent claims $\{\mathfrak{v}_{S_i} : i \in \mathbb{Z}^n_+, |i| \leq N\}$ with inception time t, expiration time T and the payoffs $v_T^{S_i}$ such that $v_T^{S_i}(s_T) = s_T^i$ is traded for each t and T in $\mathcal{T}$ with $t \leq T$.

8.114. Remark. We comment that throughout this Subsection s_t^i stands for the s_t in $\mathbb{R}^n_{++}$ to the power i in $\mathbb{Z}^n_+$. We recall that

$$s^i = s_1^{i_1}, s_1^{i_2}, \dots, s_1^{i_n}$$

for each $i = (i_1, i_2, \dots, i_n)$ in $\mathbb{Z}^n_+$ and $s = (s_1, s_2, \dots, s_n)$ in $\mathbb{R}^n_{++}$.

8.115. Remark. We comment that the number of the European contingent claims in the set $\{\mathfrak{v}_{S_i} : i \in \mathbb{Z}^n_+, |i| \leq N\}$ is equal to the number of solutions to $i_1 + i_2 + \cdots + i_n \leq N$ in nonnegative integers which, in turn, is equal to $\binom{N+n}{n}$ (see, for example, [53] page 15).

8.116. Remark. It is clear that the European contingent claim $\mathfrak{v}_{S_i}$ with $i = 0$ is nothing but the pure discount bond $\mathfrak{v}_{\omega_B}$ with inception time t, maturity time T and the face value of one unit of account. It is also clear that the European contingent claim $\mathfrak{v}_{S_i}$ with

$$i = (i_1 = 0, \dots, i_{k-1} = 0, i_k = 1, i_{k+1} = 0, \dots, i_n = 0)$$

is nothing but the k-th underlying security $\mathfrak{v}_{\omega_{S_k}}$ itself.

Since the European contingent claims $\mathfrak{v}_{S_i}$ with $|i| \leq N$ are traded, their values $v_{S_i} = v_{S_i}(t)$ are the solutions of the Cauchy problem (6.45), that is

$$\overset{2}{\frac{d}{dt}} \boldsymbol{u}'(\overset{3}{t}, \overset{1}{t})\, v_{S_i} + \mathfrak{L}(\overset{2}{t})\, \boldsymbol{u}'(\overset{3}{t}, \overset{1}{t})\, v_{S_i} = 0, \quad t < T, \quad |i| \leq N,$$
$$v_{S_i}(T) = v_T^{S_i}. \tag{8.158}$$

At the same time the values $v_{S_i} = v_{S_i}(t)$ of the European contingent claims $\mathfrak{v}_{S_i}$, $|i| \leq N$ incepted at time t and expiring at time T an instant later can be formally represented as follows

$$v_{S_i} = e^{-\int_{\overset{1}{(t)}}^{\overset{3}{(t)}} \mathfrak{d}_i(\overset{3}{s}_t, \tau) d\tau} s^i_t, \quad |i| \leq N, \tag{8.159}$$

so that the evolution equation in (8.158) can be rewritten as follows

$$(\overset{2}{\frac{d}{dt}} + \mathfrak{L}(\overset{2}{t}))\, \boldsymbol{u}'(\overset{3}{t}, \overset{1}{t})\, e^{-\int_{\overset{1}{(t)}}^{\overset{3}{(t)}} \mathfrak{d}_i(\overset{3}{s}, \tau) d\tau} \overset{1}{s^i} \mathbf{1} = 0, \quad t < T, \quad |i| \leq N,$$

or equivalently

$$(\overset{2}{\frac{d}{dt}} + \mathfrak{L}(\overset{2}{t}))\, \boldsymbol{u}'(\overset{3}{t}, \overset{1}{t})\, \overset{1}{s^i}\, \mathbf{1} + \mathfrak{d}_i(s, t)\, s^i = 0, \quad t < T, \quad |i| \leq N, \tag{8.160}$$

where $\mathfrak{d}_i(s, t)$ is the operator of multiplication by the function $\mathfrak{d}_i(s, t)$ and where the indexes over the operators indicate the order in which these operators act. We comment that here $\mathbf{1}$ is the function in $\Pi(\mathbb{R}^n_{++} \times \mathcal{T})$ identically equal to unity.

8.117. Remark. We comment that $\overset{1}{s^i}$ is the operator on Π of multiplication by the function $h(s) = s^i$ in Π. We also comment that $\overset{1}{s^i}$ can be interpreted as the operator on $\Pi(\mathbb{R}^n_{++} \times \mathcal{T})$ in the standard way as indicated in Remark (6.50).

8.118. Remark. We comment that the functions $\mathfrak{d}_i(s_t, t)$ with $|i| \leq N$, or more precisely their values $\mathfrak{d}_i(s_t, t)$ at the state of the market as expressed by the prices of the underlying securities s_t at time t, are observable directly from the market data. Indeed

$$\mathfrak{d}_i(s_t, t)\, s^i_t = \frac{d}{dt} \mathbf{V}(t, T)|_{t=T}\, s^i_T, \tag{8.161}$$

or equivalently

$$\mathfrak{d}_i(s_t, t)\, s^i_t = -\frac{d}{dT} \mathbf{V}(t, T)|_{T=t}\, s^i_T, \tag{8.162}$$

where $\mathbf{V}(t,T)\, s^i_T$ is the value $v_{S_i} = v_{S_i}(t)$ at inception time t of the European contingent claims $\mathfrak{v}_{S_i}$ with expiration time T and the payoff $v^{S_i}_T(s_T) = s^i_T$, and where the derivatives with respect to time are understood in an appropriate sense. We also note that the preceding relation (8.161), or equivalently (8.162) can be rewritten in terms of the generators $\boldsymbol{L}(t)$ of the market environment $\mathbf{V}$ with the evolution operators $\mathbf{V}(t,T)$ as follows

$$\mathfrak{d}_i(s_t, t)\, s^i_t = -\boldsymbol{L}(t)\, s^i_t. \tag{8.163}$$

In this regard the fact that the functions $\mathfrak{d}_i(s_t, t)$ with $|i| \leq N$ are observable directly from the market data also follows from the fact that, according to Remarks (6.28) and (6.63), the generators $\boldsymbol{L}(t)$ are directly observable from the market data.

8.119. Remark. It is clear that $\mathfrak{d}_i(s_t, t)$ with $i = 0$ and $i = (i_1 = 0, \ldots, i_{k-1} = 0, i_k = 1, i_{k+1} = 0, \ldots, i_n)$ are nothing but the continuously compounded interest rate $r(s_t, t)$ and the continuously compounded dividend yield $d_k(s_t, t)$ of the k-th stock in terms of the underlying securities being stocks.

8.120. Remark. We comment that it is in the sense of relation (8.161), or equivalently (8.162) that we interpret the formal expressions in (8.159) for the values $v_{S_i} = v_{S_i}(t)$ of the European contingent claims $\mathfrak{v}_{S_i}$ with $|i| \leq N$ incepted at time t and expiring at time T an instant later. In more detail, the formal expressions in (8.159) imitate the following two crucial properties of the values $v_{S_i} = v_{S_i}(t)$ of the European contingent claims $\mathfrak{v}_{S_i}$ with $|i| \leq N$ incepted at time t and expiring at time T an instant later. The first property is that the time derivative $\frac{\overset{2}{d}}{dt}$ of the values $v_{S_i} = v_{S_i}(t)$ of the European contingent claims $\mathfrak{v}_{S_i}$ with $|i| \leq N$ incepted at time t and expiring at time T an instant later given by

$$\frac{\overset{2}{d}}{dt} e^{-\int_{\overset{1}{(t)}}^{\overset{3}{(t)}} \mathfrak{d}_i(\overset{3}{s}_t, \tau) d\tau} s^i_t = \mathfrak{d}_i(s_t, t)\, s^i_t, \quad |i| \leq N,$$

coincides with the time derivative with respect to t evaluated at t equal to T understood in an appropriate sense of the value $v_{S_i} = v_{S_i}(t)$ equal to $\mathbf{V}(t,T)\, s_T^i$ at inception time t of the European contingent claims $\mathfrak{v}_{S_i}$ with expiration time T and the payoffs $v_T^{S_i}(s_T) = s_T^i$ given by relation (8.161). The second property is that the action of the generator $\mathfrak{L}(\overset{2}{t})$ on the values $v_{S_i} = v_{S_i}(t)$ of the European contingent claims $\mathfrak{v}_{S_i}$ with $|i| \le N$ incepted at time t and expiring at time T an instant later given by

$$\mathfrak{L}(\overset{2}{t})\, e^{-\int_{\overset{1}{(t)}}^{\overset{3}{(t)}} \mathfrak{d}_i(\overset{3}{s}_t,\tau)d\tau}\, s_t^i = \mathfrak{L}(t)\, s_t^i, \quad i = 0,\ldots,N,$$

coincides with the action of the generator $\mathfrak{L}(\overset{2}{t})$ on the values $v_{S_i} = v_{S_i}(t)$ equal to $\mathbf{V}(t,T)\, s_T^i$ at the inception time t of the European contingent claims $\mathfrak{v}_{S_i}$ with expiration time T and the payoffs $v_T^{S_i}(s_T) = s_T^i$ when $t = T$. Finally, we note that the formal expressions in (8.159) for the values $v_{S_i} = v_{S_i}(t)$ of the European contingent claims $\mathfrak{v}_{S_i}$ with $|i| \le N$ incepted at time t and expiring at time T an instant later can be also rewritten as follows

$$v_{S_i} = \mathbf{V}(\overset{1}{t},\overset{3}{t})\, s_t^i, \quad |i| \le N.$$

This completes the Remark.

Now we consider the set of portfolios $\{\mathfrak{p}_i : i \in \mathbb{Z}_+^n, |i| \le N\}$, or simply $\{\mathfrak{p}_i : |i| \le N\}$ such that each $\mathfrak{p}_i$ is a portfolio of the European contingent claims $\mathfrak{v}_{S_j}$, $j \le i$ with operator weights $\binom{i}{j}(-1)^{i-j}\, s_t^{i-j}$, where -1 is the member of $\mathbb{R}^n$ with each entry equal to minus unity.

8.121. Remark. We comment that the number of the portfolios in the set $\{\mathfrak{p}_i : i \in \mathbb{Z}_+^n, |i| \le N\}$ is equal to the number of solutions to $i_1 + i_2 + \cdots + i_n \le N$ in nonnegative integers which, in turn, is equal to $\binom{N+n}{n}$ (see, for example, [53] page 15).

8.122. Remark. We comment that each portfolio $\mathfrak{p}_i$, $|i| \le N$ of the European contingent claims $\mathfrak{v}_{S_j}$, $j = 0,\ldots,i$ with operator weights $\binom{i}{j}(-1)^{i-j}\, s_t^{i-j}$ is, from the financial standpoint, nothing but the portfolio of the European contingent claims $\mathfrak{v}_{S_j}$, $j \leq i$ with weights $\binom{i}{j}(-1)^{i-j}\, s_t^{i-j}$ that depend on the state of the market as expressed by the prices of the underlying securities s_t at the inception time t. In this regard the portfolio $\mathfrak{p}_i$ with $i = 0$ is nothing but the pure discount bond with inception time t, maturity time T and the face value of one unit of account.

8.123. Remark. It is clear that the values $p_T^{(i)} = p_T^{(i)}(s_T)$ in Π of the portfolios $\mathfrak{p}_i$, $|i| \leq N$ at expiration time T are given by

$$\begin{aligned} p_T^{(i)} &= \sum_{j \leq i} \binom{i}{j} (-1)^{i-j}\, s_t^{i-j}\, s_T^j = \\ &(s_T - s_t)^i, \quad |i| \leq N. \end{aligned} \tag{8.164}$$

In this regard each portfolio $\mathfrak{p}_i$, $|i| \leq N$ itself is, from the financial standpoint, nothing but a European contingent claim with the inception time t, expiration time T and the payoff $p_T^{(i)} = p_T^{(i)}(s_T)$ in Π for each state of the market as expressed by the prices of the underlying securities s_t in $\mathbb{R}^n_{++}$ at the inception time t. We note that since each payoff $p_T^{(i)} = p_T^{(i)}(s_T)$ in Π is contingent upon the state of the market as expressed by the prices of the underlying securities s_t in $\mathbb{R}^n_{++}$ at the inception time t, then the payoff $p_T^{(i)} = p_T^{(i)}(s_T)$ as a Π-valued function of s_t in $\mathbb{R}^n_{++}$ can be interpreted as a member of $\Pi(\mathbb{R}^n_{++} \times \mathbb{R}^n_{++})$.

8.124. Remark. Since each of the European contingent claims $\mathfrak{v}_{S_i}$, $|i| \leq N$ with inception time t, expiration time T and the payoff $v_T^{S_i}$ is traded for each t and T in $\mathcal{T}$ with $t \leq T$ then, by the no-arbitrage argument, each portfolio $\mathfrak{p}_i$, $|i| \leq N$, or equivalently each European contingent claim $\mathfrak{p}_i$, $|i| \leq N$ with inception time t, expiration time T and the payoff $p_T^{(i)}$ is effectively traded for each t and T in $\mathcal{T}$ with $t \leq T$.

Since the portfolios, or equivalently, the European contingent claims $\mathfrak{p}_i$, $|i| \leq N$ are traded, or more precisely, effectively traded, their values $p_i = p_i(t)$ are, by the no-arbitrage argument, the solutions of the Cauchy problem (6.45), that is:

$$\overset{2}{\frac{d}{dt}}\boldsymbol{u}'(\overset{3}{t},\overset{1}{t})\, p_i + \mathfrak{L}(\overset{2}{t})\,\boldsymbol{u}'(\overset{3}{t},\overset{1}{t})\, p_i = 0, \quad t < T, \quad |i| \le N,$$
$$p_i(T) = p_T^{(i)}. \tag{8.165}$$

Due to relation (8.159) we can formally represent the values $p_i = p_i(t)$ of portfolios, or equivalently, of the European contingent claims $\mathfrak{p}_i$, $|i| \le N$ incepted at time t and expiring at time T an instant later as follows

$$p_i = \sum_{j \le i} \binom{i}{j} (-1)^{i-j}\, \overset{3}{s_t^{i-j}}\, e^{-\int_{\overset{1}{(t)}}^{\overset{3}{(t)}} \mathfrak{d}_j(\overset{3}{s}_t,\tau)d\tau}\, s_t^j, \quad |i| \le N, \tag{8.166}$$

so that the evolution equation in (8.165) can be rewritten as follows

$$\Big(\overset{2}{\frac{d}{dt}} + \mathfrak{L}(\overset{2}{t})\Big)\,\boldsymbol{u}'(\overset{3}{t},\overset{1}{t})\,\Big(\sum_{j \le i} \binom{i}{j} (-1)^{i-j}\, \overset{3}{s^{i-j}}\, e^{-\int_{\overset{1}{(t)}}^{\overset{3}{(t)}} \mathfrak{d}_j(\overset{3}{s},\tau)d\tau}\, \overset{1}{s^j}\Big)\,\mathbf{1} = 0,$$

or equivalently

$$\Big(\overset{2}{\frac{d}{dt}} + \mathfrak{L}(\overset{2}{t})\Big)\,\boldsymbol{u}'(\overset{3}{t},\overset{1}{t})\,(\overset{1}{s} - \overset{3}{s})^i\,\mathbf{1} + \Big(\sum_{j \le i} \binom{i}{j} (-1)^{i-j}\,\mathfrak{d}_j(s,t)\Big)\, s^i = 0, \tag{8.167}$$

where $t < T$ and $|i| \le N$.

8.125. Remark. We comment that the values $v_{S_i} = v_{S_i}(t)$ at the inception time t of the European contingent claims $\mathfrak{v}_{S_i}$, $|i| \le N$, with expiration time T and the payoffs $v_T^{S_i}$ can be expressed in terms of the evolution operator $\mathbf{V}(t,T)$ from the market environment $\mathbf{V}$ as follows

$$v_{S_i}(t) = \mathbf{V}(t,T)\, v_T^{S_i}, \quad |i| \le N,$$

where $v_T^{S_i}(s_T) = s_T^i$. Similarly, the values $p_i = p_i(t)$ at the inception time t of the portfolios, or equivalently, of the European contingent claims $\mathfrak{p}_i$, $|i| \leq N$, with the expiration time T and the payoffs $p_T^{(i)}$ can be expressed in terms of the evolution operator $\mathbf{V}(t,T)$ from the market environment $\mathbf{V}$ as follows

$$p_i(t) = \mathbf{V}(t,T)\, p_T^{(i)}, \quad |i| \leq N,$$

where $p_T^{(i)}(s_T) = (s_T - s_t)^i$. More precisely, the values $p_i = p_i(t)$ at the inception time t of the portfolios, or equivalently, of the European contingent claims $\mathfrak{p}_i$, $|i| \leq N$ with the expiration time T and the payoffs $p_T^{(i)}$ can be expressed in terms of the evolution operator $\mathbf{V}(t,T)$ from the market environment $\mathbf{V}$ as follows

$$p_i(t, s_t) = \big(\mathbf{V}(t,T)\,(\cdot - s_t)^i\big)(s_t), \quad |i| \leq N,$$

or equivalently as

$$p_i(t) = \overset{2}{\mathbf{V}}(t,T)\,(\overset{1}{s} - \overset{3}{s})^i \mathbf{1}, \quad |i| \leq N,$$

where $\mathbf{1}$ is the function in Π identically equal to unity.

Since $\mathbf{V}(t,T)$ is an absolutely positive operator and since each $v_T^{S_i} = v_T^{S_i}(s_T) > 0$ for each s_T in $\mathbb{R}_{++}^n$ we have that each $v_{S_i}(t, s_t) > 0$ for each s_t in $\mathbb{R}_{++}^n$. Therefore, each function $\mathfrak{d}_i(t, s_t)$ defined in (8.159), or equivalently in (8.161), (8.162) or (8.163) is not singular in the sense that, roughly speaking, $\mathfrak{d}_i(t, s_t) \neq \infty$ for each t in $\mathcal{T}$ and s_t in $\mathbb{R}_{++}^n$. At the same time since each $p_T^{(i)} = p_T^{(i)}(s_T) \geq 0$ for each s_T in $\mathbb{R}_{++}^n$ and $p_T^{(i)}(s_T)|_{s_T = s_t} = 0$, that is, since each $p_T^{(i)}$ is only in Π_{++}, the fact that $\mathbf{V}(t,T)$ is an absolutely positive operator implies only that each $p_i(t, s_t) \geq 0$ and $p_i(t, s_t) \not\equiv 0$, that is, that each $p_i(t)$ is in Π_{++}. Therefore, if we would formally represent the values $p_i = p_i(t)$ of the portfolios, or equivalently, of the European contingent claims $\mathfrak{p}_i$, $|i| \leq N$, incepted at time t and expiring at time T an instant later as follows

$$p_i = e^{-\int_{\overset{1}{(t)}}^{\overset{3}{(t)}} \mathfrak{d}'_i(\overset{3}{s}_t, \tau)\, d\tau} (s_t - \overset{3}{s}_t)^i, \quad |i| \leq N,$$

where each $\mathfrak{d}'_i(t,s)$ is the operator of multiplication by the function $\mathfrak{d}'_i(t,s)$, then $\mathfrak{d}'_i(t,s_t)$ might be singular in the sense that, roughly speaking, $\mathfrak{d}'_i(t,s_t)=\infty$ for some s_t in $\mathbb{R}^n_{++}$. Indeed

$$\mathfrak{d}'_i(s'_t,t)\,(s'_t-s_t)^i=\frac{d}{dt}\mathbf{V}(t,T)|_{t=T}\,(\cdot-s_t)^i, \tag{8.168}$$

or equivalently

$$\mathfrak{d}'_i(s'_t,t)\,(s'_t-s_t)^i=-\frac{d}{dT}\mathbf{V}(t,T)|_{T=t}\,(\cdot-s_t)^i, \tag{8.169}$$

where s_t in $\mathbb{R}^n_{++}$ is treated as a parameter, and where the derivatives with respect to time are understood in an appropriate sense. We also note that the preceding relation (8.168), or equivalently (8.169) can be rewritten in terms of the generators $\boldsymbol{L}(t)$ of the market environment $\mathbf{V}$ with the evolution operators $\mathbf{V}(t,T)$ as follows

$$\mathfrak{d}'_i(s'_t,t)\,(s'_t-s_t)^i=-\boldsymbol{L}(t)\,(\cdot-s_t)^i, \tag{8.170}$$

where s_t in $\mathbb{R}^n_{++}$ is again treated as a parameter. It is the possible singularity of $\mathfrak{d}'_i(t,s_t)$ that is one of the main reasons why we have considered $\mathfrak{v}_{S_i}$, $|i|\le N$ as the traded European contingent claims and $\mathfrak{p}_i$, $|i|\le N$ only as the portfolios of $\mathfrak{v}_{S_i}$, $|i|\le N$, and not vice versa. This completes the Remark.

Now we assume that the set of the portfolios, or equivalently, of the European contingent claims $\{\mathfrak{p}_i : i\in\mathbb{Z}_+, |i|\le N\}$ approximately, in the sense to be specified below, dynamically replicates each European contingent claim $\mathfrak{v}$ with inception time t, expiration time T and payoff v_T.

Due to the fact that the portfolios, or equivalently European contingent claims $\mathfrak{p}_i$, $|i|\le N$ are effectively traded and since the portfolio, or equivalently European contingent claim $\mathfrak{p}_i$ with $i=0$ is nothing but the pure discount bond, for the operator weights $\boldsymbol{\pi}_v(t,P_i)$ of the portfolios, or equivalently European contingent claims $\mathfrak{p}_i$, $|i| \leq N$ in the dynamically replicating portfolio for the European contingent claim $\mathfrak{v}$ with the value $v = v(t)$, with the help of the equation (6.59) or equivalently (6.60), we obtain the following equation

$$[[(\overset{2}{\frac{d}{dt}} + \mathfrak{L}(\overset{2}{t})), \boldsymbol{v}], \boldsymbol{u}'(\overset{3}{t}, \overset{1}{t})]\, \mathbf{1} =$$

$$\sum_{1\leq|i|\leq N} \left(\boldsymbol{\pi}_v(t, P_i)[[(\overset{2}{\frac{d}{dt}} + \mathfrak{L}(\overset{2}{t})), \boldsymbol{p}_i], \boldsymbol{u}'(\overset{3}{t}, \overset{1}{t})]\, \mathbf{1} \right), \tag{8.171}$$

or equivalently

$$[[\mathfrak{L}(\overset{2}{t}), \boldsymbol{v}], \boldsymbol{u}'(\overset{3}{t}, \overset{1}{t})]\, \mathbf{1} =$$

$$\sum_{1\leq|i|\leq N} \left(\boldsymbol{\pi}_v(t, P_i)[[\mathfrak{L}(\overset{2}{t}), \boldsymbol{p}_i], \boldsymbol{u}'(\overset{3}{t}, \overset{1}{t})]\, \mathbf{1} \right), \tag{8.172}$$

where $\boldsymbol{v} = \boldsymbol{v}(t)$ and $\boldsymbol{p}_i = \boldsymbol{p}_i(t)$ are the operators on Π of multiplication by the functions $v = v(t)$ and $p_i = p_i(t)$.

Now we formally represent each generator $\mathfrak{L}(t)$ in $\mathfrak{L}$ from $\mathbb{L}$ as a real quasidifferential operator on an appropriate space of real-valued functions on Ω equal to $\mathbb{R}^n_{++}$, that is, on an appropriate subspace of Π. Let the defining sequence of $\mathfrak{L}(t)$ be given by

$$\mathfrak{L}_M(t) = \sum_{1\leq|m|\leq M} \mathfrak{L}_m(M, t, \hat{s}) \frac{\partial}{\partial s}^{m}. \tag{8.173}$$

8.126. Remark. We comment that due to relation (3.101) the terms $\mathfrak{L}_m(M, t, \hat{s})$ with $m = 0$ in the preceding relation (8.173) can be put equal to zero for each $M \geq 0$.

8.127. Remark. We comment that due to relation (8.86) each generator $\mathfrak{L}(t)$ in $\mathfrak{L}$ from $\mathbb{L}$ can be formally represented as an analytic quasidifferential operator with the defining sequence given in relations (8.87) and (8.88).

Approximating the generator $\mathfrak{L}(t)$ by $\mathfrak{L}_M(t)$ defined in expression (8.173), equations (8.171) and (8.172) can be approximated by the following equations

$$
\begin{aligned}
&[[(\frac{\overset{2}{d}}{dt} + \mathfrak{L}_M(\overset{2}{t})), \boldsymbol{v}], \boldsymbol{u}'(\overset{3}{t}, \overset{1}{t})]\, \mathbf{1} = \\
&\sum_{1\le|i|\le N} \Big(\boldsymbol{\pi}_v(t, P_i)[[(\frac{\overset{2}{d}}{dt} + \mathfrak{L}_M(\overset{2}{t})), \boldsymbol{p}_i], \boldsymbol{u}'(\overset{3}{t}, \overset{1}{t})]\, \mathbf{1}\Big), \qquad (8.174)
\end{aligned}
$$

or equivalently

$$
\begin{aligned}
&[[\mathfrak{L}_M(\overset{2}{t}), \boldsymbol{v}], \boldsymbol{u}'(\overset{3}{t}, \overset{1}{t})]\, \mathbf{1} = \\
&\qquad \sum_{1\le|i|\le N} \Big(\boldsymbol{\pi}_v(t, P_i)[[\mathfrak{L}_M(\overset{2}{t}), \boldsymbol{p}_i], \boldsymbol{u}'(\overset{3}{t}, \overset{1}{t})]\, \mathbf{1}\Big). \qquad (8.175)
\end{aligned}
$$

With the help of identity (8.51) we rewrite the preceding equation (8.174), or equivalently (8.175) as follows

$$
\begin{aligned}
&\sum_{1\le|l|\le M-1} \Big(\sum_{|m|\le M} I_{l<m} \binom{m}{l} \mathfrak{L}_m(M, t, s) \times \\
&\qquad (\frac{\partial}{\partial s}^{(m-l)^+} v(s,t))\Big)(\overset{1}{\frac{\partial}{\partial s}}^{l} u(t, t, \overset{2}{s}, s)) = \\
&\sum_{1\le|i|\le N} \boldsymbol{\pi}_v(t, P_i)\Big(\sum_{1\le|l|\le M-1} \Big(\sum_{|m|\le M} I_{l<m} \binom{m}{l} \times \qquad (8.176) \\
&\qquad \mathfrak{L}_m(M, t, s)\,(\frac{\partial}{\partial s}^{(m-l)^+} p_i(s,t))\Big)(\overset{1}{\frac{\partial}{\partial s}}^{l} u(t, t, \overset{2}{s}, s))\Big).
\end{aligned}
$$

Since the preceding equation (8.176) has to hold for all $u(t, T, s_t, s_T)$, we obtain the following system of $\binom{M-1+n}{n} - 1$

equations

$$
\begin{aligned}
\sum_{|m|\le M} I_{l<m} \binom{m}{l} \mathfrak{L}_m(M,t,s) \Big({\frac{\partial}{\partial s}}^{(m-l)^+} v\Big) = \\
\sum_{1\le|i|\le N} \boldsymbol{\pi}_v(t,P_i)\Big(\sum_{|m|\le M} I_{l<m} \binom{m}{l} \times \\
\mathfrak{L}_m(M,t,s) \Big({\frac{\partial}{\partial s}}^{(m-l)^+} p_i\Big)\Big),
\end{aligned}
\tag{8.177}
$$

for $1 \le |l| \le M-1$.

8.128. Remark. We comment that the number of the equations in the preceding system (8.177) is equal to the number of solutions to $1 \le l_1 + l_2 + \cdots + l_n \le M-1$ in nonnegative integers which is equal to the number of solutions to $l_1 + l_2 + \cdots + l_n \le M-1$ in nonnegative integers less one, that is, $\binom{M-1+n}{n} - 1$.

Our goal is to solve the preceding system (8.177) of $\binom{M-1+n}{n} - 1$ equations explicitly. In order to do this we need the following obvious identity

$$
\begin{aligned}
{\frac{\partial}{\partial s}}^{k} p_i = & \overset{2}{\frac{\partial}{\partial s}}^{k} \Big(\sum_{j\le i} \binom{i}{j} (-1)^{i-j}\, \overset{3}{s}^{i-j}\, e^{-\int_{\overset{1}{(t)}}^{\overset{3}{(t)}} \mathfrak{d}_j(\overset{3}{s},\tau)d\tau} s^j\Big) = \\
& \overset{2}{\frac{\partial}{\partial s}}^{k} \Big(\sum_{j\le i} \binom{i}{j} (-1)^{i-j}\, \overset{3}{s}^{i-j}\, s^j\Big) = \\
& \overset{2}{\frac{\partial}{\partial s}}^{k} (s - \overset{3}{s})^i = \\
& k!\,\delta(k-i),
\end{aligned}
\tag{8.178}
$$

where

$$
\delta(k) = \delta(k_1)\delta(k_2)\ldots\delta(k_n),
$$

for each $k = (k_1, k_2, \ldots k_n)$ in $\mathbb{Z}_+^n$.

With the help of the preceding identity (8.178) we can rewrite the system (8.177) as follows

$$\sum_{|m|\le M} I_{l<m} \binom{m}{l} \mathfrak{L}_m(M,t,s) \, \Big(\frac{\partial}{\partial s}^{(m-l)^+} v\Big) =$$

$$\sum_{|m|\le M} I_{l<m} \binom{m}{l} \mathfrak{L}_m(M,t,s) \times \tag{8.179}$$

$$\big(\boldsymbol{\pi}_v(t, P_{m-l})\,(m-l)!\big),$$

for $1 \le |l| \le M-1$.

8.129. Remark. We comment that in the preceding system (8.179) we have used the same notation for the function in Π, or more precisely in $\Pi(\mathbb{R}^n_{++} \times \mathcal{T})$ identically equal to $(m-l)!$ and for the integer $(m-l)!$ itself.

Finally, if we choose N equal to $M-1$ then we obtain that the solution to the system (8.179) and therefore to the original equation (8.174) or equivalently (8.175) is given by

$$\boldsymbol{\pi}_v(t, P_i) = \frac{1}{i!}\,\boldsymbol{v}^{(i)}(t), \quad 1 \le |i| \le N, \tag{8.180}$$

where $\boldsymbol{v}^{(i)}(t)$ stands for the operator of multiplication by the function $\frac{\partial}{\partial s}^{i} v(t)$. In more detail

$$\big(\boldsymbol{\pi}_v(t, P_i)\, h\big)(s_t) = \pi_v(t, s_t, P_i)\, h(s_t), \quad h \in \Pi, \tag{8.181}$$

where

$$\pi_v(t, s_t, P_i) = \frac{1}{i!}\,\frac{\partial}{\partial s_t}^{i} v(s_t, t). \tag{8.182}$$

8.130. Remark. It is clear that we have obtained the solution (8.180) of the equation (8.174) or equivalently (8.175) under the assumption that the value $v = v(t)$ of the European contingent claim $\mathfrak{v}$ is in an appropriate sense $N = M-1$ times differentiable with respect to the prices of the underlying securities.

8.131. Remark. Assume that according to relation (8.86) each generator $\mathfrak{L}(t)$ in $\mathfrak{L}$ from $\mathbb{L}$ is formally represented as an analytic quasidifferential operator with the defining sequence given in relations (8.87) and (8.88). Then with the help of relation (8.54) it is easy to see that expression (8.180) determines the exact formal solution to the original equation (8.171) or equivalently (8.172) where $N = \infty$.

For the operator weight $\boldsymbol{\pi}_v(t, P_0)$ of the pure discount bond $\mathfrak{p}_0$ with the help of relation (6.57) we obtain the following expression

$$\begin{aligned}
\boldsymbol{\pi}_v(t, P_0) &= \boldsymbol{v}(t) - \sum_{1\leq|i|\leq N} \frac{1}{i!}\boldsymbol{v}^{(i)}(t)\,\boldsymbol{p}_i(t) = \\
&\boldsymbol{v}(t) - \sum_{1\leq|i|\leq N} \frac{1}{i!}\boldsymbol{v}^{(i)}(t)\,\Big(\sum_{j\leq i}\binom{i}{j}(-1)^{i-j}\,\overset{3}{s}{}^{i-j}\,e^{-\int_{\overset{1}{(t)}}^{\overset{3}{(t)}} \mathfrak{d}_j(\overset{3}{s},\tau)d\tau}\,\overset{1}{s}{}^{j}\Big)= \\
&\boldsymbol{v}(t) - \sum_{1\leq|i|\leq N} \frac{1}{i!}\boldsymbol{v}^{(i)}(t)\,\Big(\sum_{j\leq i}\binom{i}{j}(-1)^{i-j}\,\overset{3}{s}{}^{i-j}\,\overset{1}{s}{}^{j}\Big)= \qquad (8.183) \\
&\boldsymbol{v}(t) - \sum_{1\leq|i|\leq N} \frac{1}{i!}\boldsymbol{v}^{(i)}(t)\,(\overset{1}{s} - \overset{3}{s})^{i} = \\
&\boldsymbol{v}(t)
\end{aligned}$$

where $N = M - 1$.

8.132. Remark. We comment that the reason we have used notation $\boldsymbol{\pi}_v(t, P_0)$ for the operator weight of the pure discount bond instead of $\mathfrak{v}_{\omega_B}$ as used in Section (6) is that, contrary to the set $\{\mathfrak{v}_\omega : \omega \in \Omega\}$ that dynamically replicates a European contingent claim $\mathfrak{v}$, the set of portfolios or equivalently of European contingent claims $\{\mathfrak{p}_i : i \in \mathbb{Z}_+^n, |i| \leq N\}$ dynamically replicates the European contingent claim $\mathfrak{v}$ only approximately.

8.133. Remark. According to Remarks (6.72) and (8.131), define for each ω_i in $\Omega = \{\omega_i : i \in \mathbb{Z}_+^n\}$ and for each t in T the linear operators

$$\hat{\pi}(t, P_i) = \hat{\pi}(t, \omega_i) : \Pi \longrightarrow \Pi$$

by

$$\hat{\pi}(t, P_i)\, v = \pi_v(t, P_i)$$

where $\pi_v(t, P_i) = \pi_v(t, \omega_i)$ are the Π-valued measures of ω_i in Ω associated as in Remark (6.41) with the operator-valued measures, or equivalently operator weights $\boldsymbol{\pi}_v(t, P_i) = \boldsymbol{\pi}_v(t, \omega_i)$ of the portfolios, or more precisely European contingent claims $\{\mathfrak{p}_i : i \in \mathbb{Z}_+^n\}$ in the dynamically replicating portfolio for the European contingent claim $\mathfrak{v}$ with the value $v = v(t)$. In the case under consideration $\boldsymbol{\pi}_v(t, P_i)$, $i \in \mathbb{Z}_+^n$, are the linear operators on Π of multiplication by the functions $\pi_v(t, P_i) = \pi_v(t, \cdot, P_i)$ in Π.

It is clear that due to relations (8.183) and (8.180) the linear operators $\hat{\pi}(t, P_i)$, $i \in \mathbb{Z}_+^n$, on Π are explicitly given by

$$\hat{\pi}(t, P_i) = \frac{1}{i!} \frac{\partial}{\partial s}^{i} .$$

It is also clear that the linear operators $\hat{\pi}(t, P_i)$, $i \in \mathbb{Z}_+^n$, on Π and linear operators on Π of multiplication by functions in Π do not commute in general. Indeed with the help of relation (8.46) we obtain

$$[\hat{\pi}(t, P_i), h(\hat{s})] = \frac{1}{i!} \sum_{l<m} l! \binom{m}{l} \Big(\frac{\partial}{\partial s}^{m-l} h(\hat{s}) \Big)\, \hat{\pi}(t, P_l)$$

where $h(\hat{s})$ is the operator on Π of multiplication by the function $h = h(s)$ in Π, and where the function h in Π is assumed to be sufficiently smooth in an appropriate sense.

In this regard we note that the linear operators $\hat{\pi}(t, P_i)$, $i \in \mathbb{Z}_+^n$, on Π form a basis of the Lie module $\mathfrak{D}(\mathbb{R}_{++}^n)$ with the structure constants determined according to relation (8.47). Finally we note that it is this noncommutativity of the linear operators $\hat{\pi}(t, P_i)$ on Π and linear operators on Π of multiplication by arbitrary admissible functions in Π that is, in the essence, financially responsible for the randomness of the prices of the underlying securities, that is, for the first quantization in finance in the case under consideration. This issue will be presented in detail in forthcoming articles.

8.134. Remark. Let

$$\mathfrak{Q}_M = \sum_{|m| \leq M} \mathfrak{q}_m(\hat{\xi}) \frac{\partial}{\partial \xi}^m, \quad \mathfrak{q}_m(\xi) \in R^{\infty}(\Omega)$$

be a linear partial differential operator of order M on $R^{\infty}(\Omega)$. It is clear that the stochastic dimensionality of $\mathfrak{Q}_M$ does not exceed $\binom{M-1+n}{n}$, and in fact is equal to $\binom{M-1+n}{n}$.

8.135. Remark. Let

$$\mathfrak{Q} = \sum_{m \in \mathbb{Z}_+^n} \mathfrak{q}_m(\hat{\xi}) \frac{\partial}{\partial \xi}^m, \quad \mathfrak{q}_m(\xi) \in R^{\infty}(\Omega)$$

be a real analytic quasidifferential operator. It is clear that the stochastic dimensionality of $\mathfrak{Q}$ does not exceed the cardinality of an infinite countable set, and in fact is equal to this cardinality.

8.136. Remark. Let

$$Q_M = \sum_{|m| \leq M} q_m(M, \hat{\xi}) \left(-i \frac{\partial}{\partial \xi}\right)^m, \quad q_m(M, \xi) \in C^{\infty}(\Omega)$$

be a linear partial differential operator of order M on $C^{\infty}(\Omega)$. It is clear that the stochastic dimensionality of $\mathfrak{Q}_M$ does not exceed $\binom{M-1+n}{n}$, and in fact is equal to $\binom{M-1+n}{n}$.

8.137. Remark. Let

$$Q = \sum_{m \in \mathbb{Z}_+^n} q_m(M, \hat{\xi}) \left(-i \frac{\partial}{\partial \xi}\right)^m, \quad q_m(M, \xi) \in C^{\infty}(\Omega)$$

be an analytic quasidifferential operator. It is clear that the stochastic dimensionality of Q does not exceed the cardinality of an infinite countable set, and in fact is equal to this cardinality.

8.138. Remark. In light of Remarks (6.48), (8.134) and (8.135) the formal representation of a generator $\mathfrak{L}(t)$ in $\mathfrak{L}$ from $\mathbb{L}$ in relation (8.86) as an analytic quasidifferential operator with the defining sequence $\mathfrak{L}_M(t)$ given in relations (8.87) and (8.88), that is, the expansion of $\mathfrak{L}(t)$ in a formal power series over the vector-operator $\frac{\partial}{\partial s}$ corresponds to the expansion of the generator $\mathfrak{L}(t)$ over increasing measures of randomness.

Now with the help of the evolution equation (6.64), for the approximate value $v_M = v_M(t)$ of the European contingent claim $\mathfrak{v}$ we obtain the following evolution equation

$$\Big(\overset{1}{\frac{d}{dt}} + \mathfrak{L}_M(\overset{1}{t})\Big)\Big(v_M(t) - \sum_{1\le|i|\le M-1} \overset{2}{\boldsymbol{\pi}}_{v_M}(t, P_i) p_i(t)\Big) = \boldsymbol{v}_M(t)\, r(s,t), \tag{8.184}$$

or equivalently

$$\begin{aligned}&\Big(\frac{d}{dt} + \mathfrak{L}_M(t)\Big)\, v_M(t) - \\ &\quad \Big(\overset{2}{\frac{d}{dt}} + \mathfrak{L}_M(\overset{2}{t})\Big)\Big(\sum_{1\le|i|\le M-1} \frac{1}{i!} \overset{4}{\boldsymbol{v}}{}^{(i)}_M(t) \times \\ &\qquad \Big(\sum_{j\le i} \binom{i}{j} (-1)^{i-j}\, \overset{3}{s}{}^{i-j}\, e^{-\int_{\overset{1}{(t)}}^{\overset{3}{(t)}} \mathfrak{d}_j(\overset{3}{s},\tau)\, d\tau}\, s^j\Big)\Big) = \\ &\qquad \boldsymbol{v}_M(t)\, r(s,t),\end{aligned} \tag{8.185}$$

or equivalently

$$\begin{aligned}&\Big(\frac{d}{dt} + \mathfrak{L}_M(t)\Big)\, v_M(t) - \\ &\quad \sum_{1\le|i|\le M-1} \frac{1}{i!} \boldsymbol{v}^{(i)}_M \Big(\sum_{j\le i} \binom{i}{j} (-1)^{i-j}\, \mathfrak{d}_j(s,t)\Big) s^i - \\ &\quad \mathfrak{L}_M(\overset{1}{t}) \sum_{1\le|i|\le M-1} \frac{1}{i!} \overset{3}{\boldsymbol{v}}{}^{(i)}_M(t)(s - \overset{2}{s})^i = \\ &\quad \boldsymbol{v}_M(t)\, r(s,t),\end{aligned} \tag{8.186}$$

or equivalently

$$\begin{aligned}
&\Big(\frac{d}{dt} + \sum_{1\le|m|\le M} \mathfrak{L}_m(M,t,\hat{s})\frac{\partial}{\partial s}^m\Big)\, v_M(t) - \\
&\sum_{1\le|i|\le M-1} \Big(\frac{s^i}{i!}\big(\sum_{j\le i}\binom{i}{j}(-1)^{i-j}\,\mathfrak{d}_j(s,t)\big)\Big)\frac{\partial}{\partial s}^i v_M(t) - \\
&\Big(\sum_{1\le|m|\le M} \mathfrak{L}_m(M,t,\hat{s})\frac{\partial}{\partial s}^m\Big) \sum_{1\le|i|\le M-1} \frac{1}{i!}\boldsymbol{v}_M^{(i)}(t)(s-\hat{s})^i = \\
&\boldsymbol{v}_M(t)\, r(s,t),
\end{aligned} \tag{8.187}$$

or equivalently

$$\begin{aligned}
&\Big(\frac{d}{dt} + \sum_{1\le|m|\le M} \mathfrak{L}_m(M,t,\hat{s})\frac{\partial}{\partial s}^m\Big)\, v_M(t) - \\
&\sum_{1\le|i|\le M-1} \Big(\frac{s^i}{i!}\big(\sum_{j\le i}\binom{i}{j}(-1)^{i-j}\,\mathfrak{d}_j(s,t)\big)\Big)\frac{\partial}{\partial s}^i v_M(t) - \\
&\sum_{1\le|m|\le M-1} \mathfrak{L}_m(M,t,\hat{s})\frac{\partial}{\partial s}^m v_M(t) = \\
&\boldsymbol{v}_M(t)\, r(s,t),
\end{aligned} \tag{8.188}$$

or finally as

$$\begin{aligned}
&\frac{d}{dt}v_M + \sum_{|m|=M} \mathfrak{L}_m(M,t,\hat{s})\frac{\partial}{\partial s}^m v_M - \\
&\sum_{1\le|i|\le M-1} \Big(\frac{s^i}{i!}\big(\sum_{j\le i}\binom{i}{j}(-1)^{i-j}\,\mathfrak{d}_j(s,t)\big)\Big)\frac{\partial}{\partial s}^i v_M - \\
&r(s,t)v_M = 0.
\end{aligned} \tag{8.189}$$

8.139. Remark. It is clear that in order to determine the approximate value $v_M = v_M(t)$ of the European contingent claim $\mathfrak{v}$ with inception time t, expiration time T and payoff v_T the preceding evolution equation (8.189) must be equipped with the initial, or more precisely, final condition $v_M(T) = v_T$.

8.140. Remark. We comment that the time derivative $\frac{d}{dt}$ in the evolution equation (8.189) can be interpreted as the partial time derivative $\frac{\partial}{\partial t}$.

8.141. Remark. It is clear that if the generators $\mathfrak{L}(t)$ are of the form (5.54) then for $M = 2$ the evolution equation (8.189) is nothing but the Black and Scholes equation (5.100). In this regard for the generators $\mathfrak{L}(t)$ of a general form the Black and Scholes equation (5.100) can be considered as the evolution equation (8.189) for the approximate value $v_M = v_M(t)$ of the European contingent claim $\mathfrak{v}$ with $M = 2$.

If in the evolution equation (8.189) M goes to infinity then under the assumption that the term

$$\sum_{|m|=M} \mathfrak{L}_m(M, t, \hat{s}) \frac{\partial}{\partial s}^m v_M(t)$$

tends in an appropriate sense to the zero function in $\Pi(\mathbb{R}^n_{++} \times \mathcal{T})$ we obtain the following evolution equation for the value $v = v(t)$ of the European contingent claim $\mathfrak{v}$

$$\frac{d}{dt}v - \sum_{|i|\geq 1}\Big(\frac{s^i}{i!}\big(\sum_{j\leq i}\binom{i}{j}(-1)^{i-j}\mathfrak{d}_j(s,t)\big)\Big)\frac{\partial}{\partial s}^i v - r(s,t)v = 0. \tag{8.190}$$

8.142. Remark. We comment that in the preceding evolution equation (8.190) we have also assumed that the approximate value $v_M = v_M(t)$ of the European contingent claim $\mathfrak{v}$ tends in an appropriate sense to the value $v = v(t)$ of the European contingent claim $\mathfrak{v}$ as M goes to infinity.

8.143. Remark. We note that a generator $\boldsymbol{L}(t)$ in $\boldsymbol{L}$ of a market environment $\mathbf{V}$ with the help of the evolution equation (8.190) can be represented as the following analytic quasidifferential operator

$$\boldsymbol{L}(t) = -\sum_{|i|\geq 1}\Big(\frac{s^i}{i!}\big(\sum_{j\leq i}\binom{i}{j}(-1)^{i-j}\boldsymbol{\mathfrak{d}}_j(s,t)\big)\Big)\frac{\partial}{\partial s}^i - \boldsymbol{r}(s,t),$$

or equivalently

$$\boldsymbol{L}(t) = -\sum_{i\in\mathbb{Z}_+^n}\Big(\frac{s^i}{i!}\big(\sum_{j\leq i}\binom{i}{j}(-1)^{i-j}\,\mathfrak{v}_j(s,t)\big)\Big)\frac{\partial}{\partial s}^{i}.$$

We make the following crucial observation. The evolution equation (8.190) does not depend on the generator $\mathfrak{L}(t)$ at all. The reason for this is as follows. Consider a market in which each European contingent claim $\mathfrak{v}$ with inception time t and expiration time T has payoff $v_T = v_T(s_T)$ in Π such that it is an analytic function of s_T at s_t. It is clear that the set of portfolios, or more precisely European contingent claims $\{\mathfrak{p}_i : i \in \mathbb{Z}_+^n\}$ spans such a market. Indeed

$$v_T(s_T) = \sum_{i\in\mathbb{Z}_+^n}\Big(\frac{1}{i!}\big(\frac{\partial}{\partial s_T}^{i} v_T(s_T)\big)(s_t)\Big)p_T^{(i)}(s_T) =$$

$$\sum_{i\in\mathbb{Z}_+^n}\Big(\frac{1}{i!}\big(\frac{\partial}{\partial s_T}^{i} v_T(s_T)\big)(s_t)\Big)(s_T - s_t)^i. \qquad (8.191)$$

Then the instantaneous return on the European contingent claim $\mathfrak{v}$ with the value $v = v(t)$ has to be equal to that of the portfolios of $\{\mathfrak{p}_i : i \in \mathbb{Z}_+^n\}$ with operator weights $\boldsymbol{\pi}_v(t, P_i)$ given in relations (8.180) and (8.183):

$$\frac{d}{dt}v(t, s_t) =$$

$$\frac{\overset{2}{d}}{dt}\mathbf{V}(\overset{1}{t},\overset{3}{t})\Big(\sum_{i\in\mathbb{Z}_+^n}\Big(\frac{1}{i!}\big(\frac{\partial}{\partial s_t}^{i} v(\overset{3}{t}, s_t)\big)\Big)(\cdot - s_t)^i\Big) =$$

$$\frac{\overset{2}{d}}{dt}\sum_{i\in\mathbb{Z}_+^n}\Big(\frac{1}{i!}\big(\frac{\partial}{\partial s_t}^{i} v(\overset{3}{t}, s_t)\big)\Big(\mathbf{V}(\overset{1}{t},\overset{3}{t})(\cdot - s_t)^i\Big) = \qquad (8.192)$$

$$\frac{\overset{2}{d}}{dt}\sum_{i\in\mathbb{Z}^n_+}^{\infty}\Big(\frac{1}{i!}\big(\big(\frac{\partial}{\partial s_t}\big)^i v(\overset{3}{t}, s_t)\big)\Big) \times$$

$$\Big(\sum_{j\le i}\binom{i}{j}(-1)^{i-j}\,\overset{3}{s}{}_t^{i-j}\, e^{-\int_{\overset{1}{(t)}}^{\overset{3}{(t)}} \mathfrak{d}_j(\overset{3}{s}_t,\tau)d\tau}\, s_t^j\Big)=$$

$$\sum_{i\in\mathbb{Z}^n_+}\Big(\frac{1}{i!}\big(\big(\frac{\partial}{\partial s_t}\big)^i v(t, s_t)\big)\Big)\Big(\sum_{j\le i}\binom{i}{j}(-1)^{i-j}\,\mathfrak{d}_j(s_t,t)\Big)s_t^i,$$

which coincides with the evolution equation (8.190).

8.144. Remark. We comment that in the preceding chain of equalities (8.192) we have again used the following expression for the instantaneous return on the portfolio, or more precisely European contingent claim $\mathfrak{p}_i$ with $i \in \mathbb{Z}^n_+$:

$$\begin{aligned}
&\frac{d}{dt}p_i(s_t, t) = \\
&\quad \frac{\overset{2}{d}}{dt}\mathbf{V}(\overset{1}{t},\overset{3}{t})(\cdot - s_t)^i = \\
&\quad \frac{\overset{2}{d}}{dt}\Big(\sum_{j\le i}\binom{i}{j}(-1)^{i-j}\,\overset{3}{s}{}_t^{i-j}\, e^{-\int_{\overset{1}{(t)}}^{\overset{3}{(t)}} \mathfrak{d}_j(\overset{3}{s}_t,\tau)d\tau}\, s_t^j\Big) = \qquad (8.193)\\
&\quad \Big(\sum_{j\le i}\binom{i}{j}(-1)^{i-j}\,\mathfrak{d}_j(s_t,t)\Big)s_t^i.
\end{aligned}$$

8.145. Remark. The discussion preceding the chain of equalities (8.192) provides the financial indication of when the term

$$\sum_{|m|=M}\mathfrak{L}_m(M,t,\hat{s})\Big(\frac{\partial}{\partial s}\Big)^m v_M(t)$$

in the evolution equation (8.189) tends in an appropriate sense to the zero function in $\Pi(\mathbb{R}^n_{++}\times\mathcal{T})$ as M goes to infinity. It is natural to expect this to happen when the value $v = v(t)$ of the European contingent claim $\mathfrak{v}$, in addition to being a sufficiently regular function of time, is an analytic function of the prices of the underlying securities.

Now our goal is to examine the error due to the approximation of the generators $\mathfrak{L}(t)$ by $\mathfrak{L}_M(t)$ and the value $v = v(t)$ of the European contingent claim $\mathfrak{v}$ by $v_M = v_M(t)$ in equation (8.171), or equivalently (8.172).

Define the linear operator $\Delta\mathfrak{L}_M(t)$ on Π by

$$\mathfrak{L}(t) = \mathfrak{L}_M(t) + \Delta\mathfrak{L}_M(t). \tag{8.194}$$

With the help of the preceding expression (8.194) we can rewrite equations (8.171) and (8.172) as follows

$$\begin{aligned} &[[(\overset{2}{\frac{d}{dt}} + \mathfrak{L}_M(\overset{2}{t}) + \Delta\mathfrak{L}_M(\overset{2}{t})), \boldsymbol{v}_M], \boldsymbol{u}'(\overset{3}{t}, \overset{1}{t})]\,\mathbf{1} = \\ &\sum_{1\le|i|\le M-1} \Big(\boldsymbol{\pi}_{v_M}(t, P_i)[[(\overset{2}{\frac{d}{dt}} + \mathfrak{L}_M(\overset{2}{t}) + \\ &\qquad \Delta\mathfrak{L}_M(\overset{2}{t})), \boldsymbol{p}_i], \boldsymbol{u}'(\overset{3}{t}, \overset{1}{t})]\,\mathbf{1}\Big), \end{aligned} \tag{8.195}$$

or equivalently

$$\begin{aligned} &[[(\mathfrak{L}_M(\overset{2}{t}) + \Delta\mathfrak{L}_M(\overset{2}{t})), \boldsymbol{v}_M], \boldsymbol{u}'(\overset{3}{t}, \overset{1}{t})]\,\mathbf{1} = \\ &\sum_{1\le|i|\le M-1} \Big(\boldsymbol{\pi}_{v_M}(t, P_i)[[(\mathfrak{L}_M(\overset{2}{t}) + \\ &\qquad \Delta\mathfrak{L}_M(\overset{2}{t})), \boldsymbol{p}_i], \boldsymbol{u}'(\overset{3}{t}, \overset{1}{t})]\,\mathbf{1}\Big), \end{aligned} \tag{8.196}$$

where $\boldsymbol{v}_M = \boldsymbol{v}_M(t)$ is the operator of multiplication by the function $v_M = v_M(t)$.

Using the linearity of the commutator $[,]$ we can rewrite the preceding equations (8.195) and (8.196) as follows

$$
\begin{aligned}
&[[(\overset{2}{\frac{d}{dt}} + \boldsymbol{\mathfrak{L}}_M(\overset{2}{t})), \boldsymbol{v}_M], \boldsymbol{u}'(\overset{3}{t}, \overset{1}{t})]\,\mathbf{1} + \\
&\qquad [[\Delta \boldsymbol{\mathfrak{L}}_M(\overset{2}{t})), \boldsymbol{v}_M], \boldsymbol{u}'(\overset{3}{t}, \overset{1}{t})]\,\mathbf{1} = \\
&\sum_{1\le|i|\le M-1} \Big(\boldsymbol{\pi}_{v_M}(t, P_i)[[(\overset{2}{\frac{d}{dt}} + \boldsymbol{\mathfrak{L}}_M(\overset{2}{t})), \boldsymbol{p}_i], \boldsymbol{u}'(\overset{3}{t}, \overset{1}{t})]\,\mathbf{1}\Big) + \\
&\qquad \sum_{1\le|i|\le M-1} \Big(\boldsymbol{\pi}_{v_M}(t, P_i)[[\Delta \boldsymbol{\mathfrak{L}}_M(\overset{2}{t}), \boldsymbol{p}_i], \boldsymbol{u}'(\overset{3}{t}, \overset{1}{t})]\,\mathbf{1}\Big),
\end{aligned} \tag{8.197}
$$

or equivalently

$$
\begin{aligned}
&[[\boldsymbol{\mathfrak{L}}_M(\overset{2}{t}), \boldsymbol{v}_M], \boldsymbol{u}'(\overset{3}{t}, \overset{1}{t})]\,\mathbf{1} + \\
&\qquad [[\Delta \boldsymbol{\mathfrak{L}}_M(\overset{2}{t}), \boldsymbol{v}_M], \boldsymbol{u}'(\overset{3}{t}, \overset{1}{t})]\,\mathbf{1} = \\
&\sum_{1\le|i|\le M-1} \Big(\boldsymbol{\pi}_{v_M}(t, P_i)[[\boldsymbol{\mathfrak{L}}_M(\overset{2}{t}), \boldsymbol{p}_i], \boldsymbol{u}'(\overset{3}{t}, \overset{1}{t})]\,\mathbf{1}\Big) + \\
&\qquad \sum_{1\le|i|\le M-1} \Big(\boldsymbol{\pi}_{v_M}(t, P_i)[[\Delta \boldsymbol{\mathfrak{L}}_M(\overset{2}{t}), \boldsymbol{p}_i], \boldsymbol{u}'(\overset{3}{t}, \overset{1}{t})]\,\mathbf{1}\Big).
\end{aligned} \tag{8.198}
$$

Due to the fact that the operator weights $\boldsymbol{\pi}_{v_M}(t, P_i)$ defined in (8.180) are the solutions of equation (8.174) or equivalently (8.175) with $N = M - 1$, we conclude that the preceding equations (8.197) and (8.198) and hence (8.171) and (8.172) are satisfied up to the following defect

$$
\begin{aligned}
&[[\Delta \boldsymbol{\mathfrak{L}}_M(\overset{2}{t}), \boldsymbol{v}_M], \boldsymbol{u}'(\overset{3}{t}, \overset{1}{t})]\,\mathbf{1} - \\
&\qquad \sum_{1\le|i|\le M-1} \Big(\boldsymbol{\pi}_{v_M}(t, P_i)[[\Delta \boldsymbol{\mathfrak{L}}_M(\overset{2}{t}), \boldsymbol{p}_i], \boldsymbol{u}'(\overset{3}{t}, \overset{1}{t})]\,\mathbf{1}\Big).
\end{aligned} \tag{8.199}
$$

Finally, our goal is to examine the error due to the approximation of the generators $\boldsymbol{\mathfrak{L}}(t)$ by $\boldsymbol{\mathfrak{L}}_M(t)$ and the value $v = v(t)$

of the European contingent claim $\mathfrak{v}$ by $v_M = v_M(t)$ in the evolution equation (6.58), which in the case under consideration can be rewritten as follows

$$\begin{aligned}\Big(\big[\big(\frac{d}{dt}+\mathfrak{L}(t)\big),\boldsymbol{v}\big] + \big[\big[\big(\frac{\overset{2}{d}}{dt}+\mathfrak{L}(\overset{2}{t})\big),\boldsymbol{v}\big],\boldsymbol{u}'(\overset{3}{t},\overset{1}{t})\big]\Big)\mathbf{1} = \\ \sum_{1\le|i|\le M-1}\Big(\boldsymbol{\pi}_v(t,P_i)\Big(\big[\big(\frac{d}{dt}+\mathfrak{L}(t)\big),\boldsymbol{p}_i\big] + \\ \big[\big[\big(\frac{\overset{2}{d}}{dt}+\mathfrak{L}(\overset{2}{t})\big),\boldsymbol{p}_i\big],\boldsymbol{u}'(\overset{3}{t},\overset{1}{t})\big]\Big)\mathbf{1}\Big) + \\ \boldsymbol{\pi}_v(t,P_0)\,r(s,t),\end{aligned} \tag{8.200}$$

where $\mathbf{1}$ is the function in $\Pi(\mathbb{R}^n_{++}\times\mathcal{T})$ identically equal to unity.

8.146. Remark. In the preceding evolution equation (8.200) we have used the fact that $\mathfrak{d}_i(s_t,t)$ with $i=0$ is nothing but the continuously compounded interest rate $r(s_t,t)$.

With the help of relation (6.62) we can rewrite the preceding evolution equation (8.200) in the case under consideration as follows

$$\begin{aligned}\big(\frac{d}{dt}+\mathfrak{L}(t)\big)\,v + \big[\big[\big(\frac{\overset{2}{d}}{dt}+\mathfrak{L}(\overset{2}{t})\big),\boldsymbol{v}\big],\boldsymbol{u}'(\overset{3}{t},\overset{1}{t})\big]\mathbf{1} = \\ \sum_{1\le|i|\le M-1}\Big(\boldsymbol{\pi}_v(t,P_i)\Big(\big(\frac{d}{dt}+\mathfrak{L}(t)\big)\,p_i + \\ \big[\big[\big(\frac{\overset{2}{d}}{dt}+\mathfrak{L}(\overset{2}{t})\big),\boldsymbol{p}_i\big],\boldsymbol{u}'(\overset{3}{t},\overset{1}{t})\big]\,\mathbf{1}\Big)\Big) + \\ \boldsymbol{\pi}_v(t,P_0)\,r(s,t).\end{aligned} \tag{8.201}$$

With the help of expression (8.194) from the preceding evolution equation (8.201) we obtain

$$
\begin{aligned}
&\Big(\frac{d}{dt} + \mathfrak{L}_M(t) + \Delta\mathfrak{L}_M(t)\Big)\, v_M + \\
&\qquad [[(\overset{2}{\frac{d}{dt}} + \mathfrak{L}_M(\overset{2}{t}) + \Delta\mathfrak{L}_M(\overset{2}{t})), \boldsymbol{v}_M], \boldsymbol{u}'(\overset{3}{t}, \overset{1}{t})]\mathbf{1} = \\
&\sum_{1\leq|i|\leq M-1} \Big(\boldsymbol{\pi}_{v_M}(t, P_i)\Big(\Big(\frac{d}{dt} + \mathfrak{L}_M(t) + \Delta\mathfrak{L}_M(t)\Big)\, p_i + \\
&\qquad [[(\overset{2}{\frac{d}{dt}} + \mathfrak{L}_M(\overset{2}{t}) + \Delta\mathfrak{L}_M(\overset{2}{t})), \boldsymbol{p}_i], \boldsymbol{u}'(\overset{3}{t}, \overset{1}{t})]\,\mathbf{1}\Big)\Big) + \\
&\boldsymbol{\pi}_{v_M}(t, P_0)\, r(s, t).
\end{aligned}
\tag{8.202}
$$

Using the linearity of the commutator $[,]$ we can rewrite the preceding equation (8.202) as follows

$$
\begin{aligned}
&\Big(\Big(\frac{d}{dt} + \mathfrak{L}_M(t)\Big)\, v_M + \Delta\mathfrak{L}_M(t)\, v_M + \\
&\qquad [[(\overset{2}{\frac{d}{dt}} + \mathfrak{L}_M(\overset{2}{t})), \boldsymbol{v}_M], \boldsymbol{u}'(\overset{3}{t}, \overset{1}{t})]\mathbf{1} + \\
&\qquad [[\Delta\mathfrak{L}_M(\overset{2}{t}), \boldsymbol{v}_M], \boldsymbol{u}'(\overset{3}{t}, \overset{1}{t})]\mathbf{1} = \\
&\sum_{1\leq|i|\leq M-1} \Big(\boldsymbol{\pi}_{v_M}(t, P_i)\Big(\Big(\frac{d}{dt} + \mathfrak{L}_M(t)\Big)\, p_i + \\
&\qquad [[(\overset{2}{\frac{d}{dt}} + \mathfrak{L}_M(\overset{2}{t})), \boldsymbol{p}_i], \boldsymbol{u}'(\overset{3}{t}, \overset{1}{t})]\Big)\mathbf{1}\Big) + \\
&\sum_{1\leq|i|\leq M-1} \Big(\boldsymbol{\pi}_{v_M}(t, P_i)\Big(\Delta\mathfrak{L}_M(t)\, p_i + \\
&\qquad [[\Delta\mathfrak{L}_M(\overset{2}{t}), \boldsymbol{p}_i], \boldsymbol{u}'(\overset{3}{t}, \overset{1}{t})]\,\mathbf{1}\Big)\Big) + \\
&\boldsymbol{\pi}_{v_M}(t, P_0)\, r(s, t).
\end{aligned}
\tag{8.203}
$$

Due to the fact that $v_M = v_M(t)$ is the solution of the evolution equation (8.189) and hence (8.184) and due to the fact that the operator weights $\boldsymbol{\pi}_{v_M}(t, P_i)$ defined in (8.180) are the solutions of the equation (8.174) or equivalently (8.175) with $N = M - 1$, we conclude that the preceding evolution equation (8.203) and hence (8.200) are satisfied up to the following defect

$$\begin{aligned} &\Delta\mathfrak{L}_M(t)\, v_M + [[\Delta\mathfrak{L}_M(\overset{2}{t}), \boldsymbol{v}_M], \boldsymbol{u}'(\overset{3}{t}, \overset{1}{t})]\mathbf{1} - \\ &\sum_{1\le|i|\le M-1} \Big(\boldsymbol{\pi}_{v_M}(t, P_i) \Big(\Delta\mathfrak{L}_M(t)\, p_i + \\ &\qquad [[\Delta\mathfrak{L}_M(\overset{2}{t}), \boldsymbol{p}_i], \boldsymbol{u}'(\overset{3}{t}, \overset{1}{t})]\, \mathbf{1} \Big) \Big). \end{aligned} \tag{8.204}$$

In the case when the generator $\mathfrak{L}(t)$ is formally represented as an analytic quasidifferential operator the preceding expression for the defect (8.204) can be rewritten as follows

$$\begin{aligned} &\Delta\mathfrak{L}_M(t)\, v_M + [[\Delta\mathfrak{L}_M(\overset{2}{t}), \boldsymbol{v}_M], \boldsymbol{u}'(\overset{3}{t}, \overset{1}{t})]\mathbf{1} - \\ &\sum_{1\le|i|\le M-1} \Big(\boldsymbol{\pi}_{v_M}(t, P_i) [[\Delta\mathfrak{L}_M(\overset{2}{t}), \boldsymbol{p}_i], \boldsymbol{u}'(\overset{3}{t}, \overset{1}{t})]\, \mathbf{1} \Big). \end{aligned} \tag{8.205}$$

Indeed, each term $\Delta\mathfrak{L}_M(t)\, p_i$ in expression (8.204) is equal to the zero function in $\Pi(\mathbb{R}^n_{++} \times \mathcal{T})$ due to the following chain of equalities

$$\begin{aligned} \Delta\mathfrak{L}_M(t)\, p_i =& \Delta\mathfrak{L}_M(\overset{2}{t}) \Big(\sum_{j\le i} \binom{i}{j} (-1)^{i-j}\, \overset{3}{s}{}^{i-j}\, e^{-\int_{(\overset{1}{t})}^{(\overset{3}{t})} \mathfrak{d}_j(\overset{3}{s},\tau)d\tau}\, s^j \Big) = \\ & \Delta\mathfrak{L}_M(\overset{2}{t})(s - \overset{3}{s})^i = \\ & \sum_{|m|\ge M+1} \mathfrak{L}_m(t, \overset{2}{\hat{s}}) \overset{1}{\frac{\partial}{\partial s}}{}^m (s - \overset{3}{s})^i \end{aligned}$$

where each power $m = (m_1, m_2, \ldots, m_n)$ in $\mathbb{Z}^n_+$ of the vector operator of differentiation

$$\overset{1}{\frac{\partial}{\partial s}} = (\overset{1}{\frac{\partial}{\partial s_1}}, \overset{1}{\frac{\partial}{\partial s_2}}, \ldots, \overset{1}{\frac{\partial}{\partial s_n}})$$

is strictly greater then the power $i = (i_1, i_2, \ldots, i_n)$ in $\mathbb{Z}^n_+$ of the vector operator

$$(s - \overset{3}{s}) = ((s_1 - \overset{3}{s}_1), (s_2 - \overset{3}{s}_2), \ldots, (s_n - \overset{3}{s}_n)).$$

8.147. Remark. The results of this Subsection can be restated verbatim for the case of the dynamic beliefs-preferences gauge symmetry group for a market populace presented in Subsection (6.1) of Section (6).

8.7 The Method of Quasidifferential Operator for an Approximate Dynamic Replication of European Contingent Claims in the Case of a Markovian Market Populace with Beliefs Determined by Jump Diffusion Processes

As an illustration of the method of quasidifferential operators for the approximate dynamic replication of European contingent claims we consider a particular case of a Markovian market populace $\mathbb{H} = \mathbb{B} \times \mathbb{U}$, or more precisely $\mathbb{H} = \mathbb{L} \times \mathbb{U}$ such that each orbit of the beliefs-preferences gauge symmetry group $\hat{\mathcal{G}}$ contains a market participant $\mathcal{H} = (\mathcal{B}, \mathcal{U})$, or more precisely $\mathcal{H} = (\mathfrak{L}, \mathcal{U})$ with the following property. Each generator $\mathfrak{L}(t)$ in $\mathfrak{L}$ is of the form

$$\begin{aligned}(\mathfrak{L}(t)\, h)(s) =& \frac{1}{2} \sum_{i,j=1}^{n} \sigma^2_{ij}(s,t) \frac{\partial^2}{\partial s_i \partial s_j} h(s) + \sum_{i=1}^{n} \mu_i(s,t) \frac{\partial}{\partial s_i} h(s) + \\ & \lambda(s,t) \int_{\mathbb{R}^n_{++}} (h(s\, s') - h(s)) q(s, t, \frac{ds'}{s'}), \qquad (8.206)\end{aligned}$$

for each admissible h in Π.

8.148. Remark. We comment that in the preceding expression (8.206)

$$s\, s' = (s_1\, s'_1, s_2\, s'_2, \cdots, s_n\, s'_n),$$

is in $\mathbb{R}^n_{++}$ for each $s = (s_1, s_2, \cdots, s_n)$ and $s' = (s'_1, s'_2, \cdots, s'_n)$ in $\mathbb{R}^n_{++}$, and that

$$\frac{ds}{s} = \frac{ds_1}{s_1}\frac{ds_2}{s_2} \cdots \frac{ds_n}{s_n}.$$

8.149. Remark. We also comment that in the preceding expression (8.206) the operator

$$\frac{1}{2}\sum_{i,j=1}^{n} \sigma^2_{ij}(s,t)\frac{\partial^2}{\partial s_i \partial s_j} + \sum_{i=1}^{n} \mu_i(s,t)\frac{\partial}{\partial s_i}$$

is defined in relation (5.54).

In order to define $\lambda(s,t)$ and $q(s,t,\frac{ds'}{s'})$ we need the following expression of the generator $\mathfrak{L}(t)$ of the form (8.206) in the x-basis

$$\begin{aligned}(\mathfrak{L}_*(t)\, f)(x) = (\Upsilon_{s\mapsto x}\mathfrak{L}(t)\Upsilon_{x\mapsto s}\, f)(x) = \\ \frac{1}{2}\sum_{i,j=1}^{n} \sigma^2_{*ij}(x,t)\frac{\partial^2}{\partial x_i \partial x_j} f(x) + \sum_{i=1}^{n} \mu_{*i}(x,t)\frac{\partial}{\partial x_i} f(x) + \\ \lambda_*(x,t)\int_{\mathbb{R}^n} (f(x+y) - f(x))q_*(x,t,dy),\end{aligned} \tag{8.207}$$

for each admissible function f in $\Pi(\mathbb{R}^n)$.

8.150. Remark. We comment that

$$\lambda_*(x,t) = \lambda(\mathbf{exp}\, x, t)$$

and

$$q_*(x,t,dy) = q(\mathbf{exp}\, x, t, dy).$$

8.151. Remark. We also comment that the operator

$$\frac{1}{2}\sum_{i,j=1}^{n} \sigma^2_{*ij}(x,t)\frac{\partial^2}{\partial x_i \partial x_j} + \sum_{i=1}^{n} \mu_{*i}(x,t)\frac{\partial}{\partial x_i}$$

is defined in relation (5.76).

It is well known that $\mathfrak{L}_*(t)$ is nothing but the generator of a jump diffusion process $x(\cdot)$ such that $\lambda_*(x,t)\,\Delta t + o(\Delta t)$ is the probability that the process has a jump in the interval $[t, t + \Delta t)$ given that $x(t) = x$, and $q_*(x,t,dy)$ is the associated jump distribution (see, for example, [41] pages 21 and 42).

Now assuming that f is an admissible analytic function in $\Pi(\mathbb{R}^n)$ we can formally represent $\mathfrak{L}_*(t)$ of the form (8.207) as a real analytic quasidifferential operator

$$\mathfrak{L}_*(t) = \frac{1}{2}\sum_{i,j=1}^{n} \sigma^2_{*ij}(\hat{x},t)\frac{\partial^2}{\partial x_i \partial x_j} + \sum_{i=1}^{n} \mu_{*i}(\hat{x},t)\frac{\partial}{\partial x_i} + \sum_{m\in\mathbb{Z}^n_{++}} \mathfrak{j}_{*m}(\hat{x},t)\frac{\partial}{\partial x}^m, \tag{8.208}$$

where

$$\mathfrak{j}_{*m}(x,t) = \frac{1}{m!}\,\lambda_*(x,t)\int_{\mathbb{R}^n} y^m\, q_*(x,t,dy).$$

8.152. Remark. We comment that for the sake of consistency of notation in this Section, whenever ambiguity is likely we distinguish between $\xi = (\xi_1, \xi_2, \ldots, \xi_n)$ in Ω and the vector operator $\hat{\xi} = (\hat{\xi}_1, \hat{\xi}_2, \ldots, \hat{\xi}_n)$ such that each entry $\hat{\xi}_i$ is the operator of multiplication by ξ_i.

8.153. Remark. It is clear that the real analytic quasidifferential operator $\mathfrak{L}_*(t)$ in (8.207), or equivalently in (8.208) admits the following representation

$$\mathfrak{L}_*(t) = \sum_{m\in\mathbb{Z}^n_{++}} \mathfrak{L}_{*m}(t,\hat{x})\frac{\partial}{\partial x}^m \tag{8.209}$$

where

$$\mathfrak{L}_{*m}(t,x) = \begin{cases} \mu_{*i}(x,t) + \mathfrak{j}_{*m_i}(x,t) & \text{if } |m| = 1, \\ \frac{1}{2}\sigma^2_{*ij}(x,t) + \mathfrak{j}_{*m_{ij}}(x,t) & \text{if } |m| = 2, \\ \mathfrak{j}_{*m}(x,t) & \text{if } |m| \geq 3, \end{cases} \tag{8.210}$$

with m_i standing for a multi-index in $\mathbb{Z}^n_+$ whose only nonzero i-th entry is equal to 1, and m_{ij} standing for a multi-index in $\mathbb{Z}^n_+$ whose only nonzero i-th and j-th entries are equal to either 1 whenever $i \neq j$ or to 2 whenever $i = j$.

In this regard it is clear that the defining sequence of the $\mathfrak{L}_*(t)$ in (8.207), or equivalently in (8.208) is given by

$$\mathfrak{L}_{*M}(t) = \sum_{1 \leq |m| \leq M} \mathfrak{L}_{*m}(t, \hat{x}) \frac{\partial}{\partial x}^m. \tag{8.211}$$

With the help of identity (4.24) and expression (8.208) we can formally represent the generator $\mathfrak{L}(t)$ in (8.206) as follows

$$\begin{aligned} \mathfrak{L}(t) =& \frac{1}{2} \sum_{i,j=1}^{n} \sigma^2_{ij}(\hat{s}, t) \frac{\partial^2}{\partial s_i \partial s_j} + \sum_{i=1}^{n} \mu_i(\hat{s}, t) \frac{\partial}{\partial s_i} + \\ & \sum_{m \in \mathbb{Z}^n_{++}} \mathfrak{j}_m(\hat{s}, t) \big(\hat{s} \frac{\partial}{\partial s}\big)^m, \end{aligned} \tag{8.212}$$

where

$$\mathfrak{j}_m(s, t) = \frac{1}{m!} \lambda(s, t) \int_{\mathbb{R}^n{}_{++}} (\mathbf{log}\, s')^m \, q(s, t, ds'),$$

and where $\hat{s} \frac{\partial}{\partial s}$ is a vector operator defined by

$$\hat{s} \frac{\partial}{\partial s} = (\hat{s}_1 \frac{\partial}{\partial s_1}, \hat{s}_2 \frac{\partial}{\partial s_2}, \ldots, \hat{s}_n \frac{\partial}{\partial s_n}).$$

8.154. Remark. It is clear that with the help of relation (5.77) we can express the generator $\mathfrak{L}(t)$ in (8.206), or equivalently in (8.212) solely as a function of the vector operators $\hat{s}$ and $\hat{s} \frac{\partial}{\partial s}$

$$\begin{aligned} \mathfrak{L}(t) = & \frac{1}{2} \sum_{i,j=1}^{n} \hat{\sigma}^2_{ij}(\hat{s}, t) \big(\hat{s}_i \frac{\partial}{\partial s_i}\big) \big(\hat{s}_j \frac{\partial}{\partial s_j}\big) + \\ & \sum_{i=1}^{n} \big(\hat{\mu}_i(\hat{s}, t) - \frac{1}{2} \hat{\sigma}^2_{ii}(\hat{s}, t)\big) \hat{s}_i \frac{\partial}{\partial s_i} + \\ & \sum_{m \in \mathbb{Z}^n_{++}} \mathfrak{j}_m(\hat{s}, t) \big(\hat{s} \frac{\partial}{\partial s}\big)^m. \end{aligned} \tag{8.213}$$

Due to the fact that the operators $\hat{s}_i$ and $\frac{\partial}{\partial s_i}$ on Π with $i = 1, 2, \ldots, n$ and the identity operator $\boldsymbol{I}$ on Π generate a nilpotent Lie algebra we can formally represent the operator

$$\sum_{m \in \mathbb{Z}^n_{++}} \mathfrak{j}_m(\hat{s}, t)\big(\hat{s}\frac{\partial}{\partial s}\big)^m$$

as a real analytic quasidifferential operator

$$\sum_{m \in \mathbb{Z}^n_{++}} \mathfrak{j}_m(\hat{s}, t)\big(\hat{s}\frac{\partial}{\partial s}\big)^m = \sum_{m \in \mathbb{Z}^n_{++}} \mathfrak{J}_m(\hat{s}, t)\frac{\partial}{\partial s}^m . \tag{8.214}$$

It is clear that in order to explicitly determine the operator coefficients $\mathfrak{J}_m(\hat{s}, t)$ with $m \in \mathbb{Z}^n_{++}$ in the preceding expression (8.214) it is enough to explicitly determine for each j in $\mathbb{Z}^n_+$ the real numbers $\mathfrak{K}(j, i)$ with i in $\mathbb{Z}^n_+$ and $i \leq j$ such that

$$\big(\hat{s}\frac{\partial}{\partial s}\big)^j = \sum_{i \leq j} \mathfrak{K}_n(j, i)\hat{s}^i \frac{\partial}{\partial s}^i . \tag{8.215}$$

The existence of $\mathfrak{K}_n(j, i)$ is guaranteed by the following Theorem.

8.155. Theorem. For each j in $\mathbb{Z}^n_+$ there exist nonnegative integer numbers $\mathfrak{K}_n(j, i)$ with i in $\mathbb{Z}^n_+$ and $i \leq j$ such that relation (8.215) holds.

Proof. Due to the fact that the operators $\hat{s}_i$ and $\frac{\partial}{\partial s_j}$ commute whenever $i \neq j$ it is enough to prove the Theorem only for the case of $n = 1$. Indeed if the Theorem is proven for the case of $n = 1$ then for each $j = (j_1, j_2, \ldots, j_n)$ in $\mathbb{Z}^n_+$ we have that

$$\big(\hat{s}\frac{\partial}{\partial s}\big)^j = \prod_{k=1}^{n} \big(\hat{s}_k \frac{\partial}{\partial s_k}\big)^{j_k} =$$

$$\prod_{k=1}^{n} \Big(\sum_{i_k=0}^{j_k} \mathfrak{K}_1(j_k, i_k)\hat{s}_k^{i_k} \frac{\partial}{\partial s_k}^{i_k}\Big) = \tag{8.216}$$

$$\sum_{i_1=0}^{j_1}\sum_{i_2=0}^{j_2}\cdots\sum_{i_n=0}^{j_n}\Big(\prod_{k=1}^{n}\mathfrak{K}_1(j_k,i_k)\hat{s}_k^{i_k}\frac{\partial}{\partial s_k}^{i_k}\Big)=$$
$$\sum_{i\le j}\mathfrak{K}_n(j,i)\hat{s}^i\frac{\partial}{\partial s}^i,$$

where

$$\mathfrak{K}_n(j,i)=\prod_{k=1}^{n}\mathfrak{K}_1(j_k,i_k),$$

with $i=(i_1,i_2,\ldots,i_n)$.

Now we prove the Theorem in the case of $n=1$. We will prove the Theorem by induction. For $j=0$ it is clear that $\mathfrak{K}_1(j,i)=1$. We assume that the Theorem is proven for j in $\mathbb{Z}_+$ and we will prove it for $j+1$. The proof follows from the following chain of equalities

$$\begin{aligned}&\Big(\hat{s}\frac{\partial}{\partial s}\Big)^{j+1}=\\&\hat{s}\frac{\partial}{\partial s}\Big(\sum_{i=0}^{j}\mathfrak{K}_1(j,i)\hat{s}^i\frac{\partial}{\partial s}^i\Big)=\\&\sum_{i=0}^{j}\mathfrak{K}_1(j,i)\hat{s}^{i+1}\frac{\partial}{\partial s}^{i+1}+\\&\sum_{i=0}^{j}i\,\mathfrak{K}_1(j,i)\hat{s}^i\frac{\partial}{\partial s}^i=\\&\sum_{i=0}^{j+1}\mathfrak{K}_1(j+1,i)\hat{s}^i\frac{\partial}{\partial s}^i,\end{aligned}\tag{8.217}$$

where $\mathfrak{K}_1(j+1,i)$ is defined by the recurrence

$$\mathfrak{K}_1(j+1,i)=\mathfrak{K}_1(j,i-1)+i\,\mathfrak{K}_1(j,i),\tag{8.218}$$

with the initial conditions $\mathfrak{K}_1(0,0) = 1$ and $\mathfrak{K}_1(j,i) = 0$ whenever $j < i$. □

8.156. Remark. It is clear that $\mathfrak{K}_n(j,0) = 0$ for each j in $\mathbb{Z}^n_{++}$ and hence $\mathfrak{J}_m(\hat{s},t)$ is the zero operator for $m = 0$. This is the reason that the summand $\mathfrak{J}_m(\hat{s},t)$ with $m = 0$ is not present in the sum in expression (8.214) as should be expected.

Now with the help of relation (8.215) we obtain the explicit formal expressions for the operators $\mathfrak{J}_m(\hat{s},t)$

$$\begin{aligned}
&\sum_{l\in\mathbb{Z}^n_{++}} \mathfrak{j}_l(\hat{s},t)\big(\hat{s}\frac{\partial}{\partial s}\big)^l = \\
&\quad\sum_{l\in\mathbb{Z}^n_{++}} \mathfrak{j}_l(\hat{s},t)\Big(\sum_{m\le l} \mathfrak{K}_n(l,m)\hat{s}^m \frac{\partial}{\partial s}^m\Big) = \\
&\quad\sum_{l\in\mathbb{Z}^n_{++}} \mathfrak{j}_l(\hat{s},t)\Big(\sum_{m\in\mathbb{Z}^n_{++}} I_{m\le l}\,\mathfrak{K}_n(l,m)\hat{s}^m \frac{\partial}{\partial s}^m\Big) = \\
&\quad\sum_{m\in\mathbb{Z}^n_{++}} \Big(\sum_{l\in\mathbb{Z}^n_{++}} I_{m\le l}\,\mathfrak{K}_n(l,m)\,\mathfrak{j}_l(\hat{s},t)\Big)\hat{s}^m \frac{\partial}{\partial s}^m = \\
&\quad\sum_{m\in\mathbb{Z}^n_{++}} \mathfrak{J}_m(\hat{s},t)\frac{\partial}{\partial s}^m
\end{aligned} \tag{8.219}$$

where

$$\begin{aligned}
&\mathfrak{J}_m(\hat{s},t) = \\
&\quad\big(\sum_{l\in\mathbb{Z}^n_{++}} I_{m\le l}\,\mathfrak{K}_n(l,m)\,\mathfrak{j}_l(\hat{s},t)\big)\hat{s}^m = \\
&\quad\big(\sum_{l\ge m} \mathfrak{K}_n(l,m)\,\mathfrak{j}_l(\hat{s},t)\big)\hat{s}^m.
\end{aligned} \tag{8.220}$$

It is clear that instead of the nonnegative integers $\mathfrak{K}_1(j,i)$ we can use the nonnegative integers $K(j,i)$ defined by

$$\big(\frac{\partial}{\partial s}\hat{s}\big)^j = \sum_{i=0}^{j} K(j,i)\hat{s}^i \frac{\partial}{\partial s}^i, \tag{8.221}$$

where j and i are in $\mathbb{Z}_+$ and $i \leq j$.

The existence of $K(j,i)$ is guaranteed by the following Theorem.

8.157. Theorem. For each j in $\mathbb{Z}_+$ there exist nonnegative integer numbers $K(j,i)$ with i in $\mathbb{Z}_+$ and $i \leq j$ such that relation (8.221) holds.

Proof. We prove the Theorem by induction. For $j = 0$ it is clear that $K(j,i) = 1$. We assume that the Theorem is proven for j in $\mathbb{Z}_+$ and we will prove it for $j+1$. The proof follows from the following chain of equalities

$$\begin{aligned}
&\Big(\frac{\partial}{\partial s}\hat{s}\Big)^{j+1} = \\
&\quad\Big(\frac{\partial}{\partial s}\hat{s}\Big)\Big(\sum_{i=0}^{j} K(j,i)\hat{s}^i \frac{\partial}{\partial s}^i\Big) = \\
&\quad\Big(\boldsymbol{I} + \hat{s}\frac{\partial}{\partial s}\Big)\Big(\sum_{i=0}^{j} K(j,i)\hat{s}^i \frac{\partial}{\partial s}^i\Big) = \\
&\quad\sum_{i=0}^{j} K(j,i)\hat{s}^i \frac{\partial}{\partial s}^i + \\
&\qquad\sum_{i=0}^{j} K(j,i)\hat{s}^{i+1} \frac{\partial}{\partial s}^{i+1} + \\
&\qquad\sum_{i=0}^{j} i\,K(j,i)\hat{s}^i \frac{\partial}{\partial s}^i = \\
&\quad\sum_{i=0}^{j+1} K(j+1,i)\hat{s}^i \frac{\partial}{\partial s}^i,
\end{aligned} \tag{8.222}$$

where $\boldsymbol{I}$ is the identity operator, and where $K(j+1,i)$ is defined by the recurrence

$$K(j+1,i) = K(j,i-1) + (i+1)\,K(j,i), \tag{8.223}$$

with the initial conditions $K_1(0,0) = 1$ and $K_1(j,i) = 0$ whenever $j < i$. □

Now with the help of relation (8.214), the generator $\mathfrak{L}(t)$ in (8.206), or equivalently in (8.212) can be formally represented as a real analytic quasidifferential operator

$$\mathfrak{L}(t) = \sum_{m \in \mathbb{Z}^n_{++}} \mathfrak{L}_m(t, \hat{s}) \frac{\partial}{\partial s}^m \tag{8.224}$$

with the defining sequence given by

$$\mathfrak{L}_M(t) = \sum_{1 \le |m| \le M} \mathfrak{L}_m(t, \hat{s}) \frac{\partial}{\partial s}^m \tag{8.225}$$

where

$$\mathfrak{L}_m(t, s) = \begin{cases} \mu_i(s,t) + \mathfrak{J}_{m_i}(s,t) & \text{if } |m| = 1, \\ \frac{1}{2}\sigma^2_{ij}(s,t) + \mathfrak{J}_{m_{ij}}(s,t) & \text{if } |m| = 2, \\ \mathfrak{J}_m(s,t) & \text{if } |m| \ge 3, \end{cases} \tag{8.226}$$

with m_i standing for a multi-index in $\mathbb{Z}^n_+$ whose only nonzero i-th entry is equal to 1, and m_{ij} standing for a multi-index in $\mathbb{Z}^n_+$ whose only nonzero i-th and j-th entries are equal to either 1 whenever $i \neq j$ or to 2 whenever $i = j$.

8.158. Remark. We comment that due to the fact that the operators $\hat{s}_i$ and $\frac{\partial}{\partial s_i}$ on Π with $i = 1, 2, \dots, n$ and the identity operator $\boldsymbol{I}$ on Π generate a nilpotent Lie algebra we can also formally represent the operator

$$\sum_{m \in \mathbb{Z}^n_{++}} \mathfrak{j}_m(\hat{s}, t) \left(\hat{s} \frac{\partial}{\partial s}\right)^m$$

as a real quasidifferential operator with the defining sequence given by

$$\sum_{1 \le |m| \le M} \mathfrak{j}_m(\hat{s}, t) \left(\hat{s} \frac{\partial}{\partial s}\right)^m = \sum_{1 \le |m| \le M} \mathfrak{J}_m(M, \hat{s}, t) \frac{\partial}{\partial s}^m, \tag{8.227}$$

where $\mathfrak{J}_m(M, \hat{s}, t)$ can be explicitly found with the help of relation (8.215). Indeed

$$
\begin{aligned}
&\sum_{1\le|l|\le M} \mathfrak{j}_l(\hat{s},t)\big(\hat{s}\frac{\partial}{\partial s}\big)^l = \\
&\quad \sum_{1\le|l|\le M} \mathfrak{j}_l(\hat{s},t)\Big(\sum_{m\le l} \mathfrak{K}_n(l,m)\hat{s}^m \frac{\partial}{\partial s}^m\Big) = \\
&\quad \sum_{1\le|l|\le M} \mathfrak{j}_l(\hat{s},t)\Big(\sum_{1\le|m|\le M} I_{m\le l}\, \mathfrak{K}_n(l,m)\hat{s}^m \frac{\partial}{\partial s}^m\Big) = \\
&\quad \sum_{1\le|m|\le M}\Big(\sum_{1\le|l|\le M} I_{m\le l}\, \mathfrak{K}_n(l,m)\, \mathfrak{j}_l(\hat{s},t)\Big)\hat{s}^m \frac{\partial}{\partial s}^m = \\
&\quad \sum_{1\le|m|\le M} \mathfrak{J}_m(M,\hat{s},t)\frac{\partial}{\partial s}^m
\end{aligned}
\tag{8.228}
$$

where

$$
\begin{aligned}
&\mathfrak{J}_m(M,\hat{s},t) = \\
&\quad \big(\sum_{1\le|l|\le M} I_{m\le l}\, \mathfrak{K}_n(l,m)\, \mathfrak{j}_l(\hat{s},t)\big)\hat{s}^m.
\end{aligned}
\tag{8.229}
$$

Now it is clear that the generator $\mathfrak{L}(t)$ in (8.206), or equivalently in (8.212) can also be formally represented as a real quasidifferential operator with the defining sequence given by

$$
\mathfrak{L}_M(t) = \sum_{1\le|m|\le M} \mathfrak{L}_m(M,t,\hat{s})\frac{\partial}{\partial s}^m \tag{8.230}
$$

where

$$
\begin{aligned}
&\mathfrak{L}_m(M,t,s) = \\
&\quad \begin{cases} \mu_i(s,t) + \mathfrak{J}_{m_i}(M,s,t) & \text{if } |m| = 1, \\ \frac{1}{2}\sigma_{ij}^2(s,t) + \mathfrak{J}_{m_{ij}}(M,s,t) & \text{if } |m| = 2, \\ \mathfrak{J}_m(M,s,t) & \text{if } |m| \ge 3, \end{cases}
\end{aligned}
\tag{8.231}
$$

with m_i standing for a multi-index in $\mathbb{Z}_+^n$ whose only nonzero i-th entry is equal to 1, and m_{ij} standing for a multi-index in $\mathbb{Z}_+^n$ whose only nonzero i-th and j-th entries are equal to either 1 whenever $i \neq j$ or to 2 whenever $i = j$.

Now in the case of the Markovian market populace under consideration, relations (8.180) and (8.183) and the evolution equation (8.189) with the help of expressions (8.225) or (8.230) determines the approximate dynamically replicating portfolio and the approximate value for an arbitrary European contingent claim with any degree of accuracy which is given by expressions (8.199) and (8.204).

For example, for $M = 2$ the generator $\mathfrak{L}(t)$, due to expression (8.225), can be approximated by

$$\begin{aligned}\mathfrak{L}_2(t) = \sum_{1\le|m|\le2} \mathfrak{L}_m(t,\hat{s})\frac{\partial}{\partial s}^m = \\ \frac{1}{2}\sum_{i,j=1}^{n}\left(\sigma_{ij}^2(\hat{s},t) + 2\,\mathfrak{I}_{m_{ij}}(\hat{s},t)\right)\frac{\partial^2}{\partial s_i \partial s_j} + \\ \sum_{i=1}^{n}\left(\mu_i(\hat{s},t) + \mathfrak{I}_{m_i}(\hat{s},t)\right)\frac{\partial}{\partial s_i}.\end{aligned} \tag{8.232}$$

In this case the evolution equation (8.189) with the help of the preceding expression (8.232) can be considered as a correction to the Black and Scholes equation (5.100) due to the presence of the jumps in which $\sigma_{ij}^2(s,t) = \hat{\sigma}_{ij}^2(s,t)\, s_i s_j$ is replaced by $\sigma_{ij}^2(s,t) + 2\,\mathfrak{I}_{m_{ij}}(s,t)$.

Similarly, for $M = 2$ the generator $\mathfrak{L}(t)$, due to expression (8.230), can be approximated by

$$\mathfrak{L}_2(t) = \sum_{1\le|m|\le2} \mathfrak{L}_m(2,t,\hat{s})\frac{\partial}{\partial s}^m = \tag{8.233}$$

$$\frac{1}{2}\sum_{i,j=1}^{n}\left(\sigma_{ij}^2(\hat{s},t) + 2\,\mathfrak{J}_{m_{ij}}(2,\hat{s},t)\right)\frac{\partial^2}{\partial s_i \partial s_j} + \sum_{i=1}^{n}\left(\mu_i(\hat{s},t) + \mathfrak{J}_{m_i}(2,\hat{s},t)\right)\frac{\partial}{\partial s_i},$$

where $\mathfrak{J}_{m_i}(2,\hat{s},t)$ and $\mathfrak{J}_{m_{ij}}(2,\hat{s},t)$ are explicitly given by

$$\mathfrak{J}_{m_i}(2,\hat{s},t) = \left(\mathfrak{j}_{m_i}(\hat{s},t) + \mathfrak{j}_{m_{ii}}(\hat{s},t)\right)\hat{s}_i \tag{8.234}$$

and

$$\mathfrak{J}_{m_{ij}}(2,\hat{s},t) = \mathfrak{j}_{m_{ij}}(\hat{s},t)\hat{s}_i\hat{s}_j, \tag{8.235}$$

with m_i standing for a multi-index in $\mathbb{Z}_+^n$ whose only nonzero i-th entry is equal to 1, and m_{ij} standing for a multi-index in $\mathbb{Z}_+^n$ whose only nonzero i-th and j-th entries are equal to either 1 whenever $i \neq j$ or to 2 whenever $i = j$.

In this case the evolution equation (8.189) with the help of the preceding expression (8.233) can be considered as another correction to the Black and Scholes equation (5.100) due to the presence of the jumps in which $\sigma_{ij}^2(s,t) = \hat{\sigma}_{ij}^2(s,t)\, s_i s_j$ is replaced by $\sigma_{ij}^2(s,t) + 2\,\mathfrak{J}_{m_{ij}}(2,t,s)$. Due to the fact that $\mathfrak{J}_{m_{ij}}(2,t,s)$ is given explicitly with the help of expression (8.235), this correction is simpler but possibly rougher than the preceding one based on expression (8.232) in which $\sigma_{ij}^2(s,t) = \hat{\sigma}_{ij}^2(s,t)\, s_i s_j$ is replaced by $\sigma_{ij}^2(s,t) + 2\,\mathfrak{J}_{m_{ij}}(t,s)$.

Finally, we note that the results of this article are not limited to the analysis of financial capital markets. For example, these results can also be applied to the analysis of the dynamics of a multiple species population in ecology and to the behavioral sciences in general.

References

[1] R. A. Adams. *Sobolev Spaces.* Academic Press, New York, 1975.

[2] M. Agranovich. Spectral properties of diffraction problems. In N. Voytovich, B. Katsenelenbaum, and A. Sivov, editors, *The Generalized Method of Eigen Vibrations in Diffraction Theory,* pages 289–416, Moscow, Russia, 1977. Nauka.

[3] M. Agranovich. On elliptic pseudodifferential operators on a closed curve. *Transactions of the Moscow Mathematical Society,* 47:22–67, 1984.

[4] B. Amosov. *Elliptic Pseudodifferential Equations on a Smooth Closed Curve.* PhD thesis, Moscow Institute of Electronics and Mathematics, 1987.

[5] L. Asimow and A. Ellis. *Convexity Theory and its Applications in Functional Analysis.* Academic Press, New York, 1980.

[6] J. M. Ball. Measurability and continuity conditions for evolutionary processes. In L. Cesari, J. K. Hale, and J. P. LaSalle, editors, *Dynamical Systems, Volume II,* pages 91–94, New York, 1976. Academic Press.

[7] F. Black and M. Scholes. The pricing of options and corporate liabilities. *Journal of Political Economy,* 81:637–657, May-Jun 1973.

[8] D. T. Breeden. Consumption, production, inflation and interest rates. *Journal of Financial Economics,* 16:3–39, 1986.

[9] D. T. Breeden and R. H. Litzenberger. Prices of state-contingent claims implicit in option prices. *Journal of Business,* 51(4):621–651, 1978.

[10] M. Brennan and E. Schwartz. A continuous time approach to the pricing of bonds. *Journal of Banking and Finance*, 3:133–155, 1979.

[11] P. L. Butzer and H. Berens. *Semi-Groups of Operators and Approximation.* Springer Verlag, New York, 1967.

[12] C. Cohen-Tannoudji, B. Diu, and F. Laloë. *Quantum Mechanics.* John Wiley and Sons, New York, 1977.

[13] G. Debreu. *Theory of Value.* John Wiley and Sons, New York, 1959.

[14] J. B. Donaldson. Comparative dynamics of an equilibrium intertemporal asset pricing model. *Review of Economic Studies*, 51:491–508, 1984.

[15] B. Dubrovin, S. Novikov, and A. Fomenko. *Modern Geometry: Methods and Applications.* Nauka, Moscow, Russia, 1986.

[16] D. Duffie. *Security Markets: Stochastic Models.* Academic Press, San Diego, California, 1988.

[17] N. Dunford and J. Schwartz. *Linear Operators, Volume II.* Interscience Publishers, New York, 1963.

[18] E. Dynkin. *Markov Processes, Volume I.* Springer-Verlag, Berlin, 1965.

[19] H. O. Fattorini. *The Cauchy Problem.* Addison-Wesley, Reading, Massachusetts, 1983.

[20] P. C. Fishburn. *The Foundations of Expected Utility.* D. Reidel Publishing Company, Boston, Massachusetts, 1982.

[21] A. Friedman. *Partial Differential Equations.* Robert E. Krieger Publishing Company, Inc., Malabar, Florida, 1983.

[22] M. B. Garman. Towards a semigroup pricing theory. *Journal of Finance*, 40:847–861, July 1985.

[23] J. A. Goldstein. *Semigroups of Linear Operators and Applications.* Oxford University Press, New York, 1985.

[24] E. G. Harris. *A Pedestrian Approach to Quantum Field Theory.* Wiley-Interscience, New York, 1972.

[25] T. W. Hungerfold. *Algebra.* Springer-Verlag, New York, 1989.

[26] V. A. Kholodnyi. The linear operator method for the analysis of problems in classical electrodynamics. *Reports of Moscow Institute of Electronics and Mathematics*, 1:67–88, 1987.

[27] V. A. Kholodnyi. *The Operator Method for Classical Electrodynamics.* MS thesis, Moscow Institute of Electronics and Mathematics, 1987.

[28] V. A. Kholodnyi. Methods of pseudodifferential operators for the analysis of boundary-value problems in classical electrodynamics. *Reports of Moscow Institute of Electronics and Mathematics*, pages 53–76, 1988.

[29] V. A. Kholodnyi. The analysis of a coupled meander-line slow-wave system by the method of pseudodifferential operators. In N. Kopylova, editor, *The 44th All-Union Research Conference Devoted to the Day of Radio, Volume II*, pages 123–124, Moscow, Russia, 1989. Radio and Communication.

[30] V. A. Kholodnyi. *Invention and elaboration of the method of quasidifferential operators for the analysis of slow-wave systems.* PhD thesis, Moscow Institute of Electronics and Mathematics, 1990.

[31] V. A. Kholodnyi. The method of quasidifferential operators for the analysis of slow-wave systems. In *The Workshop on Electrodynamics of Periodic and Irregular Structures*, page 10, Orjonikidze, Russia, 1990.

[32] V. A. Kholodnyi. A nonlinear partial differential equation for American options. *Preprint, Integrated Energy Services, Inc.*, 1995.

[33] V. A. Kholodnyi. On the linearity of Bermudan and American options with general time-dependent payoffs in partial semimodules. *Preprint, Integrated Energy Services, Inc.*, 1995.

[34] V. A. Kholodnyi. On weighted function spaces related to the Cauchy problem for the heat equation arising in valuation of contingent claims in the Black and Scholes market environment. *Preprint, Integrated Energy Services, Inc.*, 1995.

[35] V. A. Kholodnyi. Reduction of an integral equation of potential type on a circular boundary in the plane to a sequence of ordinary differential equations of increasing order on the boundary. *Preprint, Integrated Energy Services, Inc.*, 1995.

[36] V. A. Kholodnyi. Reduction of an integrodifferential equation for an electric current on a circular curve in the plane to a sequence of ordinary differential equations of increasing order on the curve. *Preprint, Integrated Energy Services, Inc.*, 1995.

[37] V. A. Kholodnyi. Reduction of the Dirichlet problem for the Helmholtz equation in the plane to Cauchy problems for a sequence of ordinary differential equations of increasing order on the boundary. *Preprint, Integrated Energy Services, Inc.*, 1995.

[38] V. A. Kholodnyi. Semilinear evolution equation for general derivative contracts. *Preprint, Integrated Energy Services, Inc.*, 1995.

[39] V. A. Kholodnyi. Semilinear evolution equation for universal contingent claims. *Preprint, Integrated Energy Services, Inc.*, 1995.

[40] V. A. Kholodnyi. Universal contingent claims. *Preprint, Integrated Energy Services, Inc.*, 1995.

[41] H. J. Kushner. *Approximation and Weak Convergence Methods for Random Processes.* The MIT Press, Cambridge, Massachusetts, 1984.

[42] V. P. Maslov. *Operational Methods.* Mir, Moscow, Russia, 1976.

[43] W. S. Massey. *Algebraic Topology: An Introduction.* Springer-Verlag, New York, 1977.

[44] R. C. Merton. *Continuous Time Finance.* Blackwell, Cambridge, Massachusetts, 1990.

[45] J. Mickelsson. *Current Algebras and Groups.* Plenum Press, New York, 1989.

[46] H. Müller-Kirsten and A. Wiedemann. *Supersymmetry: An Introduction with Conceptual and Calculational Details.* World Scientific, Teaneck, New Jersey, 1987.

[47] J. V. Neuman and O. Morgenstern. *Theory of Games and Economic Behavior.* John Wiley and Sons, New York, 1967.

[48] A. Pazy. *Semigroups of Linear Operators and Applications to Partial Differential Equations.* Springer-Verlag, New York, 1983.

[49] W. Rudin. *Functional Analysis.* McGraw-Hill, New York, 1973.

[50] H. H. Schaefer. *Banach Lattices and Positive Operators.* Springer-Verlag, New York, 1974.

[51] A. N. Shiryaev. *Probability.* Springer-Verlag, New York, 1996.

[52] M. A. Shubin. *Pseudodifferential Operators and Spectral Theory.* Springer-Verlag, New York, 1987.

[53] R. P. Stanley. *Enumerative Combinatorics, Volume I.* Wadsworth and Brooks/Cole, Monterey, California, 1986.

[54] F. Treves. *Introduction to Pseudodifferential Operators, Volume I.* Plenum Press, New York, 1980.

[55] J. A. van Casteren. *Generators of Strongly Continuous Semigroups.* Pitman, London, U.K., 1985.

[56] W. V. Wahl. The equation $u' + A(t)u = f$ in a Hilbert space and L^p - estimates for parabolic equations. *Journal of the London Mathematical Society*, 25(2):483–497, 1982.

Index